Biochemistry of the Brain during the Process
of Dying and Resuscitation

BIOKHIMIYA MOZGA PRI UMIRANII I OZHIVLENII ORGANIZMA

БИОХИМИЯ МОЗГА ПРИ УМИРАНИИ И ОЖИВЛЕНИИ ОРГАНИЗМА

Biochemistry of the Brain during the Process of Dying and Resuscitation

by

Mariya Sergeevna Gaevskaya

Authorized translation from the Russian
by J. A. Stekol, B. S., M. S., Sc. D.

CONSULTANTS BUREAU
NEW YORK
1964

The original Russian text, published by the State Press for Medical
Literature in Moscow in 1963, has been supplemented by the author
for the English edition.

Гаевская Мария Сергеевна

**Биохимия мозга при умирании
и оживлении организма**

Library of Congress Catalog Card Number 64-17205

CONTENTS

INTRODUCTION

Theoretical developments in medicine during the second quarter of this century have directed attention to the pathophysiology and treatment of terminal states, which have become an independent division of medical science. Contributions to these developments have been made by advances in aviation medicine and in general and thoracic surgery, disciplines in which the treatment of shock, blood loss, asphyxia, and the terminal states resulting from these conditions is as important and urgent as is the problem of anesthesia. There are good reasons, therefore, why the creation of the science of the pathophysiology and treatment of terminal states (reanimatology) has occurred simultaneously and in close connection with the growth of anesthesiology as an independent medical discipline. Nevertheless, the problems confronting the pathophysiology and treatment of terminal states cover a much wider field. They include the study of the principles of development of the terminal stages of life as a result of a variety of lethal factors, and also the principles and methods of subsequent resuscitation and restoration of vital functions.

Experimental and clinical investigations have shown that despite the wide range of objects selected for study, they are united by certain common features. In the first place, however the terminal states may be caused, their development must inevitably be associated with the onset of hypoxia in some form, for some time, and to some degree. In the overwhelming majority of cases of "acute" death, the main effect of hypoxia is to cause injury to the central nervous system, and the degree of this injury determines the degree of the subsequent possible restoration of its functions and, hence, of the functions of the organism as a whole.

When death does not take place so swiftly and is preceded by a relatively long period of impending death, the whole extent of the physiological compensatory mechanisms is directed primarily towards protecting the central nervous system. A long period of impending death therefore frequently leads to irreversible changes in other vitally important organs before the brain begins to suffer damage. In these cases too, however, with the exclusion of physiological compensatory mechanisms and the onset of clinical death, irreversible changes soon take place in the brain. If, in the course of the period of impending death, the changes in the internal organs are reversible in character, the prognosis of resuscitation will also be determined by the degree of injury to the central nervous system.

It is along these lines that the widely accepted view of the decisive importance of the central nervous system in the restoration of vital functions after a state of agony or clinical death has developed. It will be clear why, during the study of the pathophysiology of impending death and resuscitation, attention has been directed principally to the central nervous system, as is apparent from the surveys of research in this field given in the monographs by V. A. Negovskii, I. R. Petrov, Stephenson, and others. The central nervous system has been studied by various methods: physiological, including the method of conditioned reflexes, electrophysiological, histological, and biochemical.

Biochemical studies have shed light on the metabolic changes forming the material basis of the physiological processes which have been observed.

Sechenov and Pavlov demonstrated the dominant role of the central nervous system and, in particular, of the cerebral cortex in integrating the parts of the animal organism into a unified whole, and in maintaining its relationships with the external environment. It is this importance of the higher divisions of the central nervous system to every process taking place within the animal or human organism that is responsible for the considerable volume of research undertaken into the normal and pathological physiology of the central nervous system. During recent years, its biochemistry has also received intensive study. "The principal task of the biochemistry of the central nervous system, and especially of the brain," writes A. V. Palladin, "is to elucidate the specific features of its composition and metabolism as a result of which the central nervous system performs its biological role as the organ maintaining the constant equilibrium of the relationships between the animal organism and the external environment" (1954a).

Until recently biochemical investigations were used in medicine mainly for diagnostic purposes, and to a lesser degree to analyze the causes of the onset and development of pathological processes, with the possible exception of the phenomena of hyper- and hypofunction of the endocrine glands. It is only in modern times that the biochemical method of investigation has begun to be used extensively in pathology for providing information on the nature of pathological processes.

Moreover, it has been found that the nature of certain diseases may be explained by changes in the structure of a certain type of protein molecule in the body tissues. "At the present time," says V. A. Engel'gardt, "we can think in terms, not of a cellular, but of a molecular pathology" (1959).

Most information has so far been obtained on the biochemistry of hypoxic states. This is due, firstly, to the fact that hypoxia is of considerable interest, for it accompanies many diseases, and, secondly, because it can be easily produced in experimental conditions.

The slowness of the introduction of biochemistry into medicine and of its conversion into pathochemistry has been determined largely by technical difficulties. Although for diagnostic purposes it is usually sufficient to carry out a biochemical analysis of the excretions of the human organism, for a more fundamental investigation it is necessary to analyze the tissues, and of these only the blood is easily accessible in man. This is yet another reason why hypoxic states have been among the first to be studied by biochemical methods, for analysis of the blood in these states provides sufficient information for the study of their pathogenesis and development. But when the need arises to analyze other tissues, for example the brain, ways have to be found to reproduce the particular pathological process experimentally, and the findings must then be transferred to man. Although this technique introduces unavoidable errors, it is the only one available at present, and it has given remarkable results, for example in the study of the pathophysiology and treatment of various forms of diabetes. On the other hand, in psychiatry, concerned with specifically human diseases which cannot be studied experimentally, it will be clear that the absence of information regarding metabolism in the brain must retard and complicate the study of the pathogenesis and the development of the treatment of these diseases.

The study of the metabolism of the brain, whether in normal or pathological conditions, introduces many more technical difficulties arising from the special structural, functional, and metabolic features of its tissue, distinguishing it from all other tissues of the warm-blooded animal. Foremost among these difficulties is the exceptionally high velocity of the physiological processes and the correspondingly high metabolic rate, the negligible reserves of energy, and hence the complete dependence of the brain tissue on a supply of blood and its very high sensitivity to hypoxia. The peculiar structure of the brain, the complexity of its morphological composition, the close interweaving of its gray and white matter, and the variety of its cells and conducting elements—all these factors add to make the results of biochemical investigations very relative, so that large amounts of tissue must be used for the chemical analysis. Consequently, the results of biochemical analysis cannot be correlated with the precise details of the morphological structure, and they must always be to some extent aggregates.

Strictly speaking, only histochemical investigations can reveal the precise relationships between the chemistry of nerve tissue and the structure and functions of its individual elements, but this field of science is only in its infancy, and the technical difficulties in its path are even greater than those hindering biochemistry.

In principle, four methods are available for the experimental study of the biochemistry of the nervous system. The first of these, introduced by Ludwig and improved by E. S. London and his pupils, seeks to determine the metabolism of the brain from the changes in the composition of the incoming and outgoing blood. This method has the undoubted advantage over all others that it enables prolonged observations to be made in chronic experiments on the same animal.

Nevertheless, it also has certain drawbacks: the need to measure the volume velocity of the blood flow in order to ensure that the results are correctly interpreted, the difficulty of obtaining blood simultaneously from a vein and an artery, and, most important of all, the impossibility of forming an accurate idea of the processes taking place in the brain from an analysis of the inflowing and outflowing blood (A. D. Bernshtein and S. V. Zakharov, 1949; S. V. Zakharov, 1952). This is demonstrated especially clearly by comparing the data relating to brain metabolism obtained by this method and by the radioactive isotope method (G. E. Vladimirov, 1946).

The second method attempts to determine the metabolism on the basis of the chemical analysis of brain tissue. Although this method is historically older than the others, for a long time its application was very restricted, for due regard was not always paid to the scale of the postmortem changes in brain tissue, and incorrect conclusions were drawn concerning substances with a high rate of metabolism.

This technique has developed intensively only during the last two decades, following the discovery by Kerr and his collaborators (1935-42) of the importance of instantaneous tissue fixation, i.e., the instantaneous arrest of metabolic processes in living tissue.

The principal advantage of this method is that is provides a chemical picture of the brain at a given moment, corresponding to the functional state of the nerve tissue at that moment. If sufficient of these "instant photographs" are available in a time sequence, and a sufficient number of parallel determinations are carried out at each instant, the course of the metabolic processes taking place in the brain tissue can be assessed.

The main disadvantages of this method are as follows: it is not possible to make a series of investigations on one animal and many animals have to be used; existing methods of fixation of brain tissue (freezing and injection of fixing agent into the blood vessels) require general anesthesia, particularly in large animals, or the possibility must be accepted that the functional state of the animal's central nervous system may be modified at the moment of fixation of the brain.

The third method used to study the metabolism of the nervous system is to investigate the rate at which elements are incorporated into organic compounds by the use of radioactive isotopes. This method can be used to judge the intensity of metabolism and, in particular, to introduce the proper corrections into the apparent constancy of the composition of the brain tissue as determined by the ordinary method of chemical analysis. However, before the compounds under investigation can be isolated from the brain tissue and the concentration of radioactive isotopes in these compounds determined, the animal's brain must be fixed in situ. This factor introduces all the disadvantages into this method which are found in the second, purely analytical method described above. Moreover, when labeled compounds are injected into the blood stream, subcutaneously, or intraperitioneally the existence of the blood-brain barrier, permeable to many substances only with difficulty, may mask the true intensity of their metabolism in the brain tissue. Even if the labeled substance is injected directly into the cerebrospinal fluid, the low permeability of the cell membrane for the substance in question may mask the rate of its renewal within the cell itself.

The fourth method aims to study metabolic processes in isolated, living tissue (including nerve tissue). This method, strictly speaking, demonstrates what can be done by the enzyme systems of the particular tissue in certain artificially created conditions, rather than the actual metabolism of the nerve tissue of the experimental animal. Nevertheless, this method has given useful information concerning the presence of various enzyme systems in brain tissue and the variations in their activity in comparative investigations.

Similar methods have been used to study metabolism in the mitochondria, microsomes, and hyaloplasm, i.e., in the separate elements of the nerve tissue cells. These methods have developed rapidly in recent years, since modern apparatus capable of identifying the elements of cells without injuring their structure has become available to biochemical laboratories.

Since each of these methods has its own drawbacks, the results obtained from them must be compared, and if special problems affecting the metabolism of the nervous system are being studied, material from adjacent fields of research must be used to the widest possible extent.

It is because of the technical difficulties that have arisen during the study of the metabolism of brain tissue in experimental conditions and during the transfer of the results to man that this field of research has not been developed sufficiently, although many biochemists have given it their attention.

Investigations of the biochemistry of the nervous system have developed in the direction of the study of the qualitative and quantitative composition of nerve tissue and of various divisions of the brain, the composition and properties of the enzymes isolated from brain tissue, the metabolism of the brain in different functional conditions of the central nervous system, and the metabolism of the brain in phylo- and ontogenesis and in pathological states of the organism. The latter subdivision, in turn, covers many categories: exposure to ionizing radiation, certain infectious diseases, tumors of the brain, hyperoxia. As we pointed out above, most attention has been paid to the action of hypoxia on brain metabolism. Notwithstanding all the technical difficulties, the results of these investigations in the various subdivisions of the biochemistry of the nervous system constitute a vast number of facts of great scientific value. They have been summarized in collections of papers, monographs, and surveys (McIlwain; Elliott, Page, and Quastel; Richter; A. V. Palladin; V. S. Shapot; Heald) and also in two collections of papers by Soviet workers in this field during the last ten years (Biochemistry of the Nervous System, Kiev, 1954; Problems in the Biochemistry of the Nervous System, Kiev, 1957).

There is now a considerable volume of factual evidence on the biochemistry of terminal states, including the biochemistry of the brain. Nevertheless, despite the undoubted importance of this problem, no attempt has yet been made to analyze this evidence. So far as the author is aware, the present volume is the first such attempt. At this point it must be noted that most of the material to be presented in the following pages deals with the carbohydrate-phosphorus metabolism of the brain, for which several factors are responsible.

Carbohydrate-phosphorus metabolism is the principal source of energy for the brain tissue, and it undergoes the greatest changes during hypoxia. In most studies of the brain metabolism in hypoxic states, it is this aspect of its metabolism that has been investigated. For instance, much of the work on the pathochemistry of terminal states, including our own investigations undertaken at the Laboratory of the Experimental Physiology of Resuscitation (USSR Academy of Medical Sciences), is devoted to this problem. This, naturally, is the field in which an attempt should be made to draw general principles from the existing data.

Recently, research into the nitrogen metabolism of brain tissue has attracted increasing attention. Some papers have now been published on the nitrogen metabolism of the brain in terminal states. Some experimental findings on this subject have been obtained in our laboratory. This information on the nitrogen metabolism of the brain in terminal states will be included in the appropriate section of this book.

Having set out to analyze the facts relating to the changes in the brain metabolism of the warm-blooded animal during impending death and subsequent resuscitation, we deemed it advisable to begin by summarizing, as briefly as possible, the facts concerning the metabolism of the brain in a state of relative rest (the "norm"), in states of excitation and inhibition of the central nervous system not associated with hypoxia, and in narcosis caused by various drugs, in order to give an idea of the metabolism of the brain in the initial state of the animal before the terminal state.

When classifying the existing (including our own) data on the pathochemistry of the brain during the development of terminal states, we attempted to compare them with the general pathophysiological and pathochemical picture of impending death and resuscitation. We paid particular attention to finding the relationship between metabolism in the brain and the functional state of the central nervous system as this changed under the influence of the external conditions associated with impending death and subsequent resuscitation. The biochemical investigations formed part of a general study of the pathophysiological principles governing terminal states, which must be understood before these states can be treated rationally in clinical conditions.

With this in view, we deemed it advisable to devote a separate chapter to the problem of the influence of hypothermia in the changes in brain metabolism in terminal states, since artificial hypothermia, firstly, is the most favorable condition enabling the warm-blooded animal to survive terminal states of the greatest depth and duration, and, secondly, has already been applied in clinical practice.

We consider that our purpose will have been served if our remarks on the pathochemistry of the brain in terminal states arouse the interest of both biochemists and practicing physicians, and provide them with material for use in the development of methods of treatment of patients in terminal states.

The author is grateful to Professor V. A. Negovskii and to the staff of his laboratory for their constant advice and help in these investigations.

CHAPTER I

CARBOHYDRATE – PHOSPHORUS AND NITROGEN METABOLISM
OF BRAIN TISSUE DURING PHYSIOLOGICAL REST (NORMAL STATE)

At the start, it is essential to note that in spite of the vagueness of the generally accepted term "normal," one has to employ it. This can be explained by the fact that biochemical investigations of nerve tissue up to the present still do not take into consideration the interdependence of the processes of excitation and inhibition in the central nervous system of the experimental animal as revealed by Pavlovian methods. The usual methods are limited to observations of normal animals, and for this reason the term "normal" is meaningful only as contrasted with a sharply expressed excited state, related to muscular activity or as contrasted with obvious inhibitions, and with definite pathological states elicited by the experimental procedures. In this sense only shall we employ the term "normal" in our further discussions.

Investigations employing angiostomic methods have shown that brain tissue avidly utilizes glucose supplied by the blood (London, 1931-1935; Kassil, 1938; Himwich, 1932-1951; Bernshtein, 1948; Komissarenko, 1949, 1952; Batrak et al., 1951; Zakharov, 1952; Lubovskaya, 1952; Bunyatyan, 1957; Prokhorova, 1960; Rodnight, 1959; and others). It has also been established during studies of respiration in intact organisms that the brain differs from other organs by greatly augmented metabolism and that its respiratory quotient approaches unity (London, 1935; Himwich, Nahum, 1932; Soskin, Levin, 1946). There was a close correlation between the amount of glucose supplied to the brain by the blood and the amount of oxygen consumed by the brain. Ketone bodies were not secreted by the brain into the blood, while lactic and pyruvic acids were either absorbed by the brain or were removed from it in small amounts by the blood. According to the data of London, the brain of the dog releases a certain amount of glycogen into the blood.

Thus it is considered established that under normal conditions the brain receives its necessary energy entirely by oxidation of carbohydrates.

The content of carbohydrate-phosphorus compounds — most vital energy sources — in the brain tissue of warm-blooded animals was adequately determined only after suitable methods for the fixation of the brain tissue had been perfected. Small animals (mice and rats) were immersed in liquid air; the brain of larger animals was frozen after anesthesia. In the latter case, the "normal state" is considered to be that prevailing under a more or less intensive state of inhibition of the central nervous system.

In chronic experiments Ivanenko and Voinar (1942), in an attempt to bypass this difficulty, employed dog brain which was removed through sincipital-occipital orifices which were made several days before the experiments. Yet, in spite of the use of local anesthesia for the surgical opening of the orifices, and of the rapid removal of the brain sample and its rapid immersion in liquid air, the variability of the data on the carbohydrate content of the dog brain was such that the authors found the data unreliable.

Chesler and Himwich (1943) used sodium iodoacetate intraperitoneally in dogs instead of liquid air in order to block the metabolic processes in the brain. The authors noted that about 15-30 minutes had elapsed from the time of administration of iodoacetate to the time of removal of the brain. Under such conditions it is difficult to assume that the inhibition of the metabolic processes in the brain was instantaneous. Indeed, the data obtained by these authors on the content of glycogen, for instance, in the brain of dogs and rabbits were somewhat lower than those obtained by other workers who employed freezing of the brain in situ.

For small animals (mice, rats) it has been proposed (Gromova, Kudritskaya, Petrov, and Shapot, 1952; Alekseeva and Magazanik, 1956) to employ ether anesthesia and to immerse only the occipital portion of the head in liquid air. The authors assumed that by these means it would be possible to bypass the inhibition of respiration and blood circulation during the fixation of the tissue. Veksler (1957) considered it more reasonable to decapitate the animals, letting the head fall instantly into liquid air.

Table 1 summarizes the data of several authors on the content of carbohydrate-phosphorus derivatives in the brain of warm-blooded animals. Whenever possible, average values and limits of variation are given; otherwise, only average values are given. It was considered necessary to express the content of glucose, glycogen, and lactic acid in milligrams per 100 grams of wet tissue (mg%); phosphorus derivatives and, as will be seen later, nitrogenous compounds—in micromoles per gram of wet tissue (μmoles/gm). This was done for the following reasons. In medical literature concerning carbohydrate metabolism, it is customary to express the content of glucose, glycogen, and lactic acid in tissues, including blood, in milligram per cent. Considering that the present dissertation would be of interest not only to biochemists but also to medical workers, an attempt was made to permit comparison of data, as given here, with those available elsewhere. As is known, the quoted data can be converted into micromoles/gm by multiplication by the following factors: for glucose and glycogen (expressed as glucose), 0.055; and for lactic acid, 0.111. The data on the content of phosphorus-containing and nitrogenous compounds in tissues entered medical literature considerably later than those on carbohydrates, and these data were generally expressed in micromoles per gram of tissue. The expression of data in such units is thus convenient not only for a biochemist but for a physician as well

As can be seen from Table 1, various authors are generally in agreement regarding the content of individual components of carbohydrate-phosphorus metabolism in the brain of the warm-blooded animals. We have obtained somewhat greater maximal values for the content of sugar in the brain tissue of several dogs. This could be explained by hyperglycemia which was induced by narcosis, averaging 200 mg%. It is generally accepted that the sugar content of the brain is about 50-75% of the sugar content of the blood flowing to the brain. In the dogs employed by us which were under pantopone-ether narcosis, the average sugar content in the brain was 63% of its content in the arterial blood. According to our data it would appear that, if, generally speaking, the sugar level in the brain reflects the level of sugar in the blood, no direct quantitative relationship exists between these two values. It was found that in different dogs with identical blood sugar levels the sugar content in the brain differed (occasionally twofold). In individual cases greater concentration of sugar in the brain tissue was found than in the blood.

It should be mentioned that under "sugar" of the brain we imply not only glucose, but its intermediate breakdown products was well, which would be determined as glucose. This is due to the fact that the commonly employed methods of sugar determination in the brain are based on determination of the reducing capacity of protein-free filtrates of brain tissue, which includes not only glucose but all the reducing substances.

It should be kept in mind that all the intermediary metabolism products of glucose, like glucose itself, are utilized by the brain.

In our laboratory (1953) special studies on the determination of nonfermentable substances in protein-free filtrates of the brain tissue of dogs have shown that the amount of contaminants which cannot be utilized by the living cell is small, amounting to about 15%, expressed as glucose. These contaminants depend neither on total sugar content of the brain, nor on the state of the animal (normal, acute hypoxia, postoperative state). A correction for nonfermentable contaminants has always been made by us. The values for glycogen content in brain tissue obtained by several authors are quite similar. An exception is the report of Ivanenko and Voinar. Their values appear to us somewhat high, due, perhaps, to inadequate removal of cerebrosides.

There is no doubt whatsoever about the importance of glucose in the vital activity of the brain. No such agreement existed for some time in regard to another carbohydrate, glycogen, and several authors postulated that glycogen has no significance in the energy balance of brain tissue, and that it basically represents a structural element. Rapid breakdown of glycogen during acute hypoxia of brain tissue, established by several authors (Kerr, Khaikina, Gaevskaya, and others), indirectly opposes this view. Finally, Prokhorova (1957), employing radioactive carbon, has succeeded in establishing that "the extent of glycogen metabolism in the brain exceeds that of lipids, cholesterol, and total carbon 50- to 100-fold." Furthermore, Prokhorova has established that the rate of renewal of glycogen in the brain exceeds that in the liver and muscle severalfold. Thus, according to biochemical data, glycogen of the brain plays an essential role in its metabolism, being one of the sources of energy.

TABLE 1. The Content of Sugar, Glycogen, Lactic Acid (in mg % on wet weight basis), and ATP, Creatine Phosphate, Inorganic Phosphate (in micromoles/gm wet tissue) in the Brain of Various Mammals

Author	Species of animal	Narcosis	Sugar	Glycogen	Lactic acid	ATP	Creatine phosphate	Inorganic phosphate
Kerr	Dogs	Sodium amytal	$\frac{45-86*}{57}$	$\frac{77-130}{98}$	$\frac{13-22}{17.7}$	2.5−2.8	2.4−3.7	
M. S. Gaevskaya	"	Pentothal plus pan- topone	$\frac{57-182}{104}$		$\frac{1.5-36}{21}$	1.8−2.6	2.3−3.0	0.48−3.0
E. A. Nosova	"	Nembutal plus pan- topone				$\frac{1.6-2.2}{1.7}$	$\frac{1.6-2.7}{2.1}$	$\frac{1.6-3.5}{2.5}$
A. V. Palladin and B. I. Khaikina	"	Ether + chloroform		41−105				
M. S. Gaevskaya	"	Ether + pantopone	$\frac{62-159}{111}$	$\frac{61-132}{91}$	$\frac{15-70}{41}$			
M. I. Shuster	"	Same				1.3−2.7		6.1−9.3
Stone	"	Morphine				3.0		
Chesler and Himwich	"	Iodoacetate		73				
Kerr	Cats	Amytal		77−101				
Klein and Olsen	"	Ether	75					
A. V. Palladin and B. I. Khaikina	Rabbits	No narcosis		76−109	71			
E. F. Ivanenko and A. O. Voinar	"	No narcosis	$\frac{122-139}{130.9\pm8.2}$					
E. N. Domontovich	"	No narcosis			31−39			
G. E. Vladimirov	"	No narcosis		87	23	2.2	3.6	3.8
Kerr	"	Amytal	35−75	70−90				
G. E. Vladimirov	"	Ether		89	29	2.2	3.8	2.1
Chesler and Himwich	"	Iodoacetate		68				
Potop	Rats	No narcosis		76−100	28−54			11.1
Jakubec and Svorad	"	No narcosis		85−90				
V. B. Troitskaya	"	No narcosis	42		7.2−20.0	2.9		4.8
Richter and Dawson	"	No narcosis			$\frac{13.4-24.4}{18.8}$	2.1−2.6	3.1	4.2
N. A. Verzhbinskaya	"	No narcosis				2.3−2.8	2.7−3.7	
I. A. Sytinskii	"	No narcosis	+	+	+	3.3	3.1	5.2
M. I. Prokhorova	"	No narcosis	45−5	72−10	22−3			
Ya. I. Veksler	"	No narcosis				2.4−2.8	2.7−4.0	2.7−3.6
Albaum, Tepperman, and Bodansky	"	Amytal	85					
Le Page	"	Nembutal			11.2−12.6	1.4−2.0	2.8−3.4	4.0−6.0
V. S. Shapot and K. G. Gromova	"	Ether				2.2	3.6	4.0
Stone	Mice	No narcosis			12−23	2.7		
E. F. Ivanenko and A. O. Voinar	"	No narcosis	160±5.7					

*The numerator gives the limits of variation; the denominator shows the average value.

Brief mention should be made of the differences which exist between biochemical and histochemical data on the presence of glycogen in the cerebral cortex of normal animals. During histochemical as well as during biochemical analyses, the essential conditions are the measures taken to prevent decomposition of brain glycogen. Such measures were carefully developed by Shabadash (1937-1951) for histochemical investigation of glycogen content in the central nervous system. Special fluid was injected by the author into the blood vessels to fix the glycogen in the tissues of intact animals. In normal animals (dogs, cats, rabbits) glycogen was absent in nerve cells of the cerebral cortex, but it was present in the neuroglia and muscle fibers of the walls of blood vessels. Glycogen appeared in the cells of the cerebral cortex only during acute pathological states.

On the basis of his investigations Shabadash postulates that the glycogen which was found during general biochemical investigations in the cerebral cortex could not play a role in ensuring its functional activity, since it was absent in the neurons. Indeed, he does not exclude the possibility that the glycogen of the cerebral cortex is less stable than that of the neuroglii and motoneurons of the spinal cord (where it is present in considerable amounts), and for this reason it is degraded before the fixing fluid can reach it. From this standpoint, instantaneous fixation of the cerebral cortex by liquid air, employed during biochemical studies, appears to be more satisfactory than fixation by fixing fluids since the latter proceeds more slowly and requires preliminary displacement of the blood by physiological solutions.

However, even if the neurons of the cerebral cortex did not indeed contain glycogen, its presence in the neuroglii could serve as a store of energy for the nerve elements of the cerebral cortex. The degradation of glycogen in the neuroglii with the formation of glucose or its phosphorylated products and their diffusion into the surrounding intracellular fluid could indeed ensure the inflow of additional carbohydrates to the neurons. The presence in the cerebral cortex of active enzymic systems which synthesize and cleave glycogen (Palladin and co-workers, 1936-1954; Leloir, 1957-1959; Breckenridge, 1959-1961) also indicates the active role of glycogen in the metabolic processes of the cerebral cortex.

In considering the question of the content of lactic acid in brain tissue it is necessary to point out that inasmuch as lactic acid is a product of glycolytic transformation of carbohydrates, the amount of lactic acid is closely related to the course of metabolic processes. As has been shown by McGinty and Gesell (1925, 1929), Haldi (1932, 1933), Avery and Ghantus (1935, 1937), interruption of blood circulation for a single second is sufficient for a sharp increase in the content of lactic acid. For this reason the true content of lactic acid in the brain can be ascertained only by in situ freezing of the brain with the preservation of normal blood circulation and respiration and in total absence of hypoxia. In the brain frozen under specified conditions, one always finds a certain amount of lactic acid, and the smallest amounts, i.e., 1.5 to 20 mg % (see Table 1), appear to be the closest to normal values. Greater amounts seem to indicate that either the freezing of the brain or the narcosis conditions induced in the animal a state of hypoxia. A more detailed discussion of this state will follow shortly.

The constant presence, under normal conditions, of small amounts of lactic acid in brain tissue indicates that in spite of the predominance of oxidative processes and the induction of the Pasteur effect, there exists in the brain an equilibrium between oxidation and aerobic glycolysis. This equilibrium is easily shifted in the direction of glycolysis at the slightest alteration in respiration. It would appear that the presence of this "latent" glycolytic process, ready at any moment to become active and to compensate to a certain extent for the loss of the oxidative capacity, has a definite biological significance — this in spite of the fact that glycolysis, as is known, can ensure only 1/16 of the energy which can be produced during the oxidation of the same amount of the same product.

In 1929-1932 Engel'gardt showed that the basic role in energy metabolism is played by nucleotides which are rich in energy in their terminal phosphate bonds. Numerous workers have studied the participation of these energy-rich phosphate compounds in individual reactions of the aerobic and anaerobic cycles of carbohydrate transformations, and computations were made of the amount of energy which may be available to the organism in the course of these reactions. After the significance of the energy-rich phosphate compounds in the energy balance of the cell had been elucidated, many studies appeared which were devoted to the metabolism of these compounds in the brain. Table 1 shows data on the content of two most important energy-rich compounds, adenosine triphosphate (ATP) and creatine phosphate (CP), in the brain tissue.

As can be seen from Table 1, the ATP content in the brain tissue of dogs, rabbits, and rats is almost the same and is about 2.5 micromoles/gm brain tissue. In fact, the ATP values include the values of adenosine diphosphate (ADP), since all authors, except Le Page, Shapot and Gromova, Sytinskii, and Nosova, employed a nonspecific method of determination of ATP in trichloracetic acid filtrates of brain tissue in which phosphate phosphorus was determined after 7-10 minutes hydrolysis in 1 N HCl. Separate determination of ATP and ADP in protein-free filtrates of brain by fractionation of barium precipitates (Le Page), an enzymatic method (Shapot and Gromova), or by paper chromatography (Sytinskii, Nosova) has shown that in normal brain tissue small amounts of ADP are always present.

Shapot and Gromova administered ether to rats for 2 minutes,then froze the brain by immersion of the back of the head in liquid air. Special measures were taken by these authors to ensure continuous respiration of the rats before the freezing of the medulla. Under these conditions the authors found 1 micromole of ADP per gram of brain tissue. Le Page and Sytinskii froze intact rats in liquid air both without narcosis and using nembutal and amytal narcosis. According to Le Page, the content of ADP in unanesthetized rat brain was 1.4 micromoles per gram, and in anesthetized rats, 0.5 micromole per gram. Sytinskii was unable to find any difference in the ADP content of the brain of anesthetized or unanesthetized rats, the content being somewhat high—1.3 micromoles per gram. This seems to suggest the presence of either hypoxia or certain stimulation in rats during freezing. This is supported by the relatively high content of inorganic phosphate in the brain tissue of these animals, amounting to 5.2 micromoles per gram. According to Nosova, in dogs, the brains of which were frozen in situ after trepanation of the skull under nembutal narcosis, the ADP content of the brain tissue was within the limits of 0.06 to 0.53 micromole per gram. Parallel to the small amounts of ADP in the brain, the content of inorganic phosphate in the brain was also small, 2.5 micromoles per gram.

MacIlwain (1959), in reviewing the literature data on the ADP content of brain tissue, came to the conclusion that most of the data are unreliable, and he excluded them from his tables. We are of the opinion, however, that the information which we quoted above quite adequately supports the presence of ADP in brain tissue, and that the somewhat lowered concentration of ADP in the brain during inhibition of the central nervous system by narcotics promptly rises during wakefulness. It would appear that 0.1 to 1.0 micromole of ADP per gram brain tissue is the correct concentration during a normal state.

Chromatographic determination of ATP and the products of its dephosphorylation (Sytinskii, Nosova, 1960) has shown that in normal rats or dogs the brain tissue does not contain adenylic acid, i.e., a product which does not contain acid-labile phosphorus. Therefore the labile equilibrium between the synthesis and degradation of ATP in the complex processes of accumulation and utilization of energy by the cell is maintained in such a manner that even during absolute predominance of the oxidative processes in brain tissue there is always present not only ATP but a small amount of ADP as well. The latter is the acceptor of phosphate and as such it stimulates the oxidative processes of the cell. Herein lies the biological importance of the small amounts of ADP (and other phosphate acceptors) present in brain tissue: they maintain the necessary level of oxidative processes and the coupled phosphorylation of the intermediary metabolism products of carbohydrates.

The content of creatine phosphate (CP) in brain tissue of various species of mammals is very similar, and, as is shown in Table 1, it amounts to about 3 micromoles per gram. At the onset of hypoxia the content of CP rapidly falls (Kerr, 1942; Alekseeva, 1952; Vladimirov, 1954). This led Verzhbinskaya (1954) to doubt the values for the CP content of brain tissue of warm-blooded animals as determined by various authors. According to Verzhbinskaya, the brain of certain reptiles contains twice as much CP as that found in the brain of warm-blooded animals. At the same time the rate of turnover of certain brain components and the rate of postmortem degradation of labile phosphate derivatives is considerably slower in reptiles than in warm-blooded animals. This had led Verzhbinskaya to propose that in spite of precautionary measures, such as freezing of the brain in liquid air, the CP of the brain of warm-blooded animals is in part degraded, and the analytical values are therefore low. To this the following can be offered as rebuttal. During artificial lowering of the body temperature of warm-blooded animals to 25-20°C a retardation of the turnover of brain components and a considerable lowering of the post-mortem degradation of the carbohydrate-phosphorus derivatives is observed (Vladimirov, 1957; Gaevskaya, 1957). However, the content of CP, as determined in the brain tissue of cooled animals, is equal to that in normal warm-blooded animals. Thus, the data for CP shown in Table 1 represent the true content of CP in the brain tissue of warm-blooded animals, and they represent the net values of CP during the labile equilibrium between its synthesis and degradation.

Finally, a few words should be said about the last compound listed in Table 1, namely, inorganic phosphate (IP). The increase in IP as well as in the content of lactic acid in the brain is an index of the alteration of the normal metabolism of the carbohydrate-phosphorus compounds of the brain. The degradation of the labile phosphorus compounds, such as ATP and CP, leads to a parallel increase in the resultant IP. At the maximal content of labile phosphorus compounds in the brain, the minimal content of IP is about 2.5 micromoles per gram. This value appears to be the most relaible one for the level of IP during physiological rest.

Freezing of the living brain in liquid air was the basic method which enabled the establishment of the content of the carbohydrate-phosphorus compounds in brain tissue. The question arises, what error has been introduced during the computation of these values by the admixture of blood which has been left in the brain during freezing? This error can be calculated with a great degree of accuracy, employing the data of Vladimirova (1937) and Vladimirov (1954). These authors have determined the extent of contamination by the blood of the brain tissue of rats frozen intact in liquid air, and they found that the contamination by blood is between 4 and 6%. Taking this into account, and the content of the various carbohydrate-phosphorus compounds in the blood and brain, the error does not exceed 5%.

It is known that during the estimation of the rates of turnover of phosphorus compounds in brain tissue by means of radioactive isotopes it is essential to take into consideration the admixture of blood, since the relative specific activity of inorganic phosphate of the blood is about 100 times greater than that of inorganic phosphate of the brain (Verzhbinskaya). In the determination of the content of carbohydrate-phosphorus compounds in brain tissue the error which is introduced by the admixture of blood can be ignored. Thus, the values shown in Table 1 give an adequate idea of the content of the carbohydrate-phosphorus compounds in the brain tissue of certain warm-blooded animals while in a state which we call "normal."

The study of nitrogen metabolism in the brain during terminal states is limited thus far to the determination of ammonia, glutamine, and a series of free amino acids. The available data on the content of these components in brain tissue during the "normal" state are listed below.

In a large series of experimental observations it has been found that the level of ammonia content in nerve tissue is intimately related to its functional state. The ammonia content in brain tissue rapidly increases during excitation, hypoxia, and especially during hyperoxia. As has been demonstrated by Vladimirova (1938-1961), Richter (1952) and by others, only following rapid freezing in liquid nitrogen of rats which before that were completely immobile and which had no orientating reflexes, was it possible to observe a stable and low content of ammonia in brain tissue. According to data furnished by several authors (Weil-Malherbe, 1950, 1956; Vladimirova, 1957; Gershenovich, 1957; Richter, 1957; Pertseva, 1958; Thorn, Heimann, 1958; Klimov, 1959; Goncharova, 1960; and others), it can be assumed that the normal limit of ammonia nitrogen in the brain of mammals is from 0.1 to 0.5 micromole per gram in a wakeful state, during which the acceleration of the process of excitation or inhibition in the central nervous system within the physiological limits is possible. As regards the large animals we have no choice but to accept as "normal" the state of slight narcosis.

The literature contains much information on the content of glutamine, glutamic acid, and γ-aminobutyric acid in the brain of mammals. Considerably less information is extant on the content of other free amino acids in the brain of mammals. Waelsch (1957) has summarized data obtained by Tallan (1954), Schurr (1950), Ansell and Richter (1954) on the content of free amino acids in the brain of cats and rats. Nasy (1958) has isolated from the brain tissue of rats free amino acids by ion exchange chromatography on columns and determined them quantitatively. We (Gaevskaya and Nosova, 1961) have determined free amino acids in the dog cerebral cortex by descending paper chromatography. We were not always successful in obtaining clear-cut separation of the amino acid spots, but even during good separations we preferred to determine the total content of those amino acids which were present in the brain in small amounts.

Table 2 contains data on the content of glutamine and free amino acids in brain tissue obtained by several authors. It can be seen that the amount of glutamine in the brain in normal state varies considerably. As has been shown by Tyakhepyl'd (1958) on rats and in our laboratory on dogs, increased doses of narcotics lead to an increased content of glutamine in the brain. This explains the generally higher values for glutamine in the brain of animals whose brain was frozen in situ under narcosis.

10

TABLE 2. Content of Glutamine and Free Amino Acids in the Brain of Mammals
(in micromoles/gm wet tissue)

Author	Glutamic acid	Glutamine	γ-Aminobutyric acid	Aspartic acid	Serine	Glycine	Alanine	Cystine	Lysine+histidine+arginine	Methionine	Phenylalanine+leucine	Animals
D. L. Ferdman, 1942		7.7										Dogs
Haber and Saidel, 1948	8.5	6.5										Rats
Krebs et al.	9.9	5.2										Cats
Krebs, 1949	10.4	3.7										Sheep
Boulanger, 1951	8.5	6.5	0.83									Rats
Berl and Waelsch, 1958	11.6	5.0	2.0									Dogs
Tower, 1958	10.4	3.9	4.5									Rats
	9.5	5.3	5.3									Cats
	8.7	4.05										Dogs
V. N. Goncharova, 1960	10.0	1.4−7.3 / 5.5	1.5−4.2 / 2.5									Rats
Waelsch (summary of literature data, 1957)	10.0	4.0	2.0		1.1	1.3	0.6	—	0.3	0.08	0.26	Rats
	8.7	3.4	2.3	2.2	0.72	1.3	1.0	0.04	0.28	0.10	0.21	
Nasy, 1958	10.0	4.8	2.14	2.2	0.9	0.8	0.5	—	Each 0.1−0.2			Cats
M. S. Gaevskaya and E. A. Nosova, 1961	7.23	3.3−7.0 / 5.4	1.73	2.2			0.19	0.76	0.63	·0.17	0.10	Rats / Dogs

In normal conditions, besides glutamine, glutamic acid and γ-aminobutyric acid are present in considerable amounts. Nasy has found that in the rat brain the content of aspartic acid is approximately equal to that of γ-aminobutyric acid. According to our data, the sum of aspartic acid, serine, and glycine is also approximately equal to the amount of γ-aminobutyric acid. The content of each of the rest of the free amino acids in brain tissue was less than 1 micromole per gram.

It is essential to clear up one methodological question which has a general significance: is it essential to take into account the amount of water present in brain tissue during the computation of the content of other components in the brain? The data listed in Tables 1 and 2 have been computed on the basis of wet weight of the tissue, assuming constant water content in the brain of adult animals. Thus, we found that the water content of the cerebral cortex of adult dogs varies between 76 and 81%, and that it does not alter during the agonal state and subsequent resuscitation of the animals. For this reason the relationship between the values for various components of carbohydrate-phosphorus metabolism does not alter whether they are calculated on the basis of dry or wet tissue. There are, however, certain considerations on the basis of which it is preferable to relate the obtained values to the wet weight of the tissue. The fact of the matter is that if one follows the metabolic changes in animals during ontogenesis, during which the water content of the brain changes considerably, then the question of the water content of the brain acquires considerable importance. The same question prevails during investigations of different portions of the brain, as it is known that the dry matter increases from higher to lower divisions of the central nervous system. This is true for animals of all ages.

In this connection the data of Himwich et al. (1941-1951) are of interest. These authors showed that by the intensity of the utilization of oxygen by the homogenates of brain tissue the various anatomical divisions of the brain of adult dogs can be arranged as follows: caudal nucleus, the cortex of the large hemispheres, cerebellum, optic thalamus, mid-brain, medulla oblongata, and spinal cord. In one-week-old puppies a different picture prevails: the greatest capacity for oxygen consumption is possessed by the medulla oblongata, then the mid-brain, spinal cord, cerebellum, optic thalamus, caudal nucleus, and the least capacity for oxygen consumption is shown by the cortex of large hemispheres. In addition, all divisions of the brain of the week-old puppies, with the exception of the medulla oblongata and the spinal cord, utilize considerably less oxygen that the corresponding sections of the brain of adult dogs. A similar order of oxygen consumption by the various divisions of the brain prevails in the second and third week of life of the puppies, but absolute values for oxygen consumption by the various divisions of the brain increase. By the fifth week the levels of oxygen consumption reach values which exceed those observed for the adult brain; the order of arrangement of the brain divisions by their oxygen consumption capacity alters and approaches that observed in the adult dog.

Similar data were obtained by Craig and Beecher (1943) on cats, and by Tyler and Harreveld (1942) on rats. All these data relate oxygen consumption to wet tissue. However, the recalculation of such data on metabolism in relation to dry weight of the tissue drastically alters the above described picture: the oxygen consumption by the various divisions of the brain of puppies is the same as in the brain of adult dogs. In addition, the values for oxygen consumption by various divisions of the brain of puppies turn out to be not lower but somewhat higher than in the adult animal. According to Himwich, the calculations on the basis of wet weight of brain tissue describe the picture prevailing in vivo.

Kometiani and Klein (1950) investigated the activity of certain enzymes in various divisions of the brain of cattle. On the assumption that the bulk of chloride ions is localized in extracellular space, the authors determined the extracellular space by measurements of chloride content and recalculated the activity of the enzymes on the basis of that tissue which did not contain chloride ions, namely the intracellular phase. They found that the activity of the oxidative enzymes (succinic dehydrogenase, succinic oxidase, cholinesterase, adrenaline oxidase, and glutamic dehydrogenase) was higher in that section of the brain which contained greater amounts of cellular material. It was also found that the activity of the intracellular phase was greater, the greater its water content. Thus, the data of Kometiani and Klein generally confirmed the views of Himwich that the data expressed on a wet weight basis generally characterize more closely the true metabolism of the tissue in vivo than those calculated on a dry weight basis.

There are, however, a number of pathological states which are related to alterations in water metabolism, and in these cases it appears more reasonable to report the data on a dry weight basis or in relation to protein content. Several authors have adopted such methods.

The information on the content of carbohydrate-phosphorus compounds in brain tissue gives an idea of the state of equilibrium between the process of synthesis and degradation of these compounds in the course of metabolism, and on the basis of the alterations in the relationships of these quantities one may appraise the alteration of equilibrium in one or the other direction. However, one cannot appreciate the rate of metabolic processes on the basis of data on the quantitative content of metabolites.

The application of radioisotopic methods to studies of metabolic processes in brain tissue greatly supplemented and refined the data obtained by ordinary analytical procedures.

We mentioned earlier the data of Prokhorova concerning the rate of renewal of brain glycogen which turned out to be considerably greater than that of the liver or muscle, and greater than that of brain lipids and cholesterol. As has been demonstrated by Khaikina and Goncharova (1949-1961), glycogen exists in the brain in various forms: free and bound to lipids and proteins. The same authors further showed that free glycogen of the brain has the greatest rate of renewal which, according to these authors, is utilized by the brain along with glucose for energy purposes. The content of free glycogen comprizes about 20% of the total glycogen present in the brain.

The rate of phosphorus-containing compounds in brain tissue has been studied in greatest detail. First it has been established that P^{32} administered directly into the blood stream or subcutaneously rapidly exchanges with phosphorus which enters into organic combinations of internal organs, and then very slowly penetrates the brain tissue (Vladimirov, 1946-1954; Hevesy, 1950; Lindberg and Ernster, 1950; Kometiani, 1954; and others). Direct administration of P^{32} into brain tissue (Lindberg, Kometiani, Vladimirov) increases severalfold its rate of incorporation into organic compounds of brain tissue, which exceeds the extent of incorporation into similar compounds of internal organs. On the basis of these and other considerations, Vladimirov assumed that inorganic phosphorus must overcome two barriers before it enters the brain from the blood: the first barrier is between the contents of the capillaries and the intracellular material; the second, the cell surface. The first barrier is of decisive importance.

Lately another viewpoint has been expressed regarding the nature of the blood-brain barrier and its role in the extent of penetration of inorganic phosphorus from the blood into the brain. Thus, Verzhbinskaya (1957-1960), basing her views on the theory of Nasonov regarding the adsorption basis of cell permeability of phosphorus across the blood-brain barrier of vertebrates arranged along an evolutionary scale, came to the conclusion that "the assumption of a very slow rate of penetration of inorganic phosphate into the brain is erroneous."

On the basis of her experimental data Verzhbinskaya arrived at the conclusion that the rate of diffusion of phosphate from the blood into the brain is the same as that into other tissues. The low specific activity of inorganic P^{32} of the brain is determined by the lower solubility of the phosphate in cell protoplasm of the brain cells and by rapid attainment of isotopic equilibrium of P^{32} between blood plasma and brain. The rate of penetration of inorganic phosphate, therefore, is determined not by permeability of the barrier (the existence of which the author does not deny, but believes that it is permeable to inorganic phosphate), but by the speed of its incorporation into organic compounds in the course of metabolism.

Thus, the question regarding the relatively low rate of exchange of inorganic phosphate in the brain under normal conditions remains open, and regardless which viewpoint proves to be correct, this fact is important to keep in mind.

Vladimirov and Rubel' (1954) have shown that labile phosphate compounds of the brain undergo the most intensive metabolic activity, since P^{32} was incorporated into creatine phosphate (CP) and adenosinetriphosphate (ATP) at the greatest rate. Verzhbinskaya (1960) calculated the time of a single decomposition and resynthesis of the amount of brain ATP and showed that for the brain of white rats at body temperature it is very low, about 4-6 minutes.

Engel'gardt and Lisovskaya (1954), while studying the metabolism of phosphoproteins in brain slices, have established that under favorable conditions (presence of glucose and oxygen) the specific activity of ATP approaches that of inorganic phosphate. Consequently, the constancy of the quantities of CP and ATP in the brain in normal physiological conditions is the result of equilibration of the intensive processes of synthesis and degradation.

It should also be taken into account that in various divisions of the central nervous system the intensity of metabolic processes is not the same. Thus, Kreps, Smirnov, and Chetverikov (1954) have shown that in the dog cortex of large hemispheres the rate of exchange of phosphorus of phosphorus-containing compounds is greater than in the white tissue, cerebellum, or medulla oblongata. These authors were unable to find any difference in the rate of exchange of phosphorus in the cortex of the large hemispheres, pars intermedia, medulla, and midbrain of rabbits. The authors related this fact to the considerably lower functional development of the cortex of the large hemispheres in the rabbit than in the dog.

Skvirskaya and Silich (1954) investigated the rate of incorporated of P^{32} into nucleic acids and phospholipids of various divisions of the brain. They too have shown the direct relationship between the functional activity of the divisions of the brain and the rate of metabolic processes in these divisions.

Kreps et al. and Vladimirov et al. have shown further that, although the rate of metabolism in the white matter of the large hemispheres and other divisions of the brain is lower than in the gray matter of the cortex of the large hemispheres, it is considerably higher than in other tissues, such as the muscles. It is thus understandable that the total metabolic activity of the brain exceeds that of all organs, and, as has been pointed out by Vladimirov, the brain consumes per unit time more oxygen than the working heart.

In experiments on surviving brain tissue (slices, homogenates) it has been shown that all the intermediary reactions of oxidative and glycolytic transformation of carbohydrate-phosphorus compounds can proceed: oxidation-reduction, coupled with phosphorylation, isomerization of phosphate esters of glucose, degradation of glucose phosphate to phosphotrioses, formation of pyruvate and its further oxidation or glycolytic transformation, etc.

McFarlane and Weil-Malherbe (1941), Ochoa (1941), Huszak (1942), Palladin and Khaikina (1947), and Etling (1953) have demonstrated the presence in brain tissue of hexokinase, which phosphorylates glucose and thus is included in the cycle of energy metabolism. In experiments on brain slices, extracts, and homogenates it has been established that the metabolic steps of glucose transformation do not differ from those in the muscle, and that these steps are intimately bound with the metabolism of organic phosphorus compounds. Palladin and Shtutman (1948) have described adenosinetriphosphatase of the brain. Later, Palladin, Polyakova, and Kirsenko (1961) have shown that this adenosinetriphosphatase is more active in mitochondria and less active in the microsomes and the nuclei of the brain cells.

Cori et al. (1938-1941) have shown the presence in brain tissue of a phosphorylase which could in vitro synthesize a polysaccharide and degrade it. The phosphorylase synthesizes a polysaccharide of a starch nature which under the action of another enzyme, amylose isomerase, is transformed into glycogen. Amylose isomerase was detected in brain tissue by Khaikina and Goncharova (1949). Under the conditions of surviving brain tissue the effectiveness of these enzymes is determined by the reaction medium, the concentration of inorganic phosphate, and by the presence of a certain amount of glycogen in the reaction mixture. However, in vivo there are no practical conditions for detection of the synthetic capacity of brain phosphorylase.

During the last few years another pathway of glycogen synthesis has been discovered; first in the liver, then in the brain and other tissues, namely, from uridine phosphate of glucose by the enzyme named glycogen synthetase (Leloir et al., 1957-1959; Breckenridge et al., 1960, 1961; Stetten and Stetten, 1960). This process is independent of phosphate and is accompanied by loss of free energy, and, according to calculations in vivo, it must proceed practically irreversibly in the direction of glycogen synthesis (Robbins, Traut, and Lipmann, 1959). It has been further shown that glycogen synthetase is less active than the other enzymes which participate in glycogen synthesis (phosphoglucomutase, uridine phosphate-glucose phosphorylase) which probably limits the rate of this process.

Only contradictory data are available on the pathways of glycogen degradation in the brain and on the activity of glycogen phosphorylase. According to Breckenridge (1961), glycogen phosphorylase is 31 times more active than glycogen synthetase. The author assumes that besides the phosphorylase which is activated by adenylic acid (Cori and Cori) there exists in brain tissue active phosphorylase which does not require adenylic acid for activity. Breckenridge is inclined to believe that phosphorylase can account for the rate of degradation of glycogen in brain tissue. Khaikina (1948) observed that the degradation effect of glycogen phosphorylase in brain tissue is minimal. Besides, as has been established by Rashba (1948) the brain tissue of cows, rabbits, swine, and dogs contains active amylase of dextrinogenic type. In vitro the activity of brain amylase was several times higher than the activity of amylase from liver and muscle. Of interest is the observation of Rashba that the presence of 1% glucose in the reaction mixture inhibits the amylolytic degradation of glycogen. It can thus be assumed that under normal blood supply to brain tissue the constant presence of glucose in the surrounding medium would inhibit the degradation of glycogen in the brain, and that lowering of glucose concentration in the brain would catalyze the degradation.

It can thus be assumed that the synthesis and degradation of glycogen proceed via different pathways with the participation of various enzymes. Furthermore, the synthesis of glycogen in brain tissue is accomplished with the participation of phosphorus compounds, but the degradation of glycogen, in contrast to degradation of glycogen in other tissues, can proceed without the participation of phosphorus compounds in the process (Palladin et al.).

The peculiar character of metabolic reactions distinguishing the brain tissue is revealed also in the transformations of creatine phosphate (CP). As has been established by Tseitlin (1952, 1953) in experiments with rat brain extracts, the synthesis and degradation of CP in the brain via transesterification with the adenylic acid

14

system (characteristic for muscle and other tissues) proceed very slowly, while the hydrolytic cleavage of CP proceeds rapidly under the influence of an enzyme which has phosphoamidase properties.

Naturally, data obtained on surviving brain tissue regarding the processes of degradation of glycogen as well as CP with or without the participation of phosphorus compounds must be applied with caution to the metabolic processes of nerve tissue in intact animals.

It is known that it is possible to maintain utilization of oxygen by brain slices by the addition of various substrates, besides glucose, to the medium. However, in the living organism none of these substrates can replace glucose and thereby prevent the onset of hypoglycemic coma in cases of sharp reduction in the glucose content of the blood (Holmes, 1937; Soskin and Levin, 1946). Similarly, Acs, Balazs, and Straub (1953) have established that several compounds (glutamic, succinic, malic, lactic, and pyruvic acids), which can support oxygen utilization by brain cortex slices, could not preserve that quantity of ATP which is maintained in the presence of glucose. According to Abood and Geiger (1955), the exclusion of glucose from the nutrient medium (suspension of erythrocytes in Ringer solution) caused a loss of phosphoproteins, phospholipids, and nucleic acids from the tissue of perfused brain; i.e., the presence of glucose somewhat protected the phosphorus-containing compounds of the brain from degradation. In addition, it has been established (Engel'gardt and Lisovskaya, 1954; Lisovskaya, 1954) that it is glucose that ensures the high level of metabolism of brain phosphoproteins.

It would thus appear that basic causes which determine the prime importance of glucose in the activity of the brain have been elucidated. It can be added that according to several authors (Ashford, 1929; Haarmann, 1932; Skvirskaya, 1938; and others) who studied the glycolytic capacity of surviving brain tissue, glucose was the best substrate for the formation of lactic acid under anaerobic conditions.

In the last few years MacIlwain (1951-1959) has made an attempt to approximate in vivo conditions in experiments with surviving brain tissue by stimulating the brain slices, placed in a salt medium, by rhythmic fluctuations of an electric potential. The author has found that under these conditions the surviving brain tissue is more sensitive to various conditions (for example, glucose concentration in the medium) than similar tissue which was not exposed to electric current. It would appear that the effect of electric current on surviving brain tissue makes this tissue a better brain model than the one generally employed in Warburg experiments. However, one can hardly equate the metabolism of brain tissue in vitro with that of the brain in vivo even with the use of electric stimulation. The very technique of the preparation of brain slices inevitably leads to the conclusion that the metabolism of dying tissue, deprived of any connection with the rest of the nervous system or intimate interaction in the living animal, is in fact under investigation.

In spite of the relative value of the results obtained by various methods, the data as a whole give a correct idea of the metabolism of some compounds in the animal brain in the normal state. This finds support in the definite regularity of the evolutionary development of brain metabolism established by Kreps et al. In experiments with surviving brain tissue of several species of vertebrate animals it has been established that the predominantly anaerobic metabolism of the brain in lower vertebrates is replaced by predominantly oxidative metabolism in higher vertebrates.

As has been shown by Verzhbinskaya (1950), in the course of evolutionary development of vertebrates, the cytochrome oxidase activity and the activity of the entire cytochrome system of brain tissue increase. Of considerable interest are her data (1954-1960) on the energy-rich phosphorus compounds. She found that creatine phosphate is present in the brain not only of higher vertebrates but of lower vertebrates as well. In contrast, the content of ATP in the brain increases from lower vertebrates to higher vertebrates, in proportion to the increase in complexity of brain function and increase in the intensity of metabolism of the brain tissue. Similarly, the transphosphorylation reactions in the system of creatine phosphate and adenylic acid and its phosphorylated products appear only in vertebrates living on the earth's surface, and these are most developed in warm-blooded animals. Yet the creatine phosphate of the brain is easily degraded under the effect of various stimuli of the central nervous system in lower as well as in higher vertebrates. At the same time the brain ATP of all fishes and cold-blooded animals is remarkably constant, and only in warm-blooded animals is the ATP content easily altered during the changes in the functional state of the central nervous system or during the action of harmful factors.

As has been previously indicated, the time required for a single degradation and synthesis of the entire normal content of ATP in the brain of white rats is only 4-6 minutes. For the fish it is 75-90 minutes. Parallel with this, as we proceed along the evolutionary scale, there is an increase in the extent of coupling of phosphorylation with oxidation, and the P:O ratio (the ratio of equivalent amounts of assimilated inorganic phosphorus and utilized oxygen) increases from 0.05 in fishes to 1.0 in warm-blooded animals, according to calculations approximating the conditions in vivo.

CHAPTER II

CARBOHYDRATE – PHOSPHORUS AND NITROGEN METABOLISM OF THE BRAIN IN VARIOUS FUNCTIONAL STATES OF THE CENTRAL NERVOUS SYSTEM

Functional biochemistry of the brain is one of the youngest and most rapidly developing branches of biochemistry.

In the USSR this development is closely related to the development of Pavlovian physiology. As its objective it has the discovery of chemical regularities which are intimately related to physiological regularities which characterize the activity of the central nervous system of animals and man. In the path of these investigations, as we mentioned previously, lie great methodological difficulties. These difficulties induce the majority of investigators to study simplified models instead of natural states. For example, instead of studying natural physiological sleep, studies are made of inhibited states induced by narcotic pharmaceutical preparations; instead of studying the state of excitation of some division of the central nervous system, studies are made of the effects induced by electric current, pharmacological means, or by sleep deprivation, etc. Nevertheless, the results obtained under such conditions permit the establishment of definite regularities which elucidate the biochemical basis for physiological phenomena in the central nervous system.

Only in the past few years have reports appeared which are devoted to the study of the biochemistry of the brain during the unconditioned and conditioned reflex stimulation of the central nervous system. The first works in this field are those of Vladimirova (1950-1958). She constructed a special chamber which permitted the establishment of conditioned motor-defensive reflexes in rats and the fixation at an appropriate moment of the chemical composition of the brain by the immediate immersion of the animal in liquid air. The experimental setup preserved the physiological conditions, but the question of the effect of freezing the animal remained open. However, the constancy and similarity of the results obtained by Vladimirova permitted the assumption that the cooling of the brain proceeds a great deal faster than the changes in brain metabolism by the irritation due to immersion of the animal in liquid air.

Vladimirova has established that in the course of the first 25 seconds of unconditioned as well as of conditioned reflex excitation of the central nervous system, increased accumulation of ammonia in brain tissue takes place. On further irritation the amount of ammonia decreases and, simultaneously, the amount of glutamine increases. During change of the state of the central nervous system from excitation to inhibition, there is a reduction in the amounts of ammonia and glutamine, which, according to the author, is utilized for the synthesis of protein for the restoration of the normal chemical structure of the cells.

The data of Vladimirova were recently confirmed by Japanese workers (Tsukada, Hirano, and Nagata, 1958-1961) who consider the amounts of ammonia and glutamine in the brain as good biochemical indicators of the state of inhibition and excitation of the animal's central nervous system. However, the problem of relationship between the processes of excitation and inhibition of the central nervous system and the content of ammonia in brain tissue still remains controversial. Thus, Rozengart et al. (1959) have observed that the state of excitation is not always accompanied by an increase in ammonia in brain tissue. By comparing electroencephalographic data with ammonia content in brain tissue, these authors have established that in the early phase of the excitation process the level of ammonia actually decreases, and at the onset of spasms it sharply rises, but then, in spite of persistence of spasms, the level of ammonia returns to normal.

Troitskaya (1953) utilized the methods developed by Vladimirova in studies of carbohydrate-phosphorus metabolism in rat brain during unconditioned and conditioned reflex excitation of the central nervous system. Her data showed that the glucose levels in the brain do not alter during excitation by either unconditioned or conditioned reflex. Yet, simultaneously there was a significant increase (11-36%) in the amounts of pyruvic and lactic acids in rat brain tissue during either type of excitation.

The observations of Troitskaya suggested that in the large hemispheres of rat brain there occurred acceleration of metabolic processes, including glycolysis. The utilization of glucose was apparently at the expense of blood sugar. That the acceleration of metabolic processes indeed took place was also indicated by the data of Troitskaya on the constancy of the ATP and creatine phosphate levels in the brain with the simultaneous increase in the level of inorganic phosphate during conditioned-reflex excitation of the central nervous system.

Vladimirov (1953) has also observed that under physiologically induced excitation the levels of ATP and creatine phosphate are not decreased. Vladimirov, Ivanova, and Pravdina (1954) in experiments on rats have established that a 3-hour application of electric irritation, which produced in animals an active defensive reaction, induced an increased rate of renewal of phosphorus of ribonucleic acid and phospholipids.

The data of Serdyuk (1953) also point to an increase in metabolism of brain tissue during physiologically induced excitation. Employing the methods of Vladimirova, this author obtained data indicating that in a state of excitation there is an increase in the amount of ascorbic acid in the brain tissue of mice. A particularly high content of ascorbic acid in the large hemispheres of the brain occurs during conditioned-reflex excitation.

Bunatyan and co-workers (1951-1961) studied the effect of cortex excitation and inhibition on the utilization of blood glucose and pyruvate by the brain, employing dogs with exposed jugular veins and with established conditioned reflexes in chronic experiments. The authors took into consideration the changes in blood flow, employing P^{32}. The data obtained by these authors showed that during conditioned food reflex excitation the brain utilizes increased amounts of glucose and pyruvic acid. During the development of cortex inhibition the utilization of glucose by the brain sharply decreases, in many cases completely. The utilization of pyruvic acid by the brain is also decreased, but to a smaller extent, and during the development of cortex inhibition the brain continues to utilize pyruvic acid, although in smaller quantities than during excitation. Thus, the data of Vladimirova, Troitskaya, Serdyuk, Vladimirov, and Bunatyan experimentally confirm the well-known thesis of Pavlov that the process of excitation in the cerebral cortex is related to increase in metabolism and to predominance of processes of dissimilation over the processes of assimilation; in inhibition processes, a reverse picture is obtained; i.e., active synthesis of the products which were degraded during excitation takes place.

It should be kept in mind that the state of excitation and inhibition arising in the cortex of the large hemispheres could be accompanied by the opposite state in the other divisions of the brain, while in all the investigations mentioned above only the large hemispheres or the metabolism in the whole brain was studied. Consequently the data obtained refer to a certain integral sum of functional and biochemical interactions which take place in the large hemispheres or in the whole brain during the processes of physiological excitation and inhibition. For this reason many authors are of the opinion that it is methodologically more correct to study the metabolism of the brain in the state of excitation or inhibition induced by various excitation or inhibition factors, principally by pharmacological means. Under the influence of these factors the states of excitation and inhibition are more defined and more intense in the animal brain.

Here, however, another danger prevails: the transition from physiological states of excitation and inhibition to the states of exhaustion or narcosis is close to pathology.

Characteristic in this connection is the work of Lyubovskaya (1952), who studied the effect of experimental epilepsy (excitation) and pentothal narcosis (inhibition) in chronic experiments on brain metabolism in dogs. She determined the content of glutathione and glucose in the inflowing and outflowing blood of the brain. Blood was taken by puncture from artery and from longitudinal sinus by the method of London. On the basis of the data obtained the author concluded that during epilepsy and narcosis the brain consumes glucose and returns glutathione to the blood, as in the normal state. However, the data reported by this author indicate that during epileptic convulsions the brain releases sugar to the outflowing blood, and during narcosis the difference in sugar levels of the arterial and venous blood becomes insignificant or, in many cases, the brain also releases sugar to the blood. The impression is thus gained from the data of Lyubovskaya that during epilepsy as well as narcosis the utilization of sugar by the brain is decreased, which suggests that there we are dealing with a state of inhibition rather than excitation. This perhaps is explainable by the exhaustion of the central nervous system during epileptic convulsions.

Prokhorova and Tupikova (1957) employed caffeine or phenamine as stimulants and chloral hydrate or morphine plus ether as narcotics for the induction of changes in the functional state of the brain. The experiments were performed on sinus-ostomotized dogs. It has been shown that during excitation the utilization by the brain of glucose from inflowing blood increased, and during narcotic sleep it sharply decreased compared to normal states.

Employing the method of London, Zakharov (1949, 1952) determined the difference in glucose and lactic acid content in venous and arterial blood in dogs in a state of excitation induced by sleep deprivation and administration of benzedrine, or in a state of inhibition induced by morphine-ether narcosis. The author found that during the first hour morphine-ether narcosis increased the utilization of glucose by the brain, decreasing it thereafter. Sleep deprivation and administration of benzedrine, judging by the author's data, do not significantly alter brain metabolism. However, Zakharov emphasized that more reliable data are obtained only during such potent stimuli as massive blood loss, deep asphyxia, etc., and he correctly noted that investigations such as his own and those by other authors, who employed the London method, are only of exploratory significance.

Of the reports in which brain metabolism was investigated by analysis of brain tissue the most important are those in which the state of excitation has been induced by methods approximating physiological conditions. Thus Richter and Dawson (1948) revolved white rats in a special glass vessel and induced in the rats an active defensive reaction. On the basis of apparently purely psychological grounds the authors characterized the state of the animals as emotional excitation induced by fear. The factual material obtained by these authors is nevertheless of great interest. They found that the content of lactic acid in brain tissue of rats excited by the described method was considerably greater (47-67 mg %) than in normal animals (18.8 mg %). It has also been shown that the muscular activity of the trained animals does not increase the lactic acid content of the brain, nor does the preliminary immobilization of this activity by pharmacological means decrease the lactic acid of the brain of "excited" rats. This observation permitted Richter and Dawson to conclude that an increase in brain lactic acid is an indication of metabolic activity of the brain during excitation.

In another work by the same authors (1950) it was found that the content of inorganic phosphate and ATP in brain tissue of rats which were in a state of excitation induced by the above described method did not differ from normal, while the content of creatine phosphate was somewhat increased. It follows that the increase in metabolic activity induced by this method of induction of excitation is not accompanied by a predominance of dissimilation processes.

Palladin and co-workers (1952-1958) studied the relationships of metabolic processes which form the basis of the process of excitation. In a series of experiments these authors induced a state of excitation in rabbits by the administration of pervitin and cardiazole in doses which did not induce spasms but which led to an increase in reflex excitation and an increase in motor excitation. It was shown that the nature of biochemical alterations in the brain depended on the nature of the preparation administered. Thus, pervitin increased the content of ATP in brain tissue and lowered the lactic acid content, in contrast to data obtained after the administration of cardiazole. In addition, the brain tissue of rabbits to which pervitin was administered possessed greater glycolytic activity. These observations led the authors to assume that during excitation induced by pervitin there is an increased synthesis of ATP which is a result of increased metabolism and more complete utilization of carbohydrates resulting from the intensification of oxidative processes.

The administration of cardiazole under similar conditions resulted in a gradual fall of ATP content in rabbit brain and in lowering of brain metabolism. Simultaneously, the content of preformed lactic acid in brain tissue increased. The authors indicated that the described peculiarities in metabolism explain the effect of pervitin which increases the work capacity of the central nervous system, and the effect of cardiazole, which induces excitation without increasing the work capacity.

Khaikina, Goncharova, and Mikhailovskaya (1954) also found that 4 hours after the administration to rabbits of pervitin as well as of cardiazole the brain glycogen content increases from normal (90 mg %, average) to 140 mg % during excitation. While in normal states the predominant fraction of glycogen is "free" glycogen, during excitation the greater portion of glycogen is in a "bound" state. The activity of the enzymes which synthesize and degrade glycogen does not alter significantly. In accord with certain data in the literature, these authors assumed that the increase in the "bound glycogen" fraction, which is more active in biological reactions that the "free glycogen," indicates an increase in carbohydrate metabolism of the brain during excitation of the animals. However, in a later work (1957) the authors showed that the more biologically active fraction of brain glycogen is the "free glycogen," and that parallel with the decrease in its content during excitation there is a sharp increase in the extent of its renewal. Thus, the postulate that there was an increase in carbohydrate metabolism of the brain during excitation remained in force.

Prokhorova and Tupikova cited interesting data on the correlation between the processes of synthesis and degradation in rat brain tissue after the administration of caffeine. They showed that during an intensive state of excitation the specific activity of glucose as well as of brain glycogen significantly decreased along with an increase in the utilization of carbohydrates (as previously mentioned). This indicated the predominance of dissimilation processes in nerve tissue.

On the basis of cited literature data it could be concluded that the state of excitation of the central nervous system induced by various agents, including pharmaceuticals, which, however, do not induce spasms, leads to an intensification of brain metabolism as has been observed during unconditioned and conditioned reflex excitation. However, whether the processes of dissimilation or assimilation will predominate during these states will be determined by the nature of the action of the exciting agents on this or that aspect of the metabolic process.

Shapot and co-workers showed that an increase in the excitation state of the central nervous system, up to a state of exhaustion, leads to a significant alteration in brain metabolism with predominance of the processes of degradation. Thus, Gromova (1954) administrated phenamine to rats and observed some signs of excitation without any alterations in the metabolism of phosphorus compounds in the brain. When, however, in addition to the administration of phenamine, she "teased" the rats for 40 minutes, a considerable decrease in ATP, a decrease in creatine phosphate, and accumulation of inorganic phosphate in the rat brain were observed.

In similar experiments conducted in the same laboratory Shnyak (1962) studied the process of renewal of brain proteins by the rate of incorporation of methionine-S^{35}. She found that when methionine-S^{35} was administered at the beginning of "teasing" and the subsequent 30 minutes of irritation did not induce fatigue, the rate of renewal of proteins either did not change or it was increased somewhat. When, however, the labeled methionine was administered 1-1.5 hours after the beginning of "teasing" and the subsequent 30 minutes of irritation induced definite signs of fatigue, the rate of brain protein renewal sharply decreased. The author assumes that the data support the proposition advanced by Shapot (1952) regarding the competitive relationships between the processes of functional and protein metabolism for the utilization of common sources of energy during the exhausting excitation of the brain.

Palladin and co-workers (1954) induced a state of prolonged excitation in rats by the method of Petrova, either irritating them daily for 1-1.5 months by electric current (20-40 volts) or interrupting their sleep. In the latter case the rats were placed for 3 days in a special drum which was rotated for 30 seconds every 5 minutes. The authors showed that during chronic overstimulation, leading to alteration in nervous activity, the content of ATP is decreased and the rate of renewal of its phosphorus is also decreased. The capacity of brain tissue for anaerobic glycolysis is also decreased somewhat. As has been shown by Skvirskaya and Silich (1954), there is a lowering of nucleic acid metabolism in rat brain during prolonged stimulation by electric current. In view of the fact that ribonucleic acid is intimately bound up with protein synthesis, the authors concluded that their data indicate a decrease in the extent of protein synthesis and that this determines the functional weakening of the central nervous system by chronic excitation. However, further studies (Richter, 1956; Palladin et al., 1957; Nechaeva, Sadikova, and Skvotsevich, 1957) showed that in many instances of prolonged excitation the rate of renewal of brain proteins either does not alter or is somewhat increased. Apparently it is rather difficult to evaluate the degree of excitation of the central nervous system of animals in various experiments. Furthermore, the state of exhaustion of nervous tissue does not always set in to the same extent even under similar conditions.

More significant alterations of brain metabolism are revealed during spasms connected with excitation of the central nervous system. However, when Kerr and Antaki (1937) induced spasms in rabbits by the administration of cardiazole, strychnine, or picrotoxin and then froze the brain under ether anesthesia, it was found that the glycogen content remained unaltered, while the content of glucose and lactic acid increased somewhat. After amytal narcosis, before freezing the brain, even these minor changes have not been observed.

Stone et al. (1945) induced spasms in dogs by intravenous injection of metrazole. The brain was frozen in situ after 8-18 seconds following the onset of spasms. The authors found relative hypoxia accompanied by a fall in oxygen tension in brain tissue, yet the oxygen consumption was sharply increased. Parallel with these events there was an increase in the content of lactic and phosphoric acids and a decrease in creatine phosphate. The content of ATP remained unaltered. Thus, during spasms, as well as during hypoxia, there is an increase in glycolysis in brain tissue.

Khaikina, Goncharova, and Mikhailovskaya (1952), Palladin (1953), and Khaikina (1953) administered pervitin, cardiazole, and metrazole to rabbits and rats in amounts which induced spasms and exhaustion of the nervous system. The content of polysaccharides and ATP in the brain was decreased, accompanied by an increase in the activity of enzymes concerned with the degradation of these metabolites.

It is of interest that the rate of renewal of such labile compounds of the brain as phosphoproteins is not altered during prolonged spasms induced in rabbits by corazole and in rats by phosphacole (Balashev, Maṣlova, Panyukov, and Rozengart, 1958, 1960). Under indentical conditions the rate of incorporation of labeled methionine into brain proteins was either unaltered or significantly decreased (Rozengart and Maslova, 1956).

Gromova (1954) observed a significant decrease in the content of ATP and creatine phosphate in rat brain 2-3 hours after the administration of camphor, which induced violent spasms. An increase in the content of inorganic phosphate of almost 100% was noted at the same time. Examination of the rat brain after one to three onsets of spasms induced by camphor (Vladimirova, 1937; Gromova, 1954) showed that during this time there were not yet any changes in the content of labile phosphorus compounds in brain tissue.

During spasm excitation induced by camphor the content of ascorbic acid in the large hemispheres of rabbit and mouse brain significantly increased (Serdyuk, 1953).

Several authors induced a spasmatic state in animals by electric current. Thus, Dawson and Richter (1950) induced spasms in rats by passing electric current through electrodes in the skull. The authors found that after 1 second of electric stimulation the content of creatine phosphate in the brain falls by 50%, and after 5 seconds, by 70%. The total content of ATP and ADP also decreased somewhat. However, within a short time (15-45 seconds) after the cessation of spasms the content of the labile phosphorus compounds in the brain returns to normal.

A rapid increase in glycogen content in rat brain after electric current-induced spasms was observed by Mison-Crighel, Constantinesco, and Crighel (1959). Glycogen content rose to 1.5-2 times the initial levels.

Kudryavtseva and Kudryavtseva (1950) noted that epilepsy induced by electric current is followed by a sharp increase in the activity of catalase in the large hemispheres of rabbit brain. Reduced glutathione content increases, while that of oxidized glutathione decreases.

According to Khaikina (1953), if spasms are induced by electric current in dogs under ether anesthesia, i.e., when the higher divisions of the brain are in a state of inhibition, then in spite of this the content of brain glycogen decreases. At the same time the activity of synthesizing as well as of degrading enzymes, particularly of amylase, increases. This apparently determines the lowering of the content of polysaccharides. At the same time, the lowering of the content of glycogen occurs at the expense of its "free" fraction, while the "bound" fraction of the polysaccharides somewhat increases in some cases. According to these data of Khaikina, the spasms induced by electric current depend not on brain cortex but on subcortex, and the biochemical changes cbserved are determined by the functional alterations in this anatomical division of the brain.

We previously mentioned the relationship between the stimulation of the central nervous system and the accumulation of ammonia in nervous tissue. Many attempts have been made to connect the onset of spasms during epilepsy, irritation of the nervous system by current, or by pharmacological means (picrotoxin, phosphacole, etc.) with the accumulation of ammonia in the brain. However, this question cannot be considered settled, and what amount of ammonia in the brain can be considered toxic is not as yet clear. It is well known that the amount of ammonia in the brain during spasms induced by various means increases up to 0.7 micromole per gram. However, in order to induce spasms in animals by the administration of ammonium salts, the content of ammonia in the brain had to be raised to 6.5-7.0 micromoles per gram (Richter and Dawson, 1948; MacIlwain, 1955; Stone, 1955; Martinson and Tyakhepyl'd, 1957, 1959). For this reason the administration of glutamic acid for the purpose of binding the excess of ammonia and of relieving spasms, on which so much hope was placed, has not produced the expected results (Braksh, 1957; Klimov, 1959). In this connection the experiments of Martinson and Tyakhepyl'd (1961) are of interest. These authors induced prolonged (15-30 minutes) spasms in rabbits and guinea pigs by electric current and found that the amount of ammonia in the brain increased two-fold compared to normal levels. This was accompanied by an increase in amide nitrogen and by a change in the ultraviolet spectrum of brain proteins. In addition, the electrophoretic mobility of the various brain protein fractions was decreased, suggesting an alteration in the macrostructure of brain proteins. On the basis of available data Martinson and Tyakhepyl'd concluded that the alterations in the macrostructure of brain proteins are connected first of all with the changes in ammonia concentration in the tissue. Thus, even changes in ammonia content not exceeding those found under physiological conditions can, apparently, lead to significant but reversible biochemical changes in brain tissue. Undoubtedly, these questions require further experimental attention.

Thus, the reviewed literature data indicate that during excitation of the central nervous system coupled with spasms of sufficient degree and duration there is an increase in metabolic processes (increase in activity of several enzymes, increase in ascorbic acid, appearance of hypoxia, etc.), and the processes of dissimilation (degradation of labile phosphates and polysaccharides, accumulation of lactic acid and inorganic phosphate) begin to predominate in brain tissue. All these events determine, apparently, the extent of exhaustion and functional weakening of the nervous system as they do during prolonged excitation not accompanied by spasms.

The question as to how the process of restoration of brain metabolism which has been altered by excitation occurs has not been as yet elucidated. Dawson and Richter (1950) observed a very rapid restoration of labile phosphates in the brain after the cessation of spasms of short duration induced by electric current. It appears possible that with an increase in duration of excitation of the central nervous system the restoration processes of metabolic functions would proceed more slowly.

The state of inhibition following the state of excitation in the central nervous system, according to Pavlov, is intimately related to the restoration of metabolic processes and to the increase in assimilatory processes in the system.

In some investigations devoted to studies of brain metabolism during inhibition of the central nervous system, the latter was induced by various means, but not by pharmacological means. The conditions of these experiments are more physiological than those in which narcotics were employed.

We previously mentioned the work of Vladimirova (1951-1957) in which she investigated the content of ammonia in the brain of rats during the shift from the state of unconditioned and conditioned reflex excitation of that of inhibition. She showed that during the inhibition state active metabolic processes which remove the excess of ammonia take place in the brain.

In a series of experiments Richter and Dawson (1948) induced deep physiological sleep in rats by illuminating them with sunlight or artificial light. As in the experiments of Vladimirova, the rats were frozen in liquid air. Less lactic acid (12.2 mg %) and phosphoric acid (12 mg %) were found in the brain tissue of sleeping rats than in wide-awake rats (18.8 and 13.8 mg % respectively). The amount of labile phosphates in the brain of sleeping rats increased somewhat.

According to the view of Shapot (1952) a sharp inhibition of functional activity of nerve cells during the inhibition state following strong and prolonged excitation creates conditions for the shift of energy to the path of protein metabolism. As has been shown by Shnyak (1962), deep sleep which sets in in rats after exhausting excitation is accompanied by a significant increase in the rate of synthesis of protein in the brain cortex. The view of Shapot is also supported by the work of Geiger (1957-1960), who, employing labeled glucose, found that in rabbits during the inhibition which follows spasms only 30-35% of the glucose is directly utilized by the brain for energy purposes, the rest of the glucose being utilized for the synthesis of amino acids and proteins of the brain. As has been mentioned by Vrba (1962), the incorporation of labeled glucose into the amino acids and protein of the brain proceeds very rapidly, which indicates the intense activity of the metabolic processes in the brain.

Of interest is the brain tissue metabolism of animals during winter hibernation, i.e., during a state of very deep but physiological inhibition. In Siberian marmots during winter hibernation the content of brain glycogen is significantly greater than during wakeful states (Khaikina, 1953), which suggests the predominance of synthetic processes over those of degradation.

The studies of Ferdman and Dvornikova (1940), in which the brain metabolism of hibernating and narcotized animals was compared, showed that the content of creatine phosphate and ATP in the hibernating marmot's brain frozen in situ was considerably greater (by 42 and 27%, respectively) than in the narcotized marmot. At the same time the amount of lactic acid in the brain of hibernating animals was lower than in the narcotized animal brain. This work convincingly shows that the labile equilibrium between synthesis and degradation of various compounds in the brain is established on a higher level during physiological sleep than during sleep induced by narcotics. Apparently some aspect of the narcotics' toxicity plays a basic role in lowering this level.

Thus, the cited literature data indicate that during physiological sleep sufficiently intensive metabolism takes place in the brain. The amount of products of degradation (ammonia, lactic acid, inorganic phosphate) decreases and the energy-rich compounds accumulate in the brain (ATP, creatine phosphate, glycogen).

Quite similar results were obtained in experiments in which the state of inhibition was induced by narcotics in doses which produce normal sleep. Thus, Stone (1938, 1940) determined the content of lactic acid and phosphorus compounds in mouse brain frozen in liquid air during a wakeful state and during drug-induced sleep produced by barbiturates. He found that 30-minute drug-induced sleep leads to a certain increase in the content of creatine phosphate and to a decrease in the content of inorganic phosphate in the brain. The content of lactic acid in the brain was also decreased.

In rats frozen during drug-induced sleep produced by nembutal, Richter and Dawson (1948) found a lowered concentration of lactic and phosphoric acids as well as of ammonia in the brain compared to values obtained in rats which were frozen in the wakeful state and even compared to the values found in the brain of rats during deep physiological sleep. The concentration of labile phosphates increased to the same extent as in the brain of rats in a state of normal sleep.

Palladin and co-workers (1952-1954) observed a small accumulation of ATP and a decrease in the amount of lactic acid in the brain tissue of rabbits during drug-induced sleep. They also showed that during 4-hour sleep induced by sodium amytal the content of glycogen in the brain of rabbits increased. The activity of enzymes degrading polysaccharides somewhat decreased. The glycolytic activity of the brain tissue also remained within normal limits. Under the influence of sleep-inducing drugs there was a decrease in the activity of hexokinase, an enzyme which initiates the transformation of glucose. At the same time there was a significance increase in the activity of desoxyribonuclease, while the amounts of ribonucleic and desoxyribonucleic acids remained constant. On the basis of these data Palladin concluded that there is a predominance of the processes of synthesis over those of degradation in brain tissue during the inhibition of the central nervous system by pharmaceutical means. This conclusion characterizes biochemically the protective meaning of inhibition, which makes possible the restoration of the working capacity of the brain.

Unfortunately, in the majority of investigations devoted to studies of the effects of drug-induced sleep or narcosis on the metabolism of brain tissue, insufficient attention was paid to the description of objective indications of the depth of the state of inhibition of the central nervous system, such as the presence of eye reflexes, the width of pupils, pain sensation, the speed of awakening after the cessation of administration of narcotics, etc. The authors also do not always note the total duration of narcotic sleep at the time of fixation of the tissues for analysis. For this reason it is often difficult to judge to what extent the state of drug-induced sleep in experimental animals approximated natural physiological sleep in depth, or the duration of narcotic sleep. Of course, the duration as well as the depth of narcosis has an important bearing on the state of metabolism in the organism. Thus, Dunaeva and Ivanenko (1961) observed that during inhibition of nervous activity in rats and mice by pharmacological means the synthesis of proteins and the content of sulfhydryl groups in them increases, the viscosity of brain colloids increases, and the degree of swelling of the colloids decreases. The indicated changes depended on the concentration and the duration of action of the pharmaceutical preparations. Ether and urethane in narcotizing doses induced the greatest, and barbamil and urethane, in sleep-inducing doses, the smallest changes. The investigations of Tyakhepyl'd (1955-1958) showed that the subcutaneous administration of medinal or sodium amytal at first induced a stage of excitation during which the content of ammonia in the brain increased. Later, with the onset of sleep, the content of ammonia in the brain decreased while the content of glutamine increased. During prolonged drug-induced sleep for several days the amount of ammonia in brain tissue again increased, which was shown by Tyakhepyl'd to be due to sharply altered binding of ammonia in the liver and to an increase in its content in the blood. The lowering of the content of inorganic phosphate in the brain of rats at the beginning of narcotic sleep (chloroform, sodium amytal) and the increase in inorganic phosphate after several hours of narcosis was also observed by Paktovskii, Kozlova, and others (1958).

Contradictory data are available in the literature on the effect of narcosis on the carbohydrate-phosphorus metabolism in brain tissue. This apparently is explainable by the differences in the depth and duration of narcosis in the experiments of various authors even when the same narcotic has been employed. In addition, as we already stated, it is impossible to obtain data on brain tissue metabolism in cattle without narcosis, and the only possibility left is to compare the pictures obtained employing different narcotics. According to Khaikina (1953), ether narcosis in rats did not induce any changes in polysaccharide metabolism in the brain, while hexenal narcosis led to lowering of glycogen content at the expense of its "free" fraction. The twofold decrease in glycogen content of rabbit brain under the influence of prolonged administration of veronal (5 times throughout the day) was observed by Rustamova-Gadzhieva (1958). On the contrary, several authors observed that ether and barbiturate narcosis increases the content of carbohydrates, including glycogen, in the brain of rabbits and mice (Ivanenko and Voinar, 1942; Fregni, Malaguti, and Vaccari, 1953; Prokhorova and Tupikova, 1957). The accumulation of glycogen in rat brain under the influence of neuroplegic preparations (chlorpromazine, reserpine) was observed by Mathe and Kassay (1961).

Kerr and Antaki (1937) found no important changes in the content of glucose, glycogen, or lactic acid in rabbit brain under ether narcosis compared to narcosis under amytal. Only some increase in glucose content of the brain was noted after one hour of anesthesia, which was induced by hyperglycemia accompanying ether narcosis. Employing the isotopic tracer methodology, Prokhorova and Tupikova showed that during morphine-ether and chloral hydrate narcosis in rats there is a decrease in the rate of renewal of glycogen in the brain. For this reason the increase in the content of brain glycogen during narcosis is a result of inhibition of the processes of degradation of carbohydrates and not of increase in the synthetic processes, the intensity of which is sharply reduced. In the same work the old data of Hutchinson and Stotz (1941) on the depression of brain respiration during narcosis were confirmed. It was shown that the amount and the specific activity of carbon dioxide expired by the animal during narcotic sleep significantly decreased.

The depression of respiration in the brain during narcosis is undoubtedly connected with the decrease in its function and with the corresponding decrease in the requirement for oxygen. However, from a practical standpoint a great deal of interest is evoked by the question: is there a brain hypoxia during this state? If we refer to our data shown in Table 1 it can be seen that during pantopone-ether and pentothal-pantopone narcosis of equal depth and duration the content of sugar in brain tissue was practically the same, while that of lactic acid was twice as great during pantopone-ether narcosis. Therefore, in the latter state there was a certain degree of hypoxia of the brain. According to our data one can visualize the following most commonly encountered picture during the pantopone-ether narcosis in dogs. Subcutaneous administration of 8 mg/kg of pantopone induced significant depression in pulse rate; the respiration became accelerated and superficial. In the blood outflowing from the brain the content of lactic acid increased. Placing of an ether mask on the dog's face 40 minutes after the administration of pantopone evoked a violent defensive reaction, accompanied by a delay in respiration and by strong motor excitation leading to the onset of hyperglycemia. Then the defensive reaction ceased, and the dog fell asleep. The narcotic sleep was supported at medium depth: the dog retained lively corneal reflexes, the pupils were contracted, and after removal of the mask the animal awoke within a few minutes. The amount of ether utilized was 3-4 ml/kg. With the onset of narcotic sleep the pulse increased to the initial rate, and the respiration became deeper, which resulted in better supply of oxygen to the brain. After 30 minutes from the beginning of ether narcosis, the amount of lactic acid in the blood was decreased without reaching, however, normal levels, and after further action of ether and increase in its dose 30 minutes later the lactic acid content again increased. In some animals pantopone as well as ether induced a small progressive increase in lactic acid content of the blood outflowing from the brain. Thus, in all dogs pantopone-ether narcosis induced eventually an increase in lactic acid content in venous blood. In 3 dogs it was observed that the amount of lactic acid in venous and arterial blood exceeded that found in the brain cortex. Taking into account the data of Vladimirova (1937) and Stone (1938) that the injection of lactic acid into the blood stream does not increase significantly its concentration in the brain, it can be assumed that the increase in lactic acid in brain tissue during pantopone-ether narcosis has been induced by the hypoxia of brain tissue itself.

That narcosis-induced hypoxia in dogs under analogous experimental conditions occurs was indicated by the experiments of Smirenskaya (1946) who showed that the application of pantopone-ether narcosis induced lowered utilization of oxygen by the brain of dogs. The coefficient of utilization and the arterial-venous difference was decreased 2- to 2.5-fold. The lowered utilization of oxygen was not compensated by an increase in blood flow. The developing acidosis led to lowered CO_2-binding capacity of the blood. Smirenskaya also arrived at the conclusion that the lowered utilization of oxygen by the brain is connected not only with the lowering of its functional activity but also with the fact that the utilization of oxygen is depressed by pantopone-ether narcosis. The appearance of indications of hypoxia of the cerebral cortex during pantopone-ether narcosis was not accompanied by a detectable reduction in the content of glucose or glycogen, which, apparently, was maintained at the expense of sugar of the blood flowing to the brain at an increased rate. Thus, in dogs in which the lactic acid content of the cerebral cortex reached 58-70 mg %, the brain sugar level remained within the same limits as in dogs in which the lactic acid content of the cerebral cortex was 15-34 mg %. Therefore, compensatory physiological mechanisms, in response to hypoxia, alleviated the alterations in metabolism by increasing the flow of sugar in the blood to the brain.

In contrast to inhalation ether narcosis, intravenous dropwise administration of dilute (0.2%) solutions of barbiturates (sodium amytal, pentothal, nembutal) did not elicit defensive reactions in dogs, and the onset of narcotic sleep, accompanied by normalization of the pulse and respiration previously altered by pantopone, resulted in a normal content of lactic acid in the cerebral cortex not only after 30 minutes of narcosis of medium depth but even after an additional hour. Therefore, our data, as well as those of other workers, indicate that barbiturates are less toxic than ether to brain tissue.

Thus, the intensity of brain metabolism during narcosis is decreased, whether it concerns synthetic or degradation processes. To this we must add the more or less toxic effects of narcotics on the organism as a whole and specifically on the central nervous system. The toxic effects of narcotics, particularly during their prolonged action, may induce a state of relative hypoxia with the predominance of the processes of degradation over those of synthesis. As a result, the alteration of metabolism of brain tissue during deep and prolonged narcosis may induce in the tissue a state of exhaustion as well as a state of excitation.

It is apparent that the changes in brain metabolism under the influence of the processes of inhibition and excitation or the narcotic state cannot be insignificant to the organism during the development of terminal states under various backgrounds. As we shall see later, the depth of the terminal state and the possibility of recovery from it indeed depend to a great extent on the state of the central nervous system which preexisted in the animal.

CHAPTER III

CHANGES IN BRAIN METABOLISM IN HYPOXIA OF VARIOUS INTENSITY, IN AGONAL STATE DUE TO BLOOD LOSS, AND IN CLINICAL DEATH

As previously mentioned, regardless of how the terminal states are elicited, their development inevitably leads to the onset of hypoxia of various forms, duration, or intensity. The alteration of metabolism in brain tissue sets in only during hypoxia of definite intensity, when oxygen insufficiency can no longer be compensated by the physiological compensatory mechanisms. As is known, the latter under unfavorable changes in external and internal environment of the organism are first of all directed towards the preservation of the constancy of the conditions of survival of the central nervous system. Towards this aim are directed the redistribution of blood, changes in blood vessels capable of increasing the blood circulation in the brain, deepening and increasing the frequency of respiration leading to an increase in saturation of the blood with oxygen, and changes in the physico-chemical properties of the blood which facilitate the release of oxygen from the blood to the tissues.

The initial indications of the onset of hypoxia in brain tissue are first of all revealed in an increase in the content of lactic acid and inorganic phosphate in the brain. Opitz and Schneider (1950) have noted that an increase in brain lactic acid occurs during hypoxia earlier than the alteration in external respiration, and that it is intimately related to the amount of oxygen in the blood flowing to the brain. These authors also noted that with the increase in the extent of hypoxia the level of glycogen in the brain remains constant only up to a certain moment; then a decrease sets in.

Stone, Marchall, and Nims (1941) and Gurdjian, Stone, and Webster (1944) have shown that the increase in brain lactic acid is observed when the oxygen saturation of the arterial blood decreases to 55-65%, and the degradation of creatine phosphate and the increase in inorganic phosphate begin when the oxygen saturation of the arterial blood falls to 23-35%. If during these events the blood pressure in these animals fell, then the changes were even greater.

Kurokhtina, Malkiman, and Parfenova (1950) induced a state of intense hypoxia in dogs by inhalation of gas mixtures of low oxygen content (1.4-5%) and found that a considerable degradation of ATP (by 40%) and of creatine phosphate (by 60%) in brain tissue occurred.

The administration of cyanides to mice (Estler and Heim, 1960), rats (Albaum, Tepperman, and Bodansky, 1946), and cats (Olsen and Klein, 1947) inactivated the cytochrome oxidase of the brain, changed the aerobic metabolic pathway to an anaerobic one, and exhausted the supply of the energy-rich phosphorus compounds in the brain. The content of glycogen, creatine phosphate, and ATP in the brain significantly decreased, and the content of inorganic phosphate, lactic acid, hexose diphosphate, and phosphopyruvic acid significantly increased. The same general picture has been observed by Le Page (1946) in brain tissue of rats during the state of shock, which was induced by rotating the animals in a special drum or by the application of a tourniquet to the hind limbs.

During prolonged oxygen starvation under lowered atmospheric pressure in a decompression chamber, the changes in brain tissue metabolism have their own peculiarities. Palladin, Khaikina, Polyakova, Goncharova, and Mikhailovskaya (1952) have studied the rabbit and rat brain carbohydrate metabolism during nonlethal prolonged hypoxia. The authors have studied not only the changes in the content of lactic acid and glycogen in the brain of rabbits and rats but also the changes in the activity of several enzymes. Hypoxia was induced by placing the animals for 4 to 7 hours in a decompression chamber with atmospheric pressure reduced closely to levels which induced spasms. For the rabbits this amounted to a height of 7,000-10,000 meters, and for the rats, 6,000-8,000 meters. Such prolonged nonlethal hypoxia altered the character of brain metabolism in rabbits differently than the deep, intense hypoxia or anemia of the brain. Thus, the authors found that along with the usual increase in lactic acid content during hypoxia there was also an increase in glycogen from 90 mg % during the normal state to 140 mg % during hypoxia, an increase of 60%. In rats under similar conditions a reverse picture was noted; namely, the amount of glycogen in brain tissue decreased.

Palladin and co-workers, and later Kovach (1957-1959), noted an inhibition of the activity of hexokinase, an enzyme which initiates the phosphorylation of glucose, in the brain of rabbits and rats during hypoxic hypoxia. This is to be compared with the situation prevailing during terminal stages of traumatic shock when the fall in arterial pressure leads to development of circulatory hypoxia — the activity of brain hexokinase not only did not fall but it significantly increased (Kovach, 1957).

Of considerable interest is the observation of Palladin and co-workers according to whom the intensity of glycolysis (increase in lactic acid during autolysis of brain tissue in the presence of glucose) is somewhat lowered if one employs the brain tissue of rabbits which survived hypoxia. It would appear that during prolonged hypoxia the tissue loses the capacity not only for oxidation but for glycolytic changes as well, although to a smaller extent.

Under analogous conditions Domontovich (1952) observed in brain tissue of rats and rabbits a lowered concentration of ATP and increased amounts of lactic acid.

Thus, the studies of Palladin and co-workers confirm and further extend the assumption that the peculiarities of brain metabolism during hypoxia depend on the intensity and duration of the hypoxia and on the species of animals employed. Furthermore, the increase in the extent of glycolytic processes is the first and general indication of alteration in carbohydrate metabolism during any type of hypoxia, although the extent of glycolysis depends on the cause which induced the hypoxia.

The experiments in which the metabolism of the brain has been studied by noting the changes in the composition of the outflowing blood also illustrate the increase in glycolytic processes in brain tissue during hypoxia. Zakharov (1949-1952), in experiments on dogs with chronic "fistula" of the oblong sinus (London), examined changes in the concentration of glucose and lactic acid in the blood inflowing to and outflowing from the brain under the condition of single massive bleeding (250-350 ml of blood, depending on the condition and weight of the animal). The author noted that bleeding induced hyperglycemia and general lacticacidemia. The amount of lactic acid in the blood was very high, reaching 115 mg %. In a majority of cases after bleeding there was increased consumption of glucose by the brain, which was indicated by the increase in the arterio-venous differences. The lactic acid was flushed out of the brain and its content in the venous blood was greater than in the arterial blood. Later, during recovery from the hypoxic state, there was a definite retention of lactic acid by the brain. Asphyxia, induced by tightening of the trachea, led to the same phenomena.

McGinty (1928), Loeschke and Loeschke (1948) observed significant artero-venous differences in lactic acid concentration, indicating its removal from the brain, in dogs which inhaled gas mixtures of low oxygen content. Komissarenko (1949, 1952) found that during the development of brain hypoxia under insulin intoxication there is at first the removal of lactic acid from the brain into the blood; then, at the height of the intoxication, lactic acid begins to be removed by the brain from the blood with a simultaneous reduction in the removal of glucose. Thus, the state of hypoxia induced a significant increase in the utilization of glucose by the brain and in the production by the brain of lactic acid.

Hypoxia of the brain, induced by tightening of the neck of rabbits by a collar, by the inhalation of gas mixtures of low oxygen content, or by tightening of the trachea, elicited an increase in ammonia content in brain tissue which increased linearly at the rate of 0.027 micromole per gram per minute, reaching after 15 minutes the value of about 0.6 micromole per gram (Thorn and Heimann, 1958). Vladimirova (1938) reported data which seemingly contradicted those of Thorn and Heimann. Studying the effects of oxygen deficiency on the ammonia content in mouse brain, Vladimirova found that during hypoxia the content of ammonia sharply declined (from 0.32 micromole per gram to 0.06 micromole per gram). Hypoxia was induced by placing the mice in a medium of low oxygen content. Apparently, carbon dioxide quickly accumulated in this medium in the course of the experiment which induced in mice the state of narcosis, since the author noted that the mice became inactive, and their body temperature dropped. The state of inhibition and the drop in body temperature lowered the oxygen requirements of the nerve tissue. Essentially, the lowering of the ammonia content in brain tissue was, apparently, a response to the state of inhibition of the central nervous system and not to oxygen deficiency which actually has not been induced under these conditions.

An increase in ammonia and a concomitant decrease in glutamine in brain tissue of rats during oxygen starvation induced by ligation of both carotid arteries has been noted by Pertseva (1958).

Smirnov and Chetverikov (1953-1954) studied the metabolism of the brain during various types of hypoxia employing the isotopic tracer methods. Anemia of the brain was induced in rats by ligation of both carotid arteries which led to inhibition of exchange of phosphate between blood plasma and brain tissue, as well as to a definite inhibition of renewal of phosphorus in ribonucleic acid, phosphoproteins, and phospholipids. During hypoxia, induced by inhalation of gas mixtures of low oxygen content or by placing the animals in a decompression chamber with low atmospheric pressure, the exchange of phosphate between blood plasma and brain tissue, on the contrary, increased at the expense of compensatory brain hyperemia, and the renewal of phosphorus in nucleoproteins, phosphoproteins, and phospholipids remained practically unaltered.

The onset of various forms of hypoxia as a result of a decrease in oxygen content of inhaled air, blood loss, poisoning by sodium nitrite, alteration of blood circulation during terminal states of shock, and from other causes leads to an increase in the permeability of the blood-brain barrier to inorganic phosphate (P^{32}), which, as expected, should be reflected in the metabolic processes of phosphorus-containing compounds in the brain (Bakay, 1957; Tumanovskaya, 1960; Otomo and Michaelis, 1960; Tupikova, 1961).

Of considerable interest are the data produced by the investigations of Leningrad biochemists and pathophysiologists on the effects of partial brain anemia on the metabolism of the brain (Gromova and Shapot, 1951, 1954; Petrov, Shapot, Kudritskaya, and Gromova, 1952, 1953; Pertseva, 1958). We shall consider these investigations in some detail, since they have contributed valuable material towards the elucidation of the pathophysiology and pathochemistry of hypoxic states.

These authors employed white rats in which both carotid arteries were ligated. As is known (Petrov, 1949), following the ligation of both carotid arteries, in the majority of rats a sharp state of excitation with the onset of spasms occurs which persist up to the death of the animals within 10-12 hours ("spasm" group). In the minority of the rats ligation of the carotid arteries induces a state of inhibition which, while gradually deepening, continues for 2-4 days up to the death of the animals ("nonspasm" group). Thus, the natural development of the response of the nervous system in two opposite directions placed in the hands of the investigators means of following up the correlation of the metabolic processes in the brain during hypoxia with the above described picture. After 6-7 or 24 hours from the onset of anemia the brain was frozen in situ under light ether narcosis, and inorganic phosphate, creatine phosphate, and ATP were then determined. The latter (ATP) was determined by the usual 10-minute hydrolysis in 1 N HCl and by the enzymatic method, employing myosin. In addition, by the myokinase reaction the amount of partially dephosphorylated ATP, ADP, was also determined. The data showed that in brain tissue of rats belonging to the "spasm" group, 6-8 hours following the ligation of the carotid arteries there was a sharp drop in the concentration of ATP and creatine phosphate up to a complete disappearance of these compounds in the brain of animals in a state of agony. Simultaneously, the amount of ADP and the accumulation of inorganic phosphate in the brain of rats increased. In contrast, in rats belonging to the "nonspasm" group, after 6-8 hours following the ligation of the carotid arteries there was only a small decrease in the content of ATP and creatine phosphate and a small accumulation of inorganic phosphate in the brain. More significant changes, closely resembling those which were observed in rats belonging to the "spasm" group after 6-8 hours, were observed in rats in an inhibited state after 24 hours.

Thus, the excitation which developed during oxygen starvation deepened, leading to the predominance of the processes of degradation. On the contrary, during the state of inhibition the capacity to equilibrate the processes of dissimilation and assimilation in brain tissue was preserved considerably longer.

The application of general cooling of rats and the administration of narcotics in soporific doses with the objective of induction of defensive inhibition in the central nervous system has led, according to Shapot et al., to the prevention of the onset of spasms, to prolongation of the survival of the animals, and to smaller changes in the phosphorus metabolism of the brain, even in comparison with those in rats belonging to the "nonspasm" group. The administration of narcotics to rats which were already undergoing the first spasms (Gromova, 1954) induced sleep in animals and prevented any sharp alterations in the metabolism of the brain. The administration of narcotics after 5-9 spasmatic fits, i.e., after the nerve cells have already been exhausted, did not improve the metabolism of the brain in spite of the onset of sleep. The intensification of the inhibition up to a state of deep narcosis worsened the course of development of anemia.

As has been demonstrated by Gromova, the irritation by an electric current of rats in which for 3-4 hours after ligation of the carotid arteries no spasms were observed, led to a significant increase in the reactions of degradation of the energy-rich compounds.

On the basis of the experimental data obtained the authors came to the conclusion that the oxygen starvation of the brain elicited by partial anemia of the brain is further aggravated during the state of excitation, because expenditure of the energy-rich phosphorus compounds cannot be compensated due to the low level of oxidative phosphorylation. According to the authors, the state of inhibition, by lowering the expenditure of energy-rich phosphorus compounds, permits adjustment of the metabolism in the brain to the state of lowered supply of oxygen.

It is important to note, as it follows from these investigations, that even the partial anemia of the central nervous system leads to changes in the relationships of the energy-rich phosphorus compounds of the brain: the ATP content is lowered, the ADP content is somewhat increased, and creatine phosphate almost completely disappears. Shapot and Gromova assume that the extreme lability of creatine phosphate in the brain contributes to the relative stability of ATP. Support for this assumption is provided by Nosova (1960), and this will be discussed later.

Tseitlin (1952) noted certain peculiarities of the connection between the metabolism of creatine phosphate and the adenylic acid system in experiments with extracts of brain tissue. On the basis of Le Page's data (1946) and his own he came to the conclusion that the reaction of transesterification between creatine phosphate and the adenylic acid system in brain tissue is considerably slower than in muscle tissue. Along with this, there is an intense hydrolytic cleavage of creatine phosphate in brain extracts which does not occur in the muscle.

On the assumption that various effects (for example, opening of the cranium of the rat under ether anesthesia) induce sharp falls in creatine phosphate content in the brain, Gromova and Shapot believe that such changes cannot be considered specific for anemia of the brain. We believe that the same applies also to ATP, because the same effects induce lowering of its concentration in brain tissue.

There is evidence from the work of Domontovich (1957) for the dependence of brain metabolism during hypoxia on the functional state of the central nervous system. She employed conditioned reflex methodology for a refined determination of the functional state of rat cerebral cortex during studies of the mechanisms of adaptation to oxygen starvation under lowered atmospheric pressures. Simultaneously, biochemical studies were made on the brain of rats frozen in liquid air. It was established that the inhibition which arises in brain cortex during hypoxic hypoxia is of a different nature before adaptation than after adaptation. In the first case the inhibition is of a defensive character and represents a response to the lowered working capacity of the cortex cells. In the second case, apparently, there is an increase in the cortex differentiating inhibition. Accordingly, in the first case (unadapted rats) hypoxia elicits lowering of the content of ATP and creatine phosphate and an accumulation of inorganic phosphate and lactic acid in brain tissue. In the second case (adapted rats), the biochemical changes in brain tissue during hypoxia are insignificant.

We should recall the already mentioned work of Vladimirova in which it was shown that the ammonia content of the brain of mice kept in a medium of low oxygen content depends on whether the mice were in a state of excitation or inhibition. In the first case (excitation) there was a certain increase in ammonia; in the second, a decrease, all the more significant the lower the oxygen content of the atmosphere and the stronger the inhibition of the central nervous system.

Summarizing the discussed material on the effects of hypoxia on brain metabolism, the following points appear the most significant. Hypoxia of the brain, elicited by partial anemia of the brain, inhalation of gas mixtures poor in oxygen, tightening of the trachea for short periods, and by other methods, when the animal can spontaneously return to its initial state only by removal of the injuring factor, quickly induces a complicated series of alterations in the biochemical processes of brain tissue. First of all there occurs a certain depression of oxidative processes and an increase in the relative extent of glycolytic processes. This leads to an increase in the content of lactic acid, inorganic phosphate, and ammonia, an increase in ADP, and a decrease in creatine phosphate and ATP in the brain. The level of carbohydrates remains constant due to the inflow of carbohydrates with the blood. Undoubtedly the functional state of the central nervous system determines to a great extent the character and intensity of the biochemical alterations which occur in brain tissue during the development of hypoxia. The alterations become more intense if the effects due to the state of the central nervous system and to the pathological factor act in the same direction; the alterations become neutralized if these effects act in different directions.

Before we proceed with discussing the available material concerning brain metabolism during terminal states, it appears necessary to explain what meaning is attached at present to this terminology. By "terminal state" we refer to the last stages (III and IV) of shock, preagonal state, agony, and clinical death. The human and animal organism in such states cannot through its own efforts recover from these states, and it perishes even when the external cause of such states is removed. For example, an animal in a state of agony from excessive loss of blood cannot recover from this state and dies even when further blood loss is stopped. Therefore, during terminal states the complex of pathophysiological compensatory mechanisms is inadequate to eliminate the consequences of the pathological processes. In order to return the organism to life it is necessary to perform appropriate therapy; blood transfusion, artificial respiration, administration of pharmacological preparations, etc. It is obvious that the initial, marginal stages of terminal states, for example, shock of III and IV degree, will sometimes conform to this definition, sometimes will not, depending on a series of circumstances (causes which induced the pathological state, prior state of the organism, etc.). As regards the extreme state, such as clinical death, the organism of animal or man cannot independently recover from it under any condition.

The concept of clinical death, as one of the stages of the process of dying, has been developed in detail by Negovskii (1943-1960) on the basis of the dialectic-materialistic understanding of the essence of death. The author considers the state of clinical death from the standpoint of unity of alteration and continuity, pulse and process, during the transition from life to the state of clinical death. Clinical death is a state during which all external signs of life (consciousness, reflexes, respiration, and cardiac activity) are absent, but the organism as a whole is not yet dead; the metabolic processes of its tissues still proceed, and under definite conditions it is possible to restore all its functions; i.e., this state is reversible under appropriate therapeutic intervention. If the organism in a state of clinical death is allowed to take the natural course of events, then the state of clinical death is followed by an irreversible state—biological death. The transition from the states of clinical death to biological death is simultaneously a break and a continuous process, because in its initial stages it is already impossible to completely restore the activity of the organism in all its functions, including those of the central nervous system, but it is still possible to restore the organism with altered functions of the brain cortex, i.e., an organism which cannot function under natural conditions of existence. Thereafter it becomes possible to restore under artificial conditions the activity of only certain organs, and further on even this becomes no longer possible. During biological death metabolic activity degradation, specific for a dead organism, set in.

Attention should be called to the fact that the onset of clinical death can be easily judged by the cessation of the last visible life function—cardiac activity or respiration; but the end of the state of clinical death is much more difficult to ascertain. Here one must follow the experimental data obtained in a large number of experiments which indicate that under definite, concrete conditions animals of given species, age, etc. in a great majority of cases are capable of surviving clinical death of definite duration with full subsequent recovery. The duration of clinical death is determined mainly by the period of survival of the brain cortex during concrete conditions of dying, because this tissue is the least stable in the organism. Consequently, from a practical standpoint it is impossible to determine exactly the end of the state of clinical death for each individual organism, and one has to resort to data based on averages.

Considerable experimental material gathered by several authors indicates that 5-6 minutes is the maximum duration of the state of clinical death which the brain cortex of an adult organism can survive with full subsequent recovery of all its functions, if during this period of dying nothing was undertaken to artificially prolong its life (Heymans et al., 1935-1953; Weinberger, Gibbon, and Gibbon, 1940; Kabat, Dennis, and Barker,

1941; Asratyan, 1948-1954; Petrov, 1949-1952; Negovskii, 1943-1960; Howkins, McLanghlin, and Daniel, 1940; Gadzhiev, 1949; Bakulev, 1954; and others). Furthermore, the indicated 5-6 minutes of the survival period is correct even if the cerebral cortex, prior to the onset of clinical death, was, on the average, for 5 to 25 minutes under conditions of altered nutrition. During slow dying the duration of clinical death, naturally, is shortened, while during rapid dying, it is prolonged.

In actual work the duration of clinical death is established experimentally, and its limits are calculated from the moment of disappearance of the last visible function (cardiac activity or respiration) up to the beginning of taking measures for resuscitation. We shall employ this definition in our further discussion.

The process of dying from blood loss has been studied experimentally most extensively because blood loss is often the cause of sudden death in peace or war. Furthermore, during this type of death one often encounters cases when a completely intact organism is about to perish, i.e., when it is still possible to fully restore all its functions. Of course, it is obvious that resuscitation is impossible when vital organs are irreversibly damaged. In the Laboratory of Experimental Physiology of Resuscitation (Academy of Medical Sciences, USSR), under Professor Negovskii, employing such an experimental model of severe, lethal blood loss, the basic pathophysiological and pathochemical parameters of dying have been elucidated and the method of resuscitation of an organism in the terminal state has been developed. This method has been widely used under clinical conditions, and this fact makes it essential to discuss the biochemical aspect of the problem.

Further on we shall attempt to summarize the results of biochemical investigations which were made in this laboratory and to describe the sequential picture of brain metabolism during development of the terminal state induced by blood loss.

The experiments were conducted on dogs which were under pantopone-ether or pantopone-nembutal narcosis of average depth. Dying was induced by free flow of blood from the femoral artery. Our investigations (1951-1955) showed that at the second and third minute of exsanguination, when the blood loss amounted to about 50% of the total blood of the organism and the arterial blood pressure was lowered to 50-25 mm Hg, the lactic acid of the venous blood increased from 28 to 46 mg %. At the same time, the levels of glucose in the cerebral cortex, frozen in situ in liquid nitrogen, remained at initial levels while the content of lactic acid increased somewhat (Fig. 1). Thus, in this case, as during hypoxia induced by narcosis, the physiological compensatory mechanisms (dilation of vessels in the brain, mobilization of the blood from depot, etc.) summarily ameliorated the symptoms of hypoxia which were induced by exsanguination. Several investigations, referred to previously, also indicated that massive but not lethal blood loss leads to increased consumption of blood glucose by the brain and to an increase in acidosis of the blood due to an increase in organic acid content. The literature data as well as our own show that during the onset of hypoxia of medium intensity along with a depression of oxidative processes there occurs an increase in glycolysis in the brain, as was indicated by the rise in the content of lactic acid.

As the blood loss, the decrease in the rate of blood circulation, and the intensification of hypoxia progressed, the level of brain sugar remained constant for a while and then began to decrease. The glucose of the inflowing blood did not, apparently, compensate for the expenditure of sugar via glycolysis. This situation set in at a time when the physiological compensatory mechanisms could no longer ameliorate the alterations in metabolism induced by hypoxia. The intensification of inhibition of the higher and then of the lower divisions of the central nervous system led to the disappearance of eye reflexes and to the onset of the terminal pause in respiration. According to Smirnov and Negovskii (1949) and Gurvich (1959) at this moment there

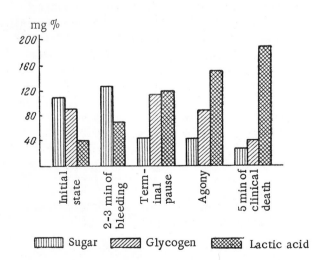

Fig. 1. Content of sugar, glycogen, and lactic acid in the cerebral cortex during dying from blood loss.

is a sharply reduced electric activity of the cortex of the large hemispheres. As has been shown by Smirenskaya (1946), exsanguination leads at this stage to an inhibition in the rate of blood circulation, and, in spite of the increase in the arteriovenous oxygen difference, the utilization of oxygen by the brain is actually negligible. As a result, severe hypoxia of the stagnant type develops (Negovskii, 1949).

In addition to the lowering of the glucose content, during the disappearance of the eye reflexes and the onset of the terminal pause in respiration, there was an increase in the lactic acid content in the brain (Fig. 1). It is important to note that there seems to be no correlation between the extent of decrease in brain glucose, increase in lactic acid, and the length of time during which the brain was under inadequate blood supply (arterial blood pressure of 30 mm Hg or less). Thus, in one of the dogs the low arterial blood pressure persisted for 7 minutes and 18 seconds, and the lactic acid content of the cerebral cortex was 90 mg %; in another dog the lactic acid content of the cerebral cortex was 143 mg%, although the low arterial blood pressure persisted only for 4.5 minutes. These facts once more confirm the observation that during almost the entire period of exsanguination up to the moment of disappearance of the eye reflexes the metabolic processes of the brain tissue were sufficiently compensated and proceeding basically along the oxidative pathway. The basic qualitative change in the metabolism of brain tissue, i.e., that it has gone over to the glycolytic pathway, took place during the onset of the terminal pause in respiration and the disappearance of the eye reflexes, i.e., during the preagonal period.

The experiments showed that the accumulation of lactic acid during the preagonal period took place while glycolysis increased and while glycogenolysis remained unaltered, since the amount of glycogen in brain tissue did not change from initial levels (Fig. 1). Our data confirmed the view of Kerr in that during the onset of hypoxia the brain lactic acid arises simultaneously from glucose and glycogen. The disagreement with our data arises, apparently, from the fact that Kerr studied the rapid processes of dying and degradation in the brain of animals whose heads were severed from the body, while we studied the process of dying under more natural conditions, being able to observe biochemical alterations extended over a period of time. The lowering of the glucose level and the maintenance of the glycogen level in the brain indicate greater stability of glycogen under hypoxia.

As was shown by Shuster (1952, 1953) and Nosova (1960), the glycolytic pathway of carbohydrates in the brain during the preagonal period did not ensure the processes of resynthesis of the energy-rich phosphate compounds, and this resulted in a sharp decrease in creatine phosphate, up to a complete disappearance of it in many cases, and to a significant lowering of the sum of ADP and ATP. We shall discuss the data of Nosova in greater detail because, in contrast to Shuster, she employed a specific method for the determination of creatine phosphate as creatine, and besides determining the total easily hydrolyzable phosphate of ATP and ADP, Nosova determined separately the ATP, ADP, and AMP content chromatographically. She demonstrated that in dog brain cortex in the preagonal state the average content of creatine phosphate was 0.2 micromole per gram, compared to 2.1 micromoles per gram at the initial level. The level of inorganic phosphate rose from 2.7 micromoles per gram at the initial level to 5.5 micromoles per gram during the preagonal period. Of great interest were the changes (Table 3) observed by Nosova in the relative content of adenosinephosphoric acids in the brain cortex of dogs during the process of dying from exsanguination. As can be seen from Table 3, during the preagonal state the true content of ATP is very low, and the products of its dephosphorylation, ADP and AMP, appear in significant amounts. The latter, AMP, is not an energy-rich compound. Consequently, the changes in the content of the energy-rich compounds in the brain in a state of partial anemia, observed by Shapot and Gromova a few hours following the tying of the carotid arteries in rats, occur within a few minutes following exsanguination during the period of disappearance of eye reflexes and the appearance of the terminal pause in respiration.

The alteration of the brain's carbohydrate-phosphorus metabolism induced by d e c o m p e n s a t e d exsanguination and the inadequate satisfaction of its energy requirements did not at the same time alter the nitrogen metabolism, and (see from Fig. 2), the content of ammonia and glutamine in the brain cortex during the preagonal state remained at the upper initial level (Gaevskaya and Nosova, 1961). Only when the "uneconomical" process of glycolysis began to predominate in brain tissue was there a deepening of the extent of inhibition of the divisions of the central nervous system situated above the medulla oblongata. Simultaneously, excitation of the nerve centers of the medulla oblongata set in, characterizing the development of the agonal state in the dogs.

TABLE 3. Content of Adenosinephosphates in the Cerebral Cortex of Dogs During Dying from Blood Loss, in micromoles/gm (average data)

Time of removal of the test tissue	ATP	ADP	AMP*
Initial period of narcosis	1.37	0.26	0
Preagonal state	0.24	0.71	1.0
Agony	0.42	0.61	1.5
5th minute of clinical death	0.07	0.26	1.0

*AMP—adenylic acid.

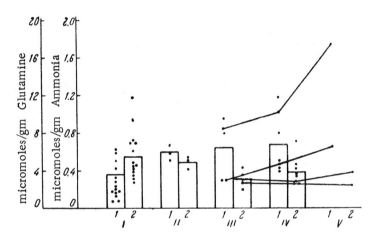

Fig. 2. Content of ammonia and glutamine in the cerebral cortex during dying from blood loss. I) Initial narcosis state; II) preagonal state; III) agony; IV) 5 minutes of clinical death; V) 15 minutes of clinical death. 1) Ammonia; 2) glutamine. Designation of the results: dots —data of individual experiments; columns—average data of all determinations; dots connected by lines—data on the same animal.

Bulanova (1954) had demonstrated, under similar conditions, that the total content of organic acids, determined by electrometric titration, sharply increased during the agonal state of the animal. In arterial blood it reached 17.3 meq as against 11.9 meq in normal conditions. At the beginning of exsanguination lactic acid constituted only 20% of the total organic acids, while during the agonal state it rose to 37%. Therefore, the alteration induced by hypoxia, of the carbohydrate metabolism in tissues resulted in the accumulation of lactic acid in the tissues and in the entry of the lactic acid into the blood during the slowdown in blood circulation.

During the agonal state there was a direct relationship between the duration of brain anemia and the degree of alterations in biochemical processes in the cortex of the large hemispheres, since the compensatory possibilities of the organism were exhausted before the agony set in. Table 4 shows data on the analysis of dog brain cortex frozen during the development of powerful agonal respiration. From the beginning of exsanguination up to this moment there were different time lapses in different dogs, and the central nervous system during various time periods was under conditions of inadequate blood supply at a level of arterial blood pressure below 30 mm Hg. The experimental data are arranged in increasing order of duration of hypoxia. In the first 3 dogs the period of duration of the low arterial pressure did not exceed 5 minutes and the content of glucose in the brain cortex remained at a fairly high level. The high content of lactic acid indicated intensive glycolysis. In the next 4 dogs the time of hypoxia of the brain extended from 6 to 23 minutes, and in 3 of these dogs the glu-

TABLE 4. Content (in mg %) of Sugar, Glycogen, and Lactic Acid in the Cortex of Large Hemispheres and in the Blood of Dogs During Agony

| Dog. No. | Sugar | | Glycogen | Lactic acid | | Time during which arterial pressure was 30 mm Hg or lower | Time from the beginning of bleeding before freezing |
	Brain	Arterial blood		Brain	Venous blood		
1	88	194	—	103	32	3 minutes 30 seconds	4 minutes 18 seconds
2	55	187	—	178	43	3 " 42 "	5 " 06 "
3	41	—	—	145	60	4 " 36 "	7 " 30 "
4	13	169	116	79	—	5 " 56 "	7 " 42 "
5	3	198	87	90	25	6 " 24 "	10 " 00 "
6	70	317	—	277	69	13 " 30 "	15 " 18 "
7	13	168	46	168	—	23 " 00	24 " 00 "

cose content of the brain cortex decreased to minimal levels of 3-13 mg %. In dog No. 6 the glucose level remained fairly high in spite of the fact that hypoxia lasted more than 13 minutes. The accumulation of very large amounts of lactic acid in the brain tissue of this animal indicates that in this case the sugar was degraded via the glycolytic pathway. It should be noted that in this particular case there was very extensive hyperglycemia (317 mg %) which, apparently, was responsible for the fairly high levels of glucose in the brain.

In experiment No. 7, in which the low arterial pressure extended over a more prolonged period, not only glucose of the brain but glycogen as well decreased. Therefore, the prolonged "decompensated" hypoxia led, apparently, to degradation of the more stable glycogen.

According to Nosova, during the agonal state the content of creatine phosphate in dog brain cortex drops almost to zero (0.1 micromole per gram), while the content of inorganic phosphate rises almost to 7.1 micromoles per gram. It can be seen from Table 3 that the process of cleavage of the phosphate groups from ATP continues and that the content of AMP increases still further. The alteration in energy metabolism during the agonal period resulted in an alteration in the synthesis of glutamine and in lowering of its content in brain tissue, accompanied by an increase in ammonia (Fig. 2). These data suggest, it seems, the following practical conclusion: if during massive exsanguination the arterial pressure persists for a long time (20 minutes) at such a low level which cannot be measured by the usual tonometry, i.e., below 30 mm Hg, with the absence of eye reflexes, then this indicates that the hypoxia of the brain resulted in almost total disappearance of carbohydrates from the brain, and it becomes essential to supply them by the administration of glucose in the blood.

The successful operations performed by Fatin (1951) and others on patients in a state of severe shock or even during a preagonal state under hexenal narcosis administered intravenously, dropwise, diluted with large amounts of glucose, are explainable, it seems to us, by the fact that hexenal narcosis lowers the energy requirements of the central nervous system, and the administered glucose replenishes the carbohydrates which, under these circumstances, are degraded by the brain via the glycolytic pathway.

The cessation of cardiac activity and respiration indicated the onset of clinical death, blood circulation ceased, and, as expected, study of the blood of the animal became impossible. However, Semirenskaya (1946) employed the following approach in order to obtain some idea of the content of oxygen in the blood of capillaries of the brain during clinical death. She took samples of blood from the site where the medulla and transverse segments of the brain sinuses merge at the moment when they become filled with blood (during clinical death they are depleted of blood) emerging from the capillaries under the pressure of the blood during the first seconds of resuscitation. Judging by the fact that the glucose content of this blood was the same as that found at the end of the process of dying (about 100 mg %), the mixing of the blood had not as yet taken place (Gaevskaya). It turned out that the oxygen content of the blood of the capillary net of the brain remained fairly high (5.9 volume %), although lower than that of the venous blood at the end of exsanguination (9.3 volume %). Correspondingly, the content of CO_2 was increased only from 50.3 to 53.7 volume %. Thus, the analysis of blood gases also showed that during the agonal state and clinical death induced by exsanguination, the metabolic processes are sharply reduced and the brain tissue cannot adequately utilize the oxygen of the blood.

It has been established by Sechenov (1907) that the oxygen of the blood of animals perishing from asphyxia completely disappears. Further on we shall describe certain considerations regarding the causes which determine the differences in the ability of tissues to utilize oxygen of the blood during death ensuing from asphyxia and exsanguination.

During clinical death, judging by the average data shown in Fig. 1, the glucose content in brain tissue decreased even more than during the period of agony; the content of glycogen sharply decreased, while that of lactic acid sharply increased. However, a more detailed examination of the numerical data (Table 5) reveals certain important details in the changes of the carbohydrate metabolism of the brain during clinical death. Indeed, while in 3 out of 7 dogs in a state of agony the glucose content of the brain cortex was minimal (3-13 mg %), only in 2 out of 13 dogs (experiment Nos. 10 and 13) in a state of clinical death could such low glucose levels in the brain cortex be observed. In the rest of the dogs the sugar content of the brain cortex was 3 to 5 times higher. It would seem that the extension of the duration of anemia of the central nervous system should result in complete disappearance of glucose from brain tissue; instead, it contained definitely determinable amounts of glucose during 10 minutes of clinical death. At the same time the amount of glycogen in the brain cortex during clinical death was considerably smaller than during the preceding period of dying, with the exception of the data in experiment No. 3 in which the period of clinical death lasted only one minute. Taking into account the fact that during clinical death the inflow of glucose to the brain is excluded due to absence of blood circulation, it seems reasonable to assume that during this period the glucose in brain tissue is formed during the degradation of glycogen (probably with participation of amylase), but this glucose cannot be converted to lactic acid, due to the alteration in the enzymatic system or in the conditions for its activity and, therefore, to general inhibition of the glycolytic process.

That the glycolytic process is indeed inhibited is indicated by the fact, as can be seen from Table 5, that there is no correlation between the duration of clinical death, the decrease in carbohydrate content, and the increase in lactic acid. It follows that during the first 2 minutes of clinical death the quantity of carbohydrates reaches a minimum and the quantity of lactic acid a maximum which remain at these levels during the subsequent 8 minutes. As we have shown (1953), the exhaustion of the carbohydrate reserves and the accumulation of lactic acid during clinical death take place not only in the brain cortex but also in the white matter of the

TABLE 5. Content (in mg %) of Sugar, Glycogen, and Lactic Acid in the Cortex of Large Hemispheres of Dog Brain During Clinical Death, and of Sugar and Lactic Acid in Dog Blood During Agony

Dog No.	Sugar		Brain glycogen	Lactic acid		Duration of clinical death			Time from the beginning of bleeding to onset of clinical death		
	Brain	Arterial blood		Brain	Venous blood						
1	36	250	—	210	44	1 min	00	sec	8 min	24	sec
2	32	206	—	156	36	1 »	00	»	9 »	34	»
3	24	135	78	151	—	1 »	00	»	11 »	40	»
4	20	221	44	315	—	3 »	00	»	38 »	00	»
5	27	244	12	192	31	5 »	00	»	23 »	20	»
6	42	—	10	148	12	6 »	00	»	6 »	00	»
7	27	198	13	146	43	6 »	00	»	6 »	26	»
8	24	303	30	196	34	6 »	00	»	6 »	32	»
9	20	233	—	218	22	6 »	00	»	8 »	00	»
10	8	208	—	178	41	6 »	00	»	10 »	30	»
11	34	321	55	196	27	9 »	00	»	11 »	00	»
12	30	243	—	195	72	10 »	00	»	14 »	53	»
13	7	—	58	161	—	10 »	00	»	8 »	27	»
Average	25	233	37	189	36						

hemispheres and in the medulla oblongata. Therefore, the carbohydrate metabolism was generally altered to a similar extent in various sections of the brain in response to hypoxia.

According to Shuster (1952), the sum of ATP and ADP of the brain cortex during the first 3 minutes of clinical death is reduced about twofold. Then the amount of ADP and ATP is decreased more gradually, but it does not reach a zero value even during 20 minutes of clinical death. At the same time in different dogs the extent of degradation of the nucleotides was different. Thus, in the brain cortex of some dogs at 5-7 minutes of clinical death there was 1-3 mg % of ADP plus ATP, while in other dogs at 11-18 minutes of clinical death the value was 9-6 mg %. As has been shown by Nosova (1960), at the 5th minute of clinical death in none of the dogs was it possible to detect even traces of creatine phosphate in brain tissue. The amount of inorganic phosphate increased insignificantly compared to that found in the brain during the agonal period, and the sum of the adenosine phosphoric acids decreased about threefold. Individual determination of the latter showed (Table 3) that along with further decrease in the content of ATP and ADP the content of AMP was also lowered. Apparently, during clinical death the process of deamination of adenylic acid prevails in brain tissue.

Unfortunately, for methodological reasons we could not conduct studies of carbohydrate metabolism in the same animal while the body temperature of the animal remained normal. Undoubtedly, only during such conditions would it be possible to determine the regularity in the slowdown of metabolic processes in the brain during clinical death. Such a possibility presented itself during studies of the process of dying under the conditions of hypothermia, and this will be discussed in Chapter V. However, while studying the changes in the amounts of ammonia and glutamine in the dog brain cortex during the agonal state and clinical death (Gaevskaya and Nosova, 1961) we removed the brain cortex sections from 2 animals and immersed them in liquid air. The time of immersion of the brain into liquid air determined the time of clinical death. Since for the first few tests this time was equal to a few seconds, we considered it proper to record the obtained data under the column marked "agony." As can be seen from Fig. 2, at the end of 5 minutes of clinical death the content of ammonia in the brain cortex increased still further. This is particularly well illustrated in 2 experiments in which the brain tissue was taken from the same animal. Study of the brain tissue in these 2 dogs at the 15th minute of clinical death showed a further increase in ammonia content, particularly in one of the animals, and some increase in glutamine content in the same animal. In several dogs the content of glutamine in the brain even at the 5th minute of clinical death was higher than the average content of glutamine in the agonal state, although we cannot state with certainty that this was due to accumulation of glutamine in the brain and not simply a reflection of its higher initial content. It would appear that during clinical death free ammonia is formed not only from glutamine, but also from proteins, adenylic acid (we previously mentioned deamination of adenylic acid), and other compounds. During this period the accumulation of a certain amount of glutamine is quite possible.

At the 5th minute of clinical death the content of the majority of free amino acids in the brain either did not change (Fig. 3) (glutamic acid, cystine, phenylalanine plus leucine) or it increased slightly (γ-aminobutyric acid, the sum of asparagine, serine, glycine, lysine, histidine, and arginine). Only the amount of alanine and methionine definitely increased. During the period of dying, apparently, changes in the physico-chemical properties of protein structure took place without any alterations in their chemical structure. Thus, on the one hand, the state of clinical death was characterized by the cessation of anabolism and by further intensification of the processes of degradation in brain tissue, while, on the other hand, it was also characterized by the fact that even after 2-3 minutes following cessation of blood circulation and respiration the extent of carbohydrate-phosphorus metabolism via the glycolytic pathway sharply decreased.

That the processes of degradation in dying brain tissue are rapidly inhibited is also indicated by the experimental data obtained on postmortem changes in the brain after decapitation of the animals. In the earliest work of this series McGinty and Gesell (1925) investigated the role of lactic acid of the brain in the mechanism of regulation of respiration. The authors decapitated the dogs with a T-shaped guillotine which separated the head from the trunk and simultaneously cleaved the head into two parts. The brain in one of the halves was immediately frozen in liquid air, while the brain in the other half was kept in a thermostat at 37° for various periods. The data of McGinty and Gesell have shown that, independently of the initial level of lactic acid in dog brain tissue, the rate of its accumulation during the first 3 minutes after decapitation is ac-

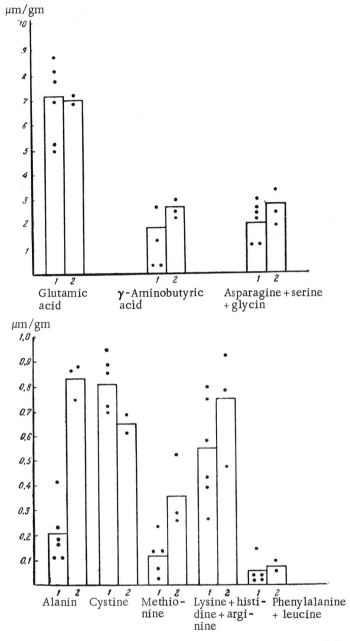

Fig. 3. Content of free amino acids in the cerebral cortex of dogs during dying from blood loss. 1) Initial narcosis period; 2) 5 minutes of clinical death.

tually a linear function of time. The rate of accumulation of lactic acid is very rapid in the first few minutes; then towards 10 minutes it reaches a definite maximum. This maximal amount of lactic acid and the absence of further accumulation of it in the brain kept in a thermostat the authors observed during 10, 15, and 30 minutes. The data of McGinty and Gesell were later confirmed by Haldi (1932, 1933). Kerr and Ghantus (1937), Stone (1940), and Vladimirov (1953) repeated these experiments employing more refined procedures and extending the investigations. The initial levels of metabolites were obtained on brain frozen in situ. Glucose, glycogen, and labile phosphorus compounds were determined in addition to lactic acid.

According to data of Kerr and Ghantus, the initial levels of lactic acid in brain tissue, amounting on the average to 18 mg %, rise to 40 mg % in 3 seconds following decapitation. Thus, even during 3-second anoxia there accumulates that quantity of lactic acid which McGinty and Gesell considered average under normal conditions. Further, during 3-5 minutes after decapitation the content of lactic acid in the brain reaches a maximum as the result of degradation of glucose as well as of glycogen of the brain. Glucose is utilized considerably faster than glycogen and it completely disappears during this period. The degradation of glycogen continues for the first 15 minutes, and the remaining 15-20 mg % disappears gradually in the next 1-2 hours. The amount of lactic acid formed in the brain during the postmortem period is intimately related to the blood sugar level before death (Holmes and Sherif, 1932; Kerr and Ghantus, 1937). Thus, according to data of Kerr, the presence of hyperglycemia (313-327 mg %) is followed by postmortem accumulation of lactic acid in the brain amounting to 304-330 mg %, while hypoglycemia at the moment of decapitation (20-32 mg %) leads to post mortem accumulation of lactic acid of only 54-98 mg %.

Kerr and then Vladimirov and Rubel (1954) have shown that during 3 seconds after decapitation the brain tissue loses 70% of its creatine phosphate. Further decrease proceeds more gradually, yet quite rapidly, and 45 seconds after decapitation creatine phosphate completely disappears from brain tissue.

ATP also is initially decomposed quite rapidly: about $\frac{2}{3}$ in the first 3 seconds. Further decomposition of ATP proceeds more slowly, and one minute after decapitation the brain tissue still contains about 0.5 micromole of ATP per gram.

Gurvich, Levyant, and Erzina (1950) induced complete temporary anemia of the central nervous system in narcotized dogs by the method of Pavlov-Chistovich, by exclusion of blood circulation, or killing the dogs by double pneumothorax. The authors first of all noted that there were no differences in the changes in the content of ADP plus ATP in brain tissue regardless what method of killing the animals was employed. In all cases after the last agonal onset there was a rapid decrease in the content of ATP plus ADP in the brain cortex, the most rapid decrease taking place in the first 5 minutes.

The postmortem accumulation of ammonia in brain tissue, as has been shown by Vladimirova (1938), takes place more gradually and regularly than the degradation of the labile phosphorus compounds, and its quantity, considerably exceeding normal levels, appears only 5 minutes after decapitation.

Comparison of the illustrated data with those of our investigations permits the conclusion that in dying brain tissue the carbohydrate-phosphorus metabolism is altered considerably earlier than the nitrogen metabolism, and the latter event is apparently the result of the first. In addition, it is necessary to emphasize that the drop in the extent of degradation processes in brain tissue, even under the conditions of decapitation, occurs before the complete utilization of glucose, glycogen, or ATP has taken place.

As has been shown in experiments with lethal exsanguination, the drop in the intensity of metabolic reactions in brain tissue occurs before glucose, glycogen, ATP, and ADP have been completely utilized. An exception was creatine phosphate, which disappeared immediately after the physiological compensatory mechanisms ceased to compensate for the occurring alterations in blood circulation. The disappearance of creatine phosphate, the donor of phosphate in transphosphorylation reactions with the adenylic acid system, determined the direction of the reactions towards degradation and towards impossibility of ATP resynthesis. It may be assumed that the parallel accumulation of the acidic degradation products (inorganic phosphate, lactic acid, and other organic acids) altered the state of the surrounding medium in such a way that the activity of several enzymes and coenzymes was inhibited, thus favoring the slowdown of the glycolytic process. However, as will be seen in the next chapter, brain tissue began to glycolyze again after the blood circulation had been restored, in spite of presence in the tissue of the same, if not even greater, amount of acidic products. This forces the assumption that the slowdown of glycolysis during clinical death depends not so much on the changes in the pH of the medium and accumulation of acidic products in it as on the inadequacy in the amount of glucose and, possibly, some other compounds, which are delivered with the blood during resuscitation.

That the acticity of the enzymes of brain tissue during clinical death is intact is indicated by the fact that homogenates of the isolated brain tissue, placed in Warburg vessels, intensively consume oxygen and undergo glycolysis in an artificial medium. The preparation of such tissue takes about 15 minutes; i.e., the tissue during this period survives the state of clinical death without any loss in the ability to respire and glycolyze.

Therefore, the enzymatic systems of the tissue cannot possibly be destroyed during clinical death, although it has been observed that the longer the period of preparation of such tissue the less intense is the consumption of oxygen or the formation of lactic acid in it (Chesler and Himwich, 1944, and others). At the same time, in the presence in the reaction mixture of an excess of substrate (glucose) which serves as the acceptor of phosphate. the initial levels of creatine phosphate or ATP are restored in brain homogenates or slices.

Let us pause at certain considerations which arise when we compare the metabolism of the brain during the process of dying from asphyxia with the metabolism during exsanguination. The most significant difference is the presence of a large amount of blood in the blood vessels of the brain of the animal dying from asphyxia, contrasted with an insignificant amount of blood in the brain tissue of the animal dying from exsanguination. The possibility of receiving additional amounts of glucose from the blood is apparently determined by the circumstance that during death from asphyxia, in spite of the presence of acidic products of degradation, tissue respiration continues up to the moment of complete utilization of the oxygen of the blood, while during death from exsanguination neither the oxygen of the blood nor the substrates of respiration and glycolysis are completely utilized. These considerations suggest that in all probability in the mechanism of the slowing of the glycolytic process in dying brain tissue the greatest role is played by the insufficient quantity of substrates (glucose, glycogen) which can serve as acceptors of phosphate and introduce it into the cycle of carbohydrate-phosphorus transformations.

Up till now we considered the changes in the metabolic processes in dying brain tissue, without paying any attention to the question of the functional state of the animal before the beginning of exsanguination. From the investigations of Shapot et al. and Petrov it appeared clear that even during partial anemia of the brain the functional state of the central nervous system markedly affects the rate of development of the alterations in metabolism of the brain.

It has been shown by Negovskii and co-workers that the functional state of the central nervous system during the dying process has a definite effect on the completeness and speed of restoration of the functions of the cerebral cortex after resuscitation. Thus, excitation and deep narcosis during dying hamper the subsequent restoration of the functions of the cerebral cortex, while medicinal sleep, on the contrary, close in depth to physiological sleep, enhances the restoration.

Grozdova (1955-1959) has established that in dogs which before and during dying were in a state of sleep induced by barbamyl, similar in depth to physiological sleep, the functions of the central nervous system were restored more fully than in dogs which were dying either under ether narcosis or without it. Thus, in experiments on 21 dogs when clinical death was of 7 minutes duration, 12 dogs could not be resuscitated, 2 were resuscitated with complete restoration of all functions, and in 7 dogs after resuscitation there was only partial restoration of the functions of the nervous system. However, after clinical death of 7 minutes duration of 13 dogs dying in a state of sleep induced by barbamyl, in depth closely resembling physiological, all 13 dogs were resuscitated with complete restoration of all functions.

It is well known that during the process of dying the functions of the cerebral cortex are switched off first of all and its influence on the lower divisions of the central nervous system ceases. Negovskii has suggested that even when the direction control of the cortex over the subcortical and stem nerve centers ceases, its prior effects continue to be reflected in the functional characteristics of these centers, determining their resistance to hypoxia. If this is so, it would be natural to expect that the course of metabolism of the cerebral tissue during the process of dying and resuscitation would proceed differently during different functional states of the cerebral cortex before the process of dying.

The elucidation of the relationship between the functional state of the central nervous system and metabolism of the cortex of the large hemispheres is greatly complicated by methodological difficulties, especially in experiments on dogs. The impossibility of making trepanation of the skull without serious alterations of the functional state of the central nervous system forced us to conduct a portion of our work on narcotized animals. The establishment of regularities in the carbohydrate metabolism of the cerebral tissue during dying from exsanguination, on the one hand, required at least partial verification of the obtained data without the use of narcosis; on the other hand, the exclusion of narcosis would permit approximation of the posed problem regarding the relationship between the functional state of the central nervous system and the metabolism of the dying brain.

The only methodological possibility which occurred to us was an attempt to perform the trepanation of the skull during the onset of clinical death in the animal when all forms of sensitivity appear to be absent. In 5 experiments on dogs all narcotics were excluded. The dogs were tied to stands. Under local procaine anesthesia the femoral vessels were bared and exsanguination commenced. The trepanation of the skull began one minute after the last agonal inspiration. Since 5 to 10 minutes were required for the operation, the duration of clinical death at the moment of freezing the brain varied from 6 minutes 30 seconds to 11 minutes 57 seconds (Table 6). The dogs were quiet before they were tied to the stand. Two of them (Nos. 1 and 2) did not object to tying, since they were inhibited by a mass of external irritants in unfamiliar surroundings. During the operation this inhibition was weakened and the dogs exhibited orientation reflexes. During exsanguination no excitation was in evidence; on the contrary, the inhibition of the cerebral cortex was deepened up to complete exclusion of all its functions. Then the inhibition extended to the middle brain, including the red nucleus; and relatively rapidly, within 3 minutes, the symptoms of decerebration rigidity appeared. In the other 3 dogs defensive reactions were in evidence during tying to the stand; they attempted to escape, barked and squealed. During the operation the animals quieted down somewhat, but with the onset of exsanguination the excitement of the dogs increased, and the attempts to get away were resumed. The symptoms of decerebration rigidity in 2 of these dogs appeared later, within 6 to 10 minutes; i.e., the functional activity of the cerebral cortex and its influence on the lower divisions of the brain were preserved for a considerably longer time. The process of dying was also longer than in inhibited dogs.

Examination of the data obtained in this series of experiments fails to establish any relationship between the state of the central nervous system during the process of dying and the content of glucose and glycogen in the cerebral cortex of dogs at the 7th to 12th minute of clinical death. Both the excited group of dogs as well as the dogs in which there were rapidly developing inhibitory processes contained the same insignificant amounts of carbohydrates in the brain tissue as in the brain of dogs which were dying in a state of narcosis (Table 5). As regards the lactic acid it could be mentioned that in all 3 dogs dying in the state of excitation (Nos. 3, 4, 5) the cerebral cortex contained significantly greater amounts of lactic acid than in the 2 dogs which were dying in the inhibited state. Although the largest amount of lactic acid was observed in dogs which at the beginning of exsanguination had slight hyperglycemia, apparently induced by the excitement of the animals, it appears un-

TABLE 6. Content of Sugar, Glycogen, and Lactic Acid (in mg %) in the Cortex of Large Hemispheres of Dogs During Clinical Death

Dog No.	Sugar	Glycogen	Lactic acid	Sugar of arterial blood at the beginning of bleeding	Duration of dying	Period of clinical death	Time of onset of symptoms of decerebration from beginning of bleeding	
							Rigidity of occipital muscles	Opistotonus
Dying without narcosis								
1	19	24	151	71	7 min. 12 sec.	8 min. 24 sec.	1 min. 36 sec.	2 min. 48 sec.
2	30	34	150	111	5 » 51 »	11 » 57 »	3 » 36 »	
3	18	18	230	160	14 » 12 »	6 » 30 »	1 » 54 »	3 » 18 »
4	28	31	230	140	16 » 26 »	7 » 22 »	6 » 12 »	10 » 06 »
5	44	17	187	99	18 » 12 »	7 » 36 »	5 » 42 »	
Dying in medicinal sleep								
6	8	22	150	106	12 » 45 »	12 » 27 »	—	—
7	16	27	93	103	7 » 06 »	8 » 18 »	—	—
8	1	29	167	69	4 » 12 »	9 » 30 »	—	—
9	16	25	163	113	8 » 00 »	10 » 48 »	—	—

likely that there is a direct relationship between these two parameters. From the experiments with narcotized animals (Table 5) we could not deduce any direct relationship between the amounts of blood sugar and the accumulation of lactic acid in the brain, as has been noted by Kerr. This is explainable by the fact that such a relationship is apparent only when hyperglycemia (300 mg %) is compared with hypoglycemia (20-30 mg %). In our experiments, however, the blood sugar values varied within much narrower limits. Therefore, as follows from Table 5, in a series of experiments and during more extensive hyperglycemia (198-208 mg %) than that in dogs in a state of excitement, the content of lactic acid in the brain was relatively low, namely, within 146 to 178 mg %.

To what then could one attribute the differences in the accumulation of lactic acid in the brain tissue of the easily excitable and easily inhibitable dogs? First of all attention is drawn to thé circumstance that the amount of glucose and glycogen in the cerebral cortex during clinical death was almost the same in all dogs and that this amount was rather small. Therefore, the reserves of carbohydrates were almost completely exhausted during dying in dogs which were in a state of excitation as well as in dogs in which inhibitory processes were rapidly developing. For this reason the smaller quantity of lactic acid in some dogs cannot be explained by poorer utilization of carbohydrates than in other dogs. Neither can it be explained by the transformation of lactic acid into glycogen in view of the presence of hypoxia. This is supported by the low content of glycogen in the brain during clinical death. The deduction follows that during the predominance of inhibitory processes in the cerebral cortex less lactic acid accumulated in the brain because a relatively greater portion of carbohydrates was subjected to oxidative transformations.

On the basis of the experiments obtained on nonnarcotized dogs one could assume that a certain deepening of the inhibition in the central nervous system before dying, in the quiet animals as well as in the excited ones, would lead to lowering of the lactic acid content in the brain. To check this assumption four experiments were performed in which the dogs before dying were in a state of medicinal sleep. Before the experiment the dogs were administered subcutaneously 4 mg per kilogram of pantopone. Then after 30-40 minutes under local procaine anesthesia the femoral vessels were bared and into the vein a 0.3% solution of sodium amytal was introduced dropwise. By regulating the rate of administration of sodium amytal the depth of sleep was kept close to physiological. The animal exhibited considerable lowering of muscle tone, the eyeballs were turned downwards, the eye reflexes were intact, the pupils were contracted to 3-4 mm, the respiration was even, rhythmical, superficial, and with some snoring, and arterial pressure was moderately lowered. During noise in the operating room the dogs began to wake up, stretch and whine, and when it was quiet again the dogs fell asleep. The state of sleep was supported for an hour, after which the exsanguination was commenced. Trepanation of the skull was performed after the onset of clinical death. It goes without saying that sodium amytal administered to dogs intravenously before dying continued to exert its effect during the subsequent exsanguination period.

The data shown in Table 6 confirmed the assumption described. The quantity of lactic acid accumulated in the cerebral cortex of dogs during the process of dying and clinical death while under medicinal sleep was lower than in dogs which were dying while in a state of excitation. It should be noted that in dog No. 8 during the preparation of the blood vessels and before the onset of anesthesia induced by the administered sodium amytal there was a state of intense excitement for almost 30 minutes: the animal attempted to get off the stand, was howling loudly, and even tried to bite the laboratory assistant. However, even in this case the amount of lactic acid, although quite large, did not reach the levels obtained in dogs which were in a state of excitation but dying without the use of anesthetic.

As is evident from Table 6 the content of glucose and glycogen in the cerebral cortex of dogs dying while in a state of medicinal sleep was just as low as in dogs which were dying while in a state of wakefulness or under narcosis. Therefore, it would appear that the reserves of carbohydrates were practically exhausted in the brain tissue of dogs of this group also, and our assumption can be applied to them as well: namely, that the smaller extent of accumulation of lactic acid during the period of dying is best explained by the better preservation of oxidative processes in dogs in which the inhibitory processes of the central nervous system predominated.

On the basis of our own observations and those recorded in the literature the following picture is visualized regarding the relationship between the ability of the brain tissue to survive the state of clinical death and the metabolic processes in this tissue. In the first 5-6 minutes of clinical death the content of carbohydrates and energy-rich phosphate compounds decreases to a minimum which induces a sharp slowdown in the process of glycolysis, and further cleavage of the carbohydrate-phosphorus compounds proceeds very slowly. Consequently, in the first 5-6 minutes of clinical death the brain tissue receives a quantity of energy which, although small, is nevertheless sufficient for the majority of the nerve cells to preserve their structure and viability. This in turn ensures, during subsequent resuscitation, complete restoration of all functions of the central nervous system.

Naturally, in different animals this period will vary in either direction. Indeed, a prolonged period of dying, as we have seen, leads to exhaustion of carbohydrate reserves even during the agonal state, and consequently the brain of such an animal could survive only a short period of clinical death compared to animals which were dying rapidly and in which the carbohydrate reserves had not yet been depleted before the onset of clinical death. The fact that the period of dying is longer the greater the extent of alterations of nervous activity obtained during resuscitation, and vice versa, confirms the observations of Negovskii, Petrov, and others as well as our own.

Besides the length of the process of dying, considerable influence on the metabolism and the survival time, during clinical death, of the brain tissue is exerted by the individual characteristics of the tissue, its specific physicochemical peculiarities which are not yet well understood, as well as by the functional state of the central nervous system before dying, and by many other factors. The data in the literature, as well as our own, indicate that during short period of anemia of the brain in various animals different quantities of energy reserves (glucose, glycogen, ATP, ADP) are expended and different quantities of degradation products accumulate. Undoubtedly, in these cases the correlation between the oxidative and glycolytic processes in various instances will be different. All this apparently has a bearing on the phenomenon that in individual animals (as, for example, in the dog named Bobik, described by Negovskii and co-workers, 1938) the functions of the central nervous system are restored after 8 minutes of clinical death, while in others the restoration of the functions proceed slowly and incompletely after only 5 minutes of clinical death.

Nevertheless, the large amount of experimental material and numerous clinical observations show that in the overwhelming majority of cases during a period of dying (period of intense hypoxia of the brain) equal to 5-25 minutes, a duration of clinical death of 5-6 minutes appears for the moment the upper limit which the central nervous system can endure with complete subsequent restoration of all its functions, if the process of dying proceeds under normal conditions of body temperature of animal or man.

During periods of clinical death longer than 5-6 minutes the energy resources of the brain tissue become so insignificant that in the majority of cases they cannot ensure the structural integrity and the viability of the nerve cells. In accord with this, longer intervals of clinical death induce irreversible morphological alterations in nerve tissue and later, in varying degrees, disturbances in the function of the central nervous system (Klosovskii, 1941; Kurkovskii, 1940, 1941, 1946; Romanova, 1956).

The data of Negovskii and co-workers indicate that hypoxia induces the greatest damage to the visual zone of the cerebral cortex. It would seem that in this zone the metabolic processes should proceed most intensively, and therefore the energy deficit would develop in this zone earlier than in any other brain division. However, the data of Kreps, Smirnov, and Chetverikov (1954) showed that the intensity of metabolism of phosphorus compounds in the motor zone of the cerebral cortex exceeded manyfold that observed in the visual and auditory zones. Apparently, while analyzing the described phenomena, one must take into account not only the intensity and nature of metabolism of the tissue, but also its individual specific biochemical structure which determines its stability. Unfortunately, this field, belonging to histochemistry, is still poorly developed.

CHAPTER IV

METABOLISM OF THE BRAIN DURING THE POSTHYPOXIC STATE, DURING THE PROCESS OF RESTORATION OF BASIC VITAL FUNCTIONS OF THE ORGANISM AFTER THE STATE OF CLINICAL DEATH, AND DURING LATER STAGES OF THE RESTORATION PERIOD

The literature devoted to biochemistry of the brain during hypoxic states contains considerably less data on the posthypoxic state than on the period of hypoxia itself. A number of authors who studied the changes in brain metabolism during hypoxia suggested that the content in the brain tissue of such substances as inorganic phosphate, lactic acid, creatine phosphate, and the sum of easily hydrolyzable phosphate compounds (ATP and ADP) very rapidly returns to normal levels after the factors which prevent the access of oxygen to the brain are removed. The restoration of blood circulation after the occlusion of brain vessels, the restoration of respiration after constriction of the trachea, the increase in oxygen content to normal in an inhalation mixture, etc. lead within a few minutes, and in some cases a few seconds, to restoration to normal levels of the energy-rich compounds, and after 30-60 minutes to lowering to normal levels of the content of inorganic phosphate and lactic acid in the brain tissue. In the majority of these investigations the depth of the hypoxia and its duration were such that after the removal of the factor which induced it the animal spontaneously returned to the initial state. However, according to Gurvich and others, the sum total of ATP and ADP was restored to almost the initial level within several minutes, even after the blood circulation was excluded for 30 minutes, when the restoration of blood circulation resulted in only partial restoration of brain functions (appearance of respiratory movements and eye reflexes).

While after the removal of factors which induce hypoxia of average depth one can observe a rapid normalization of the general state of the animal as well as of the metabolic processes in the animal, during recovery from terminal states the normalization of the physiological functions in the animal proceeds more slowly and gradually. The rate of normalization of the physiological functions is intimately connected with the duration and depth of the hypoxia. As was shown in the preceding chapter, the extent of alteration in metabolism of the brain tissue depends on the depth and duration of hypoxia, and the greatest extent of such alteration occurs during clinical death. Obviously, it is impossible to develop any rational therapeutic procedure during the restoration period without a knowledge of the biochemical picture of alterations which take place in the resuscitated brain tissue. This made it imperative to study in greater detail the metabolism of the organism recovering from the terminal state.

Such a study has been made in the greatest detail in the Laboratory of Experimental Physiology of Resuscitation of the Academy of Medical Sciences of the USSR, which is devoted to studies of the pathophysiology and therapy of terminal states. Based mainly on the work done in this laboratory, we shall attempt to give as complete a picture as possible of the process of restoration of metabolism of the brain tissue of animals which survived the state of clinical death under the conditions of normal body temperature.

The experiments were conducted on dogs under the conditions described in the preceding chapter. The resuscitation of animals after 5-6 minutes of clinical death, induced by intense, massive exsanguination, was performed by a complex method developed by Negovskii and co-workers (1938-1960).

The methodology of restoration of vital functions consists in simultaneous rhythmic inflow of blood into the cardiac artery and artificial respiration by means of an apparatus which alternately pumps air into the lungs and removes it from the lungs. The dogs were administered the previously removed, heparinized blood. After 12-10 seconds from the beginning of the pumping of the blood, 0.2-0.5 ml of 1:1000 solution of adrenaline was introduced into the blood stream. The recommended addition of glucose to the blood was not made in order not to alter the picture of the carbohydrate metabolism. The pressure of the inflowing blood was 50-60 mm Hg greater than the initial arterial pressure of the animal. The centripetal pumping of the blood into the artery restores the nourishment of the cardiac muscle, lowers the extent of its hypoxia, and restores the cardiac activity. The mechanism of the action of arterial pumping of the blood is based "on the reflex effect on the heart from irritated angioreceptors and on direct irritation of the system, which is responsible for excitation, as well of the receptors of the heart which was artificially restored by venous circulation" (Negovskii and Smirenskaya, 1954).

After the restoration of the first cardiac contractions, administration of the blood into the vein was immediately commenced, which resulted in the acceleration of the cardiac activity. The parallel pumping of the blood into the artery and its transfusion into the vein was continued for 10-20 seconds until regular and powerful cardiac activity was restored. Then the pumping of the blood into the artery was discontinued, and the available blood of the animal was administered intravenously. If during this time the arterial pressure was very high (above 180 mm Hg) the intravenous blood transfusion was made intermittently, employing a microflow.

The artificial respiration was performed by an apparatus which periodically pumped air into the lungs, inducing a mechanical dilation of the lung tissue during inhalation. The dilation of the lungs induces the appearance of impulses which travel along the vagus nerves into the bulbar centers and facilitate the restoration of the functions of the respiratory center. In terminal states during the artificial active exhalation, as well as during active inhalation, impulses arise in the ending of the vagus nerves which induce changes in the activation of the respiratory center (Negovskii), which lead to the rapid restoration of the respiration of the animal.

The artificial respiration was conducted at a frequency of 20-25 inspirations per minute. After the restoration of the respiration of the resuscitated animal the frequency of the artificial respiration was gradually reduced, and then stopped when the rhythm of the respiration of the animal itself reached 5-7 inhalations per minute. We employed several apparatuses for artificial respiration, most frequently model DP-1.

During the resuscitation of dogs after 5-6 minutes of clinical death ventricular fibrillation arises very infrequently. However, whenever this occurred the ventricular fibrillation was eliminated by the discharge of a condenser by the method of Gurvich (1952-1957).

The moment of the initiation of the pumping of blood into the artery and of artificial respiration signified the end of clinical death. 25-50 seconds after taking the measures for the resuscitation of the animals, cardiac activity was restored at a level of 40-70 mm Hg arterial pressure. The arterial pressure was then rapidly increased and at the end of the first minute of resuscitation it reached the initial level (90-120 mm Hg) and then somewhat higher levels (150-180 mm Hg). After 10-20 minutes the level of pressure returned to almost normal levels. Because of the fact that the animal was administered his own previously removed arterial blood and because of the effective artificial respiration, the brain began to be flooded with blood rich in oxygen within 20-40 seconds from the onset of resuscitation. The blood contained elevated quantities of acidic products of metabolism (Gaevskaya, 1946; Bulanova, 1954), and the physico-chemical properties of the blood were altered in a manner which ensured the supply of oxygen to the tissue (according to Bulanova, a deflection of the oxy-hemoglobin dissociation curve downward and to the right takes place). All this, it seems, should favor the removal of oxygen from the blood and the supply of it to the brain tissue. However, as has been established by Smirenskaya (1946), in the initial period of resuscitation (the period of restoration of cardiac activity, then of respiration and eye reflexes), i.e., during the first 20-30 minutes from the beginning of resuscitation, the amount of oxygen in the blood taken from the transverse brain sinus and in arterial blood was almost the same. The arterio-venous differences in oxygen varied within 0.04-1.16 volume % compared to 10.3 volume % at the initial level. Correspondingly insignificant was the coefficient of utilization of oxygen: 0.004-0.009 compared to 0.48 under normal conditions. The lowering of the arterio-venous difference in oxygen occurred mainly at the expense of the increase in oxygen in venous blood (average of 17 volume % instead of 11 volume % under normal conditions). At the same time the capacity of the blood to bind CO_2 was lowered 2- to 4-fold compared to normal, which indicated considerable acidosis.

44

TABLE 7. Content of Sugar (in mg %) in the Blood of Dogs at the Moment of Restoration of Respiration

Dog No.	Duration of clinical death	Before expt.	Beginning of bleeding	Appearance of respiration
1	2 min 41 sec	91	173	285
2	2 » 50 »	110	198	363
3	3 » 00 »	103	178	284
4	3 » 00 »	96	174	364
5	3 » 00 »	84	171	145
6	3 » 00 »	83	159	211
7	3 » 20 »	101	172	290
8	3 » 34 »	84	136	280
9	4 » 34 »	77	195	290
10	4 » 48 »	94	89	240
11	4 » 54 »	133	89	240
12	4 » 58 »	107	97	173
13	5 » 04 »	92	284	452
14	5 » 06 »	125	94	307
15	5 » 12 »	81	171	260
16	5 » 18 »	133	116	270
17	5 » 20 »	106	287	450
18	5 » 47 »	108	171	430
19	6 » 00 »	111	186	299
20	6 » 00 »	93	212	289
21	6 » 00 »	110	184	192
22	6 » 00 »	106	91	268
23	6 » 01 »	97	229	410
24	6 » 03 »	97	207	221
25	6 » 06 »	101	194	144
Average		100	166	283

It follows from the foregoing facts that in the initial period of resuscitation the intense oxygen starvation of the brain continues, determined by the decrease in its capacity to consume oxygen in spite of the adequate amounts of the latter in the arterial blood and conditions favoring its dissociation. As has been shown by Bulanova, at the same time the consumption of oxygen by the entire organism of the dog not only is not diminished but, on the contrary, is increased by 30-50%.

In spite of continuing oxygen starvation by the brain possessing histotoxic nature, the functions of the brain are gradually restored. The first to undergo restoration is the subcortex of the brain, including the medulla, which induces the appearance in dogs of external respiration. Then the functions of the middle brain are restored, judging by the appearance of the eye reflexes. At about the same time the first signs of the electric activity of the cerebral cortex appear, indicating the initiation of the restoration of its activity (Smirnov and Negovskii, 1941; Gurvich, 1961). Undoubtedly, energy was required for restoration of the activity and function of the brain utilizing only the glucose of the blood and only via the glycolytic pathway, since the oxygen was not consumed by the brain tissue at this time. In 44 experiments we investigated the amount of blood glucose in animals during resuscitation. In Table 7 the data on 25 such experiments are summarized in which, in addition, the blood under normal conditions and during exsanguination was also examined. As can be seen from the table, in dogs at the time of appearance of their own respiration (during artificial respiration) very high hyperglycemia was observed, in an overwhelming majority of the cases exceeding the normal levels 2- to 4-fold. The glucose levels of the blood during the restoration of respiration also exceeded 1.5- to 2-fold those observed during exsanguination, although in a number of animals during this time hyperglycemia was induced by narcosis. It has been established that only in 5 out of 44 dogs' was hyperglycemia absent at the moment of the appearance of respiration, and the amount of glucose in the blood was within the limits 104-145 mg % (for example, experiments Nos. 5 and 25, Table 7).

The glucose supplied by the blood was avidly consumed by the brain tissue, as indicated by the high positive arterio-venous difference in blood sugar (Table 8). If one takes into account the fact that the arterio-venous

TABLE 8. Arterio-Venous Difference in Sugar During the Period of Restoration of Respiration

Dog No.	Blood sugar, mg %		Arterio-venous difference, mg %
	Artery	Jugular	
1	410	356	+ 54
2	291	240	+ 51
3	592	544	+ 48
4	242	185	+ 57
5	202	178	+ 24
Average	345	300	+ 47

difference in glucose under normal conditions (Prokhorova and Kazimirova, 1956) and during exsanguination (Gaevskaya, 1946) in the brain tissue does not exceed 10 mg %, and that the velocity of the blood flow at the onset of resuscitation is increased (Bulanova, 1960), then one can assert with confidence that during this period there was an increased consumption of glucose by the brain. In dogs whose respiration appeared shortly after the restoration of cardiac activity, blood samples were taken at short intervals. It has been established (Table 9) that the increased levels of blood sugar, which coincided with the appearance of respiration, occurred within short intervals of time, about 25-30 seconds between the tests.

In order to study in detail the process of initiation of hyperglycemia during the resuscitation of dogs, blood sugar was determined in 4 of these dogs not only at the moment of appearance of cardiac activity, respiration, and eye reflexes, but several times at intervals between these moments. The data showed that the rise in sugar

TABLE 9. Rate of Accumulation of Sugar in the Blood at the Moment of Restoration of Respiration in a Reviving Animal

Dog No.	Blood sugar, mg %, at the moment of restoration		Time interval between tests, seconds
	Cardiac activity	Respiration	
1	161	240	25
2	192	320	30
3	149	290	43
4	124	280	45
5	107	149	60
6	158	363	90
7	185	485	90

level of the blood during the first 30 seconds reached a maximum in 1-2 minutes, after which a slow decrease in the sugar level commenced. Such a rapid increase in blood sugar level makes it all the more probable that here we are dealing with a reflex discharge of glucose from the liver analogous to the action of "la piqure" of Claude Bernard. The increase in the blood sugar level under the influence of adrenaline, for example, occurs considerably more slowly, and, as has been demonstrated experimentally, the maximum is reached only after 5-6 minutes. To elucidate the question of the mechanism of the onset of hyperglycemia during the period of restoration of respiration two experiments were performed on dogs in which both suprarenals were removed in order to exclude the effects of the basic portion of the adrenal system on the process of resuscitation. The sectioning of the abdomen in these dogs was performed along the white line and both suprarenals were removed (this is the bloodless way of removal of the suprarenals, which is most important since in the subsequent course of the experiments the dogs develop artificial hemophilia). After suturing, a solution of heparin was introduced into the vein, and exsanguination and resuscitation in the usual manner were performed. The duration of clinical death in these animals had to be shortened to 2-3 minutes, since all attempts to resuscitate the adrenalectomized dogs after longer periods of clinical death without the administration of adrenaline failed here because it was impossible to restore the cardiac activity in these animals. The data showed that in the adrenalectomized dogs as well as in dogs with intact adrenals the blood sugar content at the moment of appearance of respiration was 2-3 times higher than at the moment of appearance of cardiac activity. However, the removal of the adrenals was reflected in the time during which the blood sugar content,(increased at the moment of appearance of respiration) had returned to normal levels. As can be seen in Fig. 4, in intact animals the lowering of the blood sugar level to normal level took place within 3-4 hours, while in the adrenalectomized animals the normal level was reached in one of the animals within 30 seconds, and in another within an hour. Thereafter, the blood sugar level in the adrenalectomized animals was somewhat lower than the initial level. The lowering of the venous blood sugar continued up to the moment of death due to adrenal insufficiency, while in the arterial blood during agony the sugar level sharply increased. The mechanism of this phenomenon is apparently of a nervous reflex nature.

Thus, the removal of the basic portion of the adrenal system did not prevent hyperglycemia in the initial period of resuscitation, but it increased the subsequent rate of lowering of blood sugar levels to normal, having prevented the possibility of its continuous entry into the blood which takes place under the influence of the suprarenal hormones. In contrast to our data are the results of Kolpakov (1961) who did not observe hyperglycemia in adrenalectomized cats during resuscitation. This is apparently due to the fact that Kolpakov tested the blood 20 minutes after the restoration of respiration when, according to our data, in adrenalectomized animals hyperglycemia is already absent.

As has been previously indicated, in all experiments the time of the restoration of respiration in dogs coincided with the onset of hyperglycemia. It can hardly be deduced from this observation that a causal relationship exists between the activation of the resuscitated respiratory center and hyperglycemia. What is involved, apparently, is the activation of some region of the central nervous system which includes the respiratory center as well as the center of the sympathetic innervation of the liver or of the paths leading from this center. On the basis of our data it is difficult to determine the demarcations of this region, but it appears most likely that it is limited by the medulla, since the appearance of the eye reflexes, indicating the restoration of the functions of the middle brain, appears later.

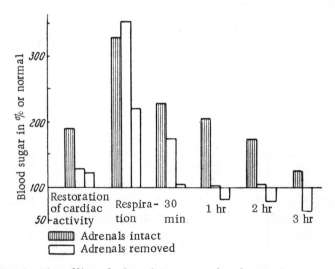

Fig. 4. The effect of adrenalectomy on the changes in amount of blood sugar in dogs after resuscitation.

Reflex hyperglycemia is one of the compensatory reactions of the organism which was elaborated in the course of evolution in the struggle with all sorts of hypoxic states. This reaction gives the organism an opportunity to satisfy the increased demands for glucose—the substrate of respiration and glycolysis—and to cancel out the deficit in energy which is necessary for the support of the vital activity and function of tissues and organs. Undoubtedly, the reflex hyperglycemia which originates during the onset of resuscitation has the same origin.

Considerable hyperglycemia during the period of restoration of the functions of the bulbar centers in asphyxiated cats has been observed by Danilov (1940) and during the resuscitation of exsanguinated cats by Kolpakov (1961). During the restoration of the functions of the bulbar centers in dogs after temporary acute anemia of the central nervous system hyperglycemia has also been noted in some cases (Petrov, Danilov, Kudritskaya, and Kachka, 1948).

We commenced the study of the metabolism in cerebral tissue of the resuscitated animals from the moment of restoration of respiration in these animals, when, in connection with the onset of blood circulation just a few minutes previously and of the resulting flow of blood to the brain, one could expect changes in the amounts of the tested compounds compared to the levels observed during clinical death. According to Shuster (1952), in the first 1.5 minutes of resuscitation, still before the appearance of respiration, the content of inorganic phosphate, organic phosphorus, and of the labile phosphate of the sum of ATP and ADP remains within the limits observed during the period of clinical death. Analysis of the brain tissue for sugar, glycogen, and lactic acid during the restoration of respiration was performed on 11 dogs which were dying in a state of ether narcosis. The obtained data are summarized in Table 10.

The data in Table 10 indicate that during the appearance of respiration the initial level of sugar in the cerebral cortex is restored. The level of glucose of 40 mg % during clinical death rose to 113 mg % during the appearance of respiration. In individual dogs the amount of glucose in the brain tissue was even considerably higher than that normally found in dogs, for example in dogs Nos. 8 and 11. In only one dog (No. 10) was the level still low, differing little from the levels characteristic of clinical death.

The studies of Negovskii convincingly showed that the sooner the respiration appears in dogs during resuscitation the sooner and more completely the functions of the central nervous system are restored. It would

TABLE 10. Content (in mg % of wet weight of tissue) of Sugar, Glycogen, and Lactic Acid in the Cortex of Large Hemispheres of Dogs During Restoration of External Respiration

Dog No.	Time of appearance of respiration from the beginning	Duration of dying	Duration of clinical death	Sugar	Glycogen	Lactic acid	Sugar of arterial blood during appearance of respiration	Lactic acid of venous blood	
								Bleeding	Appearance of respiration
1	3 min 12 sec	7 min 44 sec	6 min 04 sec	63	20	—	124	—	—
2	4 » 03 »	9 » 30 »	6 » 00 »	105	—	187	299	38	72
3	4 » 34 »	9 » 33 »	4 » 57 »	48	—	—	242	—	82
4	4 » 54 »	11 » 36 »	6 » 12 »	51	8	170	—	—	55
5	6 » 08 »	13 » 30 »	6 » 03 »	76	—	184	221	27	81
6	6 » 14 »	6 » 48 »	5 » 00 »	109	—	187	298	—	80
7	6 » 42 »	9 » 30 »	5 » 28 »	98	26	—	243	—	—
8	8 » 04 »	11 » 04 »	5 » 56 »	184	33	240	503	9	55
9	9 » 35 »	17 » 40 »	4 » 55 »	111	—	155	202	—	86
10	10 » 28 »	18 » 18 »	5 » 00 »	36	14	145	173	24	70
11	16 » 00 »	15 » 56 »	5 » 04 »	213	—	227	452	32	92
Average				98	20	187	275	26	74

appear that the more of the energy source material (glucose) supplied to the brain tissue the faster should be the restoration of its functions. However, as can be seen from Table 10, no such correlation can be established. On the contrary, in dogs Nos. 8 and 11, in which the greatest amount of sugar was present in the brain as well as in the blood, the respiration was restored later, namely, 8 to 16 minutes after the beginning of resuscitation. Apparently, the duration of the process of dying in this case also played a significant role in the outcome of the subsequent resuscitation and cancelled out the beneficial effects of the excess of glucose. This assumption, as will be shown later, finds support in the experiments in which the dogs were resuscitated by blood with an increased content of glucose. For the moment we deem it necessary to indicate that, as follows from the data in Table 10, there is a direct relationship between the degree of hyperglycemia at the moment of appearance of respiration in animals and the amount of glucose in the brain tissue. The extensive experimental material collected by Negovskii and co-workers indicates that if one follows the path suggested by nature itself and during the resuscitation adds glucose to the pumped blood the animals are revived considerably more easily and restoration of all the functions occurs sooner. One cannot ignore the fact that during resuscitation it is not only the central nervous system that craves glucose, but the internal organs as well, especially the heart.

The amount of glycogen in the cerebral cortex during the appearance of respiration was determined in 5 dogs, and all 5 showed equal amounts at a level generally found during clinical death, averaging 20 mg %. Therefore, under the conditions prevailing in the brain tissue during resuscitation the synthesis of glycogen could not as yet take place and it could not serve as the source of glucose in the brain.

Doubts have arisen as to how well one can evaluate, on the basis of data obtained on the cerebral cortex, the metabolism in the medulla in which the restoration of functions determines the appearance of respiration in the resuscitated animal.

Experiments were therefore set up in which parallel examination of the cerebral cortex and of the medulla was made. In these experiments after removal of the samples of the cerebral cortex the exposure to liquid nitrogen was continued up to the moment of cessation of natural respiration of the animal and then for 2 minutes longer during artificial respiration. In cases when the samples of the medulla were taken in dogs which were in a state of clinical death, the exposure to liquid nitrogen of the samples of the cerebral cortex was continued for 4 minutes longer. During the freezing of the brain of living animals particular attention was paid to the support of sufficient arterial pressure and to the volume of lung ventilation in order to avoid the onset of hypoxia. As can be seen from data in Table 11, the amount of glucose in the medulla at the initial state in most dogs was smaller than in the cortex of the large hemispheres. At the same time the amount of lactic acid in dog No. 1 was greater in the cerebral cortex than in the medulla, while in dog No. 4 the reverse relationship prevailed. This apparently is due to transient alteration in the oxidative processes which took place in spite of the precautionary measures taken. Judging by the increase in the lactic acid content one may assume that in dog No. 4 the actual amount of sugar in the medulla was somewhat greater. Because of the small amount of tissue of the medulla available the content of glycogen in it was determined at the initial stage only in dog No. 3, and different values were obtained in parallel determinations. It has been further shown (dogs Nos. 6, 7, and 8) that during the process of dying and 5-6 minutes of clinical death the amount of glucose and glycogen in the medulla is decreased, compared to the initial level, to the same extent as in the cerebral cortex. Therefore, at the initiation of resuscitation the medulla has at its disposal the same small amount of the substrates of respiration and glycogen as the cerebral cortex. Towards the end of clinical death lactic acid accumulates in the medulla in somewhat smaller amounts than in the cortex of the hemispheres. This is understandable if one takes into account that the initial level of glucose in the medulla was lower than in the cortex.

Thus, the study of the metabolism of carbohydrates in the medulla of dogs during the process of dying and resuscitation has shown that the metabolism is subject to the same interdependencies as have been observed in the cortex of the large hemispheres.

Returning to the analysis of the material shown in Table 10, it should be noted that during the period of the appearance of respiration the cerebral cortex of dogs (as well as the medulla, as shown in Table 11) contained a large amount of lactic acid. On the average, the amount of lactic acid was 187 mg %, which was close to that found in dogs in a state of clinical death (189 mg %). This large amount of lactic acid in brain tissue was maintained in spite of the continuous removal of lactic acid with the blood. As can be seen from

TABLE 11. Content (in mg %) of Sugar, Glycogen, and Lactic Acid
in the Cortex of Large Hemispheres of the Brain and in the Medulla

Dog No.	Brain tissue taken	Sugar		Glycogen		Lactic acid	
		Brain cortex	Medulla	Brain cortex	Medulla	Brain cortex	Medulla
1	At initial	95	75	107	—	62	22
2	narcosis	98	102	63	—	32	38
3		150	76	68	19	26	30
4		117	78	61	62	30	80
5		137	—	132	154	—	—
	Average	115	82	—	—	—	—
6	During clinical	34	31	55	18	196	149
7	death	30	48	20	30	171	119
8		27	39	12	16	192	152
	Average	29	39	29	21	186	140
9	At appearance	36	57	14	16	145	72
10	of respiration	51	71	8	—	170	180
11		109	125	—	—	187	251
12		201	184	—	—	117	97
13		172	172	—	—	148	108
14		87	147	22	44	136	102
	Average	109	126	—	—	150	135

Table 10, the content of lactic acid in the blood during the period of appearance of respiration averaged about 3-fold greater compared to the amount of lactic acid in the blood during the process of dying in the animal. At the same time, the simultaneous determination of the content of lactic acid in venous blood (jugular vein) and in arterial blood (carotid artery) showed (Table 12) that in the majority of cases there was a positive venous-arterial difference in lactic acid, indicating intensive removal of it from the brain into the blood.

It appeared possible that the extensive hyperglycemia, while increasing the glycolytic metabolism in the brain tissue, could also lead to the accumulation of a large amount of lactic acid in it, and that this event would create unfavorable conditions for the restoration of the activity of the respiratory center and slow down the appearance of the first inspiration during resuscitation. To elucidate this possibility experiments were set up in which during the resuscitation of dogs glucose in the amounts of 0.5 to 1 gm per kilogram body weight was added to the pumped blood. The experiments showed that high hyperglycemia, reaching 700 mg %, was conducive to a somewhat greater accumulation of glucose in the cerebral cortex at the moment of restoration of respiration, compared to that in dogs which did not receive glucose (Fig. 5, composed from average data in 7 experiments of each series). At the same time the amount of glucose in the cerebral cortex in both series of dogs was about the same. These results were somewhat unexpected, as it is known that the presence of extensive hyperglycemia in animals before dying leads to an increase in the amount of lactic acid in the autolyzing brain tissue (Kerr and Ghantus, 1937), and that only during normally proceeding oxidative metabolism of the brain does an increase in blood sugar not lead to an increase in the content of lactic acid in the brain (Klein and Olsen, 1947; Dawson and Richter, 1948). It should be recalled that during the period of restoration of respiration in animals the consumption of oxygen by the brain is very small (Smirenskaya, 1946), and consequently the lowering of the content of lactic acid in the brain could not have taken place through its oxidation. It should be further noted that the fact of poor consumption of oxygen by the brain at the beginning of resuscitation has been established by Smirenskaya on dogs into which blood was pumped which contained added glucose

TABLE 12. Content (in mg %) of Lactic Acid in Venous and Arterial Blood During the Period of Restoration of Respiration and Corneal Reflexes

| Dog No. | Lactic acid | | Venous-arterial difference |
	Vein	Artery	
1	92	41	+ 51
2	101	73	+ 28
3	141	70	+ 71
4	84	78	+ 6
5	63	43	+ 20
6	82	75	+ 7
7	86	69	+ 17
Average ..	93	64	+28

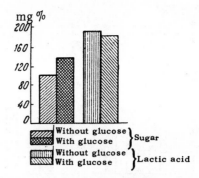

Fig. 5. Effect of administration of glucose via the blood on the content of sugar and lactic acid in the cerebral cortex during restoration of external respiration.

in the same amounts as in our experiments. Apparently, the main reason for the absence of any relationship between the intensity of hyperglycemia, exceeding 400-500 mg %, and the content of lactic acid in the brain of resuscitated dogs is the increased flushing of lactic acid from the tissue into the blood, which is confirmed by the large venous-arterial difference in lactic acid. It is also possible that the capacity of the brain tissue to consume and then utilize glucose during this period is definitely limited.

It has been further shown (Gaevskaya, 1955) that during resuscitation, the administration to dogs of blood with high glucose content was not reflected in the time at which the first inhalation appeared. The time of appearance of respiration depended mainly on the duration of the process of dying, whether glucose was administered along with the blood or not.

Thus, during the first 15 minutes after the beginning of resuscitation, the initial glucose level is restored and maintained in the brain tissue, accompanied by intensive utilization of glucose via the glycolytic pathway under the conditions of ample supply of oxygen and glucose with the blood flowing to the brain. Apparently, the resynthesis of brain ATP and creatine phosphate takes place at the expense of energy liberated by aerobic glycolysis during the initial period of resuscitation. The content of ADP is sharply reduced during this period, and AMP cannot be detected, whereas the amounts of the latter (ADP and AMP) during the process of dying and clinical death were quite considerable. The content of inorganic phosphate, which was quite high during clinical death (8.1 mg %), is reduced to initial levels (2.4 mg %). The amount of ATP in the cerebral cortex during the period of restoration in the animal of external respiration (1 micromole per gram) does not as yet reach the initial level (1.4 micromoles per gram), while the amount of creatine phosphate is only half (1.1 micromoles per gram) of the initial level (2.2 micromoles per gram). Consequently, in spite of restoration of the synthetic capacity of the brain tissue, the dynamic equilibrium of the energy-rich compounds is established at a somewhat lower level than under normal conditions, apparently because the demand for energy is being satisfied at this time by aerobic glycolysis, a process which is considerably less economical from the energy standpoint than the process of oxidation.

In accordance with what was stated during the discussion of the possible mechanism of the slowdown in glycolysis during clinical death, we assume that the accumulation of glucose in the brain tissue during resuscitation severed the vicious circle of conditions which inhibited the process of glycolysis, and increased the intensity of glycolysis. The concentration of inorganic phosphate dropped, since the inorganic phosphate, via entry into the molecule of monosaccharide, entered the cycle of organic transformations. Creatine phosphate appeared, ADP content was decreased, and the content of ATP was significantly increased in the brain tissue. The synthesis of the energy-rich phosphates predominated over their degradation, and this could occur only because the functions of the central nervous system were deeply inhibited and therefore the requirements for energy were quite small. During the process of dying accompanied by the gradual slowdown in the glycolytic process due to a shortage of substrates there occurs a degradation of the energy-rich compounds. During resusci-

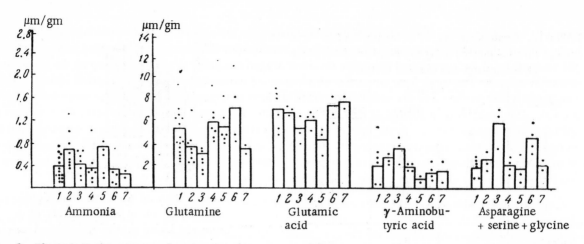

Fig. 6. Changes in the content of ammonia, glutamine, and free amino acids in the cerebral cortex during dying and after resuscitation. 1) Normal; 2) 5 minutes of clinical death; 3) 10-30 minutes after resuscitation; 4) 2 hours after resuscitation; 5) 4 hours after resuscitation; 6) 24 hours after resuscitation; 7) 6 days after resuscitation.

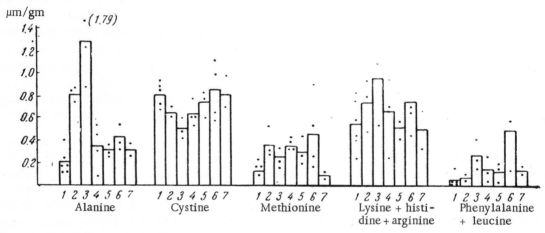

Fig. 6a. Changes in the content of free amino acids in the cerebral cortex of dogs during dying and after resuscitation. 1) Normal; 2) 5 minutes of clinical death; 3) 10-30 minutes after resuscitation; 4) 2 hours after resuscitation; 5) 4 hours after resuscitation; 6) 24 hours after resuscitation; 7) 6 days after resuscitation.

tation accompanied by the uninterrupted inflow of blood glucose, one observes an interconnected acceleration of glycolysis and the accumulation of the energy-rich substances.

Naturally, a question arises as to what determines the inhibition of oxidative processes in brain tissue during the initial period of resuscitation and the development of tissue hypoxia. It could be assumed that oxygen simply does not diffuse from the blood into the brain tissue because of alterations in the capillaries, and that there exists not a tissue but a hypoxic hypoxia of the brain. Such an assumption appears unlikely for the following reasons. It is known that during hypoxia the permeability of the capillaries increases, accompanied by perivascular edema. Furthermore, as we have seen, the permeability of the capillaries to glucose has not been altered. It should also be noted that during this time the consumption of oxygen by the other tissues of the organism is increased, and there is no reason to assume that in the brain there occurred an isolated alteration in the permeability of the capillaries to oxygen. As has been established by Fuhrman, Fuhrman, and Field (1945), who studied oxygen consumption in brain slices of rats killed by anoxic anoxia, the latter did not alter the extent of oxygen consumption by brain slices under optimal artificial conditions. Similar results were obtained by Bulanova (1958) on dogs' brains removed for analysis at the beginning of resuscitation after clinical death induced by exsanguination. However, when Bulanova placed the brain tissue in a medium which contained a large amount of suboxidized products of metabolism, considerable differences were observed in the capacity of the brain tissue of the resuscitated animal to consume oxygen compared to results obtained on the brain tissue of a normal animal. The tissue from an animal which survived intense hypoxia was less capable of utilizing the oxygen necessary for oxidation of the added suboxidized products of metabolism than was the tissue from a normal animal. This observation indicated damage to the oxidative enzymatic systems in the brain tissue of dogs in the initial period of resuscitation. As the data of Smirenskaya (1946) show, the consumption of oxygen by the brain in the initial period of resuscitation is small, although at no time was it equal to zero. This poor consumption of oxygen by brain tissue did not result in appearance of the Pasteur effect. Apparently, for the appearance of the Pasteur effect the oxidative processes must proceed at a definite intensity.

It is possible that under the conditions of our experiments a phenomenon analogous to that observed by Acs and Straub (1954) during studies of metabolism in the ascites tumor cells prevails. In accord with the view of Lynen, these authors believe that the Pasteur effect is the result of competition for the inorganic phosphate. The data of Acs and Straub show that in the surviving culture of ascites cancer cells the utilization of inorganic phosphate is more intensive during aerobic glycolysis than during respiration. At the same time during aerobic glycolysis the equilibrium between the synthesis and expenditure of the energy-rich phosphates is better maintained than during respiration.

Study of certain components of nitrogen metabolism in the cerebral tissue of dogs in the initial period of resuscitation (Fig. 6) showed that the content of ammonia and glutamic acid in the cerebral cortex was lower than that found at the end of clinical death. In spite of this, the amount of glutamine also decreased. Apparently, ammonia was removed not via the amidation of glutamic acid but in some other manner. The content of cystine and methionine, like that of glutamic acid, also decreased, while the amount of other free amino acids considerably increased. Alanine and asparagine content was increased to a particularly large extent. Taking into account the fact that during the period of resuscitation the content of acidic products of metabolism, including pyruvic acid, is increased, it could be assumed that the accumulation of alanine during this period is a result of increased transamination of glutamic acid to pyruvic acid.

It should be noted that the sharpest changes in the content of free animo acids in the brain are observed during the period of resuscitation and not at the end of clinical death. We have already expressed the opinion that during the process of dying no structural changes in the proteins have as yet occurred. During resuscitation, after restoration of blood circulation, the proteins of the brain tissue undergo changes which, possibly, lead to alteration of their chemical structure with the liberation of certain free amino acids.

In the preceding chapter it was shown that the functional state of the central nervous system has a significant influence on the metabolism of brain tissue at the onset of deep hypoxia. It appeared necessary to elucidate the influence of the functional state of the central nervous system on metabolic processes in the brain tissue after resuscitation. With this objective in mind experiments were set up in which the dogs before dying were either not administered any narcotics or they were put into a medicinal sleep close to physiological, as described above (see Chapter III). Trepanation of the skull was performed at the onset of clinical death, which lasted 5-6 minutes, and the brain was frozen in the initial period of resuscitation in the absence of any pain sensitivity in the animals. It was noted that in the resuscitating animals there was a rapid cessation of bleeding from the skull and soft tissues at the moment of restoration of cardiac activity.

Study of the brain tissue at the moment of appearance of external respiration in dogs dying in a wakeful state was performed in 6 experiments (Table 13). When the quantity of glucose in the cerebral cortex during the restoration of respiration in dogs dying in wakeful state is compared with the content of glucose in dogs dying in a state of pantopone-ether narcosis (see Table 10), it will be noted that the average values as well as the variations were almost the same in both groups of dogs. The same is true for glycogen, the amount of which in both groups of dogs was close to that found in the cerebral cortex at the end of clinical death. As far as the content of lactic acid is concerned, however, on the average it was considerably smaller in dogs which were dying without narcosis. At the same time the amount of lactic acid in venous blood outflowing from the head was about the same.

TABLE 13. Content (in mg %) of Sugar, Glycogen, and Lactic Acid in the Cortex of Large Hemispheres of Dog Brain During Period of Restoration of Respiration After Dying Without Narcosis

| Dog No. | Sugar | Glycogen | Lactic acid | Sugar of arterial blood | | Lactic acid of venous blood during appearance of respiration |
				Before bleeding	Appearance of respiration	
1	98	19	116	92	213	67
2	111	38	118	93	272	68
3	84	9	126	101	209	79
4	82	44	175	39	120	122
5	176	39	185	86	232	124
6	134	21	161	76	200	69
Average ..	114	28	147	81	207	88

In all dogs dying in a wakeful state the amount of sugar in the arterial blood at the moment of appearance of respiration was increased 2- to 3-fold compared to the amounts present during exsanguination. Therefore, hyperglycemia, characteristic for the resuscitating dogs which were dying under pantopone-ether narcosis, also appears with the same regularity in the nonnarcotized animals. The absolute value of this hyperglycemia was somewhat lower in the nonnarcotized dogs than in the narcotized animals, but in none of the 6 dogs dying without narcosis have we observed such high amounts of glucose as 400-500 mg % which occasionally appear at the moment of resuscitation in dogs narcotized with ether. It is possible, however, that an additional number of experiments would have altered these relationships.

In Chapter III the influence of the functional state of the central nervous system before dying on the accumulation of lactic acid in the brain during clinical death was illustrated. It therefore appeared necessary to correlate certain external symptoms characterizing the state of the central nervous system during operation and dying with the accumulation of lactic acid in the cerebral cortex during resuscitation.

First of all it must be pointed out that in none of the 6 dogs was there observed any aggressiveness before the operation or especially violent objection to being tied to the stand. However, during the operation and exsanguination they behaved differently. In 3 dogs (Nos. 1, 2, and 3) symptoms of excitation were not observed. Dog No. 1 was quiet during the operation, whining and licking her chops, turning her head to either side. The dog did not respond in any way to the administration of heparin or to the beginning of exsanguination, as if she were in a drowsy state with closed eyes, whining softly. Three minutes and 36 seconds from the beginning of exsanguination the dog exhibited rigidity of the cervical muscles, and, after 36 seconds, opisthotonus. The period of dying in this dog was of average duration (9 minutes, 56 seconds), and the duration of clinical death, 6 minutes. Respiration was restored within the usual time under such conditions. The amount of lactic acid in the cerebral cortex was relatively low, about 116 mg %. In dog No. 2, as in dog No. 1, none of the symptoms of excitation of the central nervous system were noted. Three minutes and 12 seconds from the beginning of exsanguination, rigidity of the cervical muscles appeared, and immediately afterwards opisthotonus. The duration of dying and clinical death was about the same as in dog No. 1. The rhythmic cardiac activity which appeared in the beginning of resuscitation shifted to fibrillation, which was stopped by a condenser discharge by the method of Gurvich, and cardiac activity was again restored by arterial pumping of the blood. Respiration appeared after 1 minute and 14 seconds after establishment of steady cardiac activity — only 36 seconds later than in dog No. 1. The amount of lactic acid in the cerebral cortex of dog No. 2 was low, 118 mg %. The next dog (No. 3), the data on which are shown in Table 13, by its behavior during the operation and exsanguination and by the duration of dying was similar to the other two dogs with the exception that the symptoms of decerebration rigidity were revealed only in sharp hypertension of the flexor muscles of the paws a few seconds before the last agonal inhalation indicating the onset of clinical death. At resuscitation the respiration in this dog was restored in the length of time usual for the duration of dying and clinical death observed in this dog. The amount of lactic acid in the cerebral cortex again was not great: 126 mg %.

In the next 3 dogs symptoms of excitation during dying were quite noticeable. Thus, in dog No. 4 intense excitation developed during exsanguination. The dog was howling, trying to get away. The excitation lasted 1.5 minutes, ending in diuresis. During the next 42 seconds the dog was quiet with closed eyes up to the appearance of the terminal pause in respiration and disappearance of eye reflexes. The dying lasted only 3 minutes and 24 seconds, and the process of inhibition embraced all stages of the central nervous system so quickly that the symptoms of decerebration rigidity had not yet developed. The state of clinical death lasted 6 minutes, 12 seconds, and the external respiration in this dog was restored in the time usual for such a duration of clinical death. The amount of lactic acid in the cerebral cortex was considerably greater than in the other 3 dogs described above, being about 175 mg %. Thus, in spite of the shortness of the period of dying, the excitation which developed during the process induced the accumulation of considerable amounts of lactic acid in the brain during the period of the restoration of respiration in the animal.

In dog No. 5 before exsanguination, pinching of the pad of the front paw (to test the presence of the spinal reflex) produce a violent defensive reaction, the excitation lasting about 2 minutes. Then the motor excitation quieted down, but the dog continued to move the head restlessly and to whine. With the beginning of exsanguination the restlessness of the dog increased, and on the 4th minute of exsanguination it shifted to a violent motor excitation which gradually subsided in the course of one minute. The eyes of the dog closed, and she ceased to make attempts to escape and to whine. Not until the 12th minute of exsanguination did the first symptoms of decerebration rigidity appear in the form of increased tonus of the muscles of the extremities. Twelve minutes and 30 seconds after the beginning of exsanguination, sharp rigidity of the cervical muscles appeared, and after a further 48 seconds opisthotonus developed. Dying in this dog lasted 18 minutes and 15 seconds, and in accordance with this the respiration in the dog was restored after only 5 minutes of resuscitation. The amount of lactic acid in the cerebral cortex was considerably higher (185 mg %) than in dogs dying in a quiet state.

In the last dog (No. 6) of this group the state during the operation and exsanguination was similar to that in dog No. 5, as above. Motor excitation with howling and barking, which began before exsanguination, increased during exsanguination and lasted almost 4.5 minutes. Seven minutes and 6 seconds from the beginning of exsanguination, hypertension of the muscles of the extremities appeared; 1 minute and 43 seconds later rigidity of the cervical muscles developed, and 12 seconds later, opisthotonus. The period of dying in this dog was also quite long (12 minutes, 30 seconds), and the respiration was correspondingly restored 4.5 minutes after the beginning of resuscitation. The amount of lactic acid in this dog also was quite high (161 mg %), although judging by the state of the dog during dying one would expect a somewhat higher value. However, one cannot assume that a simple arithmetical relationship exists between the external expression of excitation of the animal and the accumulation of lactic acid in brain tissue. One can speak only about a rough relationship, since to the basic situation are added many other factors which are difficult to assess.

While a definite relationship exists between the level of lactic acid in the brain tissue in the initial period of resuscitation and the functional state of the central nervous system during dying, no such relationship could be observed for sugar or glycogen content.

In 6 dogs (Table 14), which did not exhibit symptoms of excitation before the experiment or during the preparation of the blood vessels (local anesthesia), the state of inhibition of the central nervous system was deepened by the administration of sodium amytal. Before dying the dogs were under medicinal sleep for an hour; then they were exsanguinated by massive bleeding, and resuscitated after 5-6 minutes of clinical death. The brain was frozen during resuscitation at the moment of restoration of external respiration. As expected, the content of lactic acid in the brain tissue was considerably lower than in dogs dying in a state of excitation or under ether narcosis. The amount of lactic acid in the blood from the jugular vein at the beginning of resuscitation was also smaller than in dogs dying in medicinal sleep. Hyperglycemia in these dogs was just as high as in dogs dying in a state of ether narcosis, while the glucose content in brain tissue was, on the average, even higher by 37 mg %

What probable explanation can be given for the smaller accumulation of lactic acid in brain tissue during resuscitation of inhibited dogs compared to the amounts of lactic acid in brain tissue of more excitable dogs? As was shown in Chapter III, in wakeful dogs dying quietly towards the end of clinical death, i.e., at the beginning of resuscitation, less lactic acid accumulated in the brain than in dogs which were in an excited stage. Thus,

TABLE 14. Content (in mg %) of Sugar, Glycogen, and Lactic Acid
in the Cortex of Large Hemispheres of Dogs in the Period of Appearance of Respiration During Resuscitation After Dying in
Medicinal Sleep

Dog No.	Sugar	Glycogen	Lactic acid	Sugar of arterial blood during appearance of respiration	Lactic acid in venous blood during appearance of respiration
1	201	—	117	248	48
2	172	—	148	563	56
3	87	22	136	251	66
4	119	26	102	270	70
5	146	34	115	173	19
6	89	45	134	174	46
Average ...	135	32	125	280	51

at the beginning of resuscitation the initial level of lactic acid was different and under equal conditions of its removal from the tissue its content remained at this level. It is also possible that the oxidative processes of carbohydrate metabolism played a greater role in the brain tissue of dogs dying in an inhibited state than in dogs in excited states not only during the period of dying but at the beginning of resuscitation as well.

By this assumption we in no way wish to minimize the fact established by Gromova, Kudritskaya, Petrov, and Shapot (1952) that the lowering of utilization of the energy-rich phosphate derivatives in brain tissue plays an important role in the mechanism of the therapeutic property of the defensive inhibition during oxygen starvation. Furthermore, the economic utilization of the energy-rich phosphate derivatives in brain tissue during increased inhibition by medicinal preparations is, apparently, one of the best means of preservation of the oxidative enzymatic systems during oxygen starvation in terminal states.

The initial period of resuscitation should include not only the first few minutes when cardiac activity and external respiration are restored but also the period which includes the subsequent 20-30 minutes. During this time the external respiration, weak at first and slow, becomes deep and spasmodic, the frequency of it increasing. Then the respiration becomes no longer spasmodic and normalizes in depth as well as in frequency. During the same period of time the eye, spinal, and tendon reflexes, as well as the swallowing reflexes, are restored. All this indicates the recovery of the middle brain. The body temperature of the dogs at the beginning of the resuscitation period was 2-3 degrees lower than that before exsanguination.

During the entire initial period of resuscitation the volume velocity of the blood flow in dogs was increased, which promoted the flushing of the suboxidized metabolic products from the tissues (Bulanova, 1961). In spite of this, during this entire period the high content of lactic acid in the brain tissue persisted, indicating that the glycolytic process continued as intensively as before (Table 15). However, experimental data are available to show that towards the end of the initial period of resuscitation the brain begins to gradually recover from the state of hypotoxic hypoxia, the consumption of oxygen gradually increases (Smirenskaya, 1946), and simultaneously the content of creatine phosphate and ATP increases to initial levels (Nosova, 1960).

On the basis of the data available in the literature as well as our own, it may be considered established that the initial restoration of the functions of the bulbar centers and the region of the middle brain, as well as the vital activity of the cortex of the large hemispheres, is ensured by the energy of the glycolytic transformations of the carbohydrate-phosphorus compounds. Naturally, this is possible because of the state of deep inhibition in the cerebral cortex and because of the low level of physiological processes in the lower divisions of the central nervous system, situations which determine the low requirement for energy.

It has been shown by Negovskii (1951) and Smirenskaya (1951) that in the initial period of resuscitation any artificial excitation of the central nervous system by medicinal preparations (lobeline, cytiton, carbon di-

TABLE 15. Content (in mg%) of Sugar and Lactic Acid in the Cerebral Cortex of Dogs Which Were Resuscitated After 6 Minutes of Clinical Death

Dog No.	Time from beginning of resuscitation	Sugar	Lactic acid
1	14 minutes 14 seconds	117	192
2	14 " 59 "	185	187
3	30 " 12 "	196	79
4	30 " 30 "	88	104

oxide, ammonia) worsened the prognosis of further restoration of its functions. On the basis of the material presented we may conclude that the injurious effect of stimulating preparations is due to the fact that the increased energy requirements of the active nervous tissue cannot be met by the poor ability of this tissue to furnish the required energy which is produced via the aerobic glycolytic processes. Deepening of the extent of inhibition during this period by the use of the sleep-inducing fluid of Asratyan also resulted in difficulties in further restoration of the functions of the central nervous system (Grozdova, 1954, 1955). This, apparently, was due to the fact that for the biochemical processes in which synthesis predominates over degradation a definite intensity of the functioning of the nervous system components is required. It may be assumed with a considerable degree of certainty that lowering of the functional activity of nerve cells by medicinal means at a time when the energy supply is poor leads to further inhibition of the already inefficient metabolism in the brain.

Therefore, the study of brain metabolism in the initial period of resuscitation does not permit the use of stimulating or sedative medicinal preparations in terminal states when glycolytic processes predominate in the brain tissue.

In the subsequent period of resuscitation, in the first 10-12 hours, the dogs were as if in a state of deep sleep, although it was impossible to waken them. Temporary heightening of the muscle tonus was periodically observed. The body temperature in the first 2-4 hours after resuscitation continued to drop (by 0.5 to 1°C compared to that in the initial period of resuscitation), after which a gradual rise to the initial level took place towards the end of the first 24 hours. 1.5-2 hours after the beginning of resuscitation the process of restoration of the functions of the central nervous system spread to the subcortex region and in part to the cortex of the large hemispheres, which was reflected in the normalization of the electroencephalogram (Gurvich, 1961). In the majority of dogs sensitivity to pain appeared. The nature of the reaction to painful irritation indicated the beginning of restoration of the functions of the subcortical divisions of the brain.

The experimental data show that the observed restoration of the functions of the central nervous system in dogs was intimately connected with the beginning of the normalization of the metabolism in cerebral tissue (Table 16). As can be seen from Table 16, 1.5-2 hours after resuscitation in 5 out of 6 dogs the content of lactic acid in the cerebral cortex decreased. In dog No. 6 the high level of lactic acid in the cerebral cortex persisted; but in this dog the period of dying was the longest and the external respiration was restored later than in the other dogs. The slowing in the restoration of the physiological functions in this animal was accompanied by a slowing in the restoration of metabolic processes.

According to Smirenskaya (1946), 1.5-2 hours after resuscitation the brain began to consume oxygen avidly from the inflowing blood and the coefficient of its utilization exceeded the initial level. The decrease in lactic acid content in the brain and the increased consumption of oxygen by the brain indicated a gradual increase in the intensity of the oxidative processes, which finally made the operation of the Pasteur effect in the cerebral tissue possible, permitting the transition from the glycolytic pathway to the oxidative one. As can be seen from Table 16, the normalization of the metabolism was also reflected in the increase in the content of glycogen in the cerebral tissue, in inverse proportion to the decrease of lactic acid in the tissue. Apparently, the transition to the oxidative metabolism was accompanied by the resynthesis of lactic acid into glycogen, the levels of which in the brain increased up to initial levels from very low levels which prevailed during clinical death and in the beginning of resuscitation. The content of glucose in the cerebral tissue 1.5-2 hours after re-

TABLE 16. Content (in mg %) of Carbohydrates and Lactic Acid in the Brain and Blood of Dogs 1.5 to 2 Hours After Resuscitation (clinical death was 6 minutes)

Dog No.	Time from the beginning of resuscitation	Duration of dying	Brain			Blood	
			Sugar	Glycogen	Lactic acid	Sugar	Lactic acid
1	1 minute 23 seconds	8 minutes 00 seconds	123	—	41	192	62
2	1 " 27 "	17 " 34 "	142	53	65	200	37
3	1 " 40 "	11 " 23 "	255	—	27	291	44
4	2 " 00 "	13 " 18 "	170	101	43	191	—
5	2 " 12 "	17 " 08 "	121	85	65	311	—
6	2 " 13 "	21 " 02 "	142	47	121	306	42
Average			159			248	

suscitation was high (averaging 159 mg %), and it exceeded the amount present in the initial period of resuscitation (98 mg %). This, on the one hand, was due to persistent hyperglycemia and, on the other hand, to lower requirements of the brain for the energy substrate due to the normalization of the carbohydrate-phosphorus metabolism. The restoration of the oxidative processes and the processes of synthesis ensured not only the restoration of the energy-rich phosphate and carbohydrate reserves, but also, as can be seen from Fig. 6, of glutamine, with a simultaneous decrease in ammonia content in the brain. The content of free amino acids in the brain also began to normalize.

The use of sedatives during the described period improves the prognosis of the subsequent restoration of the functions of the central nervous system (Grozdova, 1955). We assume that the mechanism of this phenomenon consists in the reduction in energy requirements of the nervous tissue brought about by sedatives, thus lowering its functional activity. This, in turn, balances the requirements for energy by the nervous tissue with the opportunity to acquire it. The lowering of the energy requirements compensates for lowering of the intensity of the metabolic processes which is induced by sedatives administered under conditions in which the oxidative metabolism predominates. The necessity for the lowering of the functional activity of the nervous system in the resuscitated animals is motivated by the fact that the incomplete restoration of the functions of the cerebral cortex at this time determines the inefficiency of the compensatory mechanisms and the onset of secondary hypoxia. As was demonstrated by Smirenskaya and Zolotokrylina (1956) and Bulanova (1954, 1961), the total gaseous exchange in resuscitated animals is most frequently elevated, and during instances of the onset of motor excitation and even passive movements (careless transfer of animal) relative hypoxia and interruption of cardiac activity easily occurs. A similar explanation is made by Negovskii of cases of sudden death of revived humans during premature transportation of the patients from the operating room to wards. The above discussion indicates the importance of knowledge of the state and character of brain metabolism in order to judge when it is permissible to apply sedatives in the process of resuscitation.

After the normalization of the oxidative metabolism in the cerebral tissue it is also possible, if necessary, to use stimulating preparations with less risk of causing the interruption of cardiac activity because of imbalance between increase in energy requirement and means of obtaining it.

Further studies of the metabolism of the dog cerebral cortex at later stages of resuscitation—after 3.5 to 6 hours—showed (Table 17) that at this time the content of blood sugar returned to levels which prevailed before exsanguination. The glucose content of the cerebral tissue also returned to initial levels. This was equally true for animals dying in a state of ether narcosis and for those which were dying in a state of medicinal sleep induced by barbamyl or nembutal. The same picture was observed in regard to lactic acid content in cerebral tissue and in venous blood taken from the jugular vein. A different picture, however, was observed in regard to glycogen of the brain. While in animals which before dying were in a state of medicinal sleep the con-

TABLE 17. Content (in mg %) of Sugar, Glycogen, and Lactic Acid
in the Cortex of Large Hemispheres of Dog Brain 3.5 to 6 Hours
After Resuscitation (clinical death was 5-6 minutes)

Dog No.	Time from the beginning of resuscitation to freezing of the brain	Brain cortex			Sugar of arterial blood			Lactic acid of venous blood at moment of freezing of the brain
		Sugar	Glycogen	Lactic acid	Before bleeding	During appearance of respiration	At the moment of freezing of the brain	
Ether narcosis								
1	3 min 30 sec	155	155	55	—	454	221	42
2	3 » 57 »	59	225	41	124	104	89	36
3	4 » 11 »	60	186	18	210	349	170	18
4	4 » 14 »	102	167	31	—	202	108	39
5	4 » 16 »	87	198	25	166	287	141	15
6	4 » 28 »	118	198	41	252	417	171	41
7	5 » 58 »	38	224	61	53	132	62	24
	Average	88	193	39	161	269	143	33
Medicinal sleep								
8	3 min 30 sec	60	111	30	91	268	99	21
9	4 » 00 »	106	100	36	168	201	156	8
10	4 » 00 »	117	144	45	94	307	155	23
11	4 » 13 »	120	134	32	172	225	156	17
12	4 » 17 »	57	121	34	—	—	—	—
	Average	94	122	35	131	250	141	17

tent of glycogen in the cerebral cortex was at the upper limit of the normal state (normal levels varied from 61 to 132 mg %), averaging 122 mg %, in dogs dying in a state of ether narcosis the content of glycogen in the cerebral cortex was considerably greater than the initial level, being, on the average, twice as great (193 mg % against 91 mg %). Thus, 3-4 hours after revival not only was the content of glycogen restored (being very low at the beginning of resuscitation) but there was a tendency towards its excessive accumulation, particularly in dogs dying in a state of ether narcosis. Palladin and co-workers (1949) cite voluminous literature which indicates that an accumulation of glycogen in the cerebral cortex is observed in the course of several pathological states (typhus, sepsis, acute psychosis, etc.).

Of all the dogs in which we observed the excessive accumulation of glycogen in the cerebral cortex after revival, in only one did we also determine glycogen content in the white matter of the large hemispheres and in the medulla. It was found that excessive accumulation of glycogen occurs only in the cerebral cortex (163 mg %) — not in the white matter (93 mg %) or the medulla (106 mg %). Although a single determination is certainly insufficient to permit a conclusion, we draw attention to it nevertheless, particularly because the data of other authors show the same observation (Shabadash, 1949; Palladin and Khaikina, 1950).

On the basis of the foregoing it may be concluded that the excessive content of glycogen in the dog cerebral cortex 3-6 hours after revival is an indication of a pathological state of the cerebral cortex developing as a result of endured hypoxia. What can be said regarding the mechanism of the excessive accumulation of glycogen? First of all, it should be noted that 4 hours after revival the blood of the dogs contains excess insulin, for which there is convincing, although indirect, supporting evidence. According to Staub (1926), the second dose of glucose, administered at the maximal rise in the hyperglycemic curve from the first sugar dose, does not induce an additional rise in the hyperglycemic curve because of excess insulin in the blood. It was found that in dogs dying in a state of ether narcosis, 4 hours after revival the administration of glucose per os did not increase the sugar level in the blood: the hyperglycemic curves were flat and of a torpid type (Figs. 7 and 8).

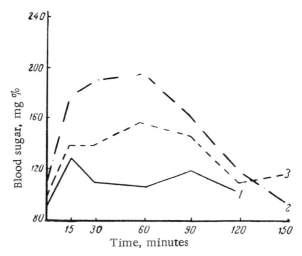

Fig. 7. Glycemic curves of dogs in normal state. 1)
Dog No. 1; 2) Dog No. 2; 3) Dog No. 3.

The presence of intense hyperglycemia during the 3 hours preceding the administration of glucose and the absence of a rise in the hyperglycemic curve after glucose administration indicated, according to Staub, the presence of excess insulin in the blood. It is possible that the presence of excess insulin in the blood could have had some significance in the mechanism of accumulation of glycogen in the cerebral cortex. Undoubtedly, the hormonal system of the animal has a significant influence on the metabolism of the brain. Supporting evidence for this was provided by data from one experiment in which the analysis of the brain was performed 4 hours after the revival of a castrated dog. It was found that in this case the cerebral cortex contained the same large amount of lactic acid (212 mg %) and small amount of glycogen (24 mg %) as in the other dogs during the appearance of respiration at the beginning of resuscitation. That is, the process of normalization of the carbohydrate metabolism in this animal had not yet commenced even 4 hours after the revival.

Turning to the purely biochemical aspect of accumulation of excessive amounts of glycogen, it should first of all be noted that we do not as yet have any data on the changes in the activity of glycogen synthetase in the cerebral tissue of dogs during dying and resuscitation. For this reason it is difficult to judge whether or not

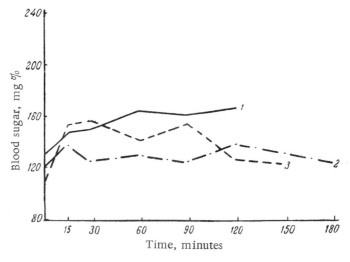

Fig. 8. Glycemic curves in dogs 4 hours after resuscitation. Notations are the same as in Fig. 7.

changes in the extent of glycogen synthesis are related to the formation of the intermediate product, glucose uridine diphosphate. As has already been stated, this path of glycogen synthesis in cerebral tissue is considered at the present time to be the basic one.

We checked the content of inorganic phosphate in the cerebral tissue 4 hours after resuscitation of the animals, since the deficiency in inorganic phosphate could have altered the normal course of the process of phosphorylation of glycogen. In 3 dogs dying in a state of ether narcosis and in 3 dogs dying in a state of medicinal sleep, the glycogen, inorganic phosphate, creatine phosphate, and ATP in the cerebral tissue were determined 4 hours after resuscitation. The data showed (Table 18) that in dogs dying in a state of ether narcosis, 4 hours after resuscitation the cerebral cortex contained increased amounts of glycogen and practically no inorganic phosphate. At the same time the creatine phosphate content was almost twice the amount found under normal conditions. In dogs dying in a state of medicinal sleep, the content of inorganic phosphate as well as of creatine phosphate was within normal limits. Therefore, the protective inhibition induced by barbamyl before dying and during drying not only increased the relative role of the oxidative processes in the brain tissue during the predominance of glycolysis during dying and in the beginning of resuscitation, but also protected the cortex from alterations in the carbohydrate-phosphorus metabolism during recovery of the organism from the hypoxic state.

Thus, the excessive accumulation of glycogen in the cerebral cortex was somewhat connected with the absence of inorganic phosphate, which apparently was fixed in significant amounts in creatine phosphate. The question of the conditions and the reasons for the accumulation of excessive amounts of creatine phosphate remains as yet unclear. It should be noted that the accumulation of glycogen in the complete absence of inorganic phosphate indicates the significance of the phosphorolytic pathway of glycogen degradation in the cerebral cortex. Apparently, the prominent amylolytic capacity of the surviving cerebral tissue, described by Palladin and co-workers, in the intact organism plays an important role only during pathological states, during which significant pH changes in the surrounding medium occur.

It should be further noted that the absence of inorganic phosphate in the dog's cerebral cortex 4 hours after resuscitation indirectly confirms the observation of Vladimirov (1954) that the phosphate is transferred from the blood to the brain very slowly. If this were not the case, the amounts of phosphorus in the brain could have been maintained at a constant level, in spite of the binding of a part of it in creatine phosphate.

It was previously mentioned that 2 hours after resuscitation the content of ammonia, glutamine, and free amino acids in cerebral tissue was relatively normal. However, 4 hours after resuscitation in the majority of dogs there was once again a significant increase in the amount of ammonia in the cerebral cortex (Fig. 6). At the same time the glutamine content was within normal limits, while that of glutamic and γ-aminobutyric acids

TABLE 18. Content of ATP, Creatine Phosphate, Inorganic Phosphate, and Glycogen in Cerebral Cortex of Dogs 4 Hours After Resuscitation

Dog No.	ATP	CP*	IP†	Glycogen mg, %	Narcosis
	micromoles/mg				
1	1.6	7.2	0.0	—	Ether
2	2.4	7.8	1.0	225	»
3	2.3	7.0	0.0	198	»
Average	2.1	7.3	0.3	211	
4	2.1	4.6	4.0	134	Barbamyl
5	1.5	3.4	6.2	—	»
6	2.0	4.6	2.2	144	»
Average	1.9	4.1	4.2	139	

*Creatine phosphate. † Inorganic phosphate.

was somewhat lowered. The normal content of creatine phosphate indicated the absence of the hypoxia of the brain during this time. The increase in ammonia could be attributed to the release of ammonia from the proteins during the continuing degradation of the brain proteins, because the primary source of ammonia (glutamine) did not alter in amount. Therefore, the accumulation of ammonia, as well as of glycogen, also indicated the development of a pathological process in the cerebral cortex as a result of endured hypoxia.

The comparison of the biochemical results of the investigations on dog brain in the course of restoration of vital functions in the animals with morphological data reveals a definite correlation between alterations in metabolism with the time of onset of the first structural alterations. Biochemical investigations showed that the alterations in nitrogen metabolism connected with the alterations in the chemical structure of brain proteins can already be detected in the initial period of resuscitation and once again 4 hours later. The first definite morphological changes in the cerebral cortex, according to Romanova (1956), appear 3-4 hours after resuscitation. They appear as dispersion and lysis of tigroid in the nerve cells. It would appear that not until this time do alterations in the protein structure of the brain reach sizable proportions as a result of the biochemical changes that preceded these alterations.

The excessive amount of glycogen in the cerebral cortex of dogs dying in a state of ether narcosis was also present 24 hours after resuscitation, if the process of the restoration of the functions of the higher divisions of the central nervous system proceeded slowly and the state of the animals was critical. Thus, in dog No. 1 (Table 19) the increased content of glycogen in the cerebral cortex was equal to that observed in dogs 4-6 hours after resuscitation. Towards the end of the first 24 hours after resuscitation this animal was in a state of deep sleep resembling the so-called anemic sleep of the first few hours of the period of resuscitation. The dog could be awakened only by severe painful irritation; she would begin to whimper and move her paws, but no signs of restoration of cortical functions could be observed. The dog was absolutely passive; she could not lap milk when her face was dipped into it. The dog could swallow when fluid was poured into her mouth, but she quickly fatigued. She could not raise her head; when her head was lifted by the experimenter, the dog could not keep it in this position. On freezing the brain of this dog, hypoxia apparently could not be avoided, since the amount of lactic acid was increased, and that of glucose decreased.

TABLE 19. Content (in mg %) of Carbohydrates and Lactic Acid in the Brain and Blood of Dogs 1 to 3 Days After Resuscitation (clinical death was 5-6 minutes)

Dog No.	Time from beginning of resuscitation	Brain cortex			Blood		Duration of dying	Time from beginning of resuscitation to appearance of respiration	Narcosis
		Sugar	Glycogen	Lactic acid	Sugar	Lactic acid			
1	22 hours	40	234	105	92	43	9 min 00 sec	1 min 45 sec	Ether
2	20 »	95	163	34	188	22	8 » 48 »	5 » 06 »	»
3	24 »	48	134	32	63	10	6 » 48 »	1 » 30 »	»
4	25 »	117	144	Traces	98	—	22 » 45 »	11 » 45 »	Nembutal
5	23 »	138	—	63	94	—	19 » 02 »	9 » 50 »	»
6	24 »	104	—	40	51	—	18 » 59 »	8 » 40 »	»
7	3 days	91	43	22	175	11	9 » 24 »	2 » 42 »	Ether
8	3 »	92	65	27	150	8	6 » 48 »	2 » 48 »	»

In dog No. 2 the content of glycogen in the cerebral cortex was also increased, although less than in dog No. 1. The state of this dog towards the end of the first 24 hours after resuscitation was less critical than that of dog No. 1. Most of the time the dog was asleep in a position usual for dogs—curled up—and the animal could easily be awakened by a simple touch. The dog could raise her head and hold it, but she made no attempt to get up; when her face was immersed in milk the dog lapped it, but she could not find food by herself and was blind and deaf. During the resuscitation of this dog ventricular fibrillation arose, but it was interrupted by the discharge of a condenser with 4,000 volts intensity through the intact breast cage. Cardiac activity was restored only after 2 minutes and 12 seconds, which in fact increased the length of clinical death to 7 minutes, and this postponed the restoration of the external respiration and the functions of the central nervous system.

In dog No. 3, also dying in a state of ether narcosis, the length of dying was the shortest, and during resuscitation restoration of the external respiration was the quickest. Towards the end of the first 24 hours the condition of the dog was much better than in the previously described 2 dogs, although in this dog also the functions of the higher divisions of the central nervous system were not yet restored, and the animal was blind and deaf. Most of the time the dog was awake, whimpered, and made unsuccessful attempts to get on its feet, could find the food by smelling it and then ate it voraciously. The content of glycogen in the cerebral cortex of this dog was within normal limits.

The next 3 dogs described in Table 19 were dying in a state of nembutal narcosis. The duration of dying in all 3 dogs was long, and the external respiration at resuscitation was restored later, which determined their state towards the end of the first 24 hours after resuscitation, resembling that in dog No. 1. However, in this experiment ether was not used, and consequently only a tendency towards increase in glycogen of the cerebral cortex in dog No. 4 was noted. Even this was only slightly above the content observed under normal conditions. In the other 2 dogs glycogen was not determined.

Of particular interest is the fact that in one of the dogs 24 hours after resuscitation, ether narcosis, administered before the skull trepanation and freezing of the brain, induced hyperglycemia. In the rest of the dogs hyperglycemia was not observed, whether ether or nembutal was administered before the freezing of the brain. In spite of this, the content of glucose in the cerebral cortex of dogs which were under nembutal narcosis was increased, although under normal conditions nembutal narcosis never raises the glucose content of the brain. In the initial period of resuscitation in dogs dying in a state of barbamyl or nembutal narcosis, the content of glucose in the cerebral cortex was also higher than in dogs dying in a state of ether narcosis. Apparently, nembutal significantly lowered the expenditure of carbohydrates in cerebral tissue.

In 2 dogs (Nos. 7 and 8) dying in a state of ether narcosis, the brain was frozen towards the end of the 3rd day after resuscitation. The dying in these dogs was of average duration, and external respiration during resuscitation was restored rather quickly. Twenty-four hours after resuscitation the dogs were in a normal position— curled up; they responded to noise, pricking up their ears, raising their heads and turning them in the direction of the noise. However, all the movements of the dogs were slowed down. The dogs were blind and could not find the food, but lapped up the milk when their faces were dipped into it. The dogs could not sit up or stand up. Most of the time they slept. Thirty-six hours after resuscitation the dogs licked their wounds, stood up and sat down, but in an attempt to walk they would fall. They could find the food, watched large objects (a chair), but would not respond to motions of small objects (pencils) before their eyes. Forty-eight hours after resuscitation the dogs adequately responded to surroundings; eyesight was completely restored, although the coordination of movements was not yet perfect, and during sharp turns of the body and attempts to run the dogs would lose balance. Dog No. 7 was friendly and approached when called. Dog No. 8, however, became very aggressive. Towards the end of 64 hours after resuscitation the coordination of movements in dog No. 7 was considerably improved, although she was slightly wobbly during running. Dog No. 8 even after 72 hours following resuscitation was still unsteady during walks and continued to be aggressive. The trepanation of the skull and freezing of the brain was performed under pantopone-ether narcosis which induced the usual increase in blood sugar. As can be seen from Table 19, the content of glucose, glycogen, and lactic acid in the cerebral cortex of these dogs was within normal limits. Therefore, with the restoration of the functions of the cerebral cortex there was a restoration of the normal content of glycogen.

That there was an inefficiently regulated mechanism of carbohydrate metabolism in the organism after resuscitation was indicated not only by the excessive accumulation of glycogen in the cerebral cortex but also by the shape of the hyperglycemic curves obtained after the dogs were administered glucose per os. Twenty-four hours after resuscitation the hyperglycemic curves were of the irritation type, with a greater rise than under normal conditions. The Boduin coefficient of the rise of the curve reached 2.24 compared to a normal rise of 1.36. Such a shape of the hyperglycemic curves is characteristic for decerebrated animals. Georgievskaya (1936), Bayandurov, Faleev, and Sitnikov (1937) observed such hyperglycemic curves in decerebrated dogs, and Anderson and Haymaker (1949) in decerebrated rats. The character of the hyperglycemic curves permitted the assumption that the influence of the cerebral cortex on biochemical processes in the organism 24 hours after re-suscitation was not yet normal, just as the restoration of its physiological functions was not yet normal at this time.

The administration of glucose 48, 64, or 120 hours or later after resuscitation showed that the hyperglycemic curves were of the usual, normal type. Therefore, the complete restoration of the functions of the cerebral cortex after resuscitation ensures the complete regulation of the physiological processes as well as the complete regulation of the intermediary metabolic processes.

CHAPTER V

THE INFLUENCE OF HYPOTHERMIA OF VARYING DEGREES ON THE CHANGES IN THE METABOLISM OF CEREBRAL TISSUE DURING DYING FROM EXSANGUINATION AND ON THE PROCESS OF ITS NORMALIZATION DURING RESUSCITATION

One of the most real and complex problems of the pathophysiology and therapy of terminal states is the question of the extent of time during which the brain, deprived of blood circulation, can retain its capacity for complete restoration of all its functions after the renewal of blood circulation. One of the approaches to this question is the application of hypothermia. In several Soviet and foreign publications, among them the recent monographs by Negovskii (1960) and Petrov and Gubler (1961), it has been shown that the resistance of the central nervous system to temporary interruption of blood circulation during artificial hypothermia is increased when the hypothermia is induced during narcosis which prevents the development of protective reactions of the organism towards lowering of the body temperature. It has been established by Negovskii, Soboleva, Gurvich, and Kiseleva (1960) that with lowered body temperature dogs can endure the state of clinical death for up to 2 hours with complete subsequent restoration of the functions of the central nervous system.

The mechanism of the increase in resistance of the organism towards hypoxia under the influence of artificial hypothermia may be generally considered as established. It consists in deep inhibition of the functions of the central nervous system, and lowering of its requirement for energy, with the corresponding decrease in the rate of its metabolic processes. Because of this, during the onset of hypoxia the available energy resources are sufficient for a considerably longer time for the support of life than under the conditions of ordinary body temperature. However, in spite of the apparent clarity of the mechanism of the favorable effects of hypothermia, many unsolved problems remain which first of all concern the possible lower limit of lowering of body temperature of the warm-blooded animals and man without the damaging effects of the hypothermia itself, the presence or absence of such damaging effects under varying degrees of hypothermia, the elucidation of the complex processes of metabolism in various tissues and organs which, in the final analysis, determine the reversibility of the functional and morphological alterations induced by hypoxia under the conditions of lowered body temperature.

Bigelow (1950-1954), Horvath (1953), Dundee (1953), Rosomoff and Holaday (1954), Gubler (1958-1961) and others have shown that during lowering of the body temperature of a narcotized warm-blooded animal the consumption of oxygen by the entire organism as well as by the brain is lowered 3- to 5-fold, the lowering of the consumption of oxygen being proportional to the fall in body temperature. Gubler believes that in the process of cooling to 28-25°C (hypothermia of average degree) the consumption of oxygen by the organism is lowered by 5% per degree. However, when deep hypothermia, i.e., body temperature lower than 20°C, is reached, further drop in oxygen consumption proceeds at a slower rate. At the same time, the inhibition of anaerobic glycolysis in brain tissue under the influence of hypothermia is considerably less prominent (Savchenko, 1958).

Vladimirov (1957 and Nikulin (1959), studying the extent of incorporation of labeled amino acids in brain tissue, found that during hypothermia of average degree the synthesis of brain protein is significantly decreased. Furthermore, Vladimirov, Ivanova, and Pravdina (1957, 1959) showed that hypothermia significantly decreased the extent of incorporation of inorganic phosphate into organic phosphorus compounds of protein and nonprotein nature. However, while decreasing the metabolism in the cerebral tissue of normal animals, hypothermia does not alter the equilibrium between synthesis and degradation of the energy-rich phosphorus compounds, and their content remains at normal levels (Vladimirov, 1957).

TABLE 20. Effect of Cooling and Subsequent Warming of Narcotized Dogs on the Content of the Components of Carbohydrate-Phosphorus Metabolism of Cerebral Cortex

Conditions for experiments	ATP	Creatine phosphate	Inorganic phosphate	Sugar	Lactic acid
	In micromoles per gram			In mg %	
Initial narcosis					
Average data of 6 experiments	2.3	2.7	1.5	104	21
Limits of variation	1.8−2.6	2.4−3.1	0.5−3.1	57−82	1.5−36
Cooling to 25°					
Average data of 6 experiments	2.3	2.6	1.0	76	28
Limits of variation	1.9−2.5	2.2−3.4	0.5−2.1	55−102	5.0−50
1 hour at 25°					
Average data of 3 experiments	2.0	3.0	1.8	100	29
Limits of variation	1.8−2.1	2.6−3.5	1.4−2.0	60−122	16−49
Cooling and subsequent warming					
Average data of 3 experiments	2.5	2.5	0.5	53	21
Limits of variation	2.3−2.6	1.8−3.2	0.5−0.5	43−63	16−26

We also found (Table 20) that cooling of narcotized dogs down to a 25°C body temperature (measured rectally), keeping the animals at this body temperature for one hour, followed by warming the animal, does not result in any substantial alterations in the equilibrium between the processes of synthesis and degradation of carbohydrate-phosphorus compounds in the cerebral cortex. It should be noted that during lowering of the dog temperature to 25°C, and particularly while holding the body temperature at this level for an hour, the arterial blood pressure dropped to 60-70 mm Hg. Furthermore, in all dogs the respiration was very slow and superficial and could hardly be recorded on the pneumogram. Arterial blood became dark (according to Bulanova, the degree of saturation of blood by oxygen dropped from 95% to 85% upon reaching 20°C body temperature). At this time the content of creatine phosphate and lactic acid (which best reflect the onset of hypoxia) in the cerebral cortex remained within normal limits. Hypoxia did not appear because of a lower requirement of the brain for oxygen. Therefore, cooling of animals under narcosis not only does not alter metabolic processes in the brain tissue, but it also prevents the alteration in equilibrium between the processes of synthesis and degradation and the onset of hypoxia during the weakening of the cardiovascular activity and respiration in dogs during the onset of hypothermia.

Nosova (1960), by chromatographic separation of the adenosine phosphoric acids, showed (Fig. 9) that in dogs under pantopone-nembutal narcosis during lowering of the body temperature to 26°C there is a tendency towards an increase in ATP of the cerebral cortex with complete absence of ADP, which is always present in small amounts at normal body temperature. Apparently, this was a result of the lowering of the rate of metabolic processes during hypothermia and of complete correlation between the energy resources and requirements of the cerebral tissue. In addition, this indirectly indicated a significant depression in brain tissue respiration. The determination of ammonia and glutamine under similar conditions in the cerebral tissue of dogs (Fig. 10) showed that the content of ammonia during hypothermia was lower and less stable than during normal body temperature. This, apparently, was a function of the state of deeper inhibition of the cerebral cortex during hypothermia. The content of glutamine in the cerebral cortex during hypothermia was about the same as under normal conditions.

According to Raiko, Petrov, and Kudritskaya (1957) and Pertsova (1958), in cats under ether-and-oxygen narcosis with the addition of hexonium and cooled to 22-25°C, the brain tissue contained high amounts of en-

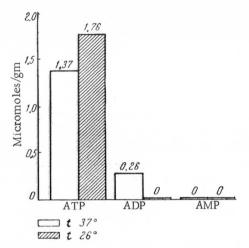

Fig. 9. Content of adenosinephosphoric acids in cerebral cortex of narcotized dogs at normal body temperatures and during hypothermia.

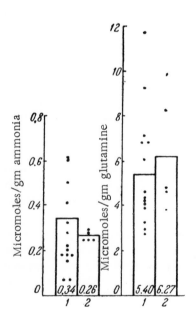

Fig. 10. Content of ammonia and glutamine in cerebral cortex of narcotized dogs under normal body temperatures and in hypothermia. 1) Normal body temperature; 2) body temperature of 25°C.

ergy-rich phosphate compounds and low amounts of inorganic phosphate and lactic acid. The content of ammonia was close to normal, and that of glutamine slightly above normal. Thus, hypothermia of average depth (25°C), induced during narcosis of average intensity, slows down the rate of metabolism in cerebral tissue, but it does not alter materially the levels of the carbohydrate-phosphorus compounds, ammonia, or glutamine.

A different situation is observed when deep hypothermia is attained in warm-blooded animals (about 20°C and lower). Cooling of narcotized dogs down to 18-20°C body temperature induced accumulation of somewhat excessive amounts of carbohydrates in the brain (Gaevskaya and Nosova, 1961). Thus, while the sum of glucose and glycogen in the brain of dogs cooled to 25°C was about 180 mg %, in dogs cooled to 18-20°C it increased to 280 mg %.

Veksler and Gershenovich (1961) observed in rats a progressive increase in ammonia of cerebral tissue with cooling of body temperature. They established that the increase in ammonia is mainly connected with the destruction of brain proteins of albumin nature. Nosova and ourselves found in the cerebral cortex of dogs cooled to 21-18°C twice as much ammonia as in dogs cooled to 26-25°C (0.4-0.6 micromole per gram and 0.25 and 0.28 micromole per gram, respectively). In the cerebral cortex of dogs in a state of deep hypothermia (body temperature 20°C) the content of glutamic acid was lower than at normal body temperature (4.98 micromoles per gram and 7.23 micromoles per gram, respectively). The content of γ-aminobutyric acid was also lower (0.68 micromole per gram at 20°C and 1.73 micromoles per gram under normal body temperature). The amount of alanine, on the other hand, increased from 0.19 micromole per gram at 37°C to 0.36 micromole per gram at 20°C. The content of other free amino acids in the cerebral tissue remained unaltered.

There is no reason to believe that these alterations are a result of an induced deficit in energy due to greater alterations in the functions of respiration and blood circulation, because none of the symptoms of brain tissue hypoxia is present at this time. Apparently an effect of hypothermia as such on the coordination of metabolic processes is taking place, and the latter can undergo a serious alteration due to the uneven extent of inhibition of various reactions with the lowering of temperature. Indications of this possibility can be found in the reports by Hannon (1958) who showed that the oxidation of tricarboxylic acids by slices of rat liver at temperatures below 21°C is progressively decreased with lower temperatures, whereas the consumption of oxygen falls considerably more slowly. However, the fact, established by Negovskii and co-workers, that lowering of the body temperature of dogs before dying to 21-20°C and further lowering of it to 10-15°C during clinical death permits the lengthening of the latter to 2 hours, proves that alterations in the metabolism of cerebral tissue under the influence of hypothermia as such are smaller than its favorable effect on the resistance of the cerebral tissue to deep hypoxia.

We (1957, 1958, 1960) and Nosova (1960, 1961) studied the process of expenditure of energy resources in the cerebral cortex of dogs during clinical death induced by exsanguination at various body temperatures. To adult dogs of both sexes weighing 7-12 kg, pantopone (0.4 mg/kg, 2% solution) and atropine (0.1 mg/kg, 0.1% solution) were administered subcutaneously; after 30-40 minutes a 0.2% solution of nembutal or pentothal was administered dropwise. The dogs in a state of mild narcosis were placed in an ice bath and the narcosis was continued in such a way as to prevent the onset of shivering. On reaching 30-28°C of body temperature, the administration of narcotics was stopped. The body temperature, measured rectally, was dropping at the rate of 1°C in 5-10 minutes. After reaching the desired body temperature the animal was killed by free flow of blood from the femoral artery, the trepanation of the skull was immediately performed, and test samples of the cerebral cortex were removed at various intervals after the onset of clinical death. Pieces of cerebral cortex were sliced off and quickly frozen in liquid nitrogen. This approach permitted the study of the cerebral tissue in the same dog at various stages of clinical death, allowing for the insignificant error in the calculation of its duration. Whenever the body temperature of the dog was above 32°C, the brain was frozen in situ, since the processes of degradation in the brain were proceeding at an accelerated rate and the error became significant. In the latter case only one piece of tissue from each dog was taken for analysis. For parallel determinations 5-7 animals were used.

During clinical death the body temperature continued to decline. In those cases when the body temperature before dying was 32-26°C, this decline in body temperature during one hour of clinical death did not exceed 2-3 degrees. Whenever the body temperature before dying was 20°C, during clinical death it declined more rapidly — down to 13-14°C at the end of 60 minutes and down to 10-12°C at the end of 120 minutes.

In accord with Negovskii and Soboleva (1956), we observed that cooling did not slow down the process of dying of the animals from exsanguination, and the duration of dying in various dogs varied within the same limits as in experiments without the use of hypothermia. Therefore, the supply of oxygen to the brain ceased within the same period of time as under normal body temperature, and the oxidative processes in the cerebral tissue should be shifted to the glycolytic pathways. In Chapter III we described how the content of energy resources of the brain alters during dying and during clinical death under normal body temperatures. Here we shall briefly describe this material once again in order to compare it with the picture prevailing during hypothermia of various extent.

The data on the changes in the content of carbohydrates (the sum of glucose and glycogen), lactic acid, ATP, ADP, and AMP in the brain at various body temperatures during the initial stage of pantopone-nembutal narcosis and during the subsequent period of dying are summarized in Fig. 11 (I-VI). At normal body temperature (37° before dying) during dying from rapid exsanguination the process of oxidative utilization of carbohydrates by the cerebral tissue began to terminate at the onset of agony, i.e., after the exhaustion of the physiological compensatory mechanisms, which compensate for the deficiency in oxygen. During this period creatine phosphate disappeared from the brain tissue, the amount of ATP decreased, the amount of ADP increased, and AMP appeared. The termination of the oxidative processes resulted in stimulation of glycolysis. As can be seen by the increase in the content of lactic acid (Fig. 11, I), glycolysis was particularly active toward the end of agony and during the first few minutes of clinical death. The final balance of the utilized carbohydrates of the brain and of the formed lactic acid showed that after 10 minutes of clinical death lactic acid accumulated by 35 mg % more than the amount of carbohydrate that was utilized. This was made possible because during agony, while the blood circulation was still partially functioning, a portion of the lactic acid of the brain was formed from the carbohydrates delivered to the brain with the blood. This once more confirms the assumption that during dying under normal body temperatures the glycolytic process in brain tissue was activated before the onset of clinical death.

Poor effectiveness of glycolysis from the energy standpoint during high requirements of the brain under normal body temperatures resulted in rapid degradation of the energy-rich phosphorus compounds. The content of ATP in the cerebral tissue towards the 5th minute of clinical death decreased 14-fold. The content of ADP, which significantly increased in the cerebral tissue during agony, markedly decreased towards the 5th minute of clinical death. Apparently, the decrease in the content of carbohydrates and of the energy-rich phosphorus compounds was the basic cause which led to the inhibition of glycolysis, which was sharply revealed towards

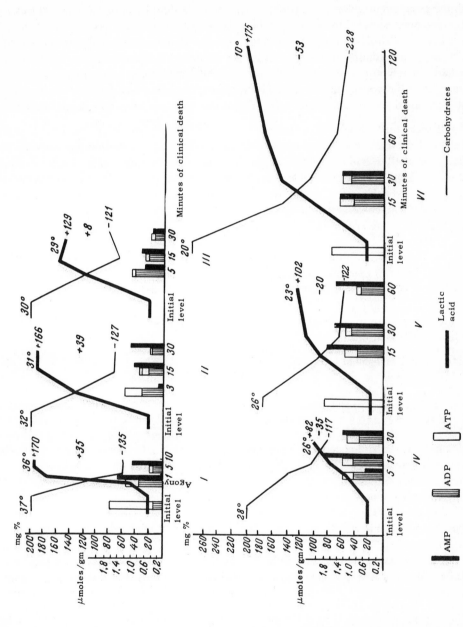

Fig. 11. Changes in the content of carbohydrate-phosphorus compounds in cerebral cortex of dogs during clinical death at various body temperatures (I-IV). Total amount of glucose and glycogen as well as of lactic acid is given in mg % of wet weight of tissue; content of adenosinephosphates, in micromoles per gram wet weight of tissue.

69

the end of the 5th minute of clinical death and which was reflected in the cessation of a further decrease in carbohydrate content and in accumulation of lactic acid.

At body temperature of 32°C before dying, as well as at 37°C, the process of glycolysis commenced while the blood circulation was still functioning. Lactic acid was formed in part from carbohydrates of the blood, and towards the 30th minute of clinical death it accumulated by 39 mg % more than the amount of carbohydrates of the brain tissue utilized. The lowering of the body temperature to 30°C resulted in a situation when the replacement of the oxidative utilization of carbohydrates by the glycolytic pathway occurred, apparently, simultaneously with the cessation of blood circulation. Lactic acid was formed only from the carbohydrates of the brain, and its amount corresponded to the amount of carbohydrates utilized. Lowering of the body temperature before dying to 32-30°C already resulted in lowering of the functional activity of the brain and in lowering of the processes of degradation during the onset of hypoxia. Creatine phosphate disappeared from cerebral tissue under these conditions only after 3-5 minutes of clinical death, and, as can be seen from Fig. 11, the degradation of ATP and ADP was markedly delayed. The reduced expenditure of the energy-rich phosphorus compounds resulted in the situation that the inhibition of glycolysis took place only after 15 minutes of clinical death.

During further intensification of hypothermia down to 28-26°C before dying, the final balance of carbohydrates utilized and of lactic acid formed during dying and clinical death showed that the amount of accumulated lactic acid was smaller than the amount of carbohydrates utilized (Fig. 11, IV and V). Apparently, during dying and even after the cessation of blood circulation, a certain portion of carbohydrates was utilized via the oxidative pathway, probably utilizing the oxygen dissolved in blood and cell plasma which remained in brain capillaries. The longer the conservation of the oxidative metabolism the longer was the preservation of the relatively higher amounts of the energy-rich phosphorus compounds. Indeed, at body temperature of 28°C at the 5th minute of clinical death the cerebral tissue still contained traces of creatine phosphate. At body temperature of 26°C at the 7th minute of clinical death, the cerebral tissue contained 0.6 micromole of creatine phosphate per gram, and traces of creatine phosphate were observed in the brain of some dogs even at the 15th minute of clinical death. The content of ATP and ADP in brain tissue at these body temperatures was several times higher than at higher body temperatures at the 30th minute of clinical death. Even at the 60th minute of clinical death at body temperature of 26°C before dying, the content of ATP and ADP in the brain was higher than at the 30th minute of clinical death at body temperature of 32-30°C.

The relatively higher content of creatine phosphate, ATP, and ADP in brain tissue during clinical death under the conditions of hypothermia of average intensity (28-26°C) facilitated the glycolytic process between the 15th and 30th minute of clinical death. During the period of the 30th to 60th minute of clinical death (Fig. 11, V) the accumulation of lactic acid in brain tissue was reduced, but not completely halted, exactly as was observed at body temperatures of 32-30°C after 15 minutes of clinical death.

During dying at the initial body temperature of 20°C (intense hypothermia) the alteration of metabolic processes began very gradually and late (Fig. 11, VI). In 3 dogs out of 5 at the 15th minute of clinical death the brain tissue contained 0.06 to 0.7 micromole of creatine phosphate per gram, while none could be found in the tissue at higher body temperatures. At the 15th minute of clinical death the cerebral cortex still contained about half the amount of initial ATP. The amount of formed ADP was equal to the decrease in ATP, and their sum was thus equal to that observed before dying. This indicated that the predominance of the processes of degradation of carbohydrate-phosphorus compounds over the processes of synthesis in cerebral tissue had not yet taken place, and that the conditions for the synthetic processes were still present. During the period of dying and 15 minutes of clinical death the expenditure of carbohydrates in the brain exceeded the amount of accumulated lactic acid by 53 mg %. Therefore, a portion of the carbohydrates must have been utilized via the oxidative pathway. The correspondence between the amount of utilized carbohydrates and the amount of lactic acid formed appeared only after 15 minutes of clinical death, and this indicated that from this moment on the brain tissue shifted to the glycolytic metabolic pathway.

At the 30th minute of clinical death under conditions of intense hypothermia (temperature of the brain was about 16°C) creatine phosphate could no longer be detected, and the content of ATP was decreased insignificantly compared to values found at the 15th minute of clinical death. Whether or not there is further decrease not only in the content of ATP but of ADP as well, as was observed between the 30th and 60th minute of clinical death under the conditions of average hypothermia (26-23°C), has not as yet been determined. It should be mentioned, however, that the accumulation of lactic acid (and therefore the glycolytic process) proceeded more intensively between the 30th and 60th minute of clinical death under the conditions of intense hypothermia than under the conditions of hypothermia of average intensity. The activity of glycolysis was noticeably decreased during the second hour of clinical death, but complete inhibition of glycolysis was not observed.

The rise in the initial amount of carbohydrates in cerebral tissue during lowering of the body temperature from 26° to 20°C ensured the supply of greater amounts of energy during dying not only via the oxidative but also via the glycolytic pathway, which could be deduced from the larger accumulation of lactic acid during clinical death. The content of lactic acid in the brain towards the end of the second hour of clinical death (temperature of the brain was about 10°C) reached the same large values as at 36°C on the 5th minute of clinical death, but the sources of its accumulation were different: at high body temperature the excess of lactic acid was accumulated during agony at the expense of blood sugar, while at low body temperature during clinical death it accumulated at the expense of excess carbohydrates in the brain.

Figure 11 shows also the data obtained by Nosova on changes in the contents of AMP in the cerebral cortex of dogs during dying under the conditions of various body temperatures. Under normal body temperature, when the animal is already in agony, a large amount of AMP which exceeded the decrease in ATP and ADP appeared in the brain. Towards the 5th minute of clinical death the content of AMP in the brain began to decline, due, apparently, to its deamination. During dying under hypothermia (32° and 30°) the accumulation of AMP and the subsequent decline in its content took place at later periods compared to conditions of normal body temperatures. At body temperature of 28-20° the accumulation of AMP also took place later than under normal body temperatures, its amounts were greater than under less intense hypothermia, and its degradation proceeded at a considerably slower rate. The latter event indicated the possibility of inhibition of the process of deamination of AMP in proportion to the intensity of hypothermia.

Under all investigated conditions of thermal changes, the accumulation of AMP in the brain during clinical death exceeded the possibility of its formation from adenosine phosphoric acids. As can be seen from Fig. 11, lowering of body temperature before dying did not inhibit the accumulation of AMP, in spite of the inhibition of degradation of ATP and ADP. As has already been indicated, during intense hypothermia the ratio of ATP and ADP altered without any changes in the sum of the two quantities, while about the same quantity of AMP accumulated (Fig. 11, VI). In this connection it may be assumed that a portion of the brain AMP was formed from other sources, perhaps from the nucleic acids.

In addition to the study of adenosine phosphoric acids in the brain tissue of dogs during dying under the conditions of hypothermia of various intensities, Nosova investigated the content of inorganic phosphate under similar conditions. The data are summarized in Fig. 12. As can be seen from the illustrated curves showing the changes in the content of inorganic phosphate in the cerebral cortex of dogs during clinical death, the accumulation of inorganic phosphate occurred rapidly and intensively under normal body temperatures as well as during hypothermia, and essentially corresponded with rapid degradation of creatine phosphate and the initial degradation of ATP. However, the amount of inorganic phosphate always exceeded that which could theroretically arise from the decomposition of the sum of creatine phosphate, ATP, and ADP. This indicated that a degradation of other phosphate-containing substances, most likely phosphoproteins, was taking place.

Apparently, the latter circumstance was the reason for the absence of a correlation between the slowdown in the degradation of the energy-rich compounds and the increase in inorganic phosphate with lowering of the body temperature down to 26°C. As can be seen from Fig. 12, only at 20°C was it possible to observe a decrease in the rate of accumulation of inorganic phosphate.

Thus, during hypothermia the requirements of brain tissue for energy are lowered, the expenditure of carbohydrates and of energy-rich phosphorus compounds is decreased, and conditions are created for a more prolonged glycolytic process which allows the brain tissue to survive clinical death for longer periods. As has been illustrated in experiments under intense hypothermia, the initial level of carbohydrates in dying brain tissue is of paramount importance for the intensive glycolytic process.

Of no smaller interest than the study of carbohydrate-phosphorus metabolism is the study of nitrogen

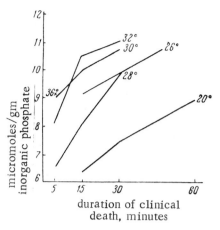

Fig. 12. Changes in the content of inorganic phosphate in cerebral cortex of dogs during clinical death at various body temperatures. X marks the content of inorganic phosphate at 5th minute of clinical death at 36°C body temperature.

metabolism in brain tissue during dying under the conditions of hypothermia, particularly because, as has been shown by Veksler, the lowering of body temperature itself induces at certain moments alterations of nitrogen metabolism in the brain. In our collaborative studies with Nosova (1961, 1962) changes in the content of ammonia and glutamine in the cerebral cortex of dogs dying from exsanguination under average and intense hypothermia were investigated. The experimental conditions were the same as those under which the carbohydrate-phosphorus metabolism was studied. It was found (Fig. 13) that under hypothermia during clinical death the content of ammonia in the cerebral cortex of dogs significantly increased, particularly at body temperatures of 26-23 °C. Under a state of intense hypothermia (20-10°C), in spite of the higher initial levels of ammonia, its content increased during the first 30 minutes twofold, and during the subsequent 1.5 hours of clinical death it remained almost the same. In addition, it was found that the content of ammonia in brain tissue on the 15th minute of clinical death was within the same limits during hypothermia as well as during normal body temperature (compare with Fig. 2). Therefore, hypothermia does not inhibit the formation of ammonia in the brain during dying, as, for example, was the case with lactic acid. As regards the degradation of glutamine in brain tissue during dying, hypothermia definitely inhibited its degradation (Fig. 14). Under normal body temperatures the content of glutamine in the cerebral cortex towards the 5th minute of clinical death was lowered from the initial

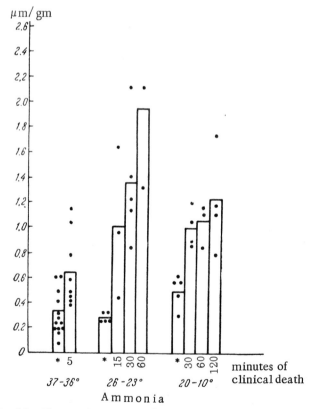

Fig. 13. Changes in content of ammonia in cerebral cortex of dogs during clinical death at various body temperatures. * Initial.

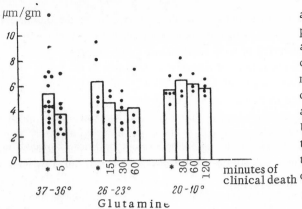

Fig. 14. Changes in content of glutamine in cerebral cortex of dogs during clinical death at various body temperatures. *Initial.

average of 5.4 micromoles per gram to 3.7 micromoles per gram. Under hypothermia of average intensity the amount of glutamine was still close to the initial level of glutamine (4.6 micromoles per gram) at the 15th minute of clinical death, and thereafter in the course of clinical death its content changed insignificantly, although there was a tendency towards a decrease. Under the conditions of intense hypothermia (20-10°C) the content of glutamine remained unaltered during the entire 2 hours of clinical death, being equal to the content observed initially.

In one of the dogs dying under the condition of hypothermia of average intensity an increase in glutamine in brain tissue from 4.8 micromoles per gram to 7.5 micromoles per gram was observed between the 30th and 60th minute of clinical death. The amount of ammonia in the brain of the same animal towards the 60th minute reached the highest levels — 2.5 micromoles per gram. Thus, in this case a phenomenon took place which was observed in one of the animals between the 5th and 15th minute of clinical death at normal body temperatures. It may be supposed that in this case also the increase in glutamine took place as a result of the onset of degradation of brain proteins.

The absence of the inhibitory effect of hypothermia on the accumulation of ammonia in brain tissue during the slowdown in the degradation of glutamine indicated that ammonia was accumulating not only at the expense of glutamine but also at the expense of other substances. It follows that hypothermia, while not preventing the release of ammonia from the proteins, adenylic acid, and other sources, preserved for longer periods the possibilities of synthesis of glutamine from ammonia and glutamine acid. As is well known, the synthesis of glutamine depends to a great extent on the availability of adequate amounts of ATP. Apparently, the conservation of greater amounts of ATP in brain tissue during clinical death under hypothermia, especially of the intensive form, ensured adequate levels of glutamine. A similar phenomenon was observed by Pertseva (1960) in the brain tissue of cats under hypothermia during temporary exclusion of the heart from circulation.

The content of free amino acids in the cerebral cortex of dogs dying in a state of intense hypothermia was also investigated. The content of glutamic acid in brain tissue during 2 hours of clinical death in a state of intense hypothermia was not altered (Fig. 15), as it did not change under normal body temperatures during 5 minutes of clinical death. The amount of γ-aminobutyric acid and the sum of asparagine, serine, and glycine, which was lowered under the influence of hypothermia, did not change during the 2 hours of clinical death. The content of alanine in brain tissue (Fig. 16), which was raised under the influence of hypothermia, continued to

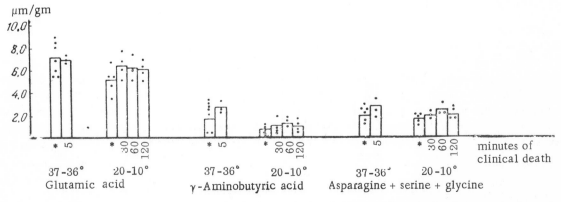

Fig. 15. Content of free amino acids (glutamic acid, γ-aminobutyric acid, and others) in cerebral cortex of dogs during clinical death at various body temperatures. * Initial.

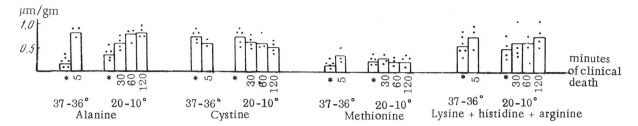

Fig. 16. Content of free amino acids (alanine, cystine, methionine, and others) in cerebral cortex of dogs during clinical death at various body temperatures. * Initial.

increase during the 2 hours of clinical death. The accumulation of alanine occurred gradually, and its content reached 0.84 micromole per gram towards the end of the second hour of clinical death, whereas under normal body temperatures the accumulation of alanine occurred rapidly during 5 minutes of clinical death, reaching the same high levels. As on the 5th minute of clinical death under normal body temperatures, during intense hypothermia the content of cystine in the brain tissue tended to decrease in the course of 2 hours of clinical death. The observed tendency for methionine of the brain to increase during clinical death under normal body temperatures was not observed during intense hypothermia. Thus, during dying in a state of intense hypothermia the changes in the contents of free amino acids of the brain were just as small as during normal body temperatures, and in addition these took place very slowly.

We shall now consider the processes of normalization of brain metabolism during resuscitation after clinical death taking place in a state of hypothermia.

Negovskii and Soboleva (1956-1960) drew attention to the fact that during the resuscitation of dogs which endured prolonged clinical death in a state of hypothermia, the restoration of external respiration and corneal reflexes took place considerably later than in dogs after 5-6 minutes of clinical death under normal body temperatures. This occurred even when the cardiac activity was restored at about the same time in both cases. Further restoration of activity of the higher divisions of the central nervous system was not only not delayed, but often took place earlier, particularly when the length of clinical death did not exceed 30 minutes during hypothermia of average intensity (25°C).

Considering that in experiments with hypothermia the body temperature of the animals was lowered during the entire initial period of resuscitation and that, in spite of the warming up of the animals, it did not rise above 25-30°C, it could be assumed that during this situation there was also a slowdown in the restoration of metabolic processes in the brain tissue. It was important to learn to what extent the character of metabolic processes in the brain tissue of dogs changes under the influence of lowered body temperature during the recovery period, particularly in relation to the oxidative and glycolytic processes, since these determine to a great extent the possibilities and the direction of the necessary therapeutic measures. The study of the metabolism of resuscitated brain tissue after it endured clinical death under hypothermia was therefore undertaken by us (1957, 1961) and by Nosova (1960, 1961).

The duration of clinical death in all experiments was 30 minutes. The restoration of the vital functions in dogs was accomplished by a complex method of resuscitation, consisting of pumping of heparinized arterial blood obtained from the same animal during exsanguination and kept at 38°C, and of artificial respiration with the aid of an apparatus which inspired and sucked out the air from the lungs. Whenever ventricular fibrillation occurred during resuscitation it was removed by the method of Gurvich by a single discharge of a condenser. The warming of the animal was commenced simultaneously with the measures for resuscitation, replacing the ice in the bath by warm water (40-43°C) and discontinuing the warming when the body temperature reached 31-32°C.

Table 21 summarizes our data on carbohydrate metabolism in dog brain and Table 22 summarizes the data of Nosova on the metabolism of the energy-rich phosphates in the same dogs during the period of restoration of the vital functions.

In dog No. 2 during clinical death and before the beginning of resuscitation the trepanation of the skull

74

TABLE 21. Changes in the Content of Components of Carbohydrate
Metabolism in Cerebral Cortex During Resuscitation of Dogs
30 Minutes After Clinical Death in Hypothermia
(expressed in mg % of wet weight of tissue)

Dog No.	Sugar	Glycogen	Lactic acid	Blood sugar	Time from beginning of resuscitation	Body temp. at the time of taking the test specimen of brain, in °C
1	61	27	61	250	9 min	25
2	101	55	317	237	10 »	25.8
3	68	41	130	247	16 »	26
4	140	42	84	235	45 »	27
5	124	12	20	147	76 »	30
6	95	23	50	105	80 »	29
7	42	209	49	—	1 day	37
8	51	—	33	—	2 days	39.3

was performed and test tissue was removed from under the soft membrane of the brain, being sure not to injure the large blood vessels so as to avoid bleeding during the recovery period. Regular cardiac activity in this dog was restored only after 2 minutes and 30 seconds from the beginning of resuscitation because of constant occurrence of ventricular fibrillation. During the subsequent 7 minutes the arterial pressure was unsteady and it fluctuated within 70 to 120 mm Hg. At the 10th minute of resuscitation freezing of the brain was begun, during which the arterial pressure stayed at the level of 50-60 mm Hg. As regards the content of glucose, glycogen, and lactic acid in the cerebral cortex during the period of resuscitation, it is possible to compare the values observed with those found in this dog on the 30th minute of clinical death before the beginning of resuscitation. The amount of glucose in the brain tissue increased from 83 mg % to 116 mg %, while the amount of glycogen, which was normal (95 mg %) at the end of clinical death, decreased twofold. Simultaneously, the amount of lactic acid sharply increased, which even before resuscitation was quite large (195 mg %). An increase in the content of sugar in the blood from 140 mg % before dying to 234 mg % at the beginning of resuscitation was also observed. Study of the energy-rich phosphates in the brain tissue of this animal (see Table 22) showed that 7.5 minutes after the restoration of blood circulation, but before the external respiration had been restored, the amount of ATP as well as of inorganic phosphate already returned to the initial levels, while the amount of creatine phosphate, absent during clinical death, was still considerably below the normal levels. The results of this experiment indicate the following peculiarities of brain metabolism at the initial period of resuscitation under the conditions of hypothermia. At the beginning of resuscitation the process of degradation of glycogen in the cerebral cortex still continued, since its quantity at the end of clinical death was not lowered to levels which indicate the inhibition of glycogenolysis. As under the conditions of normal body temperatures, hyperglycemia was present, which is characteristic for the initial period of resuscitation. Apparently, the increased content of sugar in the blood ensured the restoration of normal glucose levels in the brain and of active aerobic glycolysis which led to such a significant accumulation of lactic acid and to restoration of the levels of ATP.

In two other dogs (Nos. 1 and 3), whose brain tissue was frozen in the same manner as in experiment No. 2, at the beginning of resuscitation the arterial pressure after the restoration of the cardiac activity was high and steady (150-200 mm Hg). As in dog No. 2, extensive hyperglycemia was present in these animals; the brain tissue contained normal amounts of glucose and small amounts of glycogen. The amount of creatine phosphate was below normal, but higher than in dog No. 2, which, apparently, was due to better blood supply to the brain. The possibility is not excluded that in these dogs the oxidative processes in the brain tissue were more intense, which determined the smaller accumulation of lactic acid, particularly in dog No. 1. The content of inorganic phosphate and ATP in both dogs was already within normal limits. In dog No. 1, as was shown by chromatographic analysis, the amount of ADP was so small that the spot of ADP could not be detected by the methods employed.

Thus, during the first 15 minutes of resuscitation under the conditions of hypothermia, as under normal body temperatures, there was a restoration of initial levels of ATP with the predominance of aerobic glycolysis

TABLE 22. Content (in micromoles/gm) of Phosphorus Compounds in Cerebral Cortex of Dogs During Resuscitation 30 Minutes After Clinical Death at 26°

Dog No.	Time of taking the test sample of the brain after resuscitation	Inorganic phosphate	Creatine phosphate	ATP	ADP	AMP
1	9 min	2,3	1.4	1.7	0	0
2	10 »	3,6	0.8	2.0	—	—
3	16 »	1,9	1.8	1.4	—	—
4	45 »	2.4	1.6	1.9	—	—
5	76 »	2,3	2.2	2.1	0	0
6	80 »	1,5	3.4	1.7	—	—
7	1 day	2.6	2.1	1.6	Traces	Traces
8	2 days	1.2	2,5	1.9	0	0

in the cerebral cortex. This must have been preceded by reamination and phosphorylation of the intermediary products of degradation of ATP. One must agree with Nosova that the delay in the normalization of the content of creatine phosphate in the brain compared to ATP is explainable, apparently, by the assumption that the dynamic equilibrium between these substances was established at a lower level of creatine phosphate due to a greater rate of transfer of the phosphoric acid group from creatine phosphate to ADP.

Studying the metabolism of the brain in cats under the conditions of hypothermia (24-22°C), Raiko, Petro and Kudritskaya (1960) found that during ether narcosis and treatment with hexonium 10-12 minutes after the restoration of blood circulation, which was previously excluded for 20-40 minutes, the content of ATP in the brain tissue was restored to normal levels, while the content of creatine phosphate was somewhat lower, that of inorganic phosphate somewhat higher, and that of lactic acid much higher (140-220 mg %) than the initial levels. In spite of the latter circumstance, the authors came to the conclusion that "in experiments with hypothermia 10-minute respiration of the tissue was sufficient for a very rapid restoration in it of the synthesis of labile phosphates." We cannot agree with the postulation that the synthetic processes in the resuscitating brain tissue are connected with the processes of its respiration. On the contrary, the data of Raiko et al. also indicate that under hypothermia as well the brain tissue receives the energy necessary for synthetic processes from glycolysis which takes place aerobically since the brain is being flushed with blood rich in oxygen.

Vladimirov (1957) pointed out that during lowering of the body temperature in rabbits the oxidative processes in the brain tissue are inhibited to a greater extent than the glycolytic ones. He arrived at this conclusion on the basis of Savchenko's data, obtained under conditions of hypoxia which was considerably less intense than that employed by Raiko et al. or by us, and yet these data too indicated the predominant significance of glycolytic processes in the restoration period. These considerations provide grounds for the postulation that the character of metabolic processes in the initial period of resuscitation under hypothermia is the same as that under normal body temperatures. Therefore, all the conclusions made by us regarding the nature of therapeutic measures during this period (for example, the inadmissibility of the use of stimulating or sedative preparations) under normal body temperatures remain in force under the conditions of hypothermia.

In the next 3 dogs (see Table 21) the brain was frozen after the appearance of external respiration: in dog No. 4, 45 minutes after the beginning of resuscitation and 5 minutes and 45 seconds after the first inhalation was noted; in dog No. 6, 80 minutes after the beginning of resuscitation and 41 minutes and 10 seconds after the appearance of the first inhalation. The respiration in these two dogs was slow, and superficial; it was necessary to continue artificial respiration in order to support adequate arterial pressure. In dog No. 5 on the 34th minute of resuscitation the corneal reflexes were restored, and only after 14 minutes of resuscitation the respiration, which quickly reached high frequency and depth. The brain was frozen on the 76th minute of resuscitation, i.e., 23 minutes after the appearance of external respiration. With the beginning of resuscitation warming of the animals was begun, and the body temperature in these dogs rose to 27-30°C at the moment their brain was frozen. Thus, the extent of restoration of the functions of the central nervous system was the least in dog No. 4 and greatest in dog No. 5.

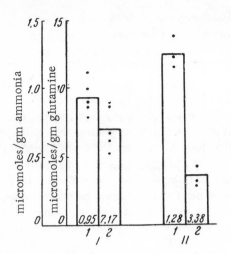

Fig. 17. Content of ammonia and glutamine in cerebral cortex of dogs after resuscitation (clinical death was 30 minutes under hypothermia). I) 30 minutes to 3 hours after resuscitation; II) one day after resuscitation. 1) Ammonia; 2) glutamine. Designations of results: dots—data for individual experiments; squares columns—overall average.

Regarding the metabolism it should be noted that while in dog No. 4 hyperglycemia was still present, in dogs Nos. 5 and 6 the amount of glucose in the blood was already within normal limits. In dog No. 5 at the beginning of resuscitation the blood sugar level reached 234 mg %. The content of glucose in the cerebral cortex of dog No. 4 was somewhat above normal, and in dogs Nos. 5 and 6 it was within normal limits. The amount of lactic acid in the cerebral cortex was the smaller the more complete the restoration of the functions of the central nervous system, and in dog No. 5 the content of lactic acid was within normal limits, indicating the restoration of the oxidative processes in the brain tissue. In spite of this, the synthesis of glycogen in the brain tissue had not yet occurred and the content of glycogen in the brain of dog No. 5 was just as low as in that of dogs Nos. 4 and 6. Parallel with the incomplete restoration of the oxidative processes in the cerebral cortex of dog No. 4, the content of creatine phosphate was still low, while in dogs Nos. 5 and 6 it was already within normal limits. The content of inorganic phosphate and ATP was within normal limits, as was indicated by chromatographic analysis. Of the adenosine phosphoric acids only ATP was present.

In dogs Nos. 7 and 8 the brain was removed for analysis 24 and 48 hours after resuscitation. At the time of the removal of the brain for analysis the body temperature was normal and in both dogs there was a complete restoration of the functions of the central nervous system; i.e., the condition of the dogs was indistinguishable from that before the experiment. In contrast to the experiments in which the brain was removed from the dogs at earlier periods of resuscitation, i.e., before the restoration of pain sensitivity, in these dogs we employed pantopone-nembutal narcosis in order to perform the trepanation of the skull and freeze the brain in situ. Basically, the content of all the investigated metabolites in the brain tissue of these dogs was within normal limits. However, in dog No. 7 there was a somewhat lowered content of ATP and traces of ADP and AMP were noted, which could not, however, be quantitatively assayed. Nosova was inclined to attribute this fact to the effect of pantopone-nembutal narcosis, since an analogous picture prevailed at the initial stages of narcosis under normal body temperatures.

Thus, in dogs which survived the clinical death of 30 minutes duration in a state of hypothermia of average intensity the carbohydrate-phosphorus metabolism of the brain (with the exception of glycogen content) was normalized in about 1.5 to 2 hours after resuscitation and thereafter was maintained at normal level.

In dog No. 8 the amount of ammonia and glutamine in the brain tissue was determined during the restoration period after 30 minutes of clinical death under hypothermia. The analyses of the brain showed (Fig. 17) that during the period of 30 minutes to 3 hours after resuscitation (the brain was frozen in situ at the 30th and 60th minute and after 2 and 3 hours) the content of ammonia in the cerebral cortex was somewhat lower than that at the 30th minute of clinical death, i.e., before resuscitation, but it remained significantly above normal levels. At the same time the content of glutamine significantly increased and even exceeded the initial level. The active aerobic glycolysis in the beginning of resuscitation, followed by oxidative metabolism, ensured the supply of energy required for the binding of the excess ammonia into glutamine. During resuscitation under hypothermia, when during the first few hours the body temperature of the animals did not exceed 30-32°C and the metabolic processes were somewhat slowed down, the elevated amounts of ammonia along with elevated amounts of glutamine indicated the alteration in the binding of ammonia into other compounds, perhaps, into brain proteins.

Comparison of the results obtained on the content of ammonia and glutamine in brain tissue during the restoration period after clinical death under hypothermia with those obtained under normal body temperatures

77

indicates that under hypothermia there is a significantly greater amount of ammonia in the brain during the initial period of resuscitation. This indicates once more that hypothermia itself induces certain alterations in nitrogen metabolism which are revealed particularly well in rats (Veksler) and which appear in dogs during the development of the hypoxic state. However, one must take into account the data of Pertseva,who observed a high content of ammonia and glutamine in cats in which the heart was excluded from the circulation for 20 minutes under hypothermia of average intensity, 5 and 12 minutes after the renewal of the blood circulation, followed by lowering of the ammonia content to normal levels after 30 minutes to 2 hours. Thus, in cats under hypothermia she obtained the same picture of changes in the content of ammonia in the brain in the initial period of resuscitation as had been observed by us in dogs at their normal body temperatures. Pertseva found, in addition, an increase in the amounts of ammonia in the brain of cats 3 hours after the renewal of blood circulation, induced by the onset of spasms and hypoxic hypoxia, which was confirmed by the lowering of the levels of the energy-rich phosphates in the brain. In our experiments, on the other hand, during normal body temperatures or during hypothermia 3-4 hours after resuscitation we never observed any symptoms of hypoxia. It may therefore be concluded that the increased amounts of ammonia in brain tissue in our experiments were determined not by hypoxia but by some other causes.

In the remaining 3 dogs the brain was studied 24 hours after resuscitation. By this time the body temperature was normal and the functions of the central nervous system were completely restored: the dogs could see and hear, they ran, and they quite adequately responded to external stimuli. The dogs, however, were somewhat drowsy and were rather quickly fatigued. In spite of the relatively satisfactory state of the animals, the ammonia content of the cerebral cortex in these animals was high, amounting to 1.3 micromoles per gram. Thus, the amount of ammonia in the brain was not only not lower than that found in the brain at the beginning of resuscitation but almost as high as at the 30th minute of clinical death.

The content of glutamine in the brain tissue of dogs 24 hours after resuscitation was lower than that in the initial period and was close to the lower limit observed in the initial period under normal body temperatures. As has been shown above, at this time the carbohydrate-phosphorus metabolism in the brain is normal and none of the signs of hypoxia can be detected. Therefore, the alteration of nitrogen metabolism took place during normal energy metabolism of the brain. This gives us grounds to postulate that the alteration of nitrogen metabolism observed during the first 24 hours after resuscitation under hypothermia is indicative of the presence of destruction of brain proteins. This seems all the more probable since the first morphologically detectable changes in nerve cells of the cerebral cortex are observed in dogs which survived clinical death under hypothermia only 29 hours after resuscitation (Romanova, 1956). Therefore, by this time the alterations of the protein structure of the brain should be clearly revealed. The externally satisfactory condition of the dogs indicates only the remarkable elasticity of the nervous system and its capacity to compensate functionally for structural defects and for alterations in protein metabolism.

Undoubtedly, our information on the changes in nitrogen metabolism in the brain during the processes of dying and resuscitation under hypothermia is too inadequate to permit any deductions regarding the mechanism of the processes involved. Yet the available data give ground for solution or at least for postulation of certain problems which are important from a practical viewpoint. Thus, in connection with the presence of high amounts of ammonia in the brain tissue (4 to 5 times exceeding normal) of animals which externally are in a satisfactory state, a question arises: what concentration of ammonia in the brain tissue should be considered toxic?

As was mentioned in Chapter II, in order to induce spasms in animals during the administration of ammonium salts intravenously it is necessary to raise the levels of free ammonia in the brain tissue to 7 micromoles per gram. Under normal physiological conditions the content of ammonia in the brain may vary within wide limits. According to Vladimirova (1957), in experiments on white rats under physiological conditions, positive motor-food and orientation-investigation reactions induce a significant (in some animals by twofold) elevation of ammonia in the brain. A weak orientation reaction also raised the average content of ammonia under normal conditions (0.27 micromole/gm) to 0.33 micromole/gm of rat brain tissue (Vladimirova, 1957).

As was shown above, in dogs at the normal body temperature the amount of ammonia in the cerebral cortex at the 5th minute of clinical death and 4 hours after resuscitation was about 0.7 micromole per gram. Still higher content of ammonia in the cerebral cortex (about 1.4 micromoles per gram) was observed in dogs under hypothermia at the 30th minute of clinical death and during the restoration period when all the functions of the central nervous system were apparently restored. In spite of the high content of ammonia in the brain of the animals which survived prolonged clinical death under hypothermia, the alterations in the central nervous system, functional as well as morphological, during the restoration period were significantly smaller than in animals which were restored from terminal states under normal body temperatures. This indicates that the toxic effects of ammonia under these conditions and at the observed concentrations have not as yet been revealed. According to Thöllen and Bosshardt (1958), the loss of consciousness in man during uremia is not related to the increase in ammonia concentration in the blood and hence in the brain.

Thus, taking into account that physiological fluctuations of ammonia content in the brain are within the limits of 0.7 micromole per gram, and that during reversible hypoxic states the ammonia concentration is within the limits of 1.4 micromoles per gram, and that the concentration of ammonia in the brain which induces spasms exceeds this value 4- to 5-fold, it may be assumed that the toxic properties of ammonia are not revealed when its concentration in the brain reaches 1.5 micromoles per gram.

Gershenovich and co-workers (1957) postulated that ammonia is not the cause of various functional states of the brain, but is a result of chemical processes, involving proteins of the brain and dicarboxylic acids, which take place during alterations in the functional state of the brain. On the basis of very thorough and methodologically excellent experiments, Rozengart et al. (1956) postulated that the increase in ammonia in brain tissue is not the cause of spasms but a result of spasms, induced by picrotoxin.

We are also inclined to assume that the increase in ammonia content of the cerebral cortex during terminal states and during recovery from these states is not the cause of alterations in the functions of the central nervous system, but a result and an indication of first physico-chemical, and then of more involved chemical processes of destruction of brain proteins, which are the actual cause of the functional and structural changes of the nervous tissue.

CONCLUSION

Restoration of vital functions of the organism during terminal states became a practical medical problem only recently. Yet in a relatively short time methods of therapy of terminal states have found wide application which permits the saving of lives of thousands of people who previously were doomed to premature death.

The scientific bases of the developed methods of resuscitation and their application in practice were experimental observations on pathophysiological regularities in the processes of obliteration and restoration of the vital functions of the organism, including studies of the peculiarities of brain metabolism during these states. The data relative to metabolism of the dying and revitalized brain tissue reviewed in this book showed that up to the present time the investigations were directed mainly towards studies of energy metabolism of the brain, which alters most distinctly during the development of terminal states. Alterations in energy metabolism determine in the final analysis all subsequent alterations taking place in the brain of animals which survive the state of severe hypoxia. So far, changes in nitrogen metabolism were studied to a smaller extent, and no studies are available to date on the metabolism of macromolecular components (enzymes, proteins, nucleic acids, etc.). In spite of the fact that the available information in such a new field as pathochemistry of the brain during terminal states is limited, this information is already of practical importance, promising perspectives for further investigations.

One of the most exciting problems for an experimental biochemist is the permissibility of the application of the results obtained on animals to the understanding of the state of the human patient. In this connection the data on brain metabolism require particularly careful approach. Because of the enormous difference in the development of the brain in man and animals one could always expect qualitatively different peculiarities in the brain of man compared to those of other mammals. Nevertheless, there are reasons to assume that during the onset of terminal states and in the initial period of recovery from these states, when the functions of the higher divisions of the central nervous system are excluded, the regularities of the metabolic processes in brain tissue are common to man and animals. A whole series of indirect data support this assumption. First of all the fact that the basic physiological regularities of the development of the terminal states are common to warm-blooded animals and man forces the assumption that the biochemical regularities are also common to animals and man.

The coincidence of the duration of clinical death which the higher divisions of the central nervous system of animals and man can endure under the usual body temperature supports this assumption. Taking into account that the duration of hypoxia which the cerebral cortex endures with subsequent restoration of its functions is basically determined by the rate of expenditure of its energy resources, it may be assumed that these resources disappear during about the same length of time in man as in animals. The application of hypothermia to clinical practice showed that the duration of the interruption of blood circulation which can be endured by the higher divisions of the central nervous system depends on the extent of lowering of the body temperature, and at moderate hypothermia (25°C) the cessation of blood circulation for about 30 minutes can well be endured by the organism.

These data are supported by experimental observations, and, as was shown in the foregoing discussions, these periods of endurance are basically determined by the rate of expenditure of the energy-rich resources of the brain.

The observations on the injurious effects of sedatives as well as of substances which stimulate the functions of the nervous system in the initial period of resuscitation could serve as an illustration. These facts were experimentally established on animals (Negovskii, Grozdova, Smirensksya, Kadetova, and others) as well as in the clinic (Negovskii, Zolotokrylina, Kiseleva, Ryabova). As was shown above (Chapter IV), in animals this is explainable by the peculiarities of the brain metabolism in the initial period of resuscitation. It seems proper to assume that the predominance of the aerobic glycolytic process which yields small amounts of energy to the brain tissue of dogs in the beginning of resuscitation is also present in the brain of the patient during the first few minutes after revival from the state of clinical death. The fact that in these patients there easily occurs an "interruption" of nervous activity, leading to the development of secondary shock and collapse, indicates that in the initial period after revival from the terminal state the resources in energy which ensure the functions of the central nervous system are inadequate. Such an "interruption" may occur under the influence of a drop in arterial pressure for short periods, secondary hypoxia, external irritations, passive movements, emotions, etc. It is significant that intravenous dropwise administration of glucose together with insulin and vitamins to patients which were revived from terminal states affects the course of the restoration period favorably, aiding the energy metabolism (Fatin, Negovskii, Zolotokrylina, Petrov, and others).

And, finally, the favorable effect of intravenous administration of sodium bicarbonate in the beginning of resuscitation on the subsequent course of the restoration period has been experimentally demonstrated in dogs (Bulanova, Kiseleva) and in patients in the clinic (Zolotokrylina, Ryabova, and Kolganova). Apparently, in the mechanism of the favorable effect of sodium bicarbonate, the neutralization of the acidic products of metabolism in the brain tissue is not insignificant, since considerable amounts of such acidic substances accumulate in the brain tissue, as our data have shown.

Among the data obtained in experiments on animals and which concern the metabolism of the brain during the processes of dying and resuscitation which are directly related to practical medicine is the dependence of the metabolism of the brain on the preceding functional state of the central nervous system. It may be expected that in man such a dependence would be revealed even more sharply.

As has been demonstrated, the functional state of the central nervous system (excitation, deep inhibition induced by ether narcosis, inhibition of average intensity, or medicinal sleep) determines the correlation between the needs of the tissue for energy and the means of obtaining it, and it also to a large extent determines the extent of the alterations in the oxidative processes in brain tissue during the development of the terminal states and during recovery from these states. The most unfavorable changes in the metabolism in brain tissue occur when the terminal state develops during excitation or deep narcosis. Inhibition of average intensity produces less severe alterations in the metabolism of the brain during terminal states. It follows that under clinical conditions for the prophylaxis of the development of the terminal states and for a more favorable course of these states it is necessary, on the one hand, to lower the excitation of the higher divisions of the central nervous system in patients who could develop such an excitation, and, on the other hand, one must avoid too deep a narcosis, particularly ether narcosis, in severely ill patients. Clinical observations on the course of traumatic shock have shown that the choice of narcosis and its depth occupies an important place in the prevention of the transition from a relatively light state of shock to a severe one. These observations have already been reflected in the instructions for the treatment of patients with traumatic shock (1961) written by Professors Shraiber, Negovskii, Krakovskii, and Sel'tsovskii.

This problem requires further study from the standpoint of the effect of various narcotics on the biochemical changes in brain tissue during hypoxia, as well as from the standpoint of the effect of inhibition of various extents induced by the same narcotic preparation on brain tissue.

The alterations of metabolism in brain tissue during terminal states, as has been shown, were studied during model anemia which was induced either by ligature of the basic arterial stems of the brain (laboratories directed by Petrov, Shapot, and others) or by lethal exsanguination (laboratory directed by Negovskii). Metabolism of the brain during other forms of the process of dying has not been adequately studied. Although hypoxia is a common pathogenic factor for various forms of dying, the peculiarities of each form of dying undoubtedly would be reflected in the qualitative and quantitative aspects of brain metabolism. For this reason one of the pressing problems which has a direct practical significance would be the study of brain metabolism during various forms of death, such as asphyxia, electrical trauma, drowning, traumatic shock, severe infections, etc.

Of great practical significance would be the study of brain metabolism during development of terminal states at various ages. It could be assumed that such studies would clarify the still debatable point of relative sensitivity and endurance towards hypoxia in the adult and in the child.

However, besides the large number of problems dictated by direct interests of practical medicine, the presented data on the metabolism of the brain during terminal states also pose some theoretical problems which demand solution. First of all, the scope of investigations of the substances in the brain should be extended to proteins, enzymes, and nucleic acids, since only by establishment of the regularities of the metabolism of the macromolecular substances in the brain tissue during the obliteration and restoration of the vital functions of the organism will it be possible to reveal the mechanisms of the injury to the morphological structure of the brain which occurs under the influence of endured hypoxia. The assumption which we expressed on the basis of indirect data regarding the fact that during clinical death no obvious chemical alterations of the proteins of the brain occur in brain tissue, but that only physico-chemical alterations take place, obviously requires direct proof. This is true also of the assumption that basic chemical alterations in the structure of proteins of the brain occur after the restoration of blood circulation in an organism which endured the state of clinical death.

Of considerable interest would be the elucidation of the dependence of the processes of degradation of proteins and of other macromolecular substances on the activity of the reaction medium and the concentration of the suboxidized metabolism products in brain tissue. Indirect evidence indicates such a dependence, as has been indicated by relatively smaller morphological alterations in the central nervous system of animals to which sodium bicarbonate was administered intravenously at the initial period of resuscitation. The neutralization of the acidic products of metabolism, raising the pH, normalization of the CO_2 of the blood—all of this was instrumental in the more rapid restoration of the functions of the central nervous system (Bulanova and Kiseleva).

Smaller morphological alterations in the brain and more rapid restoration of the functions of the central nervous system in dogs which survived the processes of dying and clinical death were observed during medicinal sleep (Grozdova, Romanova). As has been noted, in these dogs a smaller accumulation of suboxidized products of metabolism (lactic acid) in the cerebral cortex was observed in the initial period of resuscitation.

In future studies of energy metabolism in brain tissue during terminal states, the problem of the mechanism which determines the inhibition of the oxidative processes in the brain in the initial period of resuscitation and the simultaneous initiation of the intensive process of aerobic glycolysis would be of considerable interest. The elucidation of these mechanisms and the clarification of the question as to whether these mechanisms are operating extracellularly or intracellularly in the brain would greatly aid in the discovery of the means for the activation of the oxidative processes of the brain.

Besides general questions, the presented data raise many particular problems for further study. For example, many questions arise regarding glycogen metabolism in brain tissue during terminal states: is the glycogen in the brain free or in a bound state in the dying tissue; what fraction of it predominates; what is the correlation between the processes of phosphorolysis and amylolysis of glycogen in the brain during the alteration and restoration of blood circulation; is there any connection between the excessive accumulation of glycogen in the brain of revived animals and the alteration of the morphological structure of the tissue, and many others. It can be taken for granted that such questions apply as well to other substances which participate in the metabolism of brain tissue.

There is no doubt that the considerable interest which biochemists have found in studies of brain metabolism during normal and pathological states, and which has attracted a large number of investigators to attempt the solution of these problems, guarantee the further, successful development of investigations in this field.

REFERENCES

Abood, L. G., and Geiger, A., Breakdown of proteins and lipids during glucose-free perfusion of the cat's brain. Am. J. Physiol. 1955, 182, 3, 557-560.

Acs, Gy, Balazs, R., and Straub, F. B., Adenozintrifoszfat szintezis agykeregszeletekben. Kiserletes Orvostudomany. 1953, 5, 6, 466-472.

Acs, Gy, and Shtraub, F. B., The exchange of substances in ascitic cancer cells. Dokl. Akad. Nauk SSSR. 1954, 94, 5, 1021-1024.

Albaum, H. G., Tepperman, J., and Bodansky, O. The in vivo inactivation by cyanide of brain cytochrome oxidase and its effect on glycolysis and on the high energy phosphorus compounds in brain. J. Biol. Chem. 1946, 164, 1, 45-51.

Alekseeva, A. M., On the content of creatine phosphate in the brain. Biokhimiya. 1952, 17, 1, 119-122.

Alekseeva, A. M., and Magasanik, L. G., The effect of pharmacological sleep on the content of certain labile phosphorus compounds in organs and tissues. Byul. Eksperim. Biokhim. i Med. 1956, 42, 10, 19-22.

Anderson, E., and Haymaker, W., Glucose tolerance in decerebrated rats after relatively long survival. Proc. Soc. Exptl Biol. Med. 1949, 70, 1, 86.

Ashford, C. A., and Holmes, E. G., Contributions to the study of brain metabolism. V. Role of phosphates in lactic acid production. Biochem. J. 1929, 23, 748.

Asratyan, E. A., Results and perspectives of the application of a new method of anemic injury to the central nervous system of higher animals. Thirteenth Conference on Physiological Problems, Abstracts. 1948, 11-13.

Asratyan, E. A., The alteration and restoration of the functions of the central nervous system after prolonged anemia. Reports of conference on pathophysiology and therapy of terminal states. 1954, 20-37.

Avery, B. F., Kerr, J. E., and Ghantus, M., The lactic acid contents of mammalian brain. J. Biol. Chem. 1935, 110, 637.

Bakay, L., Relationship between cerebral vascularity and P^{32} uptake. Arch. Neurol. Psychiat. 1957, 78, 1, 29-36.

Bakulev, A. N., The application of intraarterial transfusion of blood in surgical clinic. Reports of Conference on Pathophysiology and Therapy of Terminal States. 1954, 109-115.

Balashova, E. K., Maslova, M. N., Panyukov, A. N., and Rozengart, V. I., Relationship between functional state of central nervous system and metabolism of ammonia and proteins in the brain. Ninth Meeting of the All-Union Society of Physiologists, Biochemists, and Pharmacologists. V, II, 31-32.

Balashova, E. K., Maslova, M. N., Panyukov, A. N., and Rozengart, V. I., Functional state of the central nervous system and metabolism of phosphoproteins of the brain. Biokhimiya. 1958, 23, 5, 674-682.

Balashova, E. K., Maslova, M. N., Panyukov, A. N., and Rozengart, V. I., The effect of excitation and inhibition of the central nervous system on the rate of incorporation of P^{32} into brain phosphoproteins. In: Phosphorylation and Function. 1960, 275-283.

Barkulis, S., Geiger, A., Kawakita, Y., and Agular, W., A study on the incorporation of C^{14} derived from glucose into the free aminoacids of the brain cortex. J. Neurochem. 1960, 5, 339-348.

Batrak, G. E., Kravchenko, A. G., and Gural'nik, G. P., On consumption of blood sugar by cerebral cortex. Farmakol. i Toksikol. 1951, 14, 6, 3-7.

Bayandurov, B. I., Faleev, A. V., and Sitnkova, G. A., On the changes in carbohydrate metabolism in decerebrated puppies. Trudy Tomsk. Gos. Med. Inst. 1937, V, 5, 207-212.

Beecher, H. K., and Craig, F. N., Tissue metabolism following shock induced by hemorrhage. J. Biol. Chem. 1943, 148, 383.

Berl, S., and Waelsch, H., Determination of glutamic acid, glutamine, glutathione and γ-aminobutyric acid and their distribution in brain tissue. J. Neurochem. 1958, 3, 2, 161-169.

Berl, S., Purpura, D. P., Girado, M., and Waelsch, H., Amino acid metabolism in epileptogenic and non-epileptogenic lesions of the neocortex (cat). J. Neurochem. 1959, 4, 4, 311-317.

Bernshtein, A. D., Materials on the biochemistry of carbohydrate metabolism in central nervous system. Byul. Eksperim. Biol. i Med. 1948, 25, 1, 69-70.

Bernshtein, A. D., and Zakharov, S. V., Can the magnitude of the arterio-venous difference serve as a reliable indicator of the dynamics of organ metabolism? Trudy Ivanovsk. Gos. Med. Inst. 1949, 76-78.

Bernshtein, A. D., Zakharov, S. V., and Yakubovskaya, V. I., The origin and role of blood glycogen. Trudy Ivanovsk. Gos. Med. Inst. 1949, 48-49.

Bigelow, W. G., Lindsy, W. K., et al., Oxygen transport and utilization in dogs at low temperature. Am. J. Physiol. 1950, 160, 1, 125-137.

Bigelow, W. G., et al.,Hypothermia. Its possible role in cardiac surgery. Ann. Surg. 1950, 132, 5, 149-157.

Bigelow, W. G., Mustard, W. T., and Evans, J. G.,Some physiological concepts of hypothermia and their application to cardiac surgery. J. Thoracic Surg. 1954, 28, 5, 463-480.

Boulanger, P., Exposés annuels de biochimie médical. 3-ème serie. 1951.

Braksh, T. A., The effect of L-glutamic acid on the higher nervous activity and certain indicators of nitrogen metabolism in dogs. Dissertation, Moscow. 1957.

Breckenridge, B. M., and Crawford, E. J., Glycogen synthesis from uridine diphosphate glucose in brain. J. Biol. Chem. 1960, 235, 3054-3057.

Breckenridge, B. M., and Crawford, E. J., The quantitative histochemistry of the brain. Enzymes of glycogen metabolism. J. Neurochem. 1961, 7, 3, 234-240.

Bronovitskaya, Z. G., and Shapovalova, N. S., Brain glucose and glycogen under the influence of increased oxygen pressure on animals. Ukrain. Biokhim. Zhur. 1957, 29, 1, 20-24.

Bulanova, O. N., Blood organic acids in the process of dying from exsanguination and subsequent resuscitation of vital functions of the organism. Biokhimiya. 1954, 19, 5, 590-598.

Bulanova, O. N., The state of oxidative processes in certain tissues of animals during the process of dying and subsequent restoration of vital functions of the organism. In: Physiology and Pathology of Respiration, Hypoxia and Oxygen Therapy. Kiev, 1958, 419-424.

Bulanova, O. N., and Kiseleva, K. S., The effect of sodium bicarbonate on the restoration of vital functions after clinical death induced by exsanguination. Patol. Fiziol. i Eksperim. Terapiya. 1959, 2, 59-67.

Bulanova, O. N., Respiratory function of the blood, hemodynamics, and total gaseous exchange during restoration period after clinical death induced by exsanguination. In: The Problem of Compensation of Altered Functions. Moscow. 1960, 314-320.

Bulanova, O. N., Ryabova, N. M., and Zaks, I. O., Certain indicators of hypoxia during the process of dying from asphyxia from excess ether and during subsequent restoration of vital functions of the organism. Materials of the Third Conference of Pathophysiologists of Siberia and Far East. Novosibirsk. 1960, 230-239.

Bunyatyam, G. Kh.,Consumption of glucose and pyruvic acid by the brain during various functional states. Problems of Biochemistry of the Nervous System. Kiev. 1957, 93-107.

Bunyatyam, G. Kh.,Newer data on functional biochemistry of the brain. Izvest. Akad. Nauk Arm. SSR, Biological Sciences. 1959, 12, 2, 13-15.

Bunyatyam, G.Kh.,Certain relationships in cortical regulation of metabolism and changes in metabolic processes of the brain during various functional states. Izvest. Akad. Nauk Arm. SSR, Biological Sciences. 1960, 13, 11, 11-26.

Chagovets, R. V., Lakhno, E. V., Rybina, A. A., Fridman, R. S., and Shtutman, Ts. M., Comparative study of the effect of physical cooling, aminazine, and evipan on the metabolic processes of nervous tissue. In: Problems of the Biochemistry of the Nervous System. Kiev. 1957, 258-268.

Chagovets, R. V., Lakhno, E. V., and Rybina, A. A., Consumption of oxygen and the activity of dehydrogenases of brain tissue and muscle during the action of evipan, aminazine, and cooling of rabbits. Farmakol. i Toksikol. 1958, 21, 1, 50-53.

Chesler, A., and Himwich, H. E., The glycogen content of various parts of the central nervous system of dogs and cats of different ages. Arch. Biochem. 1943, 2, 2, 175-181.

Chetverikov, D. A., Phosphorus metabolism of the brain in oxygen starvation. Dokl. Akad. Nauk SSSR. 1955, 105, 6, 1300-1302.

Clouet, D. H., and Richter, D., The incorporation of (35S) labelled methionine into the proteins of the rat brain. J. Neurochem. 1959, 3, 3, 219-229.

Cori, C. F., Glycogen breakdown and synthesis in animal tissues. Endocrinology. 1940, 26, 285-295.

Cori, C. F., Phosphorylation of glycogen and glucose. Biol. Symposia. 1941, 5, 131-140.

Cori, G. T., and Cori, C. F., Glycogen synthesis in vitro by the use of muscle phosphorylase. J. Biol Chem. 1940, 135, 733.

Cori, G. T., and Cori, C. F., Formation of glycogen. J. Biol. Chem. 1943, 151, 57.

Craig, F. N., and Beecher, H. K., The effect of oxygen tension on the metabolism of cerebral cortex, medulla and spinal cord. J. Neurophysiol. 1943, 6, 2, 135.

Craig, F. N., The effect of carbon dioxide tension on the metabolism of cerebral cortex and medulla oblongata. J. Gen. Physiol. 1944, 27, 4, 325-338.

Danilov, M. G., On content of blood sugar of animals resuscitated after asphyxia. Trudy Voenno-Med. Akad. im. Kirov. 1940, 21, 73-85.

Dawson, R. M. C., and Richter, D., Effect of stimulation on phosphate esters of brain. Am. J. Physiol. 1950, 160, 1, 203.

Dawson, R. M. C., and Richter, D., Biochem. J. 1953, 55, 3, 507-517; Proc. Roy. Soc. (London) B. 1951, 137, 252.

Dawson, R. M. C., The incorporation of labeled phosphate into the lipids of a brain dispersion. Biochem. J. 1953, 55, 3, 507-517.

Domontovich, E. N., Changes in certain aspects of brain metabolism during oxygen starvation and the role of adaptation. Oxygen Therapy and Oxygen Insufficiency. Kiev. 1952, 14-20.

Domontovich, E. N., Materials on the problem of adaptation of the organism to oxygen insufficiency of hypoxic form. Dissertation, Moscow. 1957.

Domontovich, E. N., Certain physiological mechanisms of adaptation of the organism to oxygen insufficiency. In: Physiology and Pathology of Respiration, Hypoxia and Oxygen Therapy. Kiev. 1958, 67-74.

Domontovich, E. N., On the question of the mechanisms of compensation of the altered functions of the organism during oxygen starvation. In: The Problem of Compensation of Altered Functions, Academy of Sciences, USSR, Moscow. 1960, 321-326.

Dunaeva, V. F., and Ivanenko, E. F., Investigation of chemical and physico-chemical properties of brain colloids during excitation and inhibition of nervous activity induced by pharmacological means. Reports of Fifth International Congress on Biochemistry. Moscow. 1961, 1, 454-455.

Dundee, J., Scott, W. E., and Meshom, R. P., The production of hypothermia. Brit. Med. J. 1953, 4848, 1244-1246.

Elliott, K. A. C., Page, J., and Quastel, J. H., Neurochemistry. Springfield, Illinois. 1955.

Engel'gardt, V. A., and Lisovskaya, N. P., Phosphoproteins and brain metabolism. In: Biochemistry of the Nervous System. Kiev. 1954, 77-86.

Engel'gardt, V. A., The summary and perspectives of the use of isotopes in biochemistry. Reports at the Session of the Academy of Sciences USSR on the Peaceful Uses of Atomic Energy. Vest. Akad. Nauk SSSR, 1955, 7, 13.

Engel'gardt, V. A., Certain Problems of Modern Biochemistry. Academy of Sciences, USSR, Moscow. 1959.

Epel'baum, S. E., Sheves, G. S., and Kobylin, A. A., Adenosinetriphosphatase of the brain. Biokhimiya. 1949, 14, 2, 107-112.

Estler, C. J., and Heim, F., Der Einfluss des Kaliumcyanid auf den Coenzym A und Milchsäuregehalt in Gehirn, Leber, Herz und Nieren und auf einige Phosphorsäureestern des Gehirns. Med. Exptl. 1960, 2, 5, 244-251.

Etling, N., Action des hypnotiques sur le métabolisme, hydrocarboné du cerveau. I. Firmation et utilisation des hexosephosphates dans le tissu cérébral normal. Bull. soc. chim. biol. 1953, 35, 8, 751-758; II. Action des hypnotiques sur divers enzymes glycolytiques. Bull. soc. chim. biol. 1953, 35, 10, 1129-1135.

Fatin, A. F., Universal apparatus for the induction of hexenal narcosis. Vopr. Neirokhirurgii. 1951, 1, 49-52.

Ferdman, D. L., and Dvornikova, P. D., Data on the chemical composition of the brain. Biokhim. Zhur. 1940, 15, 1, 69-81.

Ferdman, D. L., Frenkel', S. R., and Silakova, A. I., Glutamine in animal tissues. Biokhimiya. 1942, 7, 1-2, 43.

Fregni, R., Malaguti, G., and Vaccari, E., Il metabolismo glucidico cerebrale in corso di narcosi. Atti soc. lombarda sci. med. e biol. 1952-1953, 8, 1, 135-137.

Fuhrman, F. A., Fuhrman, G. J., and Field, J., Oxygen consumption of excised rat tissues following acute anoxic anoxia. Am. J. Physiol. 1945, 144, 1, 87-90.

Gadzhiev, Kh. D., Thousand cases of arterio-venous administration of blood and blood substitutes during severe traumatic shock and severe blood loss. Trudy Stalinabad Med. Inst. 1949, III, 82-104.

Gaevskaya, M. S., Investigation of certain aspects of carbohydrate metabolism during restoration of vital functions of organism after lethal blood losses. Arkhiv Patol. 1946, 8, 1-2, 4-12.

Gaevskaya, M. S., On the phenomena of regulation of carbohydrate metabolism during the process of restoration of vital functions of the organism after lethal blood losses. Byul. Eksperim. Biol. i Med. 1946, 21, 1-2, 72-74.

Gaevskaya, M. S., Sugar and lactic acid in cerebral tissue during extinction and restoration of vital functions of the organism. Arkhiv Patol. 1951, 13, 3, 34-40.

Gaevskaya, M. S., and Grozdova, T. N., The effect of pharmacological sleep on the course of metabolic processes in cerebral cortex during extinction and restoration of the vital functions of the organism. Byul. Eksperim. Biol. i Med. 1952, 9, 39-43.

Gaevskaya, M. S., Content of glycogen and fermentable carbohydrates in cerebral cortex during extinction and restoration of the vital functions of the organism. Zhur. Vysshei Nervnoi Deyatel'nosti im. I. P. Pavlova. 1953, 3,4, 617-625.

Gaevskaya, M. S., Content of sugar, glycogen, and lactic acid in the brain during extinction and restoration of vital functions of the organism. Byul. Eksperim. Biol. i Med. 1953, 36, 11, 29-33.

Gaevskaya, M. S., Certain peculiarities of intermediary metabolism of cerebral cortex in terminal states. Reports of the Conference on Pathophysiology and Therapy of Terminal States, Moscow. 1954, 77-87.

Gaevskaya, M. S., Carbohydrate metabolism of the brain and its relationship to the functional state of the central nervous system during extinction and restoration of vital functions of the organism. In: Biochemistry of the Nervous System. Kiev. 1954, 151-161.

Gaevskaya, M. S., Peculiarities of carbohydrate metabolism of the cerebral cortex during extinction and restoration of vital functions of the organism. Dissertation. 1956.

Gaevskaya, M. S., Carbohydrate-phosphorus metabolism of the brain during the process of dying under hypothermia and during subsequent restoration of the vital functions of the organism. In: Problems of Biochemistry of the Nervous System. Kiev. 1957, 268-277.

Gaevskaya, M. S., Nosova, E. A., and Zaks, I. O., Effect of body temperature on the degradation of energy resources of the brain during the process of dying. Ukrain. Biokhim. Zhur. 1958, 30, 4, 513-520.

Gaevskaya, M. S., and Nosova, E. A., Process of phosphorylation in brain tissue during the process of dying and resuscitation at different body temperatures. In: Phosphorylation and Function. 1960, 343-350.

Gaevskaya, M. S., and Nosova, E. A., Effect of hypothermy on ammonia and glutamine content in the cerebral cortex of dogs during the process of dying and subsequent resuscitation. Ukrain. Biokhim. Zhur. 1961, 33, 3, 407-419.

Gaevskaya, M. S., and Nosova, E. A., Effect of lethal blood loss and subsequent resuscitation on the changes in nitrogen metabolism in the brain under normal conditions and hypothermy. Fifth International Biochemical Congress. Moscow. 1961, 1, 452-453.

Galegov, G. A., and Parfanovich, M. I., Studies on transamination reactions in rat brain infected with fixed rabies virus. Byul. Eksperim. Biokhim. i Med. 1959, 47, 2, 60-62.

Geiger, A., Chemical changes accompanying activity in the brain. In: Metabolism of the Nervous System. London. 1957, 245-255.

Geiger, A., Correlation of brain metabolism and function by the use of a brain perfusion method in situ. Physiol. Revs. 1958, 38, 1, 1-19.

Geiger, A., Horvath, N., and Kawakita, Y., The incorporation of C^{14} derived from glucose into the proteins of the brain cortex at rest and during activity. J. Neurochem. 1960, 5, 4, 311-322.

Geiger, A., Kawakita, Y., and Barkulis, S., Major pathways of glucose utilization in the brain in brain perfusion experiments in vivo and in situ. J. Neurochem. 1960, 5, 4, 323-338.

Georgievskaya, L. M., On the nature of glucose curve in normal dogs and in dogs deprived of cerebral large hemispheres. Fiziol. Zhur. SSSR. 1936, 20, 5.

Gershenovich, Z. S., and Krichevskaya, A. A., Glutamic acid and tissue respiration of the brain under increased oxygen pressure. Biokhimiya. 1952, 17, 6, 684-690.

Gershenovich, Z. S., Krichevskaya, A. A., and Bronovitskaya, Z. G., The system ammonia-glutamine-glutamic acid and oxidative phosphorylation in the brain under oxygen intoxication. In: Questions of Biochemistry of the Nervous System. Kiev. 1957, 311-323.

Gershenovich, Z. S., and Krichevskaya, A. A., Decarboxylation of glutamic acid under the action of increased oxygen pressure. Uch. Zap. Rostov. Univ. 1957, 58, 123-128.

Gershenovich, Z. S., and Krichevskaya, A. A., Functional groups of brain proteins under various states of the animal. Abstracts of sections. Fifth International Congress of Biochemistry. Moscow. 1961, 1, 453.

Gesell, R., Regulation der Atmung und des Kreislaufs. Ergeb. Physiol. 1929, 340.

Goncharova, V. N., Effect of cortisone and glutamic acid on ammonia content in the brain. Problemy Endkrinol. i Gormonoterap. 1959, 5, 2, 3-7.

Goncharova, V. N., Changes in the content of certain nitrogenous fractions in the brain and the state of central nervous system during repeated injections of cortisone and glutamic acid. Dissertation. 1960.

Goncharova, E. E., Structural peculiarities of polysaccharides synthesized in vitro by brain enzymes of normal and excited rabbits. Ukrain. Biokhim. Zhur. 1959, 31, 3, 330-336.

Gordon, B. G., Acid-base relationships in rat brain during various functional states of the central nervous system induced by unconditioned and conditioned reflex agents. In: Questions of Physiology and Morphology of the Central Nervous System. Academy of Medical Sciences, USSR. Moscow. 1953, 109-115.

Gordon, B. G., Changes in ammonia and glutamine content in rat brain after administration of NaBr, caffeine, and CCl_4. Byul. Eksperim. Biol. i Med. 1959, 48, 11, 69-73.

Gromova, K. G., and Shapot, V. S., Transformations of labile phosphorus compounds in the brain during anemia. Dokl. Akad. Nauk SSSR. 1951, 78, 5, 941-944.

Gromova, K. G., Kudritskaya, T. E., Petrov, I. P., and Shapot, V. S., Metabolism of labile phosphorus compounds in the brain during anemia and under the condition of protective inhibition. Biokhimiya. 1952, 17, 1, 13-24.

Gromova, K. G., Metabolism of phosphorus compounds in the brain during anemia. Dissertation. 1954.

Gromova, K. G., On the effect of functional state of the central nervous system on metabolism of phosphorus compounds in the brain. Biokhimiya. 1954, 19, 4, 469-477.

Gromova, K. G., Content of coenzyme A in the brain during anemia and excitation. In: Phosphorylation and Function. IEM. 1960, 284-289.

Grozdova, T. N., The application of medicinal sleep in therapy of terminal states induced by lethal blood loss. Dissertation. 1955.

Grozdova, T. N., The application of medicinal sleep in therapy of terminal states induced by blood loss. Arkhiv Patol. 1959, 12, 36-41.

Gurdjian, E. S., Stoney, W. E., and Webster, J. E., Cerebral metabolism in hypoxia. Arch. Neurol. Psychiat. 1944, 51, 5, 472-477.

Gurvich, A. E., Levyant, M. I., and Erzina, G. A., Changes in the content of adenosine triphosphate, creatine phosphate, and inorganic phosphate in the cortex of large hemispheres of dogs after exclusion and restoration of blood circulation in the brain. Biokhimiya. 1950, 15, 6, 541-547.

Gurvich, A. M., The dynamics of the extinction of electric activity of dog cerebral cortex in the process of dying from extensive blood loss. Arkhiv Patol. 1959, 2, 32-40.

Gurvich, A. M., The restoration of electric activity of the dog cerebral cortex in relation to duration of preceding clinical death induced by exsanguination. Questions of Electrical Physiology and Encephalography. Akad. Nauk SSSR. Moscow-Leningrad. 1960, 235-244.

Gurvich, A. M., Respiratory center and restoration of electric activity of the brain during resuscitation after clinical death. In: Advances in Physiology and Pathology of Respiration. Moscow. 1961, 66-67.

Gurvich, N. L., Restoration of vital functions of the organism after lethal electrotrauma. Klinich. Med. 1952, 30, 6, 66-67.

Gurvich, N. L., Restoration of vital functions of the organism after lethal electrotrauma. Conference on the

Problem of Pathophysiology and Therapy of Terminal States. Medgiz. 1954, 127-134.

Gurvich, N. L., Fibrillation and Defibrillation of the Heart. Moscow. 1957.

Haarmann, W., Uber das Milchsäurebildungsvermögen der Gewebe. Biochem. Z. 1932, 255, 103-124.

Haarmann, W., Über den Abbau von Glykogen und Glucose in verschiedenen Geweben. Biochem. Z. 1932, 255, 142-150.

Haber, C., and Saidel, L., Federation Proc. 1943, 7, 47.

Haldi, J., The accumulation of lactic acid in excised brain, kidney, muscle and testicle. Am. J. Physiol. 1932, 99, 3, 702-709.

Haldi, J., Lactic acid in blood and tissues following intravenous injection of sodium bicarbonate. Am. J. Physiol. 1933, 105, 1, 43.

Hannon, J. P., Effect of prolonged cold exposure on in vitro respiration and anaerobic glycolysis of rat liver. Am. J. Physiol. 1958, 192, 2, 253-257.

Heald, P. J., Phosphorus Metabolism of Brain. London. 1960.

Hevesy, G., Radioactive Indicators, IL, 1950.

Heymans, C., and Bouckaert, J. J., Sur la survie et réanimation des centres nerveux. Compt. rend. soc. biol. 1935, 119, 324-326.

Heymans, C., Bouckaert, J. J., Jourdan, F., Nowak, S. J. G., and Farber, S., Survival and revival of nerve centers following acute anemia. Arch. Neurol. Psychiat. 1937, 38, 304-307.

Heymans, C., Survival and revival of nervous tissues after arrest of circulation. Physiol. Revs. 1950, 30, 3, 375-391.

Heymans, C., Reviviscence des centres nerveux après de la circulation sanguin. Acta Inst. Anesthesiol. 1953, 1, 56-60.

Himwich, H., and Fazekas, J., Hypoglycemia and the metabolism of the brain. Endocrinology. 1937, 21, 800.

Himwich, H. E., and Nahum, L. H., The respiratory quotient of the brain. Am. J. Physiol. 1932, 101, 446-453.

Himwich, H. E., and Fazekas, J. F., Comparative studies of the metabolism of the brain of infant and adult dogs. Am. J. Physiol. 1941, 132, 2, 454-459.

Himwich, H. E., Bernstein, A. O., Herrlinh, H., Chesler, A., and Fazekas, J. F., Am. J. Physiol. 1942, 132, 287.

Himwich, H. E., The brain and the syptomatology of the anoxia. Anesthesiology. 1949, 10, 6, 663-672.

Himwich, H., Brain Metabolism and Cerebral Disorders. Baltimore. 1951.

Holmes, E., and Sherif, C., The relationship between sugar in the blood and lactic acid in brain. Biochem. J. 1932, 2, 381-387.

Holmes, E., The Metabolism of Living Tissues. Cambridge. 1937.

Horwath, S. M., Hutt, B. R., Spurr, G. B., and Stevens, G. E., Same metabolic responses of dogs having low body temperature. Science. 1953, 118, 3056, 100-101.

Howkins, J., McLaughlin, C. R., and Daniel, P., Neuronal damage from temporary cardiac arrest. Lancet. 1946, 6397, 488-492.

Huszak, J., Über den Kohlenhydratabbau im Zentralnervensystem. Biochem. Z. 1942, 312, 319-329.

Hutchinson, M. C., and Stotz, E., Observations on inhibition of brain respiration and narcosis. J. Biol. Chem. 1941, 140, 1, lxiv−lxv.

Ivanenko, E. F., and Voinar, A. O., Effect of narcosis on glycogen content in the brain. Byul. Eksperim. Biol. i Med. 1942, 14, 5-6, 56.

Jakoubek, B., and Svorad, D., Über die Veränderungen in der Konzentration des Gehirnglykogens bei köperlicher Belastung. Pflügers Arch. ges. Physiol. 1959, 268, 5, 444-448.

Kabat, H., Dennis, C., and Barker, A. B., Recovery of function following arrest of the brain circulation. Am. J. Physiol. 1941, 132, 3, 737-747.

Kassil', G. N., Metabolism of the central nervous system. Usp. Sovrem. Biol. 1938, 9, 3, 434.

Kerr, S. E., Studies on the phosphorus compounds of brain. J. Biol. Chem. 1935, 110, 625.

Kerr, S. E., The carbohydrate metabolism of brain. I. Determination of glycogen in nervous tissue. J. Biol. Chem. 1936, 116, 1-9.

Kerr, S. E., and Ghantus, M., The carbohydrate metabolism of brain. II. Effect of varying carbohydrate and insulin supply on glycogen, free sugar and lactic acid in mammalian brain. J. Biol. Chem. 1936, 116, 9-20.

Kerr, S. E., and Ghantus, M., The carbohydrate metabolism of brain. III. On the origin of lactic acid. J. Biol. Chem. 1937, 117, 1, 217-225.

Kerr, S. E., and Antaki, A., The effect of certain narcotics and convulsant drugs upon the carbohydrate and phosphocreatine content of rabbit brain. J. Biol. Chem. 1937, 122, 1, 49-52.

Kerr, S. E., Studies on the phosphorus compounds of brain. II. Adenosinetriphosphate. J. Biol. Chem. 1941, 140, 1, 77-81.

Kerr, S. E., Studies on the phosphorous compounds of brain. J. Biol. Chem. 1942, 145, 2, 647-656.

Khaikina, B. I., and Goncharova, E. E., Data on enzymatic synthesis of brain polysaccharides. Ukrain. Biokhim. Zhur. 1949, 21, 3, 239-244.

Khaikina, B. I., Goncharova, E. E., and Mikhailovskaya, L. A., Polysaccharide metabolism in the brain of animals in various functional states. Ukrain. Biokhim. Zhur. 1952, 24, 39.

Khaikina, B. I., Polysaccharide metabolism in the brain. Dissertation, Kiev. 1953.

Khaikina, B. I., and Goncharova, E. E., Polysaccharide metabolism in the brain and its alterations in various functional states. In: Biochemistry of the Nervous System. Kiev. 1954, 63-73.

Khaikina, B. I., Goncharova, E. E., and Mikhailovskaya, L. A., Polysaccharide metabolism in the brain for various characters of excitation of the central nervous system. Dokl. Akad. Nauk SSSR. 1954, 96, 2, 347-349.

Khaikina, B. I., and Krachko, L. S., Isolation and fractionation of glycogen from animal brain tissue. Ukrain. Biokhim. Zhur. 1957, 29, 1, 10-18.

Khaikina, B. I., and Goncharova, E. E., Metabolism of various fractions of glycogen of the brain and some data on its structure. In: Questions of Biochemistry of the Nervous System. Kiev. 1957, 107-118.

Khaikina, B. I., Metabolism of glycogen fractions in the brain in various states of the organism. In: Carbohydrates and Their Metabolism in Animals and Plants. Academy of Sciences of USSR. Moscow. 1959, 130-139.

Khaikina, B. I., Carbohydrate metabolism in nervous system. Ukrain. Biokhim. Zhur. 1961, 33, 2, 272-295.

Khachatryan, G. S., Alterations in certain aspects of carbohydrate metabolism of the brain in various functional states. Abstracts of sections. Fifth International Biochemical Congress. Moscow. 1961, 1, 475.

Kheruvimova, V. A., System of ammonia-glutamine-glutamic acid of the brain in ontogenesis. Dokl. Akad. Nauk SSSR. 1961, 136, 4, 968-970.

Klein, E. E., Sourves of ammonia formation in brain homogenates. In: Questions of Biochemistry of the Nervous System. Kiev. 1957, 145-154.

Klein, E. E., On formation and elimination of ammonia in the brain under various conditions. Abstracts of sections. Fifth International Biochemical Congress. Moscow. 1961, 1, 456.

Klein, J. R., and Olsen, N. S., Effect of convulsive activity upon the concentration of brain glucose, glycogen, lactate and phosphates. J. Biol. Chem. 1947, 167, 3, 747-755.

Klimov, A. N., The effect of penicillin and streptomycin on animal metabolism. Dissertation. 1959.

Klimov, A. N., and Zezerov, E. G., Alteration in respiration and oxidative phosphorylation in animal tissues under the influence of antibiotics and other agents. In: Phosphorylation and Function. Izdatel'stvo Eksperimental'noi Meditsiny. 1959, 129-136.

Klosovskii, B. N., Histologic changes in the central nervous system in complete temporary exsanguination of animals. Arkhiv Biol. Nauk. 1941, 62, 2, 101-111.

Koldobskaya, F. D., Mironova, T. M., and Dudkovskaya, A. A., Effect of X-rays on glycogen fractions of the brain and tissues. Materials of Scientific Session, Dedicated to the Fortieth Anniversary of Belorussian Soviet Republic. Minsk. 1959, 136-138.

Kolpakov, M. G., Changes in protein composition of blood plasma after clinical death induced by blood loss. Dokl. Akad. Nauk SSSR. 1961, 134, 4, 979-982.

Kolpakov, M. G., Effect of cortisone and desoxycortisterone on the restoration of the vital functions after clinical death induced by rapid and slow blood loss. Patol. Fiziol. i Eksperim. Terapiya. 1961, 4, 16-19.

Kometiani, P. A., and Klein, E. E., Studies of activity of enzymes of various divisions of the brain. Ukrain. Biokhim. Zhur. 1950, 22, 4, 410-419.

Kometiani, P. A., and Klein, E. E., On the pathways of resynthesis of adenosine triphosphate. Reamination of inosinetriphosphate by brain homogenate. Reports of the Academy of Sciences of Georgian Soviet Republic. 1953, 14, 7, 407-412.

Kometiani, P. A., Studies on the distribution and transformations of phosphorylcholine, ethanolamine phosphate, and glutamic acid in the brain. In: Biochemistry of the Nervous System. Kiev. 1954, 98-111.

Kometiani, P. A., and Klein, E. E., On the pathways of reamination of adenylic system in nervous and muscle tissues. Biokhimiya. 1956, 21, 3, 389-396.

Kometiani, P. A., Tkeshelashvili, L. K., and Ovsyanko, T. A., Metabolism of phosphate ethers of choline, ethanolamine, and serine in the brain. In: Studies of Animal Organism. Academy of Sciences USSR. Moscow. 1958, 82-87.

Kometiani, P. A., Tkeshelashvili, L. K., and Ovsyanko, T. A., On transformations of phosphoric acid esters of choline, ethanolamine, and serine in the brain. Ukrain. Biokhim. Zhur. 1959, 31, 6, 913-936.

Kometiani, P. A., Studies on transformations of amino acids in homogenates of nervous and muscle tissues in relation to reamination of adenylic system. Biokhimiya. 1959, 24, 4, 729-737.

Kometiani, P. A., Tkeshelashvili, L. K., and Ovsyanko, T. A., The utilization of phosphoric acid esters of choline, ethanolamine, and serine in the synthesis of brain phospholipids. In: Phosphorylation and Function. Izdatel'stvo Eksperimental'noi Meditsiny. 1960, 80-86.

Komissarenko, V. P., Brain hypoxia in insulin intoxication. In: Hypoxia. Kiev. 1949, 113-121.

Komissarenko, V. P., On certain peculiarities of carbohydrate metabolism in the central nervous system. Med. Zhur. 1952, 22, 6, 7-14.

Komissarenko, V. P., Hormones and metabolism in the brain. In: Contemporary Questions of Endocrinology. First ed. Medgiz. 1960, 30-47.

Kondrasheva, M. N., and Stragitskii, K. I., Biochemical changes in cerebral cortex of puppies in natural and medicinal sleep. Vopr. Med. Khim. 1959, 5, 5, 323-327.

Konikova, A. S., Kharnas, S. Sh., Babskaya, Yu. E., Pogosova, A. V., and Avrutskii, M. Ya., Changes in metabolism in deep hypothermia. Eksperim. Khirur. i Anesteziol. 1962, 2, 58-62.

Kovach, A., Fonyo, A., Vittay, T., and Pogatsa, G., Oxygen and glucose consumption and hexokinase activity in vitro of brain tissue of rats in traumatic shock. Acta Physiol. Acad. Sci. Hung. 1957, 11, 2, 173-180.

Kovach, A., Fonyo, A., and Kovach, E., Cerebral phosphate metabolism in traumatic shock. Acta Physiol. Acad. Sci. Hung. 1959, 16, 3, 157-164.

Krebs, H. A., Eggleston, L. V., and Hems, R., Biochem. J. 1949, 7, 44, 159.

Kreps, E. M., Pigareva, Z. D., Chetverikov, D. A., and Pomazanskaya, L. F., Zhur. Vysshei Nervnoi Deyatel' nosti im. I. P. Pavlova. 1952, 11, 1, 46-56.

Kreps, E. M., Smirnov, A. A., and Chetverikov, D. A., Newer data on comparative study of phosphorus metabolism in various divisions of the brain under various functional states induced by oxygen starvation in the brain. In: Biochemistry of the Nervous System. Kiev. 1954, 125-138.

Krichevskaya, A. A., Gershenovich, Z. S., and Shcherbatykh, V. P., Formation of ammonia from amides by brain and liver homogenates under increased oxygen pressures. Biokhimiya. 1959, 24, 3, 459-464.

Kudryavtseva, A. I., and Kudryavtseva, N. G., On biochemistry of the brain in experimental epilepsy. Ukrain. Biokhim. Zhur. 1959, 22, 4, 435-441.

Kurkovskii, V. P., and Petrov, I. P., On morphological and functional changes in the central nervous system in resuscitated animals after cessation of respiration and cardiac activity induced by asphyxia. Voenno-Med. Akad. im. Kirov. 1949, 21, 3-48.

Kurkovskii, V. P., Morphological studies of the brain in severe oxygen starvation. In: Oxygen Starvation and Its Alleviation. Leningrad. 1941, 170-195.

Kurkovskii, V. P., Morphological studies of the brain in severe oxygen starvation. In: Collected Works Dedicated to Anichkov. Medgiz. 1946, 221-228.

Kurokhtina, T. P., Malkiman, I. I., and Parfenova, O. I., Changes in the content of creatine phosphate and adenosine triphosphate in the cerebral cortex in anoxia. Ukrain. Biokhim. Zhur. 1950, 22, 1, 85-90.

Kushko, V. M., and Panchenko, L. F., Incorporation of methionine-S^{35} in the proteins of the central nervous system and other organs of animals of various ages in hypoxia. Patol. Fiziol. i Eksperim. Terapiya. 1959, 3, 22-26.

Lebedeva, E. M., Maslova, M. N., and Rozengart, V. I., Functional changes and content of macroenergetic phosphorus compounds in the brain during induction of spasms. Dokl. Akad. Nauk SSSR. 1955, 102, 3, 563-566.

Leloir, L. F., and Cardini, C. E., Biosynthesis of glycogen from uridine diphosphate glucose. J. Am. Chem. Soc. 1957, 79, 6340-6345.

Leloir, L. F., Olavaria, J. M., Goldemberg, S. H., and Carminatti, A., Biosynthesis of glycogen from uridine diphosphate glucose. Arch. Biochem. Biophys. 1959, 81, 508-520.

LePage, G. A., The effects of hemorrhage on tissue metabolites. Am. J. Physiol. 1946, 147, 3, 443-446.

LePage, G. A., Biological energy transformations during shock as shown by tissue analyses. Am. J. Physiol. 1946, 146, 2, 267-281.

Lindberg, V., and Ernster, L., The turnover of radioactive phosphate injected into the subarachnoid space of the brain of the rat. Biochem. J. 1950, 46, 1, 43-47.

Lisovskaya, N. P., Phosphoproteins and metabolic processes in the brain. Dokl. Akad. Nauk SSSR. 1954, 95, 5, 1033-1036.

Lisovskaya, N. P., Phosphoproteins and brain metabolism. Biokhimiya. 1954, 19, 5, 626-637.

Lisovskaya, N. P., Phosphoproteins and brain metabolism. Dissertation, Moscow. 1954.

Lisovskaya, N. P., The role of glycolytic and oxidative mechanisms in the metabolism of phosphoproteins. Biokhimiya. 1956, 21, 3, 434-440.

Lisovskaya, N. P., Glycolysis in brain slices and phosphoprotein metabolism. In: Questions of Biochemistry of the Nervous System. Kiev. 1957, 76-83.

Lisovskaya, N. P., and Livanova, N. B., Oxidative phosphorylation and phosphoprotein metabolism. In: Phosphorylation and Function. Izd. Eksp. Med. 1960, 87-94.

Loeschke, G., and Loeschke, H. G., Über den Milchsäureaustausch zwischen arteriellem Blut und Gehirngewebe und seine Veränderungen in Sauerstoffmangel. Pflüfers Arch. 1948, 249, 6/7, 521-538.

London, E. S., and Kochneva, N. P., Inkretionsdynamik. Arch. Physiol. 1934, 234, 1-17.

London, E. S., Angiostomy and Organ Metabolism. Moscow. 1935.

Lyubovskaya, P. I., Metabolism of glutathione and glucose in dog organs in various states of the nervous system. Vopr. Med. Khim. 1952, 4, 209-218.

Makarychev, A. I., Popova, A. V., and Grozdova, T. N., Effect of ether narcosis and glucose on the restoration of the functions of the higher divisions of the central nervous system in excitable dogs after lethal blood losses. Zhur. Vysshei Nervnoi Deyatel'nosti im. I. P. Pavlova 1960, 4, 547-555.

Martison, E. E., and Tyakhepyl'd, L. Ya., On the relationship of ammonia to the processes of excitation and inhibition. Problems of Biochemistry of the Nervous System. Kiev. 1957, 176-183.

Martison, E. E., and Tyakhepyl'd, L. Ya., Effect of ammonia, glutamic acid, and urea on the in vivo changes in macrostructure of brain proteins in relation to functional state. Biokhimiya. 1961, 26, 6, 984-992.

Martison, E. E., and Tyakhepyl'd, L. Ya., Changes in macrostructure of brain proteins in relation to functional states and ammonia as a factor inducing these states. Reports of Biochemical Conference Dedicated to Twentieth Anniversary of Baltic Soviet Republics. Tartu. 1961, 26-43.

Mathe, V., and Kassay, G., Carbohydrate metabolism in the brain in various conditions of inhibition of the central nervous system. Abstracts of sections. Fifth International Biochemical Congress. Moscow. 1961, 1, 463.

McFarlane, and Weil-Malherbe, H., Changes in phosphate distribution during anaerobic glycolysis in brain slices. Biochem. J. 1941, 35, 1-34.

McGinty, D. A., and Gesell, R., On the chemical regulation of respiration. Am. J. Physiol. 1925, 75, 1, 70.

McGinty, D. A., The lactic acid of circulated brain. Am. J. Physiol. 1928, 85, 2, 395.

McIlwain, H., Metabolic response in vitro to electrical stimulation of sections of mammalian brain. Biochem. J. 1951, 49, 382-393.

McIlwain, H., Electrically excited metabolism of separated mammalian cerebral tissues. Electroencephalogr. and Clin. Neurophysiol. 1954, 6, 93-101.

McIlwain, H., Biochemistry and the Central Nervous System. London. 1955.

McIlwain, H., Measurement of reaction rates in various cerebral systems. Conferences et Rapports présentés au 3-eme Congres Intern. de Biochemie. Bruxelles, 1-6 Aout, 1955. Liege. 1956, 400-402.

McIlwain, H., Anaerobic glycolysis of cerebral tissues and a second, electrically induced metabolic defect. Biochem. J. 1956, 63, 2, 257-263.

McIlwain, H., Electrical influences and speed of chemical change in the brain. Physiol. Revs. 1956, 36, 3, 355-375.

McIlwain, H., Thiols and the control of carbohydrate metabolism in cerebral tissues. Biochem. J. 1959, 71, 2, 281-285.

McIlwain, H., Biochemistry and the Central Nervous System. London. 1959.

Miloslavskaya, L. I., Effect of barbiturates on the activity of asparaginase and glutaminase of the brain. Biokhimiya. 1958, 23, 3, 347-349.

Minaev, P. F., and Kurokhtina, G. P., Changes in the content of creatine phosphate and ATP in the cortex of large hemispheres after spasms elicited by electric current. Ukrain. Biokhim. Zhur. 1949, 21, 4, 359-369.

Minaev, P. F., Skvortsova, P. I., and Logvinova, O. F., On biochemical changes in the brain in normal and pathological conditions. Abstracts of sections. Fifth International Biochemical Congress. Moscow. 1961, 11, 35, 464.

Mison-Crighel, N., Constantinesco, E., and Crighel, E., The effect of preconvulsion functional state on the development of the convulsive seizure and the chemical changes elicited by the seizure. Ukrain. Biokhim. Zhur. 1959, 31, 6, 834-848.

Mkheyan, E. E., Consumption of glucose and pyruvate by the brain in certain functional states. In: Questions of Biochemistry. Erevan. 1961, 2, 61-70.

Nasy, H., and Leikagaku, J. Japan.Biochem. Soc. 1958, 30, 3, 205-210; 4, 264-268.

Nechaeva, G. A., Sadikova, N. V., and Skvortsevich, V. A., On renewal of amino acid composition of brain proteins in various functional states. In: Questions of Biochemistry of the Nervous System. Kiev. 1957, 31-40.

Nechaeva, G. A., Effect of deep hypothermia on carbohydrate-phosphorus metabolism of brain tissue. Byul. Eksperim. Biol. i Med. 1960, 49, 3, 54-57.

Negovskii, V. A., Restoration of Vital Functions of the Organism in Agonal State or during Clinical Death. Moscow. 1943.

Negovskii, V. A., Clinical death as a state of hypoxia. In: Hypoxia. Kiev. 1949, 63-67.

Negovskii, V. A., Clinical Death as a Reversible Stage of Dying. Moscow. 1951.

Negovskii, V. A., and Smirenskaya, E. M., On the question of therapy of patients in terminal states. Khirurgiya. 1954, 1, 56-60.

Negovskii, V. A., Pathophysiology and Therapy of Agony and Clinical Death. Medgiz, Moscow. 1954.

Negovskii, V. A., and Soboleva, V. I., Restoration of the vital functions of the organism after prolonged clinical death in hypothermia. Khirurgiya. 1955, 9, 22-26.

Negovskii, V. A., and Soboleva, V. I., Dynamics of extinction and restoration of vital functions of the organism in lethal exsanguination in hypothermia. Arkhiv Patol. 1956, 18, 6, 58-70.

Negovskii, V. A., and Soboleva, V. I., Hibernation as a method of therapy of terminal states. Farmakol. i Toksikol. 1959, 2, 172-175.

Negovskii, V. A., Soboleva, V. I., Gurvich, N. L., and Kiseleva, K. S., Restoration of vital functions of the organism two hours after clinical death in deep hypothermia. Vestnik Akad. Med. Nauk SSSR. 1960, 10, 40-44.

Negovskii, V. A., Resuscitation and Artificial Hypothermia. Medgiz. 1960. [English translation: Consultants Bureau, New York. 1962.]

Nikulin, V. I., Effect of artificial hypothermia on the extent of synthesis of proteins in organs and tissues. Dissertation. 1959.

Nikulin, V. I., Intensity of protein synthesis in organs and tissues in early posthypothermia period. Eksperim. Khirur. 1959, 2, 39-42.

Nosova, E. A., Content of macroenergetic phosphates in dog brain during the process of dying and resuscitation in hypothermia. Vopr. Med. Khim. 1960, 6, 3, 264-270.

Ochoa, S., "Coupling" of phosphorylation with oxidation of pyruvic acid in brain. J. Biol. Chem. 1941, 138, 2, 751-773.

Olsen, N. S., and Klein, J. R., Effect of cyanide on the concentration of lactate and phosphates in brain. J. Biol. Chem. 1947, 167, 3, 739-746.

Opitz, E., and Schneider, M., Über die Sauerstoffversorgung des Gehirns und den Mechanismus von Mangelwirkungen. Ergeb.Phys. biol. Chem. a. exp. Pharmakol. 1950, 46, 126-261.

Otomo, E., and Michaelis, M., Penetration of radioactive phosphorus into normal and shocked rat's brain. Proc. Soc. Exptl. Biol. Med. 1960, 104, 2, 259-260.

Paktovskii, Ya., Kozlova, M., Gracheva, G. V., Bakulin, N. D., Rudoi, B. D., and Mitina, G. V., Effect of experimental inhibition and excitation on the content of certain chemical and biochemical parameters in animal brain. Scientific Reports of Students of Kuibyshev Medical Institute. Kuibyshev. 1958, 119-127.

Palladin, A. V., Studies on the chemical composition of various divisions of the central and peripheral nervous system. Fiziol. Zhur. SSSR. 1936, 21, 4, 493-506.

Palladin, A. V., and Khaikina, B. I., Hexokinase in animal brain of various ages. Ukrain. Biokhim. Zhur. 1947, 19, 2, 177-187.

Palladin, A. V., and Shtutman, Ts. M., Adenosinetriphosphatase of the brain. Ukrain. Biokhim. Zhur. 1948, 20, 3, 311-320.

Palladin, A. V., Biochemical studies of the nervous system. Problems of Soviet Physiology, Biochemistry, and Pharmacology. Vol. II, 1949, 621-698.

Palladin, A. V., Synthesis and degradation of polysaccharides in the brain. Fiziol. Zhur. SSSR. 1949, 35, 5, 596-603.

Palladin, A. V., and Khaikina, B. I., Glycogen in animal brain. Ukrain. Biokhim. Zhur. 1950, 22, 4, 462-470.

Palladin, A. V., Metabolism in the brain during inhibition and excitation of the higher nervous activity. Biokhimiya. 1952, 17, 4, 456-461.

Palladin, A. V., Khaikina, B. I., Polyakova, N. M., Goncharova, E. E., and Mikhailovskaya, L. A., Studies of carbohydrate metabolism in the brain in hypoxia. In: Oxygen Therapy and Oxygen Insufficiency. Kiev. 1952, 7-13.

Palladin, A. V., Khaikina, B. I., and Polyakova, N. M., Glycolysis and the content of adenosinetriphosphate in excitation of the central nervous system. Dokl. Akad. Nauk SSSR. 1952, 84, 4, 777-779.

Palladin, A. V., and Rybina, A. A., Phosphorus metabolism in the brain during excitation of the higher nervous activity. Dokl. Akad. Nauk SSSR. 1953, 91, 4, 903-905.

Palladin, A. V., and Polyakova, N. M., Hexokinase in various divisions of the brain in various functional states. Dokl. Akad. Nauk SSSR. 1953, 91, 347-349.

Palladin, A. V., Summary and problems in investigations of the biochemistry of the brain. In: Biochemistry of the Nervous System. Kiev. 1954, 7-24.

Palladin, A. V., Studies of metabolism in the brain during various functional states. Ukrain. Biokhim. Zhur. 1954, 26, 2, 112-127.

Palladin, A. V., Biochemistry of the brain. Nauka i Zhizn. 1954, 5, 10-12.

Palladin, A. V., and Khaikina, B. I., Biochemistry of the brain. Usp. Biol. Khim. 1954, II, 27-50.

Palladin, A. V., Biochemistry of the brain. Reports and Communications, Third International Biochemical Congress, Brussels, August 1-6, 1955. Academy of Sciences Press, Moscow. 1955.

Palladin, A. V., Belik, Ya. V., Polyakova, N. M., and Silich, T. P., Studies of proteins of the nervous system. Problems of Biochemistry of the Nervous System. Kiev. 1957, 9-31.

Palladin, A. V., Biochemical characteristics of the functionally distinct divisions of the nervous system. Ukrain. Biokhim. Zhur. 1959, 31, 5, 765-779.

Palladin, A. V., Polyakova, N. M., and Malysheva, M. K., Content of glutaminase in various divisions of the central nervous system and in cell structures of the brain. Dokl. Akad. Nauk SSSR. 1960, 134, 5, 1236-1239.

Palladin, A. V., Polyakova, N. M., and Kirsenko, O. V., Studies on the enzymes of the structural elements of brain cells. Abstracts of sections. Fifth International Biochemical Congress. Moscow. 1961, 1, 467.

Palladin, A. V., Radioactive isotopes in the biochemistry of the nervous system. Ukrain. Biokhim. Zhur. 1961, 33, 4, 602-619.

Pertseva, M. N., Content of ammonia and glutamine in brain tissue during anemia induced by ligation of carotid artery. Byul. Eksperim. Biokhim. i Med. 1958, 7, 63-67.

Pertseva, M. N., Discussions at a Symposium, Effect of blood circulation in hypothermia on ammonia and glutamine in the brain. Vopr. Med. Khim. 1958, 4, 5, 379-384.

Pertseva, M. N., Effect of oxygen insufficiency arising during alterations of cerebral blood circulation on ammonia-glutamine system in the brain. Dissertation, Leningrad. 1959.

Pertseva, M. N., Discussion at the Symposium on Phosphorylation and Function. In: Phosphorylation and Function, Izd. Eksp. Med. 1960, 370-372.

Petrov, I. R., Oxygen Starvation of the Brain. Leningrad. 1949.

Petrov, I. R., On the Role of Nervous System in Oxygen Starvation. Moscow. 1952.

Petrov, I. R., and Gubler, E. V., The significance of general cooling in systems of prophylactic measures in severe surgical interferences. Vest. Khirurg. 1954, 74, 4, 34-46.

Petrov, I. R., Raiko, Z. A., and Kudritskaya, T. E., Comparative characteristic of functional changes and certain indicators of carbohydrate-phosphorus metabolism in brain tissue in agonal period, clinical death, and resuscitation of animals. Fiziol. Zhur. SSSR. 1957, 43, 2, 107-115.

Petrov, I. R., and Gubler, E. V., Artificial Hypothermia. Medgiz, Leningrad. 1961.

Pigareva, Z. D., Effect of the removal of the cortex of large hemispheres on the enzymatic activities of the lower divisions of the brain. Trudy Inst. Fiziol. im. Pavlova. 1954, 3, 593-599.

Pigareva, Z. D., Changes in the activity of certain enzymes in various zones of the cortex of large hemispheres of rabbits and dogs in ontogenesis. Problem of Biochemistry of the Nervous System. Kiev. 1957, 217-227.

Pigareva, Z. D., Data on the evolution of the enzymatic systems of oxidative metabolism of the central nervous system in ontogenesis of birds and mammals. Author's abstract of Dissertation, Leningrad. 1960.

Piontkovskii, I. A., Questions of hypothermia. Patol. Fiziol. i Eksperim. Terapiya. 1958, 2, 1, 55-59.

Pogodaev, K. I., and Mekhedova, A. Ya., The rate of renewal of proteins and respiration of tissues of various divisions of animal brain during and after medicinal sleep. In: Questions of Biochemistry of the Nervous System. Kiev. 1957, 40-51.

Pogodaev, K. I., Savchenko, Z. I., Osipova, M. S., and Turova, N. F., Protein metabolism in brain tissue during repeated epileptic seizures. Ukrain. Biokhim. Zhur. 1960, 32, 6, 808-820.

Pogodaev, K. I., Turova, N. F., and Savchenko, Z. I., Protein and energy metabolism in the brain during fatigue and exhaustion. Abstracts of sections. Fifth International Biochemical Congress. Moscow. 1961, 1, 468.

Potop, I., L'influence de la thyroxine sur le métabolism glucidique du tissu cérébral. Biokhimiya. 1958, 23, 1, 11-16.

Prokhorova, M. I., On the content of lactic and pyruvic acids in the blood under various stimuli. Uch. Zap. Leningrad. Gos. Univ., Biol. Ser. 1952, 24, 138, 55-70.

Prokhorova, M. I., Carbohydrate metabolism of the brain in its normal state. Uch. Zap. Leningrad. Gos. Univ. 1954, 164, 362-376.

Prokhorova, M. I., Studies with C^{14} of the intensity of renewal of glucose and glycogen in brain and liver. Vestnik Leningrad. Univ. 1955, 7, 79-88.

Prokhorova, M. I., and Kazimirova, Z. N., The importance of the method of sinusostomy for the study of metabolism in the brain in chronic experiments. Vestnik Leningrad. Univ. 1963, 3, 121-128.

Prokhorova, M. I., Brodskaya, N. I., Gubaidulina, D. Kh., Zolotareva, A. N., and Korvatskaya, A. M., Alterations in carbohydrate and gaseous metabolism in the brain during oxygen insufficiency. Uch. Zap. Leningrad. Gos. Univ. 1957, 222, 272-286.

Prokhorova, M. I., Brodskaya, N. I., and Sokolova, G. P., Extent of glycogen and glucose metabolism in the brain and liver in oxygen insufficiency. Vopr. Med. Khim. 1957, 3, 4, 279-284.

Prokhorova, M. I., and Tupikova, Z. N., The rate of renewal of carbohydrates and lipids in the brain and liver in excitation and narcotic sleep. In: Questions of Biochemistry of the Nervous System. Kiev. 1957, 118-127.

Prokhorova, M. I., Quantitative characteristic of energy expenditures in the brain during relative rest. In: Nervous System. First ed. 1960, 24-32.

Promyslov, M. Sh., Chemical changes in the brain in certain pathological processes. Dokl. Akad. Nauk SSSR. 1949, 69, 2, 235-236.

Promyslov, M. Sh., Changes in the cerebrosides of the brain in states of excitation and inhibition induced by certain toxic infections. Problems of Biochemistry of the Nervous System. Kiev. 1957, 323-331.

Raiko, Z. A., Petrov, I. R., and Kudritskaya, T. E., Phosphorus compounds and lactic acid in brain tissue and heart in cooled animals and during restoration of general blood circulation by a complex of therapeutic stimuli. Fiziol. Zhur. SSSR. 1959, 45, 12, 1489-1496.

Raiko, Z. A., Petrov, I. R., and Kudritskaya, T. E., On the effect of hypothermia and ganglionic blockade on the carbohydrate-phosphorus metabolism in the brain of animals with temporary exclusion of heart from blood circulation. Vest. Khirurg. 1957, <u>78</u>, 5, 56-63.

Raiko, Z. A., Petrov, I. R., Kudritskaya, T. E., and Pertseva, M. N., On the effect of artificial hypothermia on certain parameters of carbohydrate-phosphorus and nitrogen metabolism in the brain and heart during temporary cessation of general blood circulation. In: Phosphorylation and Function. 1960, 352-362.

Rashba, E. Ya., On amylase of nervous tissue. Ukrain. Biokhim. Zhur. 1948, <u>20</u>, 1, 34-54.

Richter, D., and Dawson, R., Brain metabolism in emotional excitement and in sleep. Am. J. Physiol. 1948, <u>154</u>, 1, 73-80.

Richter, D., The metabolic activity of the proteins of the brain. Conférences et Rupports présentés au 3-ème Congrès Internat. de Biochimie. Bruxelles, 1-6 Aout, 1955. Liege. 1956, 402-404.

Richter, D., Protein metabolism of the brain. Brit. Med. J. 1959, <u>5132</u>, 1255-1259.

Richter, D., Metabolism of the Nervous System. 1957.

Robbins, P. W., Traut, R., and Lipmann, F., Glycogen synthesis from glucose, glucose-6-phosphate and uridinediphosphate glucose in muscle preparations. Proc. Nat. Acad. Sci. 1959, <u>45</u>, 1, 6-12.

Rodnight, R., McIlwain, H., and Tresize, M. A., Analysis of arterial and cerebral venous blood from the rabbit. J. Neurochem. 1959, <u>3</u>, 3, 209-218.

Rosomoff, H. L., and Holaday, D., Cerebral blood flow and cerebral oxygen consumption during hypothermia. Am. J. Physiol. 1954, <u>179</u>, 1, 85-88.

Romanova, N. P., On dynamics of histopathological changes in the brain during experimental hypoxia. Zhur. Nevropatol. i Psikhiatr. 1956, <u>56</u>, 1, 44-55.

Rozengart, V. I., Maslova, M. N., and Panyukov, A. N., Ammonia and glutamine of the brain during spasms induced by pharmacological agents. Dokl. Akad. Nauk SSSR. 1956, <u>110</u>, 1, 122.

Rustamova-Gadzhieva, P. G., Effect of repeated medicinal sleep on the content of glucose and glycogen in the blood and tissues. Patol. Fiziol. i Eksperim. Terapiya. 1958, <u>1</u>, 1, 52.

Savchenko, O. N., Carbohydrate-phosphorus metabolism of the brain in hypothermia and hypoxia. Vopr. Med. Khim. 1958, <u>4</u>, 2, 139-148.

Sechenov, I. M., On the question of gases of the blood. Complete Works. 1907, Vol. I, 1-17.

Serdyuk, E. E., On the content of ascorbic acid in the brain in various functional states of the central nervous system. Ukrain. Biokhim. Zhur. 1953, <u>25</u>, 3, 271-275.

Shabadash, A. L., Histochemistry of Glycogen in Normal Nervous System. Moscow. 1949.

Shabadash, A. L., Glycogen in the cerebral cortex in normal and pathological states. Ukrain. Biokhim. Zhur. 1951, <u>23</u>, 3, 360-363.

Shapot, V. S., On the nature of peculiar sensitivity of the brain to oxygen insufficiency. Usp. Sovrem. Biol. 1952, <u>34</u>, 2 (5), 244-267.

Shapot, V. S., Petrov, I. R., Gromova, K. G., and Kudritskaya, T. E., On the role of excitation of the central nervous system in increased sensitivity of the organism towards oxygen insufficiency. Fiziol. Zhur. SSSR. 1953, <u>39</u>, 5, 614-617.

Shapot, V. S., and Gromova, K. G., Energy metabolism of the brain and the problem of hypoxic states. In: Biochemistry of the Nervous System. Kiev. 1954, 139-150.

Shapot, V. S., Interrelationships between the processes of oxidation, oxidative phosphorylation, and biosynthesis in the cell. Usp. Sovrem. Biol. 1954, <u>37</u>, 3, 255-278.

Shapot, V. S., Brain metabolism in relation to the functional state of the central nervous system. In: Metabolism of the Nervous System. D. Richter (ed.). 1957, 257-262.

Shnyak, E. I., The nature of renewal of brain proteins in the cortex of large hemispheres in relation to its functional state. Dokl. Akad. Nauk SSSR. 1962, <u>146</u>, 3, 734-737.

Shtutman, Ts. M., Brain adenosinetriphosphatase. Dissertation. Kiev. 1946.

Shtutman, Ts. M., On the content of ATP, creatine phosphate, and lactic acid in the brain and muscle in hypothermia. Ukrain. Biokhim. Zhur. 1958, <u>30</u>, 6, 852-859.

Shtutman, Ts. M., Peculiarities of the metabolism of phosphorus compounds in rabbits during the action of aminazine with cooling. Ukrain. Biokhim. Zhur. 1959, <u>31</u>, 3, 405-413.

Shuster, M. I., Changes in the content of inorganic phosphate and easily hydrolyzable phosphorus of ATP in dog brain during dying and resuscitation. Arkhiv Patol. 1952, <u>14</u>, 1, 36-44.

Shuster, M. I., The content of creatine phosphate in brain tissue during dying and subsequent resuscitation. Arkhi Patol. 1953, 15, 2, 55-60.

Skvirskaya, E. B., Glycolytic capacity of the various sections of the nervous system in relation to substrate. Biokhim. Zhur. 1938, 12, 1,5.

Skvirskaya, E. B., and Silich, T. P., Metabolism of phosphorus-containing compounds in the brain in various states of the nervous system. In: Biochemistry of the Nervous System. Kiev. 1954, 36-46.

Skvirskaya, E. B., and Silich, T. P., Metabolism of the brain during winter hibernation. Ukrain. Biokhim. Zhur. 1955, 27, 3, 385-393.

Skvirskaya, E. B., and Silich, T. P., The effect of winter hibernation on certain enzymes of the brain and spinal cord. Ukrain. Biokhim. Zhur. 1957, 29, 1.

Skvirskaya, E. V., and Silich, T. P., Metabolism of certain phosphorus compounds in rat brain in medicinal sleep of varying duration. Ukrain. Biokhim. Zhur. 1957, 29, 1, 33-41.

Smirenskaya, E. M., Blood gases during extinction and restoration of the vital functions of the organism. Arkhiv Patol. 1946, 8, 1-2, 12-21.

Smirenskaya, E. M., Effect of CO_2 on the restoration of respiration after clinical death. Arkhiv Patol. 1951, 13, 1, 48-55.

Smirenskaya, E. M., and Zolotokrylina, E. S., Changes in the gaseous metabolism in dogs during restoration period after clinical death. Arkhiv Patol. 1956, 18, 1, 99-100.

Smirenskaya, E. M., The role of vessel interoreception in restoration of the activity of the cardiovascular system during resuscitation after clinical death. Reports of Conference on Pathophysiology and Therapy of Terminal States. Moscow. 1954, 38-49.

Smirnov, A. A., and Chetverikov, D. A., Studies on phosphorus metabolism in the brain in hypoxia with the aid of P^{32}. Dokl. Akad. Nauk SSSR. 1953, 90, 5, 843-845.

Smirnov, A. A., and Chetverikov, D. A., Application of radioactive isotopes to studies of brain metabolism. Priroda. 1954, 2, 23-29.

Smirnov, A. A., Content of phosphorus and its metabolism in various zones of the cortex of large hemispheres of dogs at rest and during activity. Dokl. Akad. Nauk SSSR. 1955, 105, 1, 185-187.

Smirnov, G. D., and Negovskii, V. A., Changes in the electroencephalogram of dogs during increasing blood loss, during clinical death, and during subsequent resuscitation and restoration of the vital functions. Vopr. Neirokhirurg. 1941, 5, 5-6, 70-76.

Soskin, S., and Levine, R., Carbohydrate Metabolism. Chicago. 1946.

Staub, H., Über den Zuckerstoffwechsel des Menschen. Z. klin. Med. 1926, 104, 587-608.

Stephenson, H. E., Cardiac Arrest and Resuscitation. St. Louis. 1958.

Stetten, W., and Stetten, M. R., Glycogen metabolism. Physiol. Revs. 1960, 40, 3, 505-537.

Stone, W. E., The effects of anaesthetics and of convulsants on the lactic acid content of the brain. Biochem. J. 1938, 32, 11, 1908-1918.

Stone, W. E., Acid-soluble phosphorus compounds and lactic acid in brain. J. Biol. Chem. 1940, 135, 1, 43-49.

Stone, W. E., Marchall, C., and Nims, L. F., Chemical changes on the brain produced by injury and by anoxia. Am. J. Physiol. 1941, 132, 3, 770-775.

Stone, W. E., Acid-soluble phosphorus compounds of cerebral tissue. J. Biol. Chem. 1943, 149, 1, 29.

Stone, W. E., Webster, J. E., and Gurdjian, E. S., The chemical changes in cerebral cortex induced by convulsions. J. Neurophysiol. 1945, 8, 4, 233.

Stone, W. E., Acute chemical changes associated with pathological physiology of the brain. In: Neurochemistry. Springfield, Illinois. 1955, 485-514.

Sutherland, E. W., Colowick, S. P., and Cori, C. F., The enzymatic conversion of glucose-6-phophate to glycogen. J. Biol. Chem. 1941, 140, 309.

Sytinskii, I. A., Changes in the system of adenosinetriphosphoric acid in brain tissue in various functional states of the central nervous system. Dissertation, Leningrad. 1955.

Sytinskii, I. A., Changes in the system of adenosinetriphosphoric acid in brain tissue in various functional states of the central nervous system. Biokhimiya. 1956, 21, 3, 358-367.

Thölen, H., and Bosshardt, R., Über den Blutammoniakgehalt urämischer Patienten. Klin. Wochschr. 1958, 36, 12, 574-576.

Thorn, W., and Heimann, I., Beeinflussung der Ammoniakkonzentration in Gehirn, Herz, Leber, Niere und Muskulatur durch Ischämie, Anoxie, Asphyxie und Hypothermie. J. Neurochem. 1958, 2, 2-3, 166-177.

Tower, D. B., Glutamic acid metabolism in the mammalian central nervous system. Fourth Intern. Congress of Biochem. Sympos. 1958, 3, 1-38.

Troitskaya, V. B., Effect of conditioned reflex excitation of the central nervous system on carbohydrate-phosphorus metabolism in large hemispheres of the brain. Vopr. Med. Khim. 1953, 6, 17-27.

Tseitlin, L. A., Phosphoamidase activity of rat brain. Biokhimiya. 1952, 17, 2, 208-213.

Tseitlin, L. A., On transformations of creatine phosphate in brain tissue. Biokhimiya. 1953, 18, 3.

Tsukada, Y., Takagaki, G., Sugimoto, S., and Hirano, S., Changes in the ammonia and glutamine content of the rat brain induced by electric shock. J. Neurochem. 1958, 2, 4, 295-303.

Tsukada, Y., Hirano, S., and Nagata, Y., Ammonia and glutamine metabolism in rat brain in relation to conditioned reflexes. Abstracts of sections. Fifth International Biochemical Congress. Moscow. 1961, 1, 477.

Tumanovskaya, G. V., Effect of lowered atmospheric pressure on phosphorus metabolism of the brain of albino rats. In: Hypoxemia and Ionizing Radiations. Voronezh. 1960, 7-13.

Tupikova, T. M., Effect of experimental hypoxia on the permeability of certain biological barriers of the organism to radioactive phosphorus. Patol. Fiziol. i Eksperim. Terapiya. 1961, 4, 39-45.

Tyakhepyl'd, L. Ya., The process of formation and binding of ammonia in the liver and brain in relation to excitation and inhibition of the central nervous system during prolonged action of sedatives. Dissertation, Tartu. 1958.

Tyakhepyl'd, L. Ya., On the changes in ammonia and glutamine content of the brain during prolonged repeated administration of sedatives. Vopr. Med. Khim. 1958, 4, 5, 362-365.

Tyakhepyl'd, L. Ya., Changes in the extent of amidation and of certain physicochemical properties of brain proteins during alteration of binding of ammonia in the liver. Vopr. Med. Khim. 1962, 8, 3, 264-270.

Tyler, D. B., and Harreveld, A., The respiration of the developing brain. Am. J. Physiol. 1942, 136, 4, 600.

Veksler, Ya. I., Dynamics of high-energy phosphorus-containing compounds of the brain in hypothermia. In: Problems of Biochemistry of the Nervous System. Kiev. 1957, 278-285.

Veksler, Ya. I., and Gershenovich, Z. S., Ammonia-glutamic acid-glutamine of the brain in hypothermia and subsequent warming. Abstracts of sections. Fifth International Biochemical Congress. Moscow, 1961, 1, 450-451.

Veksler, Ya. I., and Gershenovich, Z. S., System ammonia-glutamic acid-glutamine of rat brain in various phases of hypothermia. Ukrain. Biokhim. Zhur. 1962, 34, 3, 406-416.

Verzhbinskaya, N. A., Cytochrome system of the brain in phylogenesis of vertebrates. Fiziol. Zhur. SSSR. 1953, 39, 1, 17-26.

Verzhbinskaya, N. A., Changes in enzymatic systems of energy metabolism of the brain in evolutionary scale of vertebrates. In: Biochemistry of the Nervous System. Kiev. 1954, 193-207.

Verzhbinskaya, N. A., Data on the evolution of energy metabolism of the brain in vertebrates. Dissertation, Leningrad. 1957.

Verzhbinskaya, N. A., Process of oxidative phosphorylation in the brain in vivo and formation of phosphorus barrier in the brain of vertebrates. In: Problems of Biochemistry of the Nervous System. Kiev. 1957, 187-200.

Verzhbinskaya, N. A., Oxidative phosphorylation in the brain of vertebrates. In: Phosphorylation and Function. IEM, 1960, 265-274.

Veselkin, N. V., and Gordon, B. G., Changes in content of ammonia and glutamine in animal brain during surgical alteration of the activity of the liver. Byul. Eksperim. Biol. i Med. 1959, 47, 3, 34-38.

Vladimirov, G. E., Regulatory changes in blood composition and metabolism in conditions of rarefied atmosphere. Fiziol. Zhur. SSSR. 1938, 25, 6, 779-784.

Vladimirov, G. E., The course of renewal of certain phosphorus-containing compounds in the liver and brain in oxygen starvation. Trudy Voenno-Med. Akad. im. Kirov. 1946, 205-214.

Vladimirov, G. E., Functional biochemistry of the brain. Fiziol. Zhur. SSSR. 1953, 39, 1, 3-16.

Vladimirov, G. E., and Ginodman, L. M., On the free energy of hydrolysis of the energy-rich phosphate bond of adenosinetriphosphate. Biokhimiya. 1953, 18, 4, 490-498.

Vladimirov, G. E., Ivanova, T. N., and Pravdina, N.I., Effect of functional state on metabolism of phosphorus compounds in brain tissue. Biokhimiya. 1954, 19, 5, 578-585.

Vladimirov, G. E., and Rubel', L. N., On the rate of renewal of adenosinetriphosphate and phosphocreatine in rat brain. Dokl. Akad. Nauk SSSR. 1954, 96, 5, 1021-1024.

Vladimirov, G. E., New data on the energy characteristics of glycolysis. Uch. Zap. Leningrad. Gos. Univ. 1954, 164, 328-349.

Vladimirov, G. E., Functional biochemistry of the brain. (Bakh Reports IX.) Moscow. Academy of Sciences USSR. 1954.

Vladimirov, G. E., Ways and means of study of functional biochemistry of the brain. Usp. Biol. Khim. 1954, 11, 50-65.

Vladimirov, G. E., The course of renewal of phosphorus-containing compounds in brain tissue in narcotic sleep and excitation of the central nervous system. In: Biochemistry of the Nervous System. Kiev. 1954, 25-35.

Vladimirov, G. E., Effect of hypothermia in conjunction with cessation of blood circulation on brain metabolism. In: Problems of Biochemistry of the Nervous System. Kiev. 1957, 241-258.

Vladimirov, G. E., Ivanova, T. N., Pravdina, N. I., and Rubel', L. N., Rate of renewal of adenosinetriphosphate in deep hypothermia. Biokhimiya. 1959, 24, 5, 891-898.

Vladimirov, G. E., On the energy function of adenosinetriphosphate in the cell. In: Phosphorylation and Function. IEM, 1960, 45-49.

Vladimirov, G. E., Ivanova, T. N., Pravdina, N. I., and Rubel', L. N., Certain aspects of phosphorus metabolism of the brain of rats in hypothermia. Abstracts. Fifth International Biochemical Congress. Moscow, 1961, 1, 11, 8, 451.

Vladimirov, G. E., and Urinson, A. P., Effect of irritation by electric current on the renewal of amino acids in the protein and glutathione of the brain. Trudy Voenno-Med. Inst. im. Kirov. 1959, 102, 49-56.

Vladimirova, E. A., Content of lactic acid and various fractions of phosphorus compounds in the central nervous system under the influence of certain spasm-inducing drugs. In: Studies of Neuro-Humoral Relationships. Third ed. VIEM, 1937, 37-49.

Vladimirova, E. A., Changes in content of ammonia and in pH of brain tissue during excitation and inhibition of central nervous system by certain pharmacological agents. Fiziol. Zhur. SSSR. 1938, 25, 6, 930-939.

Vladimirova, E. A., On the formation of ammonia in the brain. Fiziol. Zhur. SSSR. 1938, 24, 5, 915-919.

Vladimirova, E. A., On the formation of ammonia in the brain. Communication IV. Effect of oxygen deficiency on formation of ammonia in the brain. Vopr. Med. Khim. 1950, 2, 12-18.

Vladimirova, E. A., On the formation of ammonia in the brain. Communication V. Glutamine as the source of preformed ammonia in brain tissue in vitro. Byul. Eksperim. Biol. i Med. 1950, 2, 138-140.

Vladimirova, E. A., Biochemical processes in the brain in conditioned reflex changes of the functional states of the central nervous system. Byul. Eksperim. Biol. i Med. 1951, 31, 4, 228-231.

Vladimirova, E. A., The formation-removal of ammonia in rat brain during excitation of the central nervous system induced by unconditioned and conditioned reflex irritation. In: Physiology and Morphology of the Central Nervous System. Bykov (ed.). Academy of Medical Sciences USSR. Moscow. 1953, 97-108.

Vladimirova, E. A., Ammonia of the brain as a specific biochemical indicator of the functional state of the central nervous system. In: Biochemistry of the Nervous System. Kiev. 1954, 47-62.

Vladimirova, E. A., Effect of conditioned reflex excitation of the central nervous system on the content of ATP and ADP in the brain. Vopr. Med. Khim. 1956, 1, 47-52.

Vladimirova, E. A., On the binding of ammonia by glutamic acid with the formation of glutamine. Trudy Inst. Fiziol. im. Pavlova. 1956, 5, 440.

Vladimirova, E. A., Relationship between various stages of differentiated and extinguished inhibitions and performed ammonia. In: Problems of Biochemistry of the Nervous System. Kiev. 1957, 164-176.

Vladimirova, E. A., Studies of changes in the level of free ammonia in the brain during differentiated inhibition and in certain neurotic states in rats. Fiziol. Zhur. SSSR. 1960, 46, 11, 1373-1379.

Vladimirova, E. A., On the mechanism of development of cortical inhibition and certain of its properties employing biochemical data. Abstracts. Fifth International Biochemical Congress. Moscow. 1961, 1, 11, 9, 452.

Volkova, R. I., Rate of renewal of labile phosphorus compounds in the brain of cold blooded animals at different body temperatures. Biokhimiya. 1957, 22, 4, 644-651.

Volkova, R. I., Metabolism of labile phosphorus compounds in turtle brain during waking and "sleep." Izvest. Akad. Nauk SSSR, Ser. Biol. 1958, 5, 544-551.

Volkova, R. I., Effect of temperature on the metabolism of labile phosphorus compounds in the brain of cold blooded animals. Dissertation. Institute of Physiology, Academy of Sciences USSR, Leningrad, 1958.

Vrba, R., Amide bonds in the rat brain after acute carbon disulphide poisoning. In: Metabolism of the Nervous System. London, 1957, 475-479.

Vrba, R., Folbergrova, J., and Kanturek, V., On the question of ammonia formation in brain slices. In: Problems of Biochemistry of the Nervous System. Kiev, 1957, 154-164.

Vrba, R., and Folbergrova, J., Observation on endogenous metabolism in brain in vitro and in vivo. J. Neurochem. 1959, 4, 4, 338-349.

Vrba, R., Glucose metabolism in rat brain in vivo. Nature. 1962, 195, 4842, 663-665.

Vyshepan, E. D., and Porfir'eva, R. P., Content of ammonia and glutamine in the brain during bacterial intoxications. Vopr. Med. Khim. 1958, 4, 5, 365-368.

Waelsch, H., Glutamic acid and brain metabolism. Advances in Protein Chem. 1961, 6, 301-339.

Waelsch, H., Metabolism of proteins and amino acids. Symp. on Metabolism of the Nervous System, London. 1957, 431-447.

Weil-Malherbe, H., Significance of glutamic acid for the metabolism of nervous tissue. Physiol. Revs. 1950, 30, 4, 549-569.

Weil-Malherbe, H., L'ammoniaque dans le métabolisme cérébral. Schweiz. med. Wochschr. 1956, 86, 43, 1223-1227.

Weinberger, L. M., Gibbon, M. H., and Gibbon, I. H., Temporary arrest of the circulation to the central nervous system. Arch. Neurol. Psychiat. 1940, 48, 615-634.

Yavich, M. P., Effect of hypothermia on the renewal of nucleic acids of various organs and tissues. Eksperim. Khirur. 1959, 2, 55-56.

Zakharov, S. V., Metabolism of sugar and lactic acid in the central nervous system in experimental anoxemia. Trudy. Gos. Med. Inst. 1949, 74-75.

Zakharov, S. V., Content of lactic acid and sugar in the liquor and blood of brain vessels in peptone shock. Trudy Ivanovo. Gos. Med. Inst. 1949, 73.

Zakharov, S. V., On the content of lactic acid and sugar in the blood of brain vessels in enforced wakefulness and Benzidrine euphoria. Trudy Ivanovo. Gos. Med. Institute. 1949, 71-72.

Zakharov, S. V., The nature of carbohydrate metabolism of the brain under some physiological and pathological states of the organism. Vopr. Med. Khim. 1952, 4, 139-147.

Zakharov, S. V., and Orlyanskaya, R. L., Metabolism of phosphorus compounds and proteins in rat brain during excitation and spasms induced by cordiamine. Vopr. Med. Khim. 1960, 6, 3, 249-253.

SUPPLEMENTARY REFERENCES

Aprikyan, G. V., Oganesyan, V. S., Role and metabolism of N-aceyl-L-aspartic acid in the brain. In: Third All-Union Conference on Biochemistry of the Nervous System. Erevan. 1963, 121-129.

Brodskaya, N. I., Prokhorova, M. I., and Tupikova, Z. N., Rate of metabolism of glycogen fractions in the brain and liver during various functional states of the organism. In: Carbohydrates and Carbohydrate Metabolism. Izd. AN SSSR, Moscow. 1962, 151-156.

Bronovitskaya, Z. G., and Rumyantseva, L. M., Deamination of glutamine by brain slices in hyperoxia. In: Third All-Union Conference on Biochemistry of the Nervous System. Erevan. 1963, 475-481.

Bunyatyan, G. Kh. New data on the role of γ-aminobutyric acid in brain tissue. In: Third All-Union Conference on Biochemistry of the Nervous System. Erevan. 1963, 133-152.

Chikvaidze, V. N., Effect of pharmaceuticals on the content of free amino acids and on activity of enzymes involved in the metabolism of γ-aminobutyric acid in the brain. In: Third All-Union Conference on Biochemistry of the Nervous System. Erevan. 1963, 181-189.

Frenekl', S. F., and Gordienko, E. Á., Data on the nature and mechanism of alterations in the system of ammonia transformations in the brain during several alterations of its functions by means of various substances. In: Third All-Union Conference on Biochemistry of the Nervous System. Erevan. 1963, 223-235.

Gaevskaya, M. S., and Nosova, E. A., Aspects of carbohydrate-phosphorus and nitrogen metabolism of the brain during deep hypothermia. In: Third All-Union Conference on Biochemistry of the Nervous System. Erevan. 1963, 421-430.

Gershenovitch, Z. S., Krichevskaya, A. A., Lukash, A. I., and Khodykina, N. A., Amide groups of protein fractions of the brain during various functional states of the animal. In: Third All-Union Conference on Biochemistry of the Nervous System. Erevan. 1963, 91-101.

Gol'denberg, A. M., Effect of lowered barometric pressure on certain aspects of nitrogen metabolism of the brain. Ukrain. Biokhim. Zhur. 1963, 35, 6, 861-866.

Goncharova, E. E., Data on the structure of brain glycogen and polysaccharides synthesized in vitro by enzymes of the brain. In: Third All-Union Conference on Biochemistry of the Nervous System. Erevan. 1963, 455-463.

Gordon, B. G., Ammonia metabolism of brain tissue in experimental alteration of liver function. In: Third All-Union Conference on Biochemistry of the Nervous System. Erevan. 1963, 237-250.

Ivanenko, E. F., and Rudaeva, V. F., Changes in physico-chemical properties of brain proteins in relation to prolonged action of medication of various concentrations, which inhibit nervous activity. In: Third All-Union Conference on Biochemistry of the Nervous System. Erevan. 1963, 109-119.

Ivanova, T. N., Pravdina, N. I., and Rubel', L. N., On determination of "turnover time" of certain phosphorus-containing compounds in the brain. In: Third All-Union Conference on Biochemistry of the Nervous System. Erevan. 1963, 483-492.

Khachatryan, G. S., New data on metabolism of carbohydrates and glycolipids of the brain during various functional states. In: Third All-Union Conference on Biochemistry of the Nervous System. Erevan. 1963, 431-445.

Khaikina, B. I., Studies of conditions of formation of glycogen and its fractions in the brain. In: Third All-Union Conference on Biochemistry of the Nervous System. Erevan. 1963, 447-454.

Kirsenko, O. V., Properties of adenosinetriphosphatase of various cell fractions of brain tissue. In: Third All-Union Conference on Biochemistry of the Nervous System. Erevan. 1963, 55-65.

Klein, E. E., Iordanishvili, G. S., and Gvaliya, N. V., Mechanism of ammonia formation in the brain. In: Third All-Union Conference on Biochemistry of the Nervous System. Erevan. 1963, 193-205.

Martinson, E. E., and Tyakhepyl'd, L. Ya., Changes in the extent of amidation of brain proteins and in their macrostructure in relation to prolonged action of stimulants. In: Third All-Union Conference on Biochemistry of the Nervous System. Erevan. 1963, 103-108.

Maslova, M. N., and Rosengart, V. I., Content of γ-aminobutyric acid in animal brain during convulsions. In: Third All-Union Conference on Biochemistry of the Nervous System. Erevan. 1963, 153-162.

Mkheyan, E. E., Changes in the content of cerebrosides and mucolipids in the brain of white rats after unilateral extirpation of superior cervical ganglion. In: Third All-Union Conference on Biochemistry of the Nervous System. Erevan. 1963, 409-417.

Musaolyan, S. S., Effect of hypoxia on the content of γ-aminobutyric acid in the brain. In: Third All-Union Conference on Biochemistry of the Nervous System. Erevan. 1963, 175-179.

Portugalov, V. V., Pigareva, Z. D., Busnyuk, M. M., Dovedova, E. L., and Il'ina, E. I., Comparative cytochemical and biochemical characteristics of oxidative metabolism in certain cellular sections of the brain of mammals. In: Third All-Union Conference on Biochemistry of the Nervous System. Erevan. 1963, 297-309.

Putilina, F. E., Eschenko, N. D., Krestnikova, L. M., and Prokhorova, M. I., Rate of metabolism of citric acid in the brain. In: Third All-Union Conference on Biochemistry of the Nervous System. Erevan. 1963, 465-474.

Rosenfel'd, E. L., Present views on the pathways of enzymatic degradation of glycogen. In: Carbohydrates and Carbohydrate Metabolism. Izd. AN SSSR, Moscow. 1962, 99-105.

Shabadash, A. L., The significance of cytochemical detection of glycogen for evaluation of normal and pathological processes. In: Carbohydrates and Carbohydrate Metabolism. Izd. AN SSSR, Moscow. 1962, 157-164.

Shumskaya, V. I., Activity of the processes of transamination and deamination in the brain during hyperoxia. In: Third All-Union Conference on Biochemistry of the Nervous System. Erevan. 1963, 251-257.

Sytinskii, I. A., Avenirova, E. L., Dement'eva, S. P., Ostretsova, I. B., and Priyatkina, T. N., γ-Aminobutyric acid in animal brain during radial acceleration and narcotic sleep. In: Third All-Union Conference on Biochemistry of the Nervous System. Erevan. 1963, 163-173.

Tarve, U. S., Alteration in the brain of oxidative phosphorylation and certain stages of the tricarboxylic acid cycle during experimental accumulation of ammonia and the effect of glutamic acid and vitamin C. In: Third All-Union Conference on Biochemistry of the Nervous System. Erevan. 1963, 271-279.

Veksler, Ya. I., Hypothermia and metabolism of some ammonia-forming systems of the brain. In: Third All-Union Conference on Biochemistry of the Nervous System. Erevan. 1963, 259-270.

Vladimirova, E. A., Some aspects of enzymatic formation of ammonia in brain tissue and the significance of its content for elucidation of mechanisms of nervous activity. In: Third All-Union Conference on Biochemistry of the Nervous System. Erevan. 1963, 207-221.

El GED Esencial

El GED Esencial

Repaso completo y conciso para el examen de equivalencia de escuela secundaria

CB

CONTEMPORARY BOOKS

Autores que han contributo en esta obra:

Técnicas de lectura
Noreen Giles
Patricia Mulcrone

Prueba 1: Expresión Escrita
Guilherme P. Kiang-Samaniego

Prueba 2: Estudios Sociales
Dan M. Fox
Karen Gibbons
Virginia Lowe

Prueba 3: Ciencias
Bruce R. Brown
Robert P. Mitchell

Prueba 4: Arte y Literatura
Karen A. Fox
Noreen Giles
Anne V. McGravie

Prueba 5: Matemáticas
Jerry Howett
Janice Phillips

Traductores: Pedro L. Fernández y
Luis M. Pradera

Servicios editorales: Guilherme
P. Kiang-Samaniego

Patricia Mulcrone desea agradecar la colaboración de:

Janice S. Phillips, Profesora Adjunta de Desarrollo Educacional de Adultos
del William Rainey Harper College por su labor de asesoría en las
secciones de Estudios Sociales y Ciencias del *GED Esencial*.

Patricia A. Best, Profesora Adjunta de Desarrollo Educacional de Adultos
del William Rainey Harper College por su labor de asesoria en las
secciones de Estudios Sociales y Ciencias del *GED Esencial*.

Los reconocimientos se encouentran en las páginas xi–xiv que se
consideran parte de la página del copyright.

6 7 8 9 10 11 12 13 14 15 16   C U S   C U S   0 1 9 8 7 6 5 4 3 2

CONTENIDO

RECONOCIMIENTOS

Hacemos extensivo nuestro agradecimiento a las siguientes editoriales, autores y agentes por la autorización concedida para la traducción y la reproducción de las obras que se citan a continuación. Cabe recalcar que se han realizado todos los esfuerzos necesarios para determinar los propietarios de los derechos autorales. En caso de omisión, sin embargo, la Editorial tendrá el agrado de incluir los reconocimientos debidos en ediciones futuras.

Página 9: Caricatura de Jim Morin. Reproducida y traducida con autorización especial de King Features Syndicate.

Página 13: Mapa extraído de *World Geography* de Preston E. James y Nelda Davis. Reproducido y traducido con autorización de Glencoe/McGraw-Hill.

Página 23: Fragmento extraído de *Song of Solomon* de Toni Morrison. © 1977 Toni Morrison. Publicado en español por Ediciones B, S.A., Barcelona, España. Reproducido con autorización.

Página 24: Poema "Tom Merritt" de *Spoon River Anthology* de Edgar Lee Masters. Traducido con autorización de Hilary Masters.

Páginas 24–25: Fragmento extraído de *Pigmalión*. Título original en inglés: *Pygmalion* en *Four Modern Plays* de Bernard Shaw. Publicado por Santillana, S. A. Traducido con autorización.

Páginas 25–26: Fragmento extraído de "TV's Limited Visions of Hispanics" en *USA Today,* 30 de agosto, 1993. Copyright 1993, USA Today. Traducido con autorización.

Página 223: Fragmento extraído de "El hombre que vivía escondido". Título original en inglés: "The Man Who Lived Underground" en *Eight Men* de Richard Wright. Copyright © 1961 Richard Wright. Reproducido con permiso de John Hawkins & Associates, Inc.

Páginas 226–227: Fragmento extraído de "La vida corta y feliz de Francis Macomber" en *Obras Selectas II* de Ernest Hemingway. Copyright © Hemingway Foreign Rights Trust, 1969. Reproducido con autorización de Editorial Planeta, S. A.

Páginas 227–228: Fragmento extraído de "La posibilidad del mal". Título original en inglés: "The Possibility of Evil" de Shirley Jackson. Copyright © 1965 Stanley Edgar Hyman. Publicado por primera vez en *The Saturday Evening Post.* Traducido con autorización de Laurence Hyman, Barry Hyman, Jai Holly and Sarah DeWitt.

Página 229: Fragmento extraído de "Todo lo que se eleva tiene converger". Título original en inglés: "Everything That Rises Must Converge" de Flannery O'Connor. Copyright 1956, 1957, 1958, 1960, 1961, 1962, 1964, 1965 de Flannery O'Connor; copyright renovado por los sucesores de Flannery O'Connor y Regina Cline O'Connor. Reproducido con autorización de Harold Matson Co., Inc.

AL ESTUDIANTE

¿ES PARA USTED ESTE MANUAL?

El libro *GED Esencial* es el indicado para usted si reúne la mayoría de estos requisitos:

- Ha concluido dos o más años de estudios secundarios.
- No ha dejado la secundaria porque las clases le resultaban muy difíciles.
- Entiende la mayor parte de lo que lee en un periódico.
- Le es fácil hallar otras fuentes de información cuando necesita buscar más detalles. (Entre estas fuentes pueden estar personas, periódicos, revistas, libros, radio, televisión, software de computadora, etc.)
- Le gusta llevar las riendas de sus estudios y no tiene problemas en estudiar por su cuenta.

¿POR QUÉ HACER EL EXAMEN DEL GED?

Si usted está estudiando para pasar la serie de pruebas del GED, sepa que no es la única persona. En 1994, año en que se publicaron las últimas estadísticas, hubo más de 750,000 personas que se presentaron a las pruebas. De éstos, casi 450,000 recibieron sus certificados. ¿Por qué son tantas las personas que deciden hacer el Examen del GED? Hay quienes lo hacen para poder conseguir un empleo o uno mejor que el que ya tienen. Están otros que hacen las pruebas para poder ingresar a la universidad o a una escuela vocacional. Además, hay otros que deciden obtener sus diplomas del GED para superarse a sí mismos o dar un buen ejemplo a sus hijos. Son muchas y provienen de todos los ámbitos las personas que han aprobado el GED y se han diplomado. Entre éstas se encuentran conocidas figuras del espectáculo, del gobierno, del mundo de los negocios y de otras esferas.

¿EN QUÉ LE SERÁ ÚTIL ESTE MANUAL?

El *GED Esencial* consta de una variada, amena y eficaz selección de actividades diseñadas para facilitar la preparación del estudiante para el Examen del GED.

- Sección preliminar de Técnicas de Lectura que aborda los seis niveles del razonamiento crítico: conocimiento, comprensión, aplicación, análisis, síntesis y evaluación.
- Sección especial de redacción en preparación a la prueba de composición del GED.
- Variados tipos de ejercicios y preguntas que mantienen vivo el interés: pareado, rellenado de espacios en blanco, preguntas verdadero-falso, de opción múltiple y preguntas para desarrollar.
- Pruebas Posteriores de media duración que simulan las pruebas del GED, con los mismos formatos, niveles de dificultad y porcentajes que encontrará el día del examen.
- Clave de Respuestas (codificada por nivel de destreza) para cada sección, con explicaciones sobre las respuestas correctas de cada ejercicio.

- Tablas de Evaluación para las Pruebas Preliminares y las Pruebas Posteriores, útiles en la detección de puntos débiles y que proporcionan las páginas de referencia apropiadas para su repaso.

¿QUÉ QUIERE DECIR *GED?*

GED son las siglas del *General Educational Development* (Desarrollo Educativo General). El GED, que consta de una serie de pruebas, es un examen nacional creado por el *GED Testing Service* (Servicio de Pruebas del GED) del *American Council on Education* (Consejo de Educación Estadounidense). Las credenciales recibidas tras la aprobación de este examen son ampliamente reconocidas por universidades, centros de capacitación y empleadores como equivalentes a un diploma de escuela secundaria. Aunque el examen del GED mide las destrezas y los conocimientos normalmente adquiridos en cuatro años de escuela secundaria, mucho de lo que se haya aprendido a través de la experiencia o gracias a otros medios de capacitación pueden serle útil para la aprobación del examen. El GED se puede hacer en inglés, francés y español y está disponible en audiocassette, braille y en caracteres grandes.

¿QUÉ HAY QUE SABER PARA APROBAR EL EXAMEN?

El Examen del GED consta de cinco pruebas en las áreas de Expresión Escrita, Estudios Sociales, Ciencias, Arte y Literatura, y Matemáticas. La tabla siguiente describe las principales áreas de estudio, la distribución de las preguntas y el tiempo asignado a cada prueba.

PRUEBAS DEL GED			
Prueba	**Minutos**	**Preguntas**	**Porcentaje**

1: Expresión Escrita
    Parte 1: Convenciones
        del español
 	
    Parte 2: Redacción
	75
	
	45
		55
		
		1 tópico
			Estructura de la oración 35%
			Uso de la lengua 35%
			Ortografía y Puntuación 30%

2: Estudios Sociales	85	64	Historia 25% Economía 20% Ciencias Políticas 20% Geografía 15%* Ciencias del Comportamiento 20%
3: Ciencias	95	66	Ciencias de la Vida 50% Ciencias Físicas 50%
4: Arte y Literatura	65	45	Literatura Popular 50% Literatura Clásica 25% Comentarios 25%
5: Matemáticas	90	56	Aritmética 50% Álgebra 30% Geometría 20%

*En Canadá, el 20% de la Prueba es sobre Geografía y el 15% sobre Ciencias del Comportamiento.

Lo que se espera de usted en las cinco pruebas es que pueda demostrar su capacidad de razonamiento en una diversidad de temas. También se ponen a prueba sus conocimientos y destrezas adquiridos a través de la experiencia diaria, la televisión, la radio, los libros y periódicos, los productos de consumo y la publicidad.

¿QUIÉN PUEDE HACER EL EXAMEN?

En Estados Unidos y la mayor parte de sus territorios, así como en Canadá, se permite hacer este examen a personas que no se hayan graduado de la escuela secundaria y que cumplan con ciertos requisitos (edad, residencia, etc.). Dado que estos requisitos varían, recomendamos se ponga en contacto con su centro local de pruebas del GED o con el director de educación de adultos de su estado, provincia o territorio para obtener mayor información.

¿CON QUÉ PUNTUACIÓN SE APRUEBA EL EXAMEN DEL GED?

Una vez más, la puntuación varía según la región. Para enterarse de la puntuación requerida para la aprobación del examen, póngase en contacto con su centro local de pruebas del GED. Con todo, debe usted tener en mente dos puntuaciones: una de ellas es la mínima que se debe obtener en cada prueba. Por ejemplo, si el estado en que reside requiere una puntuación mínima de 40, se deberá obtener un mínimo de 40 puntos en cada prueba. Por otra parte, se deberá cumplir con los requisitos de una puntuación mínima media en las cinco pruebas. Por ejemplo, si su estado exige una puntuación mínima media de 45, usted deberá acumular un total de 225 puntos para aprobar. Estas dos puntuaciones—la mínima y la mínima media—determinan si aprueba o no el examen.

¿SE PUEDE VOLVER A HACER EL EXAMEN?

Se puede volver a hacer el examen ya sea en parte o en su totalidad. Los reglamentos que rigen el número de veces que una persona puede hacer el examen al igual que el tiempo que debe esperar esta persona antes de poder volver a presentarse están estipulados por su estado, provincia o territorio. Ciertos estados exigen que los examinados asistan a una clase de repaso o que estudien por su cuenta durante un tiempo determinado antes de volver a dar la prueba.

¿CUÁL ES LA MEJOR FORMA DE PREPARARSE PARA EL EXAMEN?

En diversas universidades locales, escuelas públicas, centros de educación de adultos, bibliotecas, iglesias y otras instituciones se ofrecen clases preparatorias al GED. Asimismo, existen determinados canales de televisión que transmiten clases de preparación para el examen. En caso de que no le sea posible encontrar una clase preparatoria al GED en el lugar donde reside, póngase en contacto con el director de educación de adultos de su estado, provincia o territorio o llame a la línea directa del GED (1-800-626-9433). Esta línea le proporcionará direcciones y números de teléfono de centros de pruebas y de centros de educación de adultos dentro de su área. La línea directa funciona las 24 horas del día, siete días a la semana.

SI ESTUDIO POR MI CUENTA, ¿CUÁNTO TIEMPO NECESITO PARA PREPARARME?

Depende de lo preparado que esté en cada una de las áreas de estudio. Con todo, es probable que le lleve de tres a seis meses realizar lo siguiente:

1. Leer la sección de introducción del libro.

2. Hacer las cinco Pruebas Preliminares y calificarlas. Decidir en qué áreas deberá concentrarse más.

3. Leer y completar los ejercicios en aquellas áreas en las que decida concentrarse.

4. Hacer las Pruebas Posteriores para determinar cuánto ha progresado.

5. Repasar las recomendaciones que se dan abajo para hacer la prueba.

6. Ponerse en contacto con el administrador del GED o con el director de educación de adultos de su estado, provincia o territorio e inscribirse para el examen.

RECOMENDACIONES PARA PASAR LAS PRUEBAS

1. **Prepárese físicamente.** Descanse y aliméntese con una comida balanceada antes del examen. Evite dejar material para estudiarlo en el último momento.

2. **Llegue temprano.** Preséntese al centro de pruebas por lo menos 15 a 20 minutos antes de la hora de inicio del examen.

3. **Piense de forma positiva.** Repítase a sí mismo que lo va a hacer bien.

4. **Relájese durante el examen.** Tómese medio minuto varias veces en el transcurso de la prueba para estirar el cuerpo y respirar profundamente, máxime si está inquieto o confundido.

5. **Lea detenidamente las instrucciones del examen.** De ser necesario, haga preguntas sobre la prueba o sobre cómo rellenar el formulario de respuestas antes del inicio del examen.

6. **Sepa cuál es el límite de tiempo para cada prueba.** Si le queda tiempo después de haber contestado todas las preguntas, repase y compruebe sus respuestas.

7. **Prepare una estrategia para contestar las preguntas.** Primero lea en su totalidad el pasaje de lectura o échele un vistazo al material por lo menos una vez, y después conteste las preguntas que siguen a continuación. Lea cada pregunta dos o tres veces para asegurarse de que la entiende. Se recomienda volver a leer el pasaje o consultar la ilustración para confirmar su respuesta. Hay quienes prefieren leer por encima las preguntas antes de leer el pasaje. De esta manera, las preguntas le servirán de guía al momento de leer el pasaje.

8. **No pierda mucho tiempo en preguntas difíciles.** Cuando no esté seguro de una respuesta, pase a la pregunta siguiente. Conteste primero

las preguntas más fáciles y vuelva luego a las preguntas más difíciles. No obstante, en caso de que se salte una o más preguntas, asegúrese de haberse saltado el mismo número de preguntas en su hoja de respuestas. No se confunda al rellenar la Clave de Respuestas.

9. **Conteste todas las preguntas del examen.** Cuando no esté seguro de una respuesta, trate de adivinarla. Cada vez que deje una pregunta sin contestar, perderá puntos; pero, si trata de adivinar la respuesta y acierta, ganará esos puntos. Si no le queda otra opción que tratar de adivinar una respuesta, elimine primero aquéllas de las que esté seguro no son correctas. Elija después de entre las respuestas restantes.

10. **Rellene claramente el círculo que corresponde a cada respuesta.** Si borra algo, bórrelo por completo. Asegúrese de dar una sola respuesta por pregunta; ya que, de lo contrario, no le valdrá ninguna de las respuestas.

11. **Practique cómo hacer el examen.** Use los ejercicios, repasos y sobre todo las Pruebas Posteriores de este manual para entender mejor sus hábitos y puntos débiles durante las pruebas. Practique distintas estrategias como, por ejemplo, leer preguntas por encima o saltarse preguntas difíciles y dejarlas para el final.

CÓMO USAR ESTE MANUAL

1. Este manual ha sido diseñado con el propósito de ayudarle a aprobar el Examen del GED. Sin embargo, puede que no le sea necesario repasar las cinco secciones de este libro. También es probable que posea un mayor dominio en ciertas áreas que en otras. Con todo, antes de empezar el libro convendría que hiciera las Pruebas Preliminares. Éstas le darán una pequeña muestra de lo que pueden contener las cinco pruebas y le ayudarán a identificar aquellas áreas en las que debe concentrarse más. Utilice las Tablas de Evaluación que se adjuntan al final de las Claves de Respuestas de las Pruebas Preliminares para marcar los tipos de preguntas contestadas de forma incorrecta y determinar qué áreas tiene que trabajar más.

2. Repase la sección de Técnicas de Lectura para comprender los seis niveles del razonamiento crítico y el modo en que dichos niveles se reflejan en el Examen del GED.

3. Creemos que la mejor forma de prepararse para el examen es estudiando el libro en su totalidad. Como método alternativo, puede usted optar por estudiar aquellas áreas que necesite reforzar según se lo indiquen los puntajes de las Pruebas Preliminares.

4. Haga las Pruebas Posteriores que aparecen al final del manual. Éstas le servirán para determinar si está listo para el día del examen y, caso no lo esté, qué áreas del libro necesita repasar. Las Tablas de Evaluación, en particular, le serán de utilidad a la hora de tomar esta decisión.

5. Realice estudios adicionales en otros libros, si fuere necesario. Si desea obtener mayor información, llame al *Library Reproduction Service (LRS)* o Servicio de Reproducción de Bibliotecas al 1-800-255-5002.

Por último, querríamos saber su opinión acerca de nuestro material. Si le ha sido de utilidad para aprobar el examen o si cree que se podría mejorar, escríbanos a la dirección que figura en la página del copyright de este manual y envíenos sus comentarios. Esperamos disfrute estudiando para el GED y desde ya le auguramos un rotundo éxito en el examen.

PRUEBAS PRELIMINARES

INSTRUCCIONES GENERALES:
El propósito de las Pruebas Preliminares es ayudarle a identificar lo que necesite estudiar de este libro. Estas pruebas, reducidas a un cuarto de su extensión normal, poseen el mismo formato y nivel de dificultad que las pruebas de un examen normal del GED. Los resultados de las mismas le servirán para trazarse un plan de estudio. En lo que respecta a las Pruebas Preliminares, hacemos las siguientes recomendaciones:

1. Hacer sólo una Prueba Preliminar cada vez. No trate de hacerlas todas de una sentada. Lea las instrucciones antes de empezar las pruebas. Use la Tabla de Respuestas del principio de las mismas para marcar sus opciones.

2. Después de acabar cada Prueba Preliminar, comprobar las respuestas en la Clave de Respuestas y llenar la Tabla de Evaluación para dicha prueba. Las Claves de Respuestas y las Tablas de Evaluación se encuentran en las páginas 429–440. En caso de haber contestado mal alguna pregunta, lea la explicación que se da de las respuestas correctas.

3. Según la información recogida en las Tablas de Evaluación, se sugieren dos planes de acción:

   • Si se ha contestado mal la mitad o más de la mitad de las preguntas de una Prueba Preliminar, trabajar esa área en su totalidad.

   • Si se ha contestado mal menos de la mitad de las preguntas, concentrarse en aquellos temas de la prueba en los que se tenga dificultad.

4. Aunque sean éstas meramente unas Pruebas Preliminares, poner en ella todo su empeño. Cuando un ejercicio le resulte difícil, señálelo y vuelva al mismo más adelante. Conteste siempre todas las preguntas, incluso si tiene que tratar de adivinar la respuesta. A veces, puede que usted sepa más de lo que cree. El día del examen del GED, cada pregunta no contestada equivaldrá a una pregunta mal contestada. Por ello, conviene siempre contestar todas las preguntas.

5. Contestar todas las preguntas lo mejor que se pueda, escogiendo la mejor de las cinco opciones y rellenando de negro la opción de la tabla. Resuelva cada ejercicio de la Prueba Preliminar de Matemáticas y escriba su respuesta en la línea en blanco. Si se encuentra con una pregunta que le cause mucha dificultad, no desperdicie su tiempo. Siga adelante y regrese luego cuando pueda pensar la respuesta con mayor detenimiento.

6. Cuando haya completado la prueba, verificar sus respuestas con las respuestas y explicaciones que se dan al final de la sección.

7. Usar las Tablas de Evaluación de las páginas indicadas para identificar aquellas áreas que se necesitan repasar:

   • Prueba Preliminar 1, pág. 430
   • Prueba Preliminar 2, pág. 433
   • Prueba Preliminar 3, pág. 435
   • Prueba Preliminar 4, pág. 437
   • Prueba Preliminar 5, pág. 440

Tiempo asignado a cada Prueba Preliminar

Expresión Escrita	Parte 1	19 minutos
	Parte 2	45 minutos
Estudios Sociales		21 minutos
Ciencias		24 minutos
Arte y Literatura		17 minutos
Matemáticas		23 minutos

PRUEBA PRELIMINAR 1: EXPRESIÓN ESCRITA

Parte 1: Convenciones del español

Instrucciones: La Parte 1 de la Prueba Preliminar de Expresión Escrita consta de 15 preguntas de opción múltiple. Las preguntas se basan en párrafos cuyas oraciones han sido numeradas. La mayor parte de estas oraciones presenta errores, pero hay unas cuantas que están bien escritas. Lea los párrafos y luego conteste las preguntas en base a ellos. Para cada pregunta, escoja ya sea la respuesta que contenga la corrección que la oración necesita, o bien la mejor de las nuevas versiones propuestas para la oración u oraciones, o la combinación de oraciones más eficaz. La respuesta elegida deberá guardar coherencia con el sentido y el estilo del resto del párrafo. Si a su parecer la versión original es la mejor, escoja la opción que así lo indique.

PRUEBA PRELIMINAR 1: TABLA DE RESPUESTAS DE EXPRESIÓN ESCRITA

1 ① ② ③ ④ ⑤	5 ① ② ③ ④ ⑤	9 ① ② ③ ④ ⑤	13 ① ② ③ ④ ⑤
2 ① ② ③ ④ ⑤	6 ① ② ③ ④ ⑤	10 ① ② ③ ④ ⑤	14 ① ② ③ ④ ⑤
3 ① ② ③ ④ ⑤	7 ① ② ③ ④ ⑤	11 ① ② ③ ④ ⑤	15 ① ② ③ ④ ⑤
4 ① ② ③ ④ ⑤	8 ① ② ③ ④ ⑤	12 ① ② ③ ④ ⑤	

Las *Preguntas 1–9* se refieren al siguiente pasaje.

(1) Las muertes relacionadas con incendios se deven en su mayor parte a incendios ocurridos en el hogar. A pesar de ello, son muchas las casas que aún no cuentan con extintores. (2) Aunque un número grande de hogares tienen detectores de humo instalados para alertar a sus residentes en caso de incendio, sólo los extintores son capaces de combatir el fuego. (3) En la mayoría de los casos, habrán todos de evacuar la casa cuando se produzca un incendio o suene la alarma del detector de humo. (4) Se deberá llamar a los bomberos desde fuera de la casa. (5) Sin embargo, si hay un extintor a mano, una persona de reflejos rápidos podrá normalmente usarlos para extinguir un incendio de pequeña magnitud. (6) Existen en el mercado varios tipos de extintores, adecuados a distintos tipos de incendios. (7) La mayor parte de los extintores venían con instrucciones y son muy fáciles de operar. (8) Pero si se desea, se puede contactar a los departamentos de bomberos para recibir capacitasión sobre cómo operar los extintores. (9) Se deberá tener en cuenta ciertas reglas básicas de seguridad al momento de tomar la decición de usar o no el extintor. (10) Al comprar un extintor, al aprender a usarlo y al ponerlo en un lugar al alcance de todos los miembros de la familia usted estará contribuyendo a proteger su hogar contra la fuerza destructora de los incendios.

1. Oración 1: **Las muertes relacionadas con incendios se deven en su mayor parte a incendios ocurridos en el hogar. A pesar de ello, son muchas las casas que aún no cuentan con extintores.**
   (1) reemplace *relacionadas* por *relasionadas*
   (2) cambie *deven* por *deben*
   (3) quite la coma después de *ello*
   (4) cambie *aún* por *aun*
   (5) no es necesario hacer correcciones

2. Oración 2: **Aunque un <u>número grande de hogares</u> tienen detectores de humo instalados para alertar a sus residentes en caso de incendio, sólo los extintores son capaces de combatir el fuego.**
   (1) numero grande de hogares
   (2) número grande de ogares
   (3) gran número de hogares
   (4) gran numero de hogares
   (5) gran numero de ogares

3. Oraciones 3–4: **En la mayoría de los casos, habrán todos de evacuar la casa cuando se produzca un incendio o suene la alarma del detector de <u>humo. Se deberá</u> llamar a los bomberos desde fuera de la casa.**
   (1) humo y se deberá
   (2) humo, se deberá
   (3) humo o se deberá
   (4) humo a menos que se deba
   (5) humo y se debrá

4. Oración 5: **Sin embargo, si hay un extintor a mano, una persona de reflejos rápidos podrá normalmente <u>usarlos</u> para extinguir un incendio de pequeña magnitud.**
   (1) usarse
   (2) usarles
   (3) usarlo
   (4) usar lo
   (5) usar los

5. Oración 6: **Existen en el mercado varios tipos de extintores, adecuados a distintos tipos de incendios.**
   (1) reemplace *Existen* por *Existe*
   (2) reemplace *Existen* por *Esisten*
   (3) reemplace *varios* por barios
   (4) reemplace *adecuados* por *adecuado*
   (5) no es necesario hacer correcciones

6. Oración 7: **La mayor parte de los extintores venían con instrucciones y son muy fáciles de operar.**
   (1) cambie *venían* por *venía*
   (2) cambie *venían* por *viene*
   (3) reemplace *mayoría* por *malloría*
   (4) cambie *fáciles* por *fásiles*
   (5) reemplace *fáciles* por *faciles*

7. Oración 8: **Pero si se desea, se puede contactar a los departamentos de bomberos para recibir capacitasión sobre cómo operar los extintores.**
   (1) reemplace *recibir* por *resibir*
   (2) reemplace *recibir* por *recivir*
   (3) cambie *cómo* por *como*
   (4) reemplace *los extintores* por *extintores*
   (5) cambie *capacitasión* por *capacitación*

8. Oración 9: **Se deberá tener en cuenta ciertas reglas básicas de seguridad al momento de tomar la decición de usar o no el extintor.**
   (1) cambie *decición* por *decisión*
   (2) cambie *decición* por *desición*
   (3) cambie *deberá* por *deverá*
   (4) reemplace *ciertas* por *siertas*
   (5) reemplace *seguridad* por *seguridá*

9. Oración 10: **Al comprar un extintor, al aprender a usarlo y al ponerlo en un lugar al alcance de todos los miembros de la familia usted estará contribuyendo a proteger su hogar contra la fuerza destructora de los incendios.**
   (1) ponga una coma después de *familia*
   (2) cambie *estará* por *estar ha*
   (3) cambie *alcance* por *alcanze*
   (4) reemplace *fuerza* por *fuersa*
   (5) cambie *proteger* por *protejer*

Las *Preguntas 10–15* se refieren al siguiente pasaje.

(1) En Estados Unidos, el concepto Europeo de alojamiento conocido como *bed and breakfast* (cama y desayuno) se está volviendo muy popular. (2) Este tipo de alojamiento lo ofrezen dueños de casa que dan en alquiler dormitorios no habitados de sus residencias y que hacen las veces de anfitrión. (3) Como se sienten más seguros en los *bed and breakfast* y porque les gusta que se los trate como a invitados, los anfitriones de estos alojamientos les hacen sentir como si estuvieran en su casa. (4) De esta manera, el viajero tiene la oportunidad de aprender algo de la historia y los habitantes de la región: hoy en día, por ejemplo, hay muchos que se hospedaron en granjas en el estado de Wisconsin o en cabañas restauradas en Kentucky. (5) El anfitrión, por su parte también se beneficia en este tipo de negocio, porque le permite trabajar sin tener que salir de su casa al mismo tiempo que le da la oportunidad de conocer a mucha gente interesante. (6) La mayoría de los departamentos de turismo así como algunas agencias de viajes disponen de listas con esta clase de alojamientos.

10. Oración 1: **En Estados Unidos, el concepto Europeo de alojamiento conocido como** *bed and breakfast* **(cama y desayuno) se está volviendo muy popular.**
(1) cambie *Europeo* por *europeo*
(2) reemplace *conocido* por *conozido*
(3) reemplace *concepto* por *consepto*
(4) reemplace *volviendo* por *bolviendo*
(5) no es necesario hacer correcciones

11. Oración 2: **Este tipo de alojamiento lo ofrezen dueños de casa que dan en alquiler dormitorios no habitados de sus residencias y que hacen las veces de anfitrión.**
(1) reemplace *veces* por *vezes*
(2) cambie *habitados* por *abitados*
(3) cambie *hacen* por *hasen*
(4) ponga una coma después de *casa*
(5) cambie *ofrezen* por *ofrecen*

12. Oración 3: **Como se sienten más seguros en los** *bed and breakfast* **y porque les gusta que se los trate como a invitados, los anfitriones de estos alojamientos les hacen sentir como si estuvieran en su casa.**
(1) ellos se sienten como en su casa.
(2) se sienten como en su casa con los anfitriones.
(3) los anfitriones de estos alojamientos se sienten como en su casa.
(4) los viajeros se sienten como en su casa gracias a la atención brindada en estos alojamientos.
(5) no es necesario hacer correcciones.

13. Oración 4: **De esta manera, el viajero tiene la oportunidad de aprender algo de la historia y los habitantes de la región: hoy en día, por ejemplo, hay muchos que se hospedaron en granjas en el estado de Wisconsin o en cabañas restauradas en Kentucky.**
(1) reemplace *región* por *rejión*
(2) sustituya *habitantes* por *havitantes*
(3) reemplace *hospedaron* por *hospedan*
(4) ponga una coma después de *Wisconsin*
(5) no es necesario hacer correcciones

14. Oración 5: **El anfitrión, por su parte también se beneficia en este tipo de negocio, porque le permite trabajar sin tener que salir de su casa al mismo tiempo que le da la oportunidad de conocer a mucha gente interesante.**
(1) quite la *a* después de *conocer*
(2) reemplace *también* por *tan bien*
(3) ponga una coma después de *por su parte*
(4) reemplace *negocio* por *negosio*
(5) reemplace *da* por *dá*

15. Oración 6: **La mayoría de los departamentos de turismo así como algunas agencias de viajes disponen de listas con esta clase de alojamientos.**
(1) cambie *como* por *cómo*
(2) cambie *viajes* por *viages*
(3) reemplace *agencias* por *ajensias*
(4) cambie *disponen de* por *disponen*
(5) no es necesario hacer correcciones

Las respuestas empiezan en la página 429.

Parte 2: Redacción

Instrucciones: El objetivo de esta sección es evaluar cómo usted escribe. La prueba consta de una pregunta donde se le pide presente una opinión acerca de un tema o explique algún tópico. Al preparar la respuesta a esta pregunta, se recomienda seguir los siguientes pasos:

1. Lea toda la información que acompaña a la pregunta.

2. Piense detenidamente la respuesta antes de empezar a escribir.

3. Use papel borrador para hacer apuntes.

4. Escriba la respuesta en una hoja de papel aparte.

5. Lea detenidamente lo que ha escrito y efectúe los cambios que contribuyan a mejorar su redacción.

6. Verifique los párrafos, la estructura de las oraciones, la ortografía, la puntuación y el uso de las mayúsculas y haga las correcciones necesarias.

Usted dispone de 45 minutos para pensar y escribir sobre el tema que se cita a continuación. Escriba con pluma y de forma legible.

Tema

Existen diversas razones por las que una persona se decide a obtener el certificado del GED. Para unas, es el deseo de cambiarse a un mejor trabajo; para otras es simplemente el deseo de terminar algo que empezaron hace muchos años. ¿Por qué se ha decidido usted a obtener su certificado del GED? Razone y argumente su respuesta y explique lo que espera lograr con ello. Asegúrese de dar ejemplos y sea específico.

En las páginas 430 y 431 encontrará información acerca de cómo evaluar su redacción.

PRUEBA PRELIMINAR 2:
ESTUDIOS SOCIALES

Instrucciones: La Prueba Preliminar de Estudios Sociales consta de 15 preguntas de opción múltiple. Algunas de las preguntas están basadas en un mapa, una tabla, una gráfica, una caricatura o un pasaje de lectura. Lea el pasaje o estudie la ilustración cuidadosamente antes de elegir una respuesta.

PRUEBA PRELIMINAR 2: TABLA DE RESPUESTAS DE ESTUDIOS SOCIALES

1 ① ② ③ ④ ⑤	**5** ① ② ③ ④ ⑤	**9** ① ② ③ ④ ⑤	**13** ① ② ③ ④ ⑤
2 ① ② ③ ④ ⑤	**6** ① ② ③ ④ ⑤	**10** ① ② ③ ④ ⑤	**14** ① ② ③ ④ ⑤
3 ① ② ③ ④ ⑤	**7** ① ② ③ ④ ⑤	**11** ① ② ③ ④ ⑤	**15** ① ② ③ ④ ⑤
4 ① ② ③ ④ ⑤	**8** ① ② ③ ④ ⑤	**12** ① ② ③ ④ ⑤	

1. El consumidor estadounidense no incurre en gastos con la misma libertad con que lo había estado haciendo en el pasado. En consecuencia, las ventas de computadoras personales se han visto afectadas. Según la dinámica de la oferta y la demanda, ¿qué sucederá con el precio de las computadoras? El precio

   (1) aumentará para compensar las pérdidas de beneficios.
   (2) seguirá igual porque el costo de la fabricación de computadoras permanece igual.
   (3) bajará para alentar a los consumidores a que compren.
   (4) aumentará para que los fabricantes mejoren la calidad de las computadoras.
   (5) permanecerá igual porque habrá menos computadoras a la venta.

La *Pregunta 2* se basa en la caricatura de abajo.

2. El caricaturista quiere dar a entender que

   (1) los terroristas cuentan con armas más grandes y mejores que antes.
   (2) los terroristas usan los medios de comunicación de forma deliberada para hacer publicidad y promover su causa.
   (3) los terroristas se cubren el rostro porque temen ser identificados por los medios de comunicación.
   (4) los medios de comunicación son el verdadero enemigo de los terroristas.
   (5) los terroristas quieren dominar el mundo.

Caricatura de Jim Morin. Reproducida y traducida con autorización de King Features Syndicate.

Las *Preguntas 3–4* se basan en la siguiente gráfica.

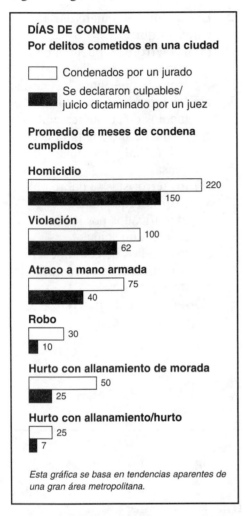

DÍAS DE CONDENA
Por delitos cometidos en una ciudad

☐ Condenados por un jurado

■ Se declararon culpables/ juicio dictaminado por un juez

Promedio de meses de condena cumplidos

Homicidio
220
150

Violación
100
62

Atraco a mano armada
75
40

Robo
30
10

Hurto con allanamiento de morada
50
25

Hurto con allanamiento/hurto
25
7

Esta gráfica se basa en tendencias aparentes de una gran área metropolitana.

3. ¿A cuál de las siguientes conclusiones respalda mejor la información de la gráfica?
   (1) Conviene que los acusados de un delito insistan en tener un juicio con jurado.
   (2) En esta ciudad, es mejor que los acusados se declaren culpables o acepten ir a juicio dictaminado por un juez.
   (3) Los miembros de un jurado no comprenden bien el impacto de sus decisiones.
   (4) Las cortes penales de esta ciudad son más severas con los criminales que las de la mayoría de las ciudades.
   (5) Las cortes penales de esta ciudad son más indulgentes con los criminales que las de la mayoría de las ciudades.

4. ¿A qué valores están dando mayor prioridad los jurados en los casos penales de esta ciudad?
   (1) al bienestar del delincuente antes que al bienestar de la comunidad
   (2) a las necesidades del delincuente antes que al consejo del juez
   (3) a las necesidades del delincuente antes que a las necesidades de la comunidad
   (4) al bienestar de la comunidad antes que al bienestar del delincuente
   (5) a los derechos del delin-cuente antes que a la estricta interpretación de la ley

La *Pregunta 5* está basada en el siguiente párrafo.

La Doctrina Monroe exigía que Europa se mantuviera al margen de los asuntos del continente americano. El Presi-dente Theodore Roosevelt se valió de esta doctrina para dar apoyo a una postura en cuanto a imperialismo que pasó a ser conocida como el "Corolario Roosevelt". Según afirmaba este corolario, Estados Unidos tenía el derecho de intervenir en aquellas zonas de América que estuvieran aquejadas de pro-blemas y que necesitaran de nuestro "poder civilizador".

5. ¿En qué incidente hubiera aplicado Roosevelt su corolario para defender las medidas que había tomado?
   (1) su aprobación a la colonización de India y Egipto por parte de Inglaterra

(2) la participación de las Naciones Unidas en una conferencia para poner fin a la rivalidad franco-alemana sobre Marruecos

(3) su apoyo a la política de puertas abiertas en el comercio con China

(4) su gestión en pro de un entendimiento entre Estados Unidos y Japón para evitar una inmigración indeseada

(5) su ayuda a los rebeldes panameños en contra del gobierno colombiano

6. Antes de la Guerra Civil, Virginia constituía un único estado. En 1863, sin embargo, West Virginia optó por independizarse. ¿Cuál es la causa más plausible de la secesión de West Virginia del resto del estado?

(1) El estado era demasiado grande para una sola legislatura.

(2) West Virginia fue derrotada por el Norte al comienzo de la guerra.

(3) Richmond, Virginia, se convirtió en la capital de la Confederación.

(4) En West Virginia no había propietarios de esclavos.

(5) Existían diferencias políticas entre la parte oeste y la parte este del estado.

Las *Preguntas 7–8* se basan en la gráfica y el pasaje siguientes.

Porcentaje de mujeres casadas empleadas en un trabajo a tiempo completo y que tienen hijos menores de 18 años y maridos que trabajan.		
	18.4%	1950
	27.8%	1960
38.7%		1970
54.1%		1980
66.3%		1990

Fuente: *Scholastic Update Magazine*

Al modo en que actúa o se espera que actúe en la sociedad un hombre o una mujer se le llama *rol*. El rol tradicional del marido en la familia estadounidense ha sido el de sostén económico, mientras que el de la mujer ha sido el de ama de casa. Sin embargo, según la gráfica de a lado, los roles familiares están cambiando.

7. ¿Cuál de los siguientes casos es *menos probable* que sea la causa del cambio del rol que desempeñan las mujeres casadas en la familia?

(1) el aumento en muchos hogares de los gastos familiares, el cual requiere un ingreso adicional

(2) el mayor número de mujeres que desean tener una profesión además de dedicarse al cuidado de la familia

(3) la poca estima asignada al rol tradicional de ama de casa

(4) la mayor disponibilidad de guarderías así como de profesionales dedicados al cuidado de niños

(5) mayores oportunidades de trabajo para las mujeres que antes

8. Según la gráfica de barras, ¿durante qué período se produjo el mayor aumento en el porcentaje de mujeres casadas dentro de la población activa?

(1) Antes de 1950
(2) 1950–1960
(3) 1960–1970
(4) 1970–1980
(5) 1980–1990

9. Entre 1937 y 1957, la tasa de natalidad aumentó de 18.7 a 25.3 por cada 1,000 habitantes. La causa más probable de este "baby boom" fue

(1) el regreso de los jóvenes estadounidenses de la guerra.

(2) el crecimiento de las áreas urbanas/residenciales después de la 2ª Guerra Mundial.

(3) la mayor movilidad de las familias estadounidenses en los años 50.

(4) la expansión continua de la clase media y su nueva riqueza.

(5) el relajamiento de las sanciones morales contra los medios artificiales de control de natalidad.

10. El aumento de los ingresos personales permite que la gente compre más bienes y servicios. Por ejemplo, los gastos de compras de casas y automóviles aumentan a medida que las personas van sintiéndose más cómodas en cuanto a la realización de inversiones a largo plazo. En semejante clima económico, es probable que las empresas

(1) aumenten su producción para proveer una mayor cantidad de bienes.

(2) disminuyan los impuestos que pesan sobre la venta de los productos.

(3) inviertan menos dinero en nuevos equipos y maquinaria.

(4) vendan sus productos en el extranjero.

(5) distribuyan uniformemente sus productos por todo el país.

La *Pregunta 11* se basa en la siguiente gráfica.

POBLACIÓN DE EE.UU., DE 65 AÑOS O MAYORES 1900-2030

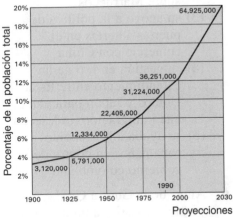

11. En Estados Unidos, el número de habitantes mayores de 65 años ha sufrido un drástico aumento. ¿Cuál de los siguientes programas gubernamentales se verá más directamente afectado por este aumento?

(1) los beneficios para los veteranos

(2) la defensa nacional

(3) los programas de capacitación y empleo

(4) los cupones de comida

(5) la seguridad social

Las *Preguntas 12–13* se basan en el siguiente pasaje.

En 1992, el Primer Ministro de Australia, Paul Keating, exhortó al país a romper los lazos políticos que aún quedan con Gran Bretaña para convertirse de esta manera en una república y terminar con su status actual de *commonwealth* (o federación). Gran Bretaña ha dejado de ser un factor importante en la estabilidad económica de Australia. Hoy en día, casi la mitad de las exportaciones de Australia van a Asia y la inmigración asiática a Australia sigue aumentando. Con una economía en declive, los australianos tienen que decidir cuál de estas regiones será la más beneficiosa a sus propios intereses.

12. Si nos basamos en la información del pasaje, podemos llegar a la conclusión de que
   (1) Paul Keating está a favor de mantener el status de *commonwealth* para Australia.
   (2) es muy probable que la economía australiana mejore si establece lazos más estrechos con Asia.
   (3) Australia está aislada para poder mantener su economía.
   (4) la política en nada tiene que ver con la situación geográfica.
   (5) hay muchos australianos que apoyan la propuesta del primer ministro.

13. La decisión a que tiene que enfrentarse el Commonwealth de Australia se asemeja más a
   (1) la decisión de traspasar Hong Kong del dominio británico al dominio chino.
   (2) la decisión del Commonwealth de Kentucky de unirse a los Estados Unidos.
   (3) la decisión de adoptar Guam como territorio de Estados Unidos.
   (4) la decisión de Puerto Rico de pasar a ser un estado de pleno derecho o seguir siendo un estado asociado.
   (5) la decisión de las trece colonias americanas originales de formar una nueva nación.

La *Pregunta 14* se basa en el mapa de abajo.

14. Según el mapa, la región del país de mayor densidad poblacional es el
   (1) Mediooeste.
   (2) Suroeste.
   (3) Noroeste.
   (4) Sureste.
   (5) Noreste.

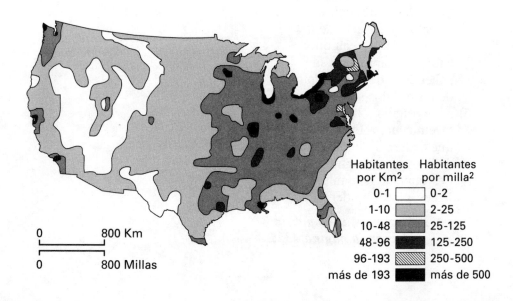

Habitantes por Km²	Habitantes por milla²
0-1	0-2
1-10	2-25
10-48	25-125
48-96	125-250
96-193	250-500
más de 193	más de 500

0   800 Km

0   800 Millas

La *Pregunta 15* se basa en el siguiente pasaje.

Tras el asesinato del Presidente Lincoln, el Vicepresidente Andrew Johnson lo sucedió en la presidencia. Johnson era de Tennessee y fue el único senador del Sur que no se unió a la Confederación al estallar la guerra. Lincoln confiaba plenamente en él, pero había muchos congresistas que no; porque, a pesar del rechazo de Johnson a unirse a la Confederación, éstos veían en todas las decisiones del presidente un matiz sospechosamente pro-Sur.

15. ¿Cuál de las siguientes decisiones tomadas por Johnson *no* respalda la opinión que los congresistas tenían de él?

    (1) su proclama que perdonaba a gran parte de los confederados

    (2) el haber exigido que los estados confederados ratificaran la Decimotercera Enmienda, que abolía la esclavitud

    (3) su veto al proyecto de ley sobre derechos civiles que garantizaba los derechos de los esclavos liberados

    (4) su veto al proyecto de ley Freedman's Bureau que había sido aprobado sin haber considerado la opinión de los estados sureños

    (5) su oposición a la Decimocuarta Enmienda, que endureció la posición del Congreso contra los que previamente habían sido leales a la Confederación

Las respuestas empiezan en la página 432.

PRUEBA PRELIMINAR 3: CIENCIAS

Instrucciones: La Prueba Preliminar de Ciencias consta de 15 preguntas de opción múltiple. Algunas de las preguntas están basadas en una tabla, una gráfica, un diagrama o un pasaje de lectura.

PRUEBA PRELIMINAR 3: TABLA DE RESPUESTAS DE CIENCIAS

1 ① ② ③ ④ ⑤	5 ① ② ③ ④ ⑤	9 ① ② ③ ④ ⑤	13 ① ② ③ ④ ⑤
2 ① ② ③ ④ ⑤	6 ① ② ③ ④ ⑤	10 ① ② ③ ④ ⑤	14 ① ② ③ ④ ⑤
3 ① ② ③ ④ ⑤	7 ① ② ③ ④ ⑤	11 ① ② ③ ④ ⑤	15 ① ② ③ ④ ⑤
4 ① ② ③ ④ ⑤	8 ① ② ③ ④ ⑤	12 ① ② ③ ④ ⑤	

Nuestra sangre se compone de un líquido de color pajizo, el *plasma*, en el que se hallan suspendidos los glóbulos rojos, los glóbulos blancos y las *plaquetas*. Los glóbulos rojos transportan el oxígeno por todo el cuerpo. Los distintos tipos de glóbulos blancos son necesarios para la lucha contra las infecciones. Las plaquetas desempeñan un papel importante en la coagulación de la sangre.

CONSUMO DE ENERGÍA	
Actividad	*Calorías por hora*
estar sentado en reposo	15
caminar	130–200
correr	500–900
montar en bicicleta	240
nadar	200–700
escribir	20

1. En base al pasaje de arriba, ¿qué componente o componentes sanguíneos se utilizarían para reparar una herida abierta?
   (1) el plasma y los glóbulos blancos
   (2) los glóbulos rojos
   (3) los glóbulos blancos
   (4) las plaquetas
   (5) los glóbulos blancos y las plaquetas

La hoja es un órgano plano compuesto por dos capas de células fotosintéticas emparedadas entre las capas epidérmicas, o externas. Las capas epidérmicas están recubiertas por una capa cerosa llamada cutícula, que evita la pérdida de gas y agua. Los estomas, diminutos agujeros, proporcionan aberturas que permiten la entrada del dióxido de carbono (anhídrido carbónico) y la salida del oxígeno.

2. Basados en la información de arriba, la hoja "respira" por
   (1) las células fotosintéticas.
   (2) las venas.
   (3) la cutícula.
   (4) las capas epidérmicas.
   (5) los estomas.

La *Pregunta 3* se basa en la siguiente tabla.

3. Si una persona deseara adelgazar, ¿cuál sería según la tabla el ejercicio más eficiente para perder peso en función del tiempo empleado?
   (1) montar en bicicleta
   (2) nadar
   (3) caminar
   (4) escribir
   (5) correr

S	N	N	S

4. A medida que se acerquen los dos imanes de arriba, ¿qué pronostica sucederá?
   (1) Se van a atraer mutuamente.
   (2) Se van a repeler.
   (3) Se anularán mutuamente sus campos magnéticos respectivos.
   (4) Crearán una corriente alterna.
   (5) No sucederá nada.

Las *Preguntas 5–6* se basan en el siguiente pasaje.

En 1859, Charles Darwin propuso su teoría de la selección natural. Esta teoría sostiene que las especies mejor adaptadas a las condiciones en que viven sobrevivirán, mientras que las que no están adaptadas perecerán.

Ilustra esta teoría lo sucedido en Manchester, Inglaterra, con la mariposa punteada—la cual era muy común en esa ciudad industrial.

Antes de la revolución industrial, la variedad de color claro de esta mariposa era común mientras que la de color oscuro era muy rara. Sin embargo, a medida que el medio ambiente de Manchester se fue contaminando, los troncos de los árboles donde vivía esta mariposa se fueron ennegreciendo a causa del hollín. Las mariposas de color claro empezaron a destacar contra el fondo oscurecido de los troncos de los árboles y fueron devoradas por los pájaros. Un 99 por ciento de las mariposas de color claro fueron exterminadas.

Con la desaparición de éstas, las mariposas de color oscuro se volvieron más comunes y pasaron a llenar la vacante que habían dejado las mariposas de color claro. Sin embargo, en la década de 1950, se redujo la cantidad de sustancias contaminantes que emitían las industrias de Manchester y la mariposa de color claro se convirtió nuevamente en la variedad más común.

5. En base a este pasaje, la causa de la desaparición de la mariposa de color claro fue
   (1) su incapacidad para tolerar un medio ambiente contaminado.
   (2) su sabor, por el cual tenían preferencia los pájaros.
   (3) un insecticida que la mató.
   (4) el reducido número de huevos que ponían las hembras de esta mariposa.
   (5) su incapacidad de esconderse en su entorno.

6. En base a la información contenida en el pasaje, se podría inferir que
   (1) las formas de vida de una comunidad se ven influidas por las leyes de la naturaleza.

(2) la actividad humana puede tener un impacto ecológico muy importante sobre el medio ambiente.
(3) la teoría de Darwin sólo es válida en condiciones ideales.
(4) todas las formas de vida deben valerse por sí mismas.
(5) las mariposas pueden prosperar en las condiciones más adversas.

7. El ácido acetilsalicílico (aspirina) tiene la propiedad de retardar el proceso de coagulación de la sangre. Este hecho puede tener efectos tanto positivos como negativos. Entre las aplicaciones positivas de esta propiedad, se encuentra el uso de la aspirina
   (1) para el alivio de dolores.
   (2) para la reducción de inflamaciones.
   (3) para la reducción de la posibilidad de derrame cerebral.
   (4) como estimulante.
   (5) en la detención de hemorragias.

Las *Preguntas 8–9* se basan en el siguiente pasaje.

Es posible que no haya en el mundo otro lugar donde se puedan estudiar los primeros períodos geológicos con tanta facilidad y precisión como en Estados Unidos. A lo largo de la frontera norte entre Canadá y Estados Unidos se extiende una cadena de cerros de baja altura conocida como Laurentian Hills. Aunque insignificantes en cuanto a altura—puesto que en ningún punto superan los dos mil pies por encima del nivel del mar— son éstas, sin embargo, las primeras montañas que rompieron el nivel uniforme de la superficie terrestre y se elevaron por encima de las aguas. La baja altura de esta cordillera—baja en comparación con la de otras cadenas montañosas más elevadas—cumple la invariable regla de estimación de edad relativa de montañas, según la cual las montañas más antiguas son las más bajas, mientras que las más jóvenes y recientes se elevan por encima de aquéllas y son más escarpadas y descoyuntadas.

8. En Estados Unidos, los primeros períodos geológicos
   (1) pueden estudiarse a lo largo de la frontera norte del país.
   (2) sólo se pueden estudiar en las Montañas Rocosas.
   (3) se pueden estudiar de forma fácil y precisa.
   (4) no son tan visibles como en otras partes del mundo.
   (5) sólo se pueden estudiar en los Montes Apalaches.

9. Al explicar la relación existente entre las cadenas montañosas bajas y las cadenas montañosas altas, se habla más bien de una relación entre
   (1) vejez y juventud.
   (2) los Laurentian Hills.
   (3) los Alpes suizos y la Cordillera del Himalaya.
   (4) descoyuntura y espesor.
   (5) su ubicación en Estados Unidos y Canadá.

La *Pregunta 10* se basa en la información de la tabla de a lado.

El calor puede pasar de una molécula a otra. A este fenómeno se le llama *conducción del calor*. En la tabla siguiente, los números (llamados coeficientes) indican la capacidad relativa de transferencia de calor de los materiales citados en la lista.

COEFICIENTES DE CONDUCCIÓN DE CALOR

Material	Coeficiente
plata	100
cobre	92
aluminio	50
hierro	11
vidrio	0.20
agua	0.12
madera	0.03
aire	0.006
vacío perfecto	0

10. Según la tabla, los mejores conductores son los
    (1) gases.
    (2) materiales naturales.
    (3) metales.
    (4) líquidos.
    (5) compuestos.

La *Pregunta 11* se basa en el siguiente pasaje.

El *loess* es un depósito de polvo transportado por el viento que va recubriendo poco a poco grandes extensiones de tierra y que suele cubrir accidentes geográficos existentes. El loess es un depósito sedimentario muy particular acumulado hace ya mucho tiempo. Puede que cubra hasta una décima parte de la superficie de la Tierra y se halla extendido sobre todo en las regiones semiáridas, bordeando los grandes desiertos. Los trópicos ecuatoriales y las áreas cubiertas por los glaciares continentales se encuentran libres de loess.

11. Hoy día es muy probable que se encuentre el loess en
    (1) la República del Congo.
    (2) Islandia.
    (3) Japón.
    (4) Estados Unidos.
    (5) Ecuador.

La *Pregunta 12* se basa en la siguiente información.

El *fathometer* (sondímetro) es un aparato que sirve para medir profundidades oceánicas. Este aparato opera con ondas sonoras que emite bajo el agua. Desde los barcos, se transmite un impulso repentino de sonido que se recibe tras rebotar en, o ecotransmitirse desde, el fondo del océano. Se registra entonces el tiempo transcurrido. Si se sabe el tiempo y la velocidad a que viajan las ondas sonoras a través del agua, se puede calcular la profundidad del mar en un punto dado, con una precisión de más o menos un pie de diferencia.

12. En base a la información del pasaje, se puede llegar a la conclusión de que
    (1) ya se conoce la profundidad del océano.
    (2) la velocidad a que se desplazan las ondas sonoras bajo el agua desde la superficie hasta el fondo del océano permanece constante.
    (3) el *fathometer* sólo muestra las profundidades aproximadas y, por lo tanto, no es fiable.
    (4) el *fathometer* funciona mejor en aguas poco profundas.
    (5) el *fathometer* se basa en principios científicos y no en principios matemáticos.

Las *Preguntas 13–14* se basan en la siguiente información.

Los ácidos orgánicos más comunes son el ácido fórmico y el ácido acético. El ácido fórmico se da en forma natural en las hormigas rojas y en las hojas de pino. En forma concentrada puede quemar la piel; sin embargo, el ácido fórmico diluido se usa por sus propiedades germicidas. El ácido acético es responsable del sabor amargo de los adobos al vinagre y de los olores penetrantes que pueden producir quemaduras en la narices. El vinagre de sidra contiene del 3 al 6 por ciento de ácido acético y se produce mediante la oxidación natural de la sidra de manzana.

13. La idea principal del pasaje es que
    (1) los ácidos orgánicos pueden a la vez ser dañinos y beneficiosos.
    (2) el ácido fórmico es una parte del vinagre.
    (3) las hojas de pino contienen ácido acético.
    (4) el ácido fórmico sin diluir se usa como germicida.
    (5) la sidra de manzana se transforma en ácido fórmico.

14. El pasaje respalda la siguiente afirmación.
    (1) Todos los ácidos son dañinos para los seres humanos.
    (2) Sólo los ácidos orgánicos son útiles para los seres humanos.
    (3) Los ácidos orgánicos en forma diluida son útiles para los seres humanos.
    (4) Los ácidos inorgánicos en forma diluida son útiles para los seres humanos.
    (5) Sólo los ácidos inorgánicos diluidos son beneficiosos para los seres humanos.

La *Pregunta 15* se basa en la siguiente tabla.

COMPATIBILIDAD SANGUÍNEA		
Tipo sanguíneo	Puede recibir sangre de	Puede donar sangre a
O	O	O, A, B, AB
A	A, O	A, AB
B	B, O	B, AB
AB	O, A, B, AB	AB

15. ¿Cuál de los siguientes tipos sanguíneos puede considerarse donante universal?
(1) O
(2) A
(3) B
(4) AB
(5) todos los tipos sanguíneos

Las respuestas empiezan en la página 434.

PRUEBA PRELIMINAR 4:
ARTE Y LITERATURA

Instrucciones: La Prueba Preliminar de Arte y Literatura consta de 12 preguntas de opción múltiple. Las preguntas se basan en fragmentos de prosa (ficción y no ficción), poesía, drama y comentarios sobre arte y literatura.

PRUEBA PRELIMINAR 4: TABLA DE RESPUESTAS DE ARTE Y LITERATURA

1 ① ② ③ ④ ⑤	4 ① ② ③ ④ ⑤	7 ① ② ③ ④ ⑤	10 ① ② ③ ④ ⑤
2 ① ② ③ ④ ⑤	5 ① ② ③ ④ ⑤	8 ① ② ③ ④ ⑤	11 ① ② ③ ④ ⑤
3 ① ② ③ ④ ⑤	6 ① ② ③ ④ ⑤	9 ① ② ③ ④ ⑤	12 ① ② ③ ④ ⑤

Lea los fragmentos y elija la mejor respuesta para las preguntas que siguen.

Las *Preguntas 1–3* se refieren al siguiente fragmento extraído de una biografía.

CÓMO ELVIS PRESLEY ALCANZÓ LA FAMA

Dicen que el éxito suele sonreír a las personas de origen humilde. Elvis Aaron Presley nació el 8 de enero de
5 1935 en Tupelo, Mississippi. Empezó a cantar en el coro de la iglesia y aprendió a tocar la guitarra por su cuenta, aunque nunca aprendió a leer música.
10 Hacia 1953, se había mudado a Memphis, Tennessee, donde concluyó sus estudios secundarios. Enseguida se matriculó en una escuela nocturna para
15 estudiar el oficio de electricista. Ese mismo año, mientras grababa unas canciones de prueba en Sun Records, el presidente de esa compañía
20 oyó a Elvis y no tardó en reconocer el talento del joven cantante. Como resultado de este casual encuentro, salió al mercado en 1954 el primer
25 disco de Presley: "That's All Right Mama".

A fin de promocionar su disco, Elvis realizó una gira por el sur del país y, en 1955,
30 se lanzaron simultáneamente cinco de sus discos. Ese mismo año se presentó por primera vez en televisión en el programa "Stage Show" de
35 Jackie Gleason; pero fue gracias al "Show de Ed Sullivan" que Elvis se dio a conocer al público. Cuando apareció en pantalla cantando su música
40 *rock 'n' roll* y realizando sugestivos movimientos de cadera al bailar, el joven causó al mismo tiempo sensación y controversia. En posteriores
45 presentaciones televisivas, la cámara pasó a enfocarlo de la cintura hacia arriba, porque sus movimientos eran considerados obscenos.
50 "Elvis the Pelvis", es decir, "Elvis Caderas", como se le dio en llamar, inició su carrera cinematográfica en 1956 con la película *Love Me Tender* y
55 firmó un contrato a largo plazo con un estudio de cine. Aunque los críticos de la pantalla grande no lo trataron de manera muy favorable, los
60 adolescentes acudían en masa a ver las películas de Presley. A los pocos años, Elvis había establecido una carrera que se extendería a lo
65 largo de veinticinco años de altibajos que le convirtieron en uno de los artistas más populares de la historia del mundo del espectáculo.
70 Muchos años después de su prematura muerte ocurrida a los 42 años de edad, Presley seguía siendo recordado como el indiscutible "Rey del *rock*
75 *'n' roll*".

1. La última oración revela que la actitud del autor hacia Presley era de
   (1) indiferencia.
   (2) admiración.
   (3) indignación.
   (4) incredulidad.
   (5) sarcasmo.

2. La idea principal que encierra este fragmento es que
   (1) la obscenidad ha existido siempre en la televisión.
   (2) los cantantes son más famosos si aparecen en las películas.
   (3) las personas se vuelven más famosas después de su muerte.

(4) el éxito sonríe siempre a las personas que se esfuerzan y se empeñan.

(5) a veces, la oportunidad y la suerte son tan importantes como el esfuerzo y la dedicación.

3. ¿A cuál de los siguientes personajes históricos se aplicaría mejor la afirmación de que "el éxito suele sonreír a las personas de origen humilde"?

(1) al multimillonario Pierre DuPont

(2) a John F. Kennedy

(3) a Franklin D. Roosevelt

(4) a Abraham Lincoln

(5) al multimillonario petrolero J. Paul Getty

Las *Preguntas 4–5* se refieren al siguiente fragmento extraído de una novela.

¿CÓMO SE SIENTE LA PERSONA?

Una vez más, hizo él sus compras navideñas en una botica Rexall. Era tarde, el día anterior a Nochebuena, y no
5 había tenido ni el espíritu ni la energía ni la presencia de ánimo para haberlas hecho con más tiempo o con más dedicación. Una sensación de
10 aburrimiento, que había empezado como una infección benigna, le invadía ahora por completo. No había actividad que valiera la pena hacer ni
15 conversación que valiera la pena mantener. El revuelo de los preparativos en la casa semejaba una farsa deprimente. Su madre se quejaba,
20 como todos los años, del precio de los árboles de Navidad y de la mantequilla. Como si el árbol fuera a ser diferente de lo que había sido siempre:
20 un bulto enorme y sombrío colocado en una esquina y sobrecargado de adornos que ella tenía desde que era niña. O como si sus pasteles de
25 fruta se pudieran comer, al igual que el pavo, asado hasta la médula. Su padre les repartió unos sobres con distintas cantidades dinero, sin que se
30 le ocurriera pensar que, aunque sea una sola vez, a ellos les habría hecho más ilusión algo que él mismo hubiera elegido y comprado
35 en un gran almacén.

—Toni Morrison, *Song of Solomon*, 1977 (fragmento)

4. El hijo espera hasta el último momento para hacer sus compras navideñas porque

(1) está siguiendo el ejemplo de su padre.

(2) no podía ir de compras hasta que no le pagaran su sueldo.

(3) no sabía qué comprarles a sus padres.

(4) no le importaba mucho lo que iba a regalar.

(5) se gastó todo el dinero en la compra de un árbol de Navidad.

5. ¿Por cuál de estos métodos muestra prefererencia la autora al crear el personaje de este fragmento?

(1) el de señalar la verdadera forma de expresión del personaje

(2) el de comunicar lo que dicen otros personajes acerca de este personaje

(3) el de revelar los pensamientos íntimos del personaje

(4) el de describir los rasgos físicos del personaje

(5) el de mostrar al personaje en acción

Las *Preguntas 6–7* se refieren al siguiente poema.

¿QUÉ LE SUCEDIÓ A TOM MERRIT?

Tom Merrit

Al principio sospeché algo—
Ella actuaba con tanta calma
   y tan distraída.
Un día escuché que se cerraba
5   la puerta de atrás,
Al entrar yo por el frente, le vi
   salir a hurtadillas
Por detrás del ahumadero
   hacia el terreno,
10 Y atravesar el campo.
Y quise matarle en ese
   mismo instante.
Pero ese día, mientras caminaba
   cerca de Fourth Bridge,
15 Sin tener un palo o una piedra
   a mano,
De repente lo vi allí
   de pie,
Muerto de miedo, sujetando
20   sus conejos,
Y todo lo que pude decir fue,
   "No, no, no",
Al tiempo que él apuntaba y
   disparaba a mi corazón.
25   –Edgar Lee Masters, 1915

6. ¿Quién es el narrador de este poema?
(1) la esposa de Merrit
(2) un asesino
(3) Tom Merrit
(4) Dios
(5) el sheriff

7. ¿De qué técnica en particular se vale la poetisa?
(1) rima: repetición del sonido de una o más vocales
(2) verso: división de un poema en partes distintas
(3) ritmo: acentuación de ciertas palabras o sílabas (tiempo)
(4) verso libre: ausencia de rima y de una serie rítmica regular

(5) personificación: atribución de cierta actividad o cualidad humana a un animal o a una cosa

Las *Preguntas 8–9* se refieren al siguiente fragmento extraído de una obra teatral.

¿QUÉ PIENSA HIGGINS DE LAS MUJERES?

PICKERING: Perdone esta pregunta tan directa, Higgins. ¿Es usted un hombre reputable en lo que a mujeres respecta?

HIGGINS: [*Con aire taciturno.*] ¿Ha conocido usted alguna vez a un hombre reputable cuando se trata de mujeres?

PICKERING: Sí, en varias oportunidades.

HIGGINS: [*Dogmáticamente, elevándose con las manos hasta el nivel del piano y sentándose en éste de un salto.*] Pues, yo no. He observado que siempre que dejo que una mujer haga amistad conmigo, se vuelve celosa, exigente, desconfiada y un fastidio inaguantable. También he observado que siempre que yo me hago amigo de una mujer, me vuelvo egoísta y tirano. Las mujeres lo alteran todo. Si usted deja que entren en su vida, acabará descubriendo que la mujer va por un camino mientras usted va por otro diferente.

PICKERING: ¿Qué camino, por ejemplo?

HIGGINS: [*Saltando del piano nerviosamente.*] ¡Sabe Dios! Supongo que la mujer quiere vivir su vida y el hombre quiere vivir la suya; y cada uno trata de arrastrar al otro por el camino equivocado. Uno quiere ir al norte y el otro al sur; y el resultado es que ambos tienen que ir al este, aunque ambos detesten el viento del este. [*Se sienta en la banqueta frente a las teclas.*] De modo que, aquí me ve, un soltero empedernido; y es probable que continúe así por mucho tiempo.

PICKERING: [*Levantándose y mirándole con gravedad.*] ¡Venga, Higgins! Usted sabe a qué me refiero. Si he de seguir en este negocio, no puedo más que sentirme responsable por esa chica. Espero que quede claro que nadie va a aprovecharse de su posición.

HIGGINS: ¡Qué! ¡Esa cosa! Sagrada, se lo aseguro. [*Levantándose para dar una explicación.*] Verá, ella será una alumna; y enseñar sería imposible si los alumnos no fueran sagrados. Yo he enseñado a hablar inglés a una buena cantidad de millonarias norteamericanas: las mujeres más atractivas del mundo. Soy un veterano. Es como si fueran bloques de madera para mí. Como si yo mismo fuera un bloque de madera.

—George Bernard Shaw,
Pigmalión, 1913 (fragmento)

8. La actitud negativa de Higgins hacia las mujeres se debe probablemente a su
   (1) reciente divorcio.
   (2) falta de contacto con las mujeres.
   (3) deseo de conocer mujeres hermosas.
   (4) experiencia previa con las mujeres.
   (5) próxima boda.

9. "Uno quiere ir al norte y el otro al sur; y el resultado es que ambos tienen que ir al este, aunque ambos detesten el viento del este".

En la obra se incluye esta referencia para señalar que
   (1) las relaciones son más firmes si ambas partes se sacrifican.
   (2) las parejas proceden a menudo de diferentes regiones del país.
   (3) las concesiones mutuas pueden tener efectos negativos en la pareja.
   (4) la confianza es el elemento más importante en la pareja.
   (5) las mujeres tienen los mismos derechos en todos los tipos de relaciones.

Las *Preguntas 10–12* se refieren al siguiente fragmento extraído de un comentario.

¿LA TELEVISIÓN CREA ESTEREOTIPOS?

Los hispanos constituyen posiblemente el grupo minoritario de más rápido crecimiento en EE.UU.; sin embargo, se
5 hallan subrepresentados en los programas de televisión que se emiten en las horas de mayor audiencia.

Aunque el 9 por ciento de
10 la población estadounidense es de origen hispano, sólo el 2 por ciento de los personajes de programas presentados en horarios de máxima teleau-
15 diencia son hispanos, según revelara una encuesta realizada a lo largo de un período de una semana por el *USA Today*.

Asimismo, los asiáticos y
20 los indios norteamericanos se encuentran subrepresentados en la pantalla chica. La encuesta indicaba que sólo el 1 por ciento de los personajes de
25 programas televisivos eran asiáticos, a pesar de constituir el 3 por ciento de la población de EE.UU. Del mismo modo,

solamente el 1 por ciento eran
30 indios norteamericanos, pese
a representar el 4 por ciento de
la población en la vida real.

"El problema estriba en
una cuestión de percep-
35 ciones", afirma Ray Blanco de
la Academia Nacional Hispana
de Artes y Ciencias de los
Medios de Comunicación.

"La gente tiende a pensar
40 que no hay ningún hispano
que hable inglés, que los hispanos sólo ven la televisión en
español y que no disponen de
ingresos; lo cual no es el
45 caso", dice Blanco.

Los pocos papeles his-
panos que se presentan, añade
Blanco, suelen venir a confirmar estereotipos despectivos.
50 El actor Marco Sánchez
está de acuerdo. "No puedo
expresar lo frustrante que era
ir a las audiciones sabiendo
que me iban a considerar para
55 cuatro posibles papeles: el de
traficante de drogas, el de
miembro de una pandilla, el de
amante o el de joven que se ha
criado en la calle pero que
60 tiene un corazón de oro".

Sánchez, hijo de inmi-
grantes cubanos, dice que su
madre le sugirió que se cambiara de nombre, "pero yo me
65 negué a renunciar a una parte
de mí sólo para poder conseguir trabajo".

—Donna Gable, fragmento del
artículo "TV's Limited Visions of
Hispanics", 30 de agosto de
1993, USA Today

10. Según este fragmento, el grupo
minoritario de más rápido
crecimiento en los Estados
Unidos lo constituyen los
(1) hispanos.
(2) asiáticos.
(3) indios norteamericanos.
(4) cubanos.
(5) afro-norteamericanos.

11. La madre del actor Marco
Sánchez le sugirió que se
cambiase de nombre porque
(1) a los agentes de reparto les
parecía difícil de recordar.
(2) la gente escribía y
pronunciaba mal su nombre.
(3) no era un nombre apropiado
para una estrella del teatro y
del cine.
(4) la gente lo confundía con
otra persona que tenía un
nombre parecido.
(5) le limitaba el tipo de
personajes que podía
representar.

12. Si a Marco Sánchez le
ofrecieran los siguientes
papeles, ¿cuál elegiría él más
probablemente?
(1) traficante de drogas en una
película para televisión
(2) personaje principal de una
comedia shakesperiana
(3) líder de una pandilla en una
serie dramática semanal
(4) joven que se ha criado en la
calle en una película de cine
(5) el amante de una mujer
casada en una telenovela

*Las respuestas empiezan
en la página 436.*

PRUEBA PRELIMINAR 5: MATEMÁTICAS

Instrucciones: La Prueba Preliminar de Matemáticas consta de 30 ejercicios, que le ofrecen la oportunidad de poner a prueba tanto sus destrezas de cálculo como de resolución de problemas. Estos ejercicios no son de opción múltiple, por lo que tendrá que trabajar de la forma más precisa y cuidadosa posible. Asegúrese de usar los diagramas y tablas proporcionados con los problemas.

PRUEBA PRELIMINAR 5: RESPUESTAS DE MATEMÁTICAS

1 _____	9 _____	17 _____	25 _____
2 _____	10 _____	18 _____	26 _____
3 _____	11 _____	19 _____	27 _____
4 _____	12 _____	20 _____	28 _____
5 _____	13 _____	21 _____	29 _____
6 _____	14 _____	22 _____	30 _____
7 _____	15 _____	23 _____	
8 _____	16 _____	24 _____	

Estas fórmulas le podrán ser de utilidad en la resolución de algunos de los problemas que siguen.

FÓRMULAS

Descripción	Fórmula
ÁREA (A) de un	
cuadrado	$A = l^2$ siendo $l = $ lado
rectángulo	$A = la$ siendo $l = $ largo; $a = $ ancho
triángulo	$A = \frac{1}{2}bh$ siendo $b = $ base; $h = $ altura
círculo	$A = \pi r^2$ siendo $\pi \cong 3.14$; $r = $ radio
PERÍMETRO (P) de un	
cuadrado	$P = 4l$ siendo $l = $ lado
rectángulo	$P = 2l + 2a$ siendo $l = $ largo; $a = $ ancho
círculo—circunferencia (C)	$C = \pi d$ siendo $\pi \cong 3.14$; $d = $ diámetro
VOLUMEN (V) de un	
cubo	$V = l^3$ siendo $l = $ lado
paralelepípedo	$V = lah$ siendo $l = $ largo; $a = $ ancho; $h = $ alto
Teorema de Pitágoras	$a^2 = b^2 + c^2$ siendo $a = $ hipotenusa; b y c catetos de un triángulo rectángulo
distancia (d) entre dos puntos de un plano	$d = \sqrt{(x_2 - x_1)^2 + (y_2 - y_1)^2}$ siendo (x_1, y_1) y (x_2, y_2) dos puntos de un plano
pendiente de una recta (m)	$m = \dfrac{y_2 - y_1}{x_2 - x_1}$ siendo (x_1, y_1) y (x_2, y_2) dos puntos de un plano

Resuelva los siguientes problemas.

1. Divida 5310 por 9.

2. ¿Cuánto es .38 dividido por .4?

3. Corey necesita $120 para comprarse un abrigo nuevo. Al momento tiene ahorrado el importe que recibió de cuatro cheques de dividendos de $16.75 cada uno. ¿Cuántos dólares más necesita para comprarse el abrigo?

4. $1\frac{1}{4} - \frac{3}{4} =$

5. $4\frac{1}{5} \times \frac{1}{2} =$

La *Pregunta 6* se basa en la tabla de abajo, que compara el incremento en las ventas de cuatro compañías locales.

	Ventas	
	1995	**1999**
Magic Marketing	$323,000	$904,400
Futures Marketing	$630,000	$925,000
Townley Agency	$264,000	$1,497,000
Billings Printing	$2,000,000	$6,000,000

6. Si Magic Marketing mantuviera aproximadamente la misma tasa de crecimiento durante los 4 años siguientes hasta el 2003. ¿cuáles serían las ventas proyectadas para el año 2003 (redondeadas al millón de dólares más cercano)?

7. En su primer día de vacaciones, la familia Morales recorrió 312 millas en 6 horas. A esa velocidad, ¿qué distancia recorrerían al día siguiente si condujeran durante 8 horas?

8. Halle el 72% de $350.

9. Halle la longitud del tirante diagonal usado para reforzar la puerta del granero.

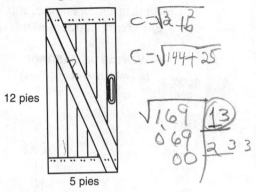

12 pies

5 pies

10. La ficha de Nick indica las horas que ha trabajado en una semana. Si para cobrar sobre-tiempo, debe trabajar más de 8 horas al día, halle la paga total de Nick previa a deducciones.

PHILLIPS CORPORATION – Ficha horaria		
Nombre: Nick Acino		**SS#:** 002-00-0021
Fecha	**De**	**A**
7/8	8:30 A.M.	4:30 P.M.
7/9	8:30 A.M.	5:15 P.M.
7/10	8:30 A.M.	4:30 P.M.
7/11	8:30 A.M.	6:00 P.M.
7/12	8:30 A.M.	4:45 P.M.

Total de horas normales: _____ a $8.40

Total de horas de sobretiempo: _____ a $12.60

(por encima de 40 horas)

11. En la fórmula de la circunferencia de un círculo, la *d* representa el diámetro, que es el doble del radio, *r*. Si $\pi \cong 3.14$ y $r = 3$, elija la expresión de abajo que pueda usarse para hallar la circunferencia del círculo.
   (1) (3.14) (3)
   (2) (3.14) (6)
   (3) (3.14) (1.5)
   (4) (3.14) (3^2)
   (5) no se da suficiente información

12. Escriba 273,000 en notación científica.

13. En un período de nueve años, se han producido varios aumentos en las ventas de gasohol. ¿Cuál es la diferencia entre el mínimo y el máximo aumento anual?

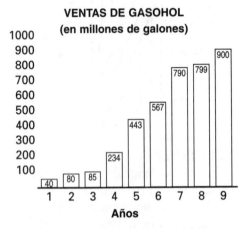

VENTAS DE GASOHOL
(en millones de galones)

14. Halle el número de yardas cuadradas de césped necesarias para cubrir el *putting green* diagramado abajo.

(*Nota:* 9 pies cuadrados = 1 yarda cuadrada)

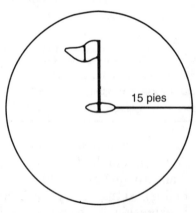

15 pies

15. Halle la medida del ángulo x en la siguiente ilustración.

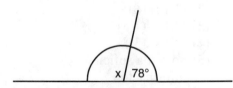

x / 78°

16. Main Street y Union Avenue son carreteras paralelas según se indica abajo.

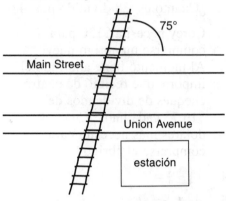

75°

Main Street

Union Avenue

estación

Las vías del ferrocarril atraviesan ambas calles. Diga cuál es la medida del ángulo del terreno en que se halla la estación, basándose en la formación indicada en el diagrama de arriba.

17. Despeje x: $14 = \frac{x}{5}$

18. Despeje x: $4x - 9 = 7$

19. Despeje x: $3(x - 2) - 3 = x + 5$

20. Resuelva: $-4 + (-3) - (-2)$

21. Si $x = -2$ e $y = 5$, halle el valor de la expresión $5y - 3x^2$.

22. Miguel tiene catorce monedas en el bolsillo. Tiene un *dime* más que *quarters* y tres *nickels* más que *dimes*. ¿Cuántas monedas tiene de cada clase?

23. Halle cuánto mide el ángulo *A* usando el diagrama de abajo.

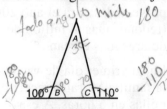

todo angulo mide 180

100° / B   C 110°

24. Si un kilogramo = 2.2 libras, ¿un paquete de 3 kilogramos pesa más o pesa menos que un paquete de 6 libras?

25. Para hallar la altura del abeto que está en su patio, Doug hizo un esquema con la información que abajo se presenta.

$$\frac{22}{4} = \frac{x}{3} = \frac{66}{4} = 16\frac{1}{2}$$

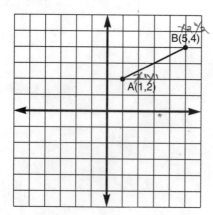

3 pies
4 pies
22 pies

$4\overline{)22}$ $5.5 \times 3 = 16.5$

Doug colocó una regla de una yarda paralela al árbol y comparó la longitud de la sombra de la regla en el terreno con la de la sombra del árbol. ¿Cuánto mide el árbol de alto?

Las *Preguntas 26–27* se basan en este dibujo.

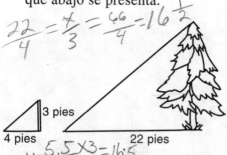

B(5,4)

A(1,2)

26. Halle la longitud del segmento comprendido entre el punto *A* y el punto *B*.

27. Halle la pendiente de la recta *AB*.

28. Observe el triángulo de abajo. ¿Cuánto mide ∠*b*?

180 midan todos los ángulos internos
b es una regla

180
110
‾‾‾
070

6 pulg   6 pulg

a 55°   55   c

29. En una baraja de 52 cartas, ¿cuál es la probabilidad de sacar un as en un solo intento?

30. Resuelva:

$$\sqrt{25} + (4 \times 3)^2 - (5 \times 2)$$

Las respuestas empiezan en la página 438.

TÉCNICAS DE LECTURA PARA EL GED

Las destrezas de lectura y de razonamiento crítico son piezas clave para la aprobación del Examen del GED. La presente sección enfoca las destrezas que se han de emplear en todas las pruebas, sobre todo en las áreas de Ciencias, Estudios Sociales, y Arte y Literatura. Estas destrezas son, a saber: comprensión, aplicación, análisis, síntesis y evaluación.

En las preguntas del GED, se pondrá a prueba su capacidad de comprender, aplicar, analizar, resumir y evaluar lo que lee. Las destrezas de lectura están íntimamente relacionadas entre sí y se encuentran estructuradas en forma de pirámide escalonada: cada destreza correspondiente a un nivel superior se basa en una destreza anterior, la cual es el escalón que permite ascender al nivel subsiguiente.

PIRÁMIDE DE DESTREZAS DE RAZONAMIENTO CRÍTICO

Memoria/Conocimiento

La *memoria (conocimiento)* constituye la base de la pirámide. A este nivel, podemos recordar datos y contestar preguntas encabezadas por *quién, qué, cuándo, dónde* y *cómo.* Usted seguramente habrá hecho exámenes que consistían en gran medida en preguntas que probaban más que nada su memoria, en las que se le pedía recordar datos determinados. Sin embargo, en el Examen del GED tendrá que manejar o trabajar tanto con la información dada como con la información almacenada en la memoria.

Comprensión

Comprender una lectura es captar e interpretar lo que quiere decir. Cuando entendemos un texto, lo podemos *parafrasear,* es decir, volver a expresar lo que dice con nuestras palabras. La destreza de **comprensión** implica la capacidad de expresar una misma idea con otras palabras, identificar la idea central o el concepto clave, y sacar conclusiones (o leer entre líneas, como en algunos casos se da en llamar).

La comprensión de un texto requiere la *comprensión de sus partes:* vocablos, frases, estructuras y giros de la lengua. Lea el párrafo siguiente y demuestre su comprensión del mismo parafraseando las palabras o frases numeradas. Escriba lo que quiere decir cada una de las expresiones.

Carmen estaba molida: a duras penas se puso el pijama y se echó a la cama. Cerró los ojos y durmió como un tronco. Llevaba casi tres días sin pegar un ojo; de verdad, la pobre estaba que no daba más. Al día siguiente, se despertó muy tarde y llegó con retraso al trabajo. El jefe le dijo: "¿Qué te pasó? ¿Se te pegaron las sábanas?"

1. _____   4. _____

2. _____   5. _____

3. _____

[Respuestas posibles: exhausta; con mucha dificultad; durmió profundamente; sin dormir; estaba muy cansada; ¿Dormiste más de la cuenta?]

Otra forma de demostrar que se comprende un texto es *resumiéndolo,* es decir, volviendo a expresar la idea principal del mismo. La idea principal encierra el contenido o mensaje básico de un texto, sin detenerse en detalles accesorios. Por ejemplo, cuando se atiende una llamada telefónica y la persona que llama da una larga explicación sobre la razón de la llamada, generalmente no se escribe todo lo que dice esa persona, sino que se resume el recado o simplemente se anotan los puntos principales de la llamada: ya sea el asunto o el motivo de ésta. Asimismo, cuando tomamos apuntes en clase, anotamos sólo los puntos esenciales o resumimos las ideas principales.

Comprender también implica el poder *identificar la idea principal* sea cual fuere su posición dentro del párrafo. En ocasiones, la idea principal se suele indicar al principio mismo, seguida por ideas secundarias que dan apoyo a la principal. El autor puede también optar por ubicar la idea principal en el medio o al final del párrafo, asegurándose siempre de que las frases que preceden o suceden a la misma, ofrezcan la información necesaria para respaldarla. Lea el pasaje siguiente e identifique la idea principal. ¿En qué parte del pasaje se encuentra?

El clima es una de las numerosas variables que afectan la economía agrícola de la nación; y su comportamiento es el más difícil de predecir. Los agricultores del norte del país, siempre a la espera de abundantes cosechas, han sufrido repetidas veces la pérdida de sus plantaciones a manos de sequías, lluvias torrenciales y temperaturas bajo cero que mantienen congelado el suelo en la primavera e imposibilitan la siembra. El lego en la materia tiende a creer que los problemas del agricultor se resuelven simplemente con mucho sol, lluvia abundante y temperaturas cálidas durante todo el año. Infelizmente esto no es tan sencillo como parece ser a simple vista. Los cultivos agrícolas requieren de gran cuidado y de condiciones meteorológicas específicas. Cualquier fluctuación o salida de los parámetros permitidos puede tener consecuencias nefastas. En los últimos años, los productores de naranjas de la Florida han experimentado graves pérdidas debido a caídas inesperadas en la temperatura por debajo del punto de congelación, lo cual ha mermado la cosecha substantivamente.

[Respuesta: en la primera oración]

La capacidad de *leer entre líneas* es también un componente esencial de la destreza de comprensión. En estos casos, el autor espera que el lector saque las conclusiones apropiadas. Lea el pasaje siguiente y trate de deducir la idea principal; luego dé un ejemplo de información accesoria que no contribuye a inferir la idea principal.

El regalo que no tenía precio

Esta dramática aventura se desarrolla muchos años antes de la desmembración de la Unión Soviética y la formación de la actual Federación de Estados Independientes. Imagínese que llega a Estados Unidos un niño ucraniano con sus padres; y que éstos luego deciden regresar a la Unión Soviética, pero el pequeño se rehúsa a acompañarlos. Seis años después, el niño, ahora un chico de doce años, recibe un regalo. El regalo es algo que los niños estadounidenses no valoran. Es un regalo para un joven que fue en bicicleta a la casa de un pariente y se escondió allí durante cinco días para no abandonar los Estados Unidos contra su voluntad. Pero este regalo conlleva un mar de trámites legales.

Antes de que el muchacho recibiera el obsequio, tuvo que hacer caso omiso de los deseos de sus padres y de su país natal. Tuvo que aprender a aceptar una nueva forma de vida sin sus padres y sin su hermano. Tuvo que aprender el inglés así como las costumbres de los alumnos de las escuelas primarias de Chicago. Tuvo que acostumbrarse a tiendas abarrotadas de alimentos, a moverse sin restricciones por las calles y a poder celebrar fiestas religiosas si lo deseaba. Tuvo que tratar de llevar una vida normal a pesar de toda la atención que le brindaban los medios de comunicación. Sabía que el regalo no se podía comprar con dinero: no tenía precio.

[Respuestas: La idea principal implícita en el texto es que el muchacho se ganó el derecho a convertirse en ciudadano estadounidense. Algunos de los datos que nos ayudan a deducir la idea principal son los siguientes: *El regalo conlleva un mar de trámites legales; El regalo es algo que los niños estadounidenses no valoran; . . . el regalo no se podía comprar con dinero. . . ; Tuvo que aprender a aceptar una nueva forma de vida. . .* Tanto la edad y la ciudad en que vivía como su condición de estudiante no aportan información que ayude a deducir la idea principal.]

Aplicación

Como su nombre lo indica, la destreza de *aplicación* consiste en hacer uso, es decir, "aplicar" lo leído. En el Examen del GED, se habrá de utilizar la información que se proporciona y aplicarla a casos de resolución de problemas. Los datos se presentan en distintas formas: definiciones, teoría científica o principio. Las preguntas de aplicación se encuentran principalmente en las áreas de Ciencias y Estudios Sociales. Asimismo, la Prueba de Arte y Literatura también contiene preguntas de este tipo. Para practicar la aplicación de definiciones, lea este pasaje sobre los subgéneros del teatro y conteste las preguntas que siguen.

Los subgéneros más importantes del teatro son la comedia, la tragedia y la tragicomedia. Las **comedias** son, por lo general, frívolas y divertidas; suelen empezar con situaciones difíciles pero divertidas; tienen un enredo festivo y un final feliz. Existen varios tipos de comedias, entre ellos la *comedia burda,* la cual es una forma de comedia física que incluye jugarretas y lanzamiento de pasteles. La *farsa* es un tipo de comedia en la que se dan circunstancias exageradas, tramas improbables y acciones y diálogos absurdos.

Las **tragedias** suelen presentar un principio feliz pero terminan siempre en desastre. El protagonista o personaje principal es normalmente bueno, pero pierde en un conflicto ante un oponente y se arruina o se muere. La razón principal del fracaso del personaje principal es el defecto trágico, la debilidad humana que ha hecho que el héroe o la heroína fuera vulnerable.

La **tragicomedia** es un subgénero intermedio que presenta a la vez rasgos propios de la tragedia y la comedia. El *melodrama* se puede en muchos casos clasificar como tragicomedia y trata de conmover al público con exageración de sentimientos (sensiblería) y actos estremecedores o enternecedores.

1. El humor tumultuoso de comediantes de la pantalla grande y chica, como los Tres Chiflados, Jerry Lewis y Charlie Chaplin se puede clasificar como
   (1) comedia.
   (2) tragedia.
   (3) comedia burda.
   (4) farsa.
   (5) melodrama.

2. Uno de los programas de televisión más populares de la última década ha sido "Seinfeld". En este programa se hacía la clásica observación de la condición humana desde el punto de vista de bulliciosos y excéntricos amigos que viven en la ciudad de New York. Se puede decir que "Seinfeld" es una
   (1) comedia.
   (2) tragedia.
   (3) comedia burda.
   (4) farsa.
   (5) melodrama.

[Respuestas: **1. (3); 2. (1)**]

En las áreas de Estudios Sociales y Ciencias se pondrá a prueba su capacidad para aplicar en situaciones diversas los conceptos presentados. Se habrá de reconocer lo que es **propaganda**—información diseminada para influir o inclinar la opinión o los sentimientos de la audiencia a quien se destina el mensaje—, así como cinco técnicas empleadas por los propagan-distas: utilización de apelativos desfavorables o despectivos para atacar la persona del adversario; uso de lenguaje altisonante y pomposo pero vago; modo de acción que sigue el modo de acción prevalente (hacer lo que hacen los demás); transferencia de respeto o poder de una persona, idea o cosa por asociación y presentación selectiva de la información, eligiendo sólo los puntos ventajosos, para asegurar un resultado favorable.

Análisis

La capacidad de *análisis* de lo leído es otra de las destrezas de razonamiento. Cuando analizamos algo, lo desmenuzamos, lo desglosamos para examinar los distintos elementos componentes y obtener una mejor comprensión de la unidad total. En arte y literatura, se emplea el análisis para identificar el *estilo* del autor, es decir, los rasgos de escritura propios de un escritor. El estilo determina el *tono* de la obra, o intención y propósito del autor.

Mediante el análisis podemos distinguir lo factual (hechos, datos) de lo subjetivo (opiniones, creencias) o hipotético (hipótesis, teorías). Los *datos factuales* se pueden demostrar a través de uno o más de los cinco sentidos. Los periódicos y los artículos de revista se basan en gran medida en lo factual. Las opiniones son creencias que pueden estar, o no, respaldadas por datos factuales. Las *opiniones* expresan sentimientos o ideas y están supeditadas a los antecedentes, los valores y la actitud ante la vida que tiene una persona. Por ejemplo, los editoriales y las columnas de periódicos presentan generalmente la opinión de un escritor junto con los hechos. Las *hipótesis* son conjeturas razonadas que tienen por objeto explicar un fenómeno o un suceso. A medida que pasa el tiempo y se va adquiriendo mayor información, se puede comprobar la veracidad o falsedad de una hipótesis.

La formulación de una hipótesis es un paso de suma importancia dentro del *método científico.* El método científico es un sistema de investigación en el que se basan todas las investigaciones científicas. La mayoría de los cursos de ciencias ofrecen al menos una breve sinopsis del procedimiento, el cual se puede resumir a seis pasos:

1. Identificar y expresar el problema.
2. Reunir información.
3. Formular una hipótesis.
4. Hacer un pronóstico en base a la hipótesis.
5. Realizar observaciones y llevar a cabo experimentos para demostrar la hipótesis.
6. Extraer una conclusión.

Cuando los resultados de un experimento u observación se pueden explicar por medio de una hipótesis, se forma entonces una *teoría.* Cuando la teoría tiene pocas excepciones, se le llama *ley.* Apliquemos ahora los seis pasos del método científico para resolver el siguiente problema.

Fuimos a pescar al lago que tanto nos gusta, pero la pesca no nos fue nada bien. El agua estaba muy transparente y no se veía ni una sola planta en el fondo del lago. Unas semanas antes, nos habían dicho que había ocurrido una gran mortandad de peces. Llamamos a la Agencia de Protección del Medio Ambiente y los funcionarios de la agencia nos dijeron que ellos creían que el lago estaba siendo afectado por la lluvia ácida. Las pruebas hechas con el agua y los exámenes de muestras de pescado congelado confirmaron la creencia de que la elevada concentración ácida del lago había acabado con todas las formas de vida.

1. *Problema:* La pesca en el lago fue mala.
2. *Información* (datos observables): El agua estaba transparente, no había plantas y recientemente habían muerto muchos peces.
3. *Hipótesis:* La lluvia ácida puede que esté afectando al lago.
4. *Predicción:* Si el lago está ácido, se habrá de observar un aumento similar de acidez en las muestras de agua y de pescado.
5. *Experimento:* Todas las pruebas son acordes a las características de la lluvia ácida; los resultados concuerdan con la predicción.
6. *Conclusión:* El lago ha sido afectado por la lluvia ácida.

El método científico se basa en un ***razonamiento lógico.*** Cuando extraemos conclusiones que respaldan la evidencia reunida en una investigación, estamos siguiendo una lógica. Entre los métodos de razonamiento lógico figuran el razonamiento inductivo y el razonamiento deductivo.

El ***razonamiento inductivo*** es aquél que extrae una conclusión, yendo de lo particular (o específico) a lo general. Al seguir la inducción, se observa el comportamiento o las características de los miembros de una clase o de un grupo y después se extrapola esta información a los miembros no observados del grupo. En otras palabras, se hacen generalizaciones sobre los otros miembros del grupo. El pasaje siguiente ilustra cómo se realiza un razonamiento inductivo.

La evidencia científica obtenida de los estudios realizados sobre las águilas doradas indica que el pesticida DDT amenaza la supervivencia de nuestras aves de rapiña. Estas aves rapaces, como los halcones y las águilas por ejemplo, ayudan a controlar la población de roedores tan perniciosa para las cosechas. Aunque el DDT no envenena a las aves directamente, puede, sin embargo, interferir con su metabolismo, haciendo que produzcan huevos de cáscaras más delgadas que se rompen con facilidad. Además, la capacidad de las aves de almacenar materiales tóxicos en los tejidos grasos debilita las crías, aumentando de esta manera su mortalidad.

[Respuesta: Uno de los juicios particulares que se puede emitir de este estudio es que el DDT amenaza la supervivencia de las águilas doradas (aves de rapiña). En base a esta observación, los científicos pueden generalizar que están igualmente amenazadas por el DDT las otras aves de rapiña que viven en esa región.]

El ***razonamiento deductivo*** es aquél que llega a una conclusión partiendo de lo general a lo particular, o sea, aplicando una generalización a un caso específico. En el caso de arriba, los científicos que han concluido que la supervivencia de nuestras aves de rapiña está amenazada por el DDT pueden deducir que las águilas calvas, los halcones de cola roja, los búhos y otras aves de rapiña de la región también están amenazados. Para extraer una conclusión válida, la generalización debe ser conocida, aceptada y verdadera. Si la generalización es errónea, no se puede aplicar a un ejemplo específico.

Los escritores y los oradores no siempre siguen una lógica al expresar sus opiniones. A veces, suelen hacer afirmaciones o escribir ensayos basados en información que no es verdadera con la intención de influenciar a su público. Lea la afirmación de abajo y considere la presuposición que encierra:

> A toda persona que reciba prestaciones de bienestar social del programa de la AFDC (ayuda para familias a cargo de niños) se le debe obligar a realizar trabajos en la comunidad si desea seguir recibiendo dicha subvención.

El orador presupone que todas las personas que reciben prestaciones sociales de la AFDC pueden trabajar. Esto no se aplica necesariamente a todos los beneficiarios. De hecho, según las estadísticas, la mayoría de los beneficiarios son niños, los que lógicamente no pueden trabajar.

Instrucciones: Identifique la presuposición que hace el escritor en las siguientes afirmaciones. Complete después las oraciones que siguen con la palabra o palabras que correspondan.

1. Se debe obligar a todas las madres solteras a terminar la escuela secundaria antes de que puedan recibir ayuda del gobierno. El orador presupone que todas las madres solteras que reciben subvención gubernamental _____.

[Respuestas posibles: *no han terminado la secundaria o son mayores de edad*]

2. Eliminaremos del ámbito deportivo tanto profesional como universitario la nefasta influencia que tienen las drogas en los deportistas. El orador supone que los deportistas profesionales y universitarios consumen _____.

[Respuesta posible: *drogas*]

Otro aspecto del análisis consiste en reconocer distintos *tipos de estructura y organización.* Los libros de texto y los pasajes de lectura de Estudios Sociales y Ciencias siguen una determinada organización. Las obras literarias, como las novelas, los cuentos, las obras de teatro y ciertas formas de literatura de no ficción se basan en una determinada estructura y organización. Tres de los tipos más comunes de estructura utilizados en la escritura son: causa-efecto, comparación/contraste, y secuencial o cronológica. Los distintos tipos de estructuras constituyen el armazón básico ya sea de párrafos aislados como de libros enteros. Es frecuente encontrar una mezcla de estos tipos de estructuras dentro de párrafos aislados o de pasajes más largos. Sin embargo, se puede ver por lo general un tipo predominante de estructura dentro de párrafos de selecciones más extensas.

La *estructura causa-efecto* indica una relación entre sucesos. Nosotros, en nuestra vida cotidiana, unimos constantemente las causas a los efectos. Por ejemplo: los de la generación del *baby-boom* de la década del 50, que decidieron esperar unos años antes de tener hijos, son ahora padres de niños en edad escolar. Este cambio en la unidad familiar estadounidense ha causado un aumento en la cantidad de alumnos matriculados en las escuelas y ha frenado el cierre de escuelas característico de la década del 70 y 80. En este caso tenemos varios resultados como consecuencia de una sola causa: el aumento del tamaño de las familias.

La relación causa-efecto suele venir indicada por palabras clave como *porque, desde que, por lo tanto, como consecuencia, puesto que, ya que, como, si. . . entonces, condujo a, originó, acarreó, produjo, ocasionó, causó, la consecuencia/el resultado final fue, fue el causante de,* etc.

El autor se vale de la **estructura comparación/contraste** para explicar o mostrar semejanzas y diferencias entre ideas, personas o cosas. Al señalar las semejanzas que hay entre dos o más cosas, se hace una comparación; mientras que, al indicar las diferencias, se hace un contraste.

Entre las palabras y las frases que indican comparación o contraste se pueden mencionar: *como, asimismo, también, de la misma forma, por una/otra parte, por un/otro lado, de la misma manera/forma, comparado con, mas, sino, sin embargo, no obstante, pero, por el contrario, mientras, aunque, aun así, por el contrario, contra, en contraste con* y *o . . . o,* etc.

Las obras también se pueden organizar en base a una **estructura secuencial** u orden cronológico. Este tipo de estructura organiza los acontecimientos en serie según el orden en que se suceden y es muy frecuente encontrarla en textos de estudios sociales en la narración de acontecimientos históricos. También se usa mucho en la literatura científica para describir los pasos de un experimento. La estructura secuencial se emplea asimismo en la organización de textos literarios: en novelas, cuentos y obras de teatro, los sucesos de la trama siguen una secuencia determinada. A menudo, esta secuencia suele presentar una relación causa-efecto. Entre las palabras y frases que indican secuencia se pueden mencionar *ahora, antes, a continuación, a seguir, seguidamente, acto seguido, después, luego, enseguida, pronto, más tarde, cuando, primero, segundo y tercero, finalmente,* etc.

Instrucciones: La **alegoría** es una narración en que los personajes u objetos son simbólicos, es decir, representan a otras personas, objetos o cualidades abstractas. Los acontecimientos que tienen lugar en una alegoría revelan una verdad o generalización sobre la vida. Lea el resumen siguiente del famoso cuento de Stephen Vincent Benét, "El diablo y Daniel Webster". Después numere los sucesos según el orden en que ocurran.

> El cuento se desarrolla en New Hampshire en los tiempos de Daniel Webster, renombrado abogado y orador que aspiraba a la presidencia de los Estados Unidos. Jabez Stone es un agricultor de la zona que está harto de lo mal que le van las cosechas y de su falta de prosperidad. Se le aparece un forastero—un abogado—, el Sr. Scratch (el diablo), que le ofrece prosperidad a cambio de su alma. Jabez Stone acepta y el Sr. Scratch redacta un contrato. Stone se da una punzada en el dedo y lo firma con su sangre. Año tras año durante seis años, el forastero pasa por la casa de Stone para recordarle el contrato.

El séptimo año, el forastero viene a llevarse el alma de Stone. Jabez le suplica que no lo haga y recibe una prórroga de tres años. Al cabo de los tres años, se cumple el plazo fijado. Jabez Stone acude a Daniel Webster y le pide que abogue por él. Cuando Daniel Webster va a casa de Stone, aparece el forastero.

Los dos discuten acaloradamente, pero el forastero exige que se le pague lo que se le debe. Daniel Webster pide que se celebre un juicio con tribunal, juez y jurado. Entran entonces doce hombres venidos de lugares lejanos y que "aún desprenden los efluvios del fuego del infierno".

Daniel Webster defiende a su cliente toda la noche y finalmente termina de presentar su caso. El jurado falla a favor del acusado, Jabez Stone; y el juez y el jurado se retiran. Finalmente, el forastero firma un documento por el que promete nunca más molestar a Jabez Stone y desaparece para siempre de New Hampshire.

_____ **a.** El extraño visita a Jabez Stone para recordarle el contrato.

_____ **b.** Jabez Stone se harta de su falta de prosperidad.

_____ **c.** Daniel Webster discute con el Sr. Scratch en casa de Stone.

_____ **d.** El Sr. Scratch viene a saldar cuentas con Jabez Stone.

_____ **e.** El jurado dictamina a favor de Jabez Stone.

[Respuestas: **a.** 2, **b.** 1,. **c.** 4, **d.** 3, **e.** 5]

Síntesis

El nivel de *síntesis* del razonamiento crítico se encuentra en la sección de Expresión Escrita de este libro. La síntesis comprende la combinación de elementos para crear un todo, como sucede con un escrito. Al escribir párrafos sobre ciencias, estudios sociales o arte y literatura, usted podrá reforzar su capacidad de síntesis.

Evaluación

Evaluar es juzgar; es determinar si una idea o un objeto cumple con su objetivo y con ciertos parámetros. Por ejemplo, al evaluar una película, se la juzga según la calidad de la actuación, dirección, cinematografía, sonido y otros parámetros. Los parámetros en base a los cuales se emite un juicio se llaman *criterios,* que pueden ser subjetivos u objetivos.

Los *criterios objetivos* son aquéllos que no se ven afectadas por los gustos, creencias u opiniones que tiene un individuo sobre lo que se juzga. La situación que se presenta abajo explica la diferencia entre un criterio objetivo y uno subjetivo. Lea el párrafo y conteste las preguntas que siguen.

Una joven pareja va a comprar su primera casa. La pareja tiene dos niños en edad escolar y debe considerar varios factores antes de tomar una decisión. En el espacio proporcionado, escriba *O* si el criterio es objetivo y *S* si es subjetivo.

_____ **1.** la distancia a pie a la escuela más próxima.

_____ **2.** el atractivo de las otras casas del bloque

_____ **3.** la tasa de impuestos de la zona comparada con la de otras áreas

[Respuestas: **1.** *O,* **2.** *S,* **3.** *O*]

Antes de tomar una decisión o sacar una conclusión hay que considerar la idoneidad de los datos: conviene, por tanto, evaluar la información de que se dispone. ¿Es suficiente la información para tomar esta decisión? ¿Respaldan los datos lo decidido?

Cuando no se dispone de todos los datos, no se puede tomar una decisión acertada. Suponga que está interesado en un tema que se ha suscitado en la zona en que vive sobre si es conveniente derribar un edificio de apartamentos de bajo alquiler para hacerle sitio a un nuevo edificio. Para poder formarse una opinión sobre el tema, es imprescindible conocer todos los datos: el número de personas que se verán afectadas con la destrucción del viejo edificio y el precio del alquiler que se cobrará en el nuevo edificio.

Asimismo, hay que saber si la compañía constructora contratará a residentes de la zona para trabajar en el proyecto. Todos estos datos (y otros más) le ayudarán a formarse una opinión sobre el tema.

Del mismo modo, cuando conteste las preguntas del Examen del GED, puede que tenga que determinar si la información presentada es suficiente para dar apoyo a la conclusión o al punto de vista del autor.

Cuando tomamos decisiones, estamos, en parte, influenciados por los hechos. Sin embargo, todos poseemos *valores* muy arraigados y *creencias* personales que influyen en gran manera en nuestras decisiones. Muchas de las selecciones literarias que aparecen en el Examen del GED consisten en comentarios u opiniones de escritores de varios tipos sobre obras artísticas y literarias. Estos comentarios se basan en los valores propios a cada escritor. En temas relacionados con los estudios sociales y las ciencias, los valores personales ejercen un gran impacto en el proceso de toma de decisiones.

Instrucciones: En cada una de las situaciones descritas a continuación existe un conflicto entre dos conjuntos divergentes de valores. Escriba en los espacios en blanco los dos valores en pugna.

1. Myrna quiere casarse con Sam, sentar cabeza y tener hijos. Aunque su familia opina que Sam es una buena persona, se opone, sin embargo, a ese matrimonio debido a que Sam profesa una religión distinta a la de ellos.

Myrna debe elegir entre _____ y

_____ .

[Respuesta: su deseo de casarse con Sam y la lealtad hacia su familia].

2. Una de las áreas más controvertidas de la investigación científica es la ingeniería genética. Los que están a favor de la ingeniería genética alegan que, gracias a ella, se podrán prevenir un sinnúmero de defectos genéticos congénitos como el síndrome de Down y la drepanocitosis.

Los que se oponen a la ingeniería genética advierten que este tipo de investigación atenta contra la naturaleza y suscitará intentos de crear una raza genéticamente "pura".

El científico al que le pidan realizar trabajos genéticos debe elegir entre

_____ y _____.

[Respuesta: la posibilidad de prevenir defectos y el posible peligro de contribuir a la creación de una raza dominante "genéticamente superior"]

EJEMPLO DE PREGUNTAS DE RAZONAMIENTO CRÍTICO

Para finalizar nuestro enfoque de los niveles del razonamiento crítico, ofrecemos a continuación una muestra de preguntas cuya contestación requiere el uso de distintas destrezas de razonamiento. Obsérvense las frases clave indicadas en cursiva.

CONOCIMIENTO

¿Cuál es el segundo paso en la resolución de. . .?

¿Dónde se puede encontrar esta especie. . .?

Cite los distintos mecanismos. . .

Identifique las características comunes de. . .

Defina el significado de. . .

COMPRENSIÓN

Cite las *funciones principales* de. . .

¿Cuál es el *propósito* del autor de. . .?

¿Son éstos *detalles accesorios* de. . .?

¿Por qué *cree* que. . . suponiendo que. . .?

Exprese. . . en forma de. . .

APLICACIÓN

Si. . . viviera en esta época, *¿qué*. . .?

Utilice la fórmula de. . . para hallar. . .

¿Cómo podemos *demostrar* la presencia de. . .?

Aplique la teoría de. . . para. . .

Siga la *regla*. . . para. . .

ANÁLISIS

Dé un *ejemplo* de. . .

Ilustre el concepto de. . .

Analice la cadena de *sucesos* que condujeron a. . .

¿Cuáles son los *efectos* de. . .?

Compare y contraste los distintos. . .

SÍNTESIS

Escriba una *redacción* sobre el siguiente tema.

Organice. . . el texto en tres partes principales: introducción, cuerpo y conclusión.

Mencione los datos más relevantes acerca de. . .

Verbalice su *opinión* respecto a. . .

¿Qué *imagen mental* evoca el texto de. . .?

Haga una *sinopsis* de lo leído en. . .

Resuma brevemente el comentario del autor de. . .

EVALUACIÓN

¿Con qué *argumentos* se podría dar apoyo a. . .?

¿Cómo *justificaría* usted la decisión tomada por. . .?

¿Son *confiables* las fuentes de información. . .?

¿Ha sido lógico o *falaz* el razonamiento presentado por. . .?

¿Ha sido *bien lograda* la imagen de. . .?

¿Ha sido *veraz o creíble* el testimonio de. . .?

PRUEBA 1: EXPRESIÓN ESCRITA

La Prueba de Expresión Escrita del GED se divide en dos partes. A continuación se describe cada una de ellas.

Parte 1: Convenciones del español

¿De qué consta la prueba?

La *Parte 1* consta de 55 preguntas de opción múltiple y se dispone de 75 minutos para contestar esta sección de la prueba. En esta parte, se presentan varios pasajes seguidos de preguntas acerca de las oraciones contenidas en los mismos. En algunas preguntas se le pedirá identificar errores dentro del pasaje; y en otras se le pedirá expresar la idea principal. Recuerde que lo que se va a poner a prueba son sus conocimientos de gramática y uso de la lengua, así como de puntuación y ortografía.

La *Parte 1* de la prueba se puede analizar según las áreas de contenido que aborda:

> Estructura de la oración: 35%
> Uso de la lengua: 35%
> Ortografía y puntuación: 30%

¿Qué clases de preguntas habrá en la prueba?

Las preguntas que aparecerán en la Prueba de Expresión Escrita del GED son básicamente de tres tipos. En las preguntas de *corrección de oraciones,* se le presentará una oración seguida por la pregunta: "¿Qué corrección debe hacerse a la oración?" Las cinco opciones que figuran en la respuesta enfocan distintas secciones de la oración y abordan distintos temas de gramática y uso de la lengua.

> *Ejemplo:* Oración 1: **El tiempo pasa volando cuándo uno se lo pasa bien.**

¿Qué corrección debe hacerse a la oración?

(1) reemplace *volando* por *bolando*
(2) sustituya *cuándo* por *cuando*
(3) reemplace *lo* por *le*
(4) ponga una coma antes y después de *volando*
(5) no es necesario hacer ninguna corrección

Observe que esta pregunta pone a prueba sus conocimientos de ortografía o norma que rige la escritura de letras y signos auxiliares. La respuesta correcta es la (2): sustituya *cuándo* por *cuando*.

El segundo tipo de pregunta es el de *revisión de oraciones,* en el cual se presentará una oración del pasaje con una sección subrayada. Le corresponderá a usted determinar cuál es la opción que ofrece la mejor versión reescrita de la parte subrayada. La primera de las opciones de la respuesta en este tipo de pregunta presenta la oración sin ningún cambio y es a veces esta versión original la respuesta correcta.

Ejemplo: Oración 2: **La frustración es una emoción que todos experimentamos, la cuestión está en cómo la encaramos.**

¿Cuál de las opciones ofrece la mejor versión reescrita de la parte subrayada de la oración? Si cree que la versión original es la mejor, elija la opción (1).

(1) experimentamos, la cuestión
(2) experimentamos la cuestión
(3) experimentamos, ya que la cuestión
(4) experimentamos. La cuestión
(5) experimentamos, a pesar de que la cuestión

Esta pregunta pone a prueba sus conocimientos de construcción y combinación de oraciones. La opción (4) reescribe de mejor manera la frase; las demás opciones producen estructuras incorrectas o sin sentido.

El último tipo de pregunta es el de *alteración de construcciones,* en que se le pedirá elegir la mejor manera de parafrasear una oración o de combinar dos o más oraciones. En este tipo de pregunta, las oraciones originales no presentan errores. En este caso, su labor consistirá en captar el modo en que están relacionadas las ideas de una oración y determinar cuál de las opciones de la respuesta posee el mismo sentido que la oración original.

Ejemplo: Oración 3: **Aunque la candidata realizó una buena campaña, no obtuvo votos suficientes.**

Si tuviera que parafrasear (volver a decir lo mismo en otras palabras) la *Oración 3* y comenzara la misma con *La candidata realizó una buena campaña,* la palabra siguiente tendría que ser:

(1) y   **(2)** que   **(3)** pero   **(4)** así   **(5)** para

Como puede ver, la oración original no presenta errores. Para contestar esta pregunta, observe el contraste entre las dos ideas de la oración y marque el (3). La palabra *pero* indica más apropiadamente este contraste.

Parte 2: Redacción

Se dispone de 45 minutos para contestar la *Parte 2* de la Prueba de Expresión Escrita. En esta sección, se le dará un tema y se le pedirá redactar una composición de unas 200 palabras de extensión. Aunque no tendrá la opción de elegir el tema, no le harán falta datos o conocimientos especiales para poder desarrollar el ensayo. La *Parte 2* de esta prueba presenta un tema que aborda conocimientos generales amplios: le pide explicar algo acerca de un tópico o problema cotidiano. En esta sección de la Prueba de Expresión Escrita, deberá plantear y organizar sus ideas respecto a un tema determinado y comunicar dichas ideas en papel de forma clara y concisa.

1
USO BÁSICO DEL ESPAÑOL

¿Qué es la norma de la lengua?

La Prueba de Expresión Escrita examina sus conocimientos sobre la *norma de la lengua* española, es decir, el conjunto de reglas a las que se ajusta la lengua que desea ser aceptable en todo momento y en todo lugar. El *español normativo* (o *estándar*) es el español que se emplea en los medios de comunicación—libros, periódicos, revistas, radio, televisión, etc.—así como en los centros de enseñanza y en las empresas. La mayor parte del material impreso utiliza, por lo general, el español normativo. Asimismo, en presentaciones, conferencias o discursos, el orador trata de ajustarse a la norma de la lengua.

El *español no normativo* es aquél que no sigue las reglas lingüísticas de gramática y uso. En las conversaciones cotidianas, solemos usar un español no normativo o no estándar. De hecho, existen diversas expresiones que no se ajustan a la norma pero que empleamos en nuestro lenguaje diario porque suenan "bien", ya que estamos acostumbrados a oírlas. En este capítulo, estudiaremos cómo corregir muchos de estos errores que cometemos tan frecuentemente al hablar y al escribir, como los problemas de concordancia, de conjugación verbal, de ortografía y otros. Lógicamente, está demás decir que, para la Prueba de Expresión Escrita se habrán de conocer estas reglas de la lengua por más que en su conversación diaria usted no se ajuste a las mismas.

Construcción de oraciones completas

Una diferencia importante entre el español hablado y el escrito es que no siempre utilizamos oraciones completas al hablar. Por ejemplo, en una conversación telefónica podemos mezclar oraciones completas con frases: grupos de palabras que tienen sentido pero que no constituyen una oración completa.

CARACTERÍSTICAS DE LA ORACIÓN COMPLETA

1. La oración completa tiene *sentido completo.* No deja preguntas sin contestar.
2. La oración completa tiene un *sujeto* (expreso o tácito), de quien se dice algo.
3. La oración completa tiene un *predicado,* que expresa algo acerca del sujeto.

En las oraciones siguientes, se indican los sujetos y los predicados. Observe en las mismas las características mencionadas en el cuadro de arriba.

Sujeto / Predicado

La tienda / está en la carretera que va al aeropuerto.
Nosotros / vendemos acondicionadores de aire.
El almacén / tiene grandes existencias de ese producto.

Aunque en el habla cotidiana solemos omitir el sujeto, el verbo, los complementos o todo el predicado, se recomienda, sin embargo, al escribir, el uso de oraciones completas. (Recuerde que también son completas aquellas oraciones en las que el sujeto está tácito o sobreentendido.) Las oraciones completas se ajustan al uso del español normativo y son un punto importante a observar en la Prueba de Expresión Escrita, tanto en la *Parte 1* como en la *Parte 2*.

Partes de la oración

Los sujetos, como los predicados, se componen de distintos elementos conocidos como *partes de la oración* (o *partes del discurso*). No será necesario en la Prueba de Expresión Escrita definir o explicar estos vocablos; no obstante se recomienda un conocimiento básico de estas partes de la oración al igual que de sus funciones para comprender cómo se constituye la oración según la norma de la lengua.

PARTES BÁSICAS DE LA ORACIÓN		
Parte de la oración	**Función**	**Ejemplos**
nombre (o sustantivo)	designa personas, lugares, cosas o ideas	**Juan** fue a **Milwaukee** a una **conferencia** de **derechos** humanos.
pronombre	sustituye al nombre	**Alguien la** vio a esa hora y **me lo** contó.
verbo	expresa una acción o un estado (**ser, estar**)	Jaime **es** alto y **juega** al básquetbol. Luis **buscaba** un trabajo.
conjunción	enlaza palabras, frases u oraciones	Margarita estuvo aquí, **pero** se tuvo que ir. Miguel **y** yo regresamos a la casa **y** alquilamos una película.
adjetivo	modifica al nombre; expresa una cualidad	¡Qué **verdes** y **frondosos** son los árboles del parque **nacional!**
adverbio	modifica al verbo u otros elementos; expresa un grado	Comió **rápidamente** y se marchó **enseguida.**

¿Qué es un nombre?

Las palabras que utilizamos para referirnos a personas, lugares y cosas son **nombres** (o **sustantivos**) fácilmente reconocibles. Sin embargo, los nombres que designan ideas suelen ser un poco más difíciles de reconocer. Entre los nombres de este tipo podemos citar: *democracia, capitalismo, coraje, amor, tiempo, enojo,* etc.

El nombre como sujeto

El nombre puede desempeñar el papel de **sujeto** de la oración. Considere el sujeto como el nombre principal o el *actor* de la oración. Pregúntese, "¿Quién o qué está realizando la acción o está siendo descrito en la oración?"

La siguiente oración contiene varios nombres en **negrita**, pero solamente uno de ellos es el sujeto. ¿Cuál es?

Los **empleados** cargaron el **camión** con una variedad de **muebles: camas, sillas** y **mesas.**

[Respuesta: *empleados*]

Número de los nombres

Según el número, el nombre puede ser *singular,* si se refiere a una sola persona o cosa, o *plural,* si se refiere a más de una. El plural de los nombres se forma de acuerdo con las reglas que se dan a continuación.

Reglas para la formación del plural de los nombres

1. **Los nombres que terminan en vocal no acentuada añaden *s*.**
   taza → tazas   despacho → despachos

2. **Los nombres que terminan en *e* acentuada añaden *es*.**
   café → cafés   té → tés

3. **Los nombres que terminan en vocal acentuada que no sea *e* añaden *es*.**
   rubí → rubíes   rondó → rondoes
   excepto:
   papá → papás   mamá → mamás

4. **Los nombres que terminan en consonante añaden *es*.**
   amistad → amistades   joven → jóvenes

5. **Los nombres compuestos forman el plural según la forma en que estén combinados sus componentes:**
   ojo de buey → ojos de buey   ricohombre → ricoshombres
   quienquiera → quienesquiera   bocacalle → bocacalles

LAS RESPUESTAS DE LOS EJERCICIOS DE ESTE CAPÍTULO EMPIEZAN EN LA PÁGINA 441.

EJERCICIO 1: NÚMERO DE LOS NOMBRES

Instrucciones: Dé el plural de las palabras siguientes. Ponga en paréntesis ( ) el número de la regla que corresponda.

Singular	Plural		Singular	Plural
1. país	_____		6. bidé	_____
2. hogar	_____		7. tren	_____
3. negocio	_____		8. vida	_____
4. aleación	_____		9. mujer	_____
5. carro	_____		10. papá	_____

Género de los nombres

Según el género, el nombre puede ser **masculino** (v. gr.: *hijo, matiz, color, empleo,* etc.) o **femenino** (v. gr.: *niña, actriz, persona, vida,* etc.). Es importante recalcar que, cuando hablamos del género en la lengua española, nos estamos refiriendo al género gramatical, el cual no debe confundirse con el género biológico.

EJERCICIO 2: GÉNERO DE LOS NOMBRES

Instrucciones: Escriba *M* si el nombre es masculino, *F* si es femenino y *A* si puede ser tanto masculino como femenino.

1. congresista _____		6. tez _____		11. joven _____
2. acción _____		7. espesor _____		12. carácter _____
3. crin _____		8. acidez _____		13. crisis _____
4. caparazón _____		9. álbum _____		14. emblema _____
5. cutis _____		10. élite _____		15. oxímoron _____

¿Qué es el verbo?

En toda oración, el **verbo** es la palabra clave que indica quién es o qué hace el sujeto. Los dos tipos de verbos son **verbos de acción** y verbos de enlace, conocidos como **verbos copulativos.** Algunos verbos expresan una acción mental (*pensar, creer, desear,* etc.) y otros una acción física (*correr, salir, nadar,* etc.).

Mientras que el verbo de acción indica lo que está haciendo el sujeto, el verbo copulativo no expresa acción alguna. Simplemente "enlaza", o sea, une el sujeto a palabras que lo califican. Observe los verbos copulativos contenidos en las oraciones que siguen: *José* y *Nosotros* están enlazados a los adjetivos calificativos *alto* y *enojados.*

Ejemplos: José **es** alto.

Nosotros **estamos** enojados

Es y *estamos* son formas conjugadas de los verbos *ser* y *estar,* los dos verbos copulativos más comunes. En el cuadro inferior se mencionan los verbos copulativos más usados.

A modo de práctica, complete los espacios en blanco de las siguientes oraciones con verbos copulativos del cuadro de arriba debidamente conjugados.

Me _____ atónito.

Te _____ cansado. Mejor sería que fueras a la cama.

David _____ rápido y puede ganar la carrera.

Conjugación de los verbos

En español, los verbos se dividen en tres grandes grupos según la manera como se conjugan. Estos tres grupos verbales se distinguen por las terminaciones del infinitivo: los verbos de 1ª conjugación presentan la desinencia -*ar;* los de 2ª conjugación terminan en -*er;* y los de 3ª conjugación en -*ir.* Cada uno de estos grupos sigue modelos distintos de conjugación.

Tiempos verbales

El *tiempo verbal* sitúa la acción o lo que expresa el verbo en un punto determinado del tiempo. Una de las formas en que los escritores nos hacen saber cuándo se producen los acontecimientos es por medio de los tiempos verbales. Algunos de éstos se forman con una sola palabra como, por ejemplo, *quiere.* Otros se forman por medio de frases como *voy a comer.* Para conjugar el verbo en todos los tiempos es indispensable contar con el *verbo principal.* Algunos tiempos requieren también un *verbo auxiliar,* como se podrá ver más adelante.

Para la Prueba de Expresión Escrita será muy importante dominar la conjugación de los verbos en los distintos tiempos.

Tiempos simples del modo indicativo

Los *tiempos simples* son los que se conjugan sin auxilio de otro verbo. En el modo indicativo tenemos los tiempos simples citados a continuación.

El *presente* expresa una acción que coincide con el momento en que se habla, una acción habitual o que expresa una verdad inmutable.

Ejemplos: Hoy **tengo** un aspecto horrible.
Jorge **lava** el auto todas las mañanas.
El sol **sale** por el este.

El *pretérito imperfecto* presenta una acción pasada en su continuidad o transcurso sin prestar atención a su principio o fin. También expresa una acción pasada habitual.

Ejemplos: **Lloraba** de alegría con la noticia.
Ella lo **miraba** y Ramón le **sonreía.**

El *pretérito indefinido* expresa una acción pasada absoluta.

> *Ejemplos:* Julio **empezó** su trabajo el mes pasado.
> Ayer **fuimos** al cine.

El *futuro imperfecto* expresa una acción futura.

> *Ejemplos:* Ya **vendrá.**
> Me **levantaré** temprano mañana.

El *condicional* expresa una acción futura supeditada a una "condición". También indica cortesía o deferencia.

> *Ejemplos:* Si tuviera dinero, **me iría** de viaje.
> ¿Me **podría** decir cuánto cuesta esta camisa?

Tiempos simples del modo subjuntivo

En el modo subjuntivo tenemos los siguientes tiempos verbales simples: *presente, pretérito imperfecto* y *futuro imperfecto.*

> *Ejemplos:* Quiero que **vengas** de inmediato.   *(presente)*
>
> **Dijera** lo que **dijese,** ya estaba   *(pretérito imperfecto)*
> hecho.
>
> Sea lo que **fuere,** no importa.   *(futuro imperfecto)*

EJERCICIO 3: TIEMPOS SIMPLES
Instrucciones: Conjugue el verbo indicado en paréntesis en el tiempo que corresponda. Preste atención a los datos temporales que ofrece la oración.

1. (*hablar*) Yo _____ con ellos mañana.

2. (*ver*) Se te _____ muy preocupada hoy.

3. (*plantar*) Ana _____ esos narcisos en marzo del año

pasado.

4. (*salir*) Ayer, justo en el momento en que (yo) _____,

sonó el teléfono.

5. (*poder*) ¿_____ (tú) ir conmigo a la fiesta?

6. (*estar*) Me urge que _____ (tú) aquí lo antes posible.

7. (*ser*) Si no _____ por Marta, no sé lo que habría hecho.

Tiempos compuestos del modo indicativo

Los *tiempos compuestos* se forman con el participio pasado del verbo principal y un tiempo del verbo auxiliar *haber.* Estos tiempos suelen indicar relaciones temporales más específicas que los tiempos simples. En el modo indicativo, los tiempos compuestos son los que se mencionan a continuación.

El *pretérito perfecto* expresa una acción que se acaba de verificar o un hecho que tiene relevancia presente.

Ejemplos: Hoy **he ido** al cine con mi hermana.

Los aztecas nos **han dejado** muchos monumentos.

El *pretérito pluscuamperfecto* expresa una acción pasada anterior a otra acción pasada.

Ejemplo: Cuando llegué, ya **te habías ido.**

El *pretérito anterior* expresa una acción pasada inmediatamente anterior a otra acción pasada. Se emplea raramente en el lenguaje hablado o escrito.

Ejemplo: Salí cuando **hubo anochecido.**

El *futuro perfecto* expresa una acción futura anterior a otra acción futura.

Ejemplo: Mañana por la tarde, **habré pintado** toda la casa.

El *condicional compuesto* expresa una acción pasada posterior y condicionada a otra acción pasada.

Ejemplo: Si hubiera sabido que el examen era tan difícil, **habría estudiado** más.

Tiempos compuestos del modo subjuntivo

En el modo subjuntivo tenemos los siguientes tiempos verbales compuestos: pretérito perfecto, pretérito pluscuamperfecto y futuro perfecto.

Ejemplos: Aunque **haya sido** él, no se *(pretérito perfecto)* lo digan.

Habría salido antes, si me *(pretérito pluscuamperfecto)* **hubieras avisado.**

Lo que **hubiere hecho** o *(futuro perfecto)* dejado de hacer no es relevante.

EJERCICIO 4: TIEMPOS COMPUESTOS

Instrucciones: Conjugue el verbo indicado en paréntesis en el tiempo compuesto que corresponda. Preste atención al sentido de la oración antes de escribir la respuesta.

1. (*asistir*) Lucía se inscribió en una clase de Lamaze. Hasta ahora

   _____ a todas las clases.

2. (*trabajar*) Antes de alistarse en el ejército, Andrés _____

   en una fábrica de conservas de pescado.

3. (*enviar*) En octubre, la Sra. Jiménez ya _____ los

   regalos de Navidad a sus parientes de Guatemala.

4. (*llamar*) Si hubiese sabido el número, de seguro le _____.

5. (*hacer*) Me cuesta creer que _____ eso.

El imperativo

El *imperativo* expresa una orden o mandato.

> *Ejemplos:* **Ven** enseguida.
> **Contesta** el teléfono.

Para expresar una prohibición, se utiliza el adverbio de negación seguido del subjuntivo presente:

> *Ejemplos:* **No vengas.**
> **No contestes** el teléfono.

EJERCICIO 5: IMPERATIVO

Instrucciones: Escriba el imperativo de los verbos indicados en paréntesis.

1. (*salir*) Niños, _____ de ahí ya.

2. (*ayudar*) Te lo pido como amigo: _____ a tu hermano.

3. (*hacer*) Oye... _____ el favor de ponerte a trabajar.

4. (*ser*) Escúchame bien: _____ bueno con tus compañeros.

5. (*inmiscuirse*) Te doy un consejo: no te _____ en los asuntos ajenos.

Verbos irregulares

El español sería un idioma mucho más sencillo si todos los verbos fueran regulares. Sin embargo, en esta lengua abundan los verbos irregulares. Los *verbos irregulares* son verbos cuya formación no se ajusta a las reglas generales de la lengua. En la lista siguiente se mencionan los verbos con irregularidad propia (como *ir*) y los de irregularidad sistemática, es decir, aquellos verbos cuyo paradigma de conjugación se ajusta al de otros verbos irregulares.

VERBOS IRREGULARES		
Desinencia -*ar*	**Desinencia -*er***	**Desinencia -*ir***
andar	caber	abrir
cerrar	caer	decir
dar	haber	dormir
estar	hacer	escribir
jugar	leer	ir
	mover	oír
	poder	reír
	saber	salir
	ser	venir
	tener	
	traer	
	ver	
	volver	

EJERCICIO 6: VERBOS IRREGULARES

Instrucciones: Escriba el verbo indicado en paréntesis en la forma que corresponda.

1. (*caber*) En esta cama yo no _____.

2. (*satisfacer*) Lo que comí anoche me _____.

3. (*oír*) Habla más fuerte, que no te _____.

4. (*haber*) Quiero que _____ paz.

5. (*estarse*) _____ quieto, Sr. Jiménez, para que pueda auscultarle.

EJERCICIO 7: USO DE LOS TIEMPOS VERBALES

Instrucciones: Lea el pasaje y conteste las preguntas que siguen. Cerciórese de que el verbo esté conjugado como corresponde en el tiempo que corresponde.

(1) La videocasetera ofrece al televidente una nueva gama de opciones en lo que a programación se refiera. (2) Un gran número de personas graban los programas de la televisión para verlos más adelante. (3) Por ejemplo, aquéllos que trabajan durante el día suelen programar su videocasetera para que les grabara en su ausencia noticieros, entrevistas, películas o telenovelas. (4) No son pocos los que no pueden prescindir de esta invención; porque, si no existiere, ¿cómo harían para no perderse sus programas predilectos?

¿Cuál es la mejor forma de expresar la parte subrayada de cada oración? Si cree que la versión original es la mejor, elija la opción (1).

1. Oración 1: **La videocasetera ofrece al televidente una nueva gama de opciones en lo que a programación se refiera.**
   (1) se refiera
   (2) se refiriera
   (3) se refiere
   (4) se refiriese
   (5) se refiére

2. Oración 2: **Un gran número de personas graban los programas de la televisión para verlos más adelante.**
   (1) graban
   (2) graba
   (3) grában
   (4) gravan
   (5) grába

3. Oración 3: **Por ejemplo, aquéllos que trabajan durante el día suelen programar su videocasetera para que les grabara en su ausencia noticieros, entrevistas, películas o telenovelas.**
   (1) grabara
   (2) grabára
   (3) grabase
   (4) grabe
   (5) grabáse

4. Oración 4: **No son pocos los que no pueden prescindir de esta invención; porque, si no <u>existiere</u>, ¿cómo harían para no perderse sus programas predilectos?**
   (1) existiere
   (2) existía
   (3) existió
   (4) existiría
   (5) existiese

Concordancia

En la lengua española existen dos clases de *concordancia:* nominal y verbal. La *concordancia nominal* se refiere a la igualdad de género y número entre un artículo o un adjetivo y un nombre, y entre el pronombre relativo, posesivo o demostrativo y su antecedente.

> *Ejemplos:* **Esa casa** se ve tan **espaciosa** y **cómoda.**
> **Aquellos días** de verano, de **los cuales** ya no me acuerdo.
> **Estas aves** son muy **exóticas.**

La *concordancia verbal* se refiere a la igualdad de número y persona entre el verbo y el sujeto.

> *Ejemplos:* **Tú** no **comprendes** muchas cosas.
> **Julio y Amalia** siempre **son** muy puntuales.

Casos particulares de concordancia

1. *Nombres colectivos:* Tanto el determinante (artículo, adjetivo y pronombre) como el verbo debe concordar con el número *gramatical* del sustantivo colectivo.

> *Ejemplos:* **La muchedumbre estaba animada.**
> No te fíes en lo que **dice la gente.**
> Una gran **cantidad** de alumnos **estuvo presente.**

2. *Nombres enlazados por cópula:* Si concurren dos o más nombres de distinto género, se hace la concordancia en masculino plural.

> *Ejemplos:* Raúl tiene una **habilidad** y una **velocidad extraordinarias.**
> Este libro está escrito con una **claridad** y un **estilo magníficos.**
> La **hija** de Juan y los **mellizos** de Sara son unos **malcriados.**

3. *Sujeto compuesto por distintas personas gramaticales:* La segunda persona tiene prioridad sobre la tercera y la primera sobre todas las demás.

> *Ejemplos:* **Tú y María** se van de paseo.
> **Tú y yo** nos vamos de paseo.

4. *Sujeto compuesto sin enlace:* El verbo puede ir tanto en singular como en plural. El determinante concuerda en género y número con el sujeto más próximo o se hace la concordancia en masculino plural si los elementos del sujeto son de distinto género.

Ejemplos: Tu **mirada,** tu **gesto,** tu **sonrisa será** por siempre **recordada.**
Tu **mirada,** tu **gesto,** tu **sonrisa serán** por siempre **recordados.**

5. *Sujeto compuesto con enlace disyuntivo:* Se aplica la misma regla anterior.

Ejemplos: El **padre** o la **hija es adinerada.**
El **padre** o la **hija son adinerados.**

6. *Sujeto compuesto resumido por elemento final:* Tanto el verbo como el determinante concuerdan en género y número con el elemento que resume a todos los demás.

Ejemplo: **Joyas, pieles, viajes, lujos, nada bastó** para contentarle.

EJERCICIO 8: CONCORDANCIA

Instrucciones: Subraye la forma correcta del adjetivo o verbo de las opciones en paréntesis.

1. Un distinguido grupo de médicos (asistió, asistieron) al congreso realizado en Bonn.
2. O Felipe o Leticia (va, van) a tener que ayudarme.
3. He comprado todo nuevo: sofá, mesa, silla, armario y poltrona (nuevas, nuevos).
4. La multitud (coreaba, coreaban) su nombre; gentes que (venía, venían) de todas partes.
5. Los novios y la suegra (está sentada, están sentados) en la terraza.
6. Botiquín, equipo, transporte y alimentos, todo (estaba, estaban) en orden.

¿Qué es un adjetivo?

El adjetivo es la palabra que modifica al nombre ya sea determinándolo, limitándolo o calificándolo.

Adjetivos calificativos

Los *adjetivos calificativos* expresan una cualidad del nombre.

Ejemplos: casa **cómoda, espaciosa** y **moderna**
joven **brillante** y **dinámica**

Adjetivos demostrativos

Los *adjetivos demostrativos* señalan el nombre.

ADJETIVOS DEMOSTRATIVOS	
Singular	**Plural**
este, esta	estos, -as
ese, esa	esos, -as
aquel, aquella	aquellos, -as

Adjetivos posesivos

Los *adjetivos posesivos* indican a quién pertenece el nombre.

ADJETIVOS POSESIVOS		
1ª persona	mi, mis	nuestro, -as
2ª persona	tu, tus	vuestro, -as
3ª persona	su, sus (de él, de ella, de usted)	su, sus (de ellos, de ellas, de ustedes)

EJERCICIO 9: ADJETIVOS

Instrucciones: Complete la oración con el adjetivo correspondiente según se indica.

1. (*posesivo*) Ésta es la casa de Armando y Pedro y éste es _____ automóvil.

2. (*posesivo*) Mis dálmatas son muy poco obedientes. ¿Cómo son _____ perros?

3. (*demostrativo*) _____ libro que tengo aquí y _____ enciclopedia que ves allí no sirven.

4. (*demostrativo*) Mira qué bien se portan Mariana e Inés. ¡Qué educadas son _____ niñas!

5. (*posesivo*) Hoy compramos un pequeño terreno Alicia y yo. Allí pensamos construir _____ casa.

¿Qué es un pronombre?

El *pronombre* es la palabra que sustituye al nombre y desempeña sus funciones. El pronombre, por lo general, se emplea por economía del lenguaje, evitando así el tener que repetir el nombre.

Pronombres personales

Los *pronombres personales* pueden desempeñar la función de sujeto u objeto de una oración.

PRONOMBRES PERSONALES		
CON FUNCIÓN SUJETO		
	Singular	**Plural**
1ª persona	yo	nosotros, -as
2ª persona	tú, usted	vosotros, -as; ustedes
3ª persona	él, ella, ello	ellos, -as
CON FUNCIÓN OBJETO		
	Singular	**Plural**
1ª persona	me, mí, conmigo	nos
2ª persona	te, ti, contigo	os
3ª persona	lo, la, le, se, sí, consigo	los, las, les, se, sí, consigo

Colocación de los pronombres personales

Regla 1: El pronombre personal se pospone al imperativo, gerundio e infinitivo.

Ejemplos: díga**me,** leyéndo**te,** esperar**lo**

Regla 2: Se pospone al verbo auxiliar en las formas compuestas del gerundio y del infinitivo.

Ejemplo: habiéndo**nos** prevenido, haber**te** visto

Regla 3: Si el gerundio y el infinitivo complementan a otro verbo, el pronombre personal puede ir antepuesto o, rara vez, enclítico al verbo principal.

Ejemplo: desea recibir**lo**—**lo** desea recibir—desé**alo** recibir
iba siguiéndo**me**—**me** iba siguiendo—íba**me** siguiendo

Regla 4: El pronombre personal normalmente va antepuesto a las demás formas verbales. La posposición del pronombre es muy poco usada en el habla coloquial.

Ejemplo: **me** voy—voy**me**
le digo—dígo**le**

Regla 5: Cuando la oración contiene más de un pronombre, el orden en que se colocan los mismos es el siguiente: *se*, si ocurre, aparece primero, seguido por el de segunda persona, luego el de primera y por último el de tercera.

Ejemplo: **te me** vas, **se le** pasó, díga**melo**

Regla 6: En el caso de los siguientes enclíticos, se elide la *s* ante *nos* y *se*; y se elide la *d* del imperativo ante *os*.

Ejemplo: vámonos (*no:* vámo**s**nos)
acercáos (*no:* acerca**d**os)
entreguémoselo (entreguémo**s**selo)

EJERCICIO 10: PRONOMBRES PERSONALES
Instrucciones: Subraye la forma correcta del verbo y el pronombre de las opciones en paréntensis.

1. Quiero que me repita lo que ha dicho. (Repítamelo, Repítamele), por favor.
2. No quiero que vengan junto a mí; no quiero que (se me, me se) acerquen.
3. (Le dirás, Dirás le) que la amas.
4. (Vayámosnos, Vayámonos) ahora.
5. (Digámosle, Digámole) lo que pensamos.

Pronombres demostrativos

Los ***pronombres demostrativos*** sustituyen al nombre y al adjetivo demostrativo que los determinan. Se recomienda prestar atención a la distinción ortográfica entre los pronombres y adjetivos demostrativos.

PRONOMBRES DEMOSTRATIVOS	
Singular	**Plural**
éste, ésta, esto	éstos, -as
ése, ésa, eso	ésos, -as
aquél, aquélla, aquello	aquéllos, -as

Pronombres posesivos

Los **pronombres posesivos,** como su nombre lo indica, denotan posesión: tanto lo poseído como el poseedor.

PRONOMBRES POSESIVOS		
	Un poseedor	**Varios poseedores**
1ª persona	mío, -a, -os, -as	nuestro, -a, -os, -as
2ª persona	tuyo, -a, -os, -as	vuestro, -a, -os, -as
3ª persona	suyo, -a, -os, -as	suyo, -a, -os, -as

EJERCICIO 11: PRONOMBRES DEMOSTRATIVOS Y POSESIVOS

Instrucciones: Subraye la forma correcta del pronombre de las opciones en paréntensis.

1. La piscina de Juan no está nada mal, pero (la tuya, el tuyo) es mejor.
2. Este caballo corre como una bala, pero (aquel, aquél) es más veloz.
3. Me sorprendió que dijera (éso, eso).
4. Prefiero tu sistema (al mío, a lo mío).
5. (Aquéllo, Aquello) que te dije no se lo cuentes a nadie.

Pronombres relativos e interrogativos

Los **pronombres relativos,** como su nombre lo indica, relacionan o enlazan una oración subordinada a un elemento de la oración principal, denominado **antecedente.** Cuide de no confundir los pronombres relativos con los interrogativos. Recuerde que los pronombres interrogativos llevan acento pintado (v. gr.: *qué, quién, cuál, cúyo,* etc.)

PRONOMBRES RELATIVOS
que
quien, quienes
el cual, lo cual, la cual, los cuales, las cuales
cuyo, cuya, cuyos, cuyas

EJERCICIO 12: PRONOMBRES RELATIVOS E INTERROGATIVOS

Instrucciones: Subraye la forma correcta del pronombre de las opciones en paréntensis.

1. ¿(Quién, Quien) es? No sé (quién, quien) pueda ser.
2. ¿(Qué, Que) sabes tú de lo (qué, que) yo sé?
3. Dime (cuál, cual) te gusta más.
4. Este es el abogado (cúyo, cuyo) padre nos conoce.
5. Le conté aquello (qué, que) me habías comentado, lo (cual, cuál) le desagradó sobremanera.

Concordancia entre el pronombre y su referente

Aquello a lo que se refiere el pronombre o aquello que el pronombre sustituye es el *referente,* llamado *antecedente* cuando está expreso en la oración. La relación entre el pronombre y su referente debe ser clara y precisa: debe concordar en género y número. Por ello es muy importante identificar el referente de un pronombre al analizar el sentido de una oración. En la Prueba de Expresión Escrita probablemente encontrará varios problemas que tratan de la concordancia entre el pronombre y su referente.

Ejemplo: **Patricia** dijo a **Roberto** cuánto **le** gustaban las rosas. **Ella** también **le** dijo que era muy feliz. [El pronombre *ella* reemplaza y se refiere a Patricia. También se refiere a Patricia el primer *le.* El segundo *le* se refiere a *Roberto.*]

Conocí al **profesor Johnson, del cual** aprendí lo que sé de los insectos. [La expresión *del cual* se refiere al *profesor Johnson.*]

EJERCICIO 13: EL PRONOMBRE Y SU REFERENTE

Instrucciones: Lea el párrafo y escriba el referente que corresponde a los pronombres subrayados.

¿Te acuerdas de Mario y Margarita? Aquellos hermanos, de <u>los que</u> <u>te</u> había comentado en una carta anterior; esos amigos <u>míos</u> tan agradables y tan serviciales. Ahora trabajan <u>conmigo</u> en la planta de empaque y siempre almorzamos juntos. Hoy <u>me</u> preguntaron si quería ir al cine y. . . te sorprenderás. . . ¡<u>les</u> dije que sí! Estoy tratando de salir más y airear la cabeza. . .

Tu hermana que te quiere un montón,

Juanita

Pronombre	Referente
1. los que	_____
2. te	_____
3. míos	_____
4. conmigo	_____
5. me	_____
6. les	_____

Ambigüedad del referente

Como anteriormente se mencionara, la función del pronombre es la economía del lenguaje. Al reemplazar al nombre, el pronombre evita que tengamos que repetirlo. Sin embargo, hay ocasiones en que se hace necesaria la repetición del nombre—por más que esta repetición no sea biensonante—para evitar la confusión del sentido de la oración. Lo mismo sucede con los adjetivos determinativos. Observe los ejemplos que se ofrecen en la siguiente página:

AMBIGUO: Esta tarde me encontré con Pablo y Arturo. **Él** [*¿Pablo o Arturo?*] me dijo que **le** [*¿A Pablo o a Arturo?*] habían dado una beca, pero que **él** [*¿Pablo o Arturo?*] no estaba satisfecho con el estipendio que iba a recibir.

CLARO: Esta tarde me encontré con Pablo y Arturo. Pablo me dijo que se había ganado una beca, pero Arturo no estaba satisfecho con el estipendio que Pablo iba a recibir.

EJERCICIO 14: AMBIGÜEDAD DEL REFERENTE

Instrucciones: Lea el pasaje y conteste las preguntas que siguen.

(1) Hoy vinieron a visitarme estas dos chicas, Natalia y Adriana. Me hablaron mucho de Jorge y me contaron del accidente de <u>su hermano Federico</u>. (2) Su padre —me dijeron— estaba muy disgustado, no sólo con él sino con ellas también. (3) Natalia y Adriana me dijeron que <u>su coche</u> había quedado inservible, pero que a Federico no le había pasado nada. (4) El padre los castigó a los tres hermanos; así que ni Natalia ni Adriana ni Federico podrán venir a la fiesta.

¿Cuál es la mejor forma de expresar la parte subrayada de cada oración? Si cree que la versión original es la mejor, elija la opción (1).

1. Oración 1: **Hoy vinieron a visitarme estas dos chicas, Natalia y Adriana. Me hablaron mucho de Jorge y me contaron del accidente <u>de su hermano Federico.</u>**
   (1) de su hermano Federico.
   (2) del hermano Federico.
   (3) del hermano de Federico.
   (4) de Federico, el hermano de las chicas.
   (5) de Federico, su hermano.

2. Oración 3: **Natalia y Adriana me dijeron que <u>su coche</u> había quedado inservible, pero que a Federico no le había pasado nada.**
   (1) su coche
   (2) el coche de él
   (3) del hermano de Federico
   (4) su coche de él
   (5) el coche del padre

2
ESTRUCTURA DE LA ORACIÓN

Tres características de la oración

Para ser completa, la oración debe constar de *sujeto* (tácito o expreso) y
predicado. Además, debe tener *sentido completo*. La palabra o grupo de
palabras que no cumplan estos requisitos constituyen *frases incompletas*.
¿Puede usted identificar las frases incompletas del diálogo?

(1)   PAPÁ: ¿Dónde está Juan?
(2) HERMANA: En una entrevista.
(3)   PAPÁ: ¿Quién le llevó?
(4) HERMANA: Su amiga Ana.

[Respuesta: Las frases incompletas son la (2) y la (4). La (1) y la (3) tienen
sentido propio y constituyen oraciones completas.]

Las frases incompletas suelen ser difíciles de detectar porque hacen
sentido cuando se las lee en el contexto de las oraciones que las rodean.
Cuando sea necesario corregir frases incompletas ambiguas, cerciórese de
que la versión corregida tenga sentido propio. Una de las técnicas que se
puede utilizar es leer las frases de final a principio para poder aislar aquéllas
que sean incompletas.

> **LAS RESPUESTAS DE LOS EJERCICIOS DE ESTE
> CAPÍTULO EMPIEZAN EN LA PÁGINA 442.**

EJERCICIO 1: CORRECCIÓN DE FRASES INCOMPLETAS
Instrucciones: Vuelva a escribir el párrafo siguiente, corrigiendo las frases
incompletas que no sean claras. Añada el sujeto o el predicado que falte o
bien combine las frases y forme oraciones completas.

En su discurso inaugural 1960, el presidente John F.
Kennedy dijo: "No pregunten lo que puede hacer su país por
ustedes; pregunten lo que ustedes pueden hacer por su
país". Esta filosofía redundó en gran beneficio de los ciudadanos de EE.UU. Y también de los países en vías de desarrollo. El caso del Cuerpo de Paz, por ejemplo. Este programa
envió a estos países voluntarios especializados en distintas
áreas. Construcción, agricultura, ganadería, salubridad y
otros. Los voluntarios del Cuerpo de Paz se dedicaron a
transmitir a los ciudadanos de dichos países sus conocimientos. Su fin, mejorar su nivel de vida. Y también mejorar las
relaciones entre Estados Unidos y estas naciones.

Oraciones compuestas

Si combinamos dos o más oraciones simples, podemos formar una *oración
compuesta*.

Ejemplo: Estos clavos son para madera. Ésos son para cemento.

[Respuesta: Estos clavos son para madera **y** ésos son para cemento.]

Las oraciones compuestas pueden ser ***coordinadas*** si la relación que guardan las oraciones simples que las conforman es de igualdad, o ***subordinadas*** si una de las oraciones predomina sobre las demás, "subordinándose" éstas a la oración principal.

Oraciones coordinadas

La oración compuesta que acabamos de formar se compone de dos oraciones independientes enlazadas por la palabra *y.* Cada oración independiente encierra en sí sentido proprio. Las siguientes palabras de enlace, llamadas ***conjunciones,*** se utilizan para combinar palabras así como oraciones independientes y se citan en la tabla adjunta. Note la diferencia en la función que desempeñan las distintas conjunciones.

CONJUNCIONES COORDINANTES		
Conjunción	**Tipo**	**Función**
y, e, que ni, ni...ni	copulativas	denotan simple enlace rechazan las opciones presentadas
o, u	disyuntivas	presentan alternativas contradictorias
bien...bien ya...ya	distributivas	presentan alternativas no contradictorias
pero mas sino sin embargo no obstante con todo	adversativas	oponen o contrastan las oraciones enlazadas

EJERCICIO 2: ORACIONES COORDINADAS
Instrucciones: Elija una conjunción de la tabla de arriba que sea apropiada para enlazar cada par de frases. Después, en una hoja aparte, forme una oración compuesta con cada par. Cerciórese de utilizar la puntuación adecuada.

Ejemplo: No quiero trabajar. Necesito trabajar

[Respuesta: *No quiero trabajar, pero necesito trabajar* o *No quiero trabajar, pero necesito hacerlo.*]

1. Vamos a dar una fiesta este viernes. Esperamos que puedan venir.
2. No estudió para su examen. Lo aprobó.
3. Diseñemos la nueva estructura. Iniciemos el proyecto.
4. Ya llueva, ya nieve, José es siempre puntual. Yo no.
5. No quiere trabajar. Tampoco quiere estudiar.

Oraciones subordinadas

La conjunción coordinante forma oraciones compuestas en las que las distintas oraciones simples mantienen una relación de igualdad: todas tienen la misma importancia. Sin embargo, la *conjunción subordinante,* como su nombre lo indica, "subordina" a la oración principal las demás oraciones simples que conforman la oración compuesta.

CONJUNCIONES SUBORDINANTES		
Conjunción	**Tipo**	**Función**
debido a que porque puesto que ya que pues dado que como	causales	enlaza la causa al efecto
como si	comparativa	expresa una semejanza
si con tal que en caso de que siempre que a menos que	condicionales	expresan una condición
aunque por más que a pesar de que aun cuando	concesivas	expresan un obstáculo o impedimento
por lo tanto por consiguiente así pues así que	consecutivas	expresan una consecuencia
a que para que a fin de que con el objeto de que	finales	expresan un propósito
cuando desde que luego que después (de) que antes (de) que mientras (que) hasta que tan pronto	temporales	expresan tiempo

Enlace de la oración subordinada a la principal

La *oración subordinada* propiamente es una oración dependiente que no tiene sentido completo si no está unida a una *oración independiente* llamada *oración principal.* Esta oración principal es una oración completa que no necesita de la subordinada para que tenga sentido. La principal y la subordinada están, como habíamos visto más arriba, unidas por una conjunción subordinante.

> *Ejemplos:* No estudió. Obtuvo una baja calificación.
> [Oración independiente. Oración independiente.]
>
> **Porque** no estudió, obtuvo una baja calificación.
> [Oración subordinada, oración principal]
>
> Obtuvo una baja calificación **porque** no estudió.
> [Oración principal, oración subordinada]

EJERCICIO 3: INTRODUCCIÓN A LAS ORACIONES SUBORDINADAS

PARTE A
Instrucciones: Complete las oraciones con las conjunciones subordinantes de la tabla que correspondan. En algunos casos, la oración admite más de una conjunción.

1. _____ le tenía mucho miedo al agua, se inscribió a la clase de natación.

2. No voy a ir a la reunión de ex-alumnos _____ mis mejores amigos no van a estar.

3. Cecilia se quedó con su madre _____ volvió la enfermera.

PARTE B
Instrucciones: Combine cada par de oraciones subordinando una de ellas a la otra mediante las conjunciones subordinantes de la tabla.

> *Ejemplo:* Andrés trató de sobornar al policía. Andrés fue arrestado.
> Cuando Andrés trató de sobornar al policía, fue arrestado.

1. Llegamos tarde a la iglesia. Nos perdimos la ceremonia de la boda.
2. Rosa se enojó con la niñera. Dijo que no la volvería a contratar.
3. Llegamos al estacionamiento. Observamos que la tienda estaba cerrada.

EJERCICIO 4: PRÁCTICA DE ORACIONES SUBORDINADAS
Instrucciones: Elija de entre las opciones la conjunción que mejor complete el sentido de la oración.

1. Vengo _____ necesito hablar contigo.

   (a) por lo tanto   **(b)** porque   **(c)** aunque

2. No lo he vuelto a ver _____ nos encontramos aquella vez en el teatro.

   (a) desde que   **(b)** antes que   **(c)** aunque

3. Llamaré a Joseph _____ me diga lo que ha ocurrido.

(a) porque   (b) para que   (c) si

4. No ha estudiado nada; _____ no me sorprende que no haya aprobado el examen.

(a) aunque   (b) por más que   (c) por lo tanto

5. He vuelto, _____ me aconsejaron no regresar.

(a) luego que   (b) puesto que   (c) a pesar de que

6. Déjame un recado, _____ no esté.

(a) en caso de que   (b) si   (c) así pues

7. Te devuelvo el libro, _____ termine de leerlo.

(a) aunque   (b) luego que   (c) por más que

8. _____ será mejor que no caigamos en el mismo error.

(a) Para que   (b) Así pues   (c) Aunque

9. _____ me supliques, no dejaré de cumplir con mi deber.

(a) Aunque   (b) Luego que   (c) A pesar de

10. _____ hubo desayunado, se marchó a la calle.

(a) Si   (b) Por más que   (c) Después que

Puntuación de las oraciones compuestas

Se puede emplear tanto la coma como el punto y coma para separar los elementos de una serie coordinada.

> *Ejemplo:* Fuimos al cine, paseamos, conversamos y nos divertimos mucho.

Se usa por lo general coma o punto y coma para separar la oración principal de la subordinada.

> *Ejemplos:* No tengo el número conmigo; pero, apenas llegue a casa, te llamo.
> En caso de que no puedas venir, te pido que me lo hagas saber.
> Me quedo porque quiero. [*o:* Me quedo, porque quiero.]

Las conjunciones consecutivas se suelen poner entre comas.

> *Ejemplos:* Por tanto, todos somos culpables.
> Estabas advertido y, a pesar de ello, seguiste adelante.
> Por consiguiente, no me dejas otra opción que sancionarte.

EJERCICIO 5: PUNTUACIÓN DE LAS ORACIONES COMPUESTAS
Instrucciones: Coloque la puntuación adecuada a cada oración.

1. La miró por largo rato trató de llamar su atención se le acercó pero ella no le hizo caso
2. Por más que me lo pidas no podré hacerlo
3. Fue a su casa pero cuando trató de abrir la puerta no pudo
4. No logró obtener la puntuación necesaria por lo tanto no podrá apobar el curso
5. Si consigue lo que se propone podrá mejorar su vida

Errores frecuentes de puntuación

Dos errores que se cometen muy a menudo son el de exceso de puntuación tanto como el de falta de puntuación hasta el extremo de enlazar oraciones que deberían ir aparte. Analicemos la oración siguiente para entender mejor estos casos.

INCORRECTO: Tienes que ver a mi hija Bernarda acaba de cumplir los quince se ha teñido el pelo de verde es horrible encima tiene el peinado más extraño del mundo.

Atendiendo al sentido de esta oración, vemos que la misma se compone de cinco oraciones completas simples, que terminan en *Bernarda, quince, verde, horrible* y *mundo* respectivamente. La frase es un extenso *texto corrido,* es decir, un desorganizado y confuso enlace de frases sin que intervenga puntuación o conjunción apropiadas. Para corregir textos corridos se los puede dividir en oraciones independientes o construir oraciones compuestas con la puntuación y conjunción necesarias.

CORRECTO: Tienes que ver a Bernarda: acaba de cumplir los quince y se ha teñido el pelo de verde. ¡Es horrible! Encima, tiene el peinado más extraño del mundo.

Otro error que es frecuente encontrar es el enlace de oraciones completas por medio de comas sin que intervenga conjunción. Este error, llamado *asíndeton imperfecto,* se puede subsanar separando las oraciones o interponiendo la conjunción apropiada entre las oraciones. Veamos entonces un ejemplo de este vicio de construcción.

INCORRECTO: Dijo eso frente a todo el mundo, ahora mis amigos y parientes van a pensar que es un troglodita.

CORRECTO: Dijo eso frente a todo el mundo: ahora mis amigos y parientes van a pensar que es un troglodita.

o:

Dijo eso frente a todo el mundo; así que ahora mis amigos y parientes van a pensar que es un troglodita.

EJERCICIO 6: ERRORES FRECUENTES DE PUNTUACIÓN

Instrucciones: Corrija las oraciones de texto corrido y de asíndeton imperfecto, ya sea separando las frases o combinándolas con conjunciones (*y, pero, porque, o, ni, por lo tanto, sin embargo*). Si, a su parecer, la oración está correctamente redactada, escriba una *C* en el espacio en blanco.

_____ 1. Vine vi vencí.

_____ 2. La llamé a su casa, me dijeron que ya se había ido, volví entonces a la oficina.

_____ 3. Buscó el paraguas. Como no lo pudo hallar, se puso el viejo impermeable y se fue.

EJERCICIO 7: PRÁCTICA DE CONSTRUCCIÓN DE ORACIONES

Instrucciones: El párrafo siguiente puede contener cualquier tipo de error estudiado hasta ahora. Realice las correcciones, según sea necesario, en los puntos críticos (subrayados).

(1) Un grupo de sicólogos ha realizado una investigación acerca del orden de nacimiento de los <u>hijos, las</u> conclusiones obtenidas sugieren que el orden en que nace el niño relativo a sus hermanos influye en el desarrollo de <u>la</u> personalidad <u>y la</u> inteligencia. (2) Una de <u>sus teorías</u> postula que el primogénito recibe más atención de los padres que sus <u>hermanos razón</u> por la cual los primogénitos tienden a ser más intelectuales. (3) El <u>segundogénito así como los que lo siguen</u> se ven obligados a compartir a sus padres con el primerizo, <u>adaptan</u> su comportamiento al de los hermanos mayores.

Otras expresiones de enlace

Existe una gran variedad de locuciones que sirven de nexo o transición entre dos o más oraciones.

Nexo o transición	Función
además asimismo	indica que se presenta información adicional
por otro lado	presenta un contraste
de lo contrario	presenta una alternativa (como *o*)
por ejemplo	presenta información específica sobre una idea general
enseguida	indica un orden temporal posterior e inmediato
de repente de pronto súbitamente	indican un suceso improviso
en consecuencia en razón de ello por ello	expresan una consecuencia

EJERCICIO 8: OTRAS EXPRESIONES DE ENLACE

Instrucciones: Complete la oración con la expresión apropiada atendiendo al sentido de la frase.

1. Era idóneo para el puesto; _____ se lo dieron.

    (a) por ello   **(b)** sin embargo   **(c)** de pronto

2. La comida aquí es muy sabrosa; _____ es bastante económica.

    (a) en consecuencia   **(b)** además   **(c)** por ejemplo

3. Tendré que estudiar con más ahínco; _____ no aprobaré el curso.

    (a) de lo contrario   **(b)** sin embargo   **(c)** en consecuencia

EJERCICIO 9: PRÁCTICA DE ORACIONES COMPUESTAS

Instrucciones: Combine cada par de oraciones según convenga: ya sea formando una oración subordinada o una coordinada. Sírvase de las tablas de conjunciones y otras expresiones de enlace de las páginas XX–XX como guía y cerciórese de puntuar correctamente las oraciones resultantes.

1. La vendedora era muy cortés. Escuchó pacientemente todas mis quejas.
2. Mis amigos me aconsejan. No siempre les escucho.
3. Puedo llevarte al trabajo por la mañana. Si prefieres, puedes ir en el subterráneo.

EJERCICIO 10: CONSTRUCCIÓN Y USO

Instrucciones: Lea el párrafo siguiente y observe si hay errores de construcción o de uso. En algunas de las oraciones, es necesario hacer correcciones; en otras, en cambio, es necesario volver a redactar la parte subrayada. Si a su parecer la frase original es mejor, elija la opción (1).

(1) La participación que tiene el accionista en la propiedad de una corporación está dada por el número de acciones que posee el accionista; sin embargo, al comprar acciones, el accionista se convierte en propietario de la compañía. (2) Cuando la corporación prospera, los accionistas reciben dividendos, es decir, beneficios basados en las ganancias de la empresa. (3) Los accionistas reciben un porcentaje de las ganancias además se benefician con el aumento del valor de sus acciones. (4) Si la compañía no tiene éxito los accionistas pueden sufrir pérdidas en sus acciones. (5) Si el valor de las mismas baja abruptamente, se puede incluso perder todo lo invertido.

1. Oración 1: **La participación que tiene el accionista en la propiedad de una corporación está dada por el número de acciones que posee el <u>accionista; sin embargo, al</u> comprar acciones, el accionista se convierte en propietario de la compañía.**
   (1) no es necesario hacer correcciones
   (2) accionista, sin embargo; al
   (3) accionista, sin embargo, al
   (4) accionista; por lo tanto, al
   (5) accionista, por lo tanto; al

2. Oración 2: **<u>Cuando la corporación prospera, los accionistas reciben dividendos,</u> es decir, beneficios basados en las ganancias de la empresa.**
   (1) no es necesario hacer correcciones
   (2) cambie *prospera* por *próspera*
   (3) elimine la coma después de *prospera*
   (4) reemplace *reciben* por *resiben*
   (5) reemplace *Cuando* por *Debido a*

3. Oración 3: **Los accionistas reciben un porcentaje de las <u>ganancias; no obstante, se benefician</u> con el aumento del valor de sus acciones.**
   (1) no es necesario hacer correcciones
   (2) reemplace *ganancias* por *ganansias*
   (3) reemplace *no obstante* por *ademas*
   (4) sustituya *no obstante* por *asimismo*
   (5) sustituya *benefician* por *benefícian*

4. Oración 4: <u>**Si la compañía no tiene éxito los accionistas pueden sufrir pérdidas en sus acciones.**</u>

    (1) no es necesario hacer correcciones

    (2) ponga una coma después de *éxito*

    (3) cambie *pérdidas* por *perdidas*

    (4) sustituya *acciones* por *acciónes*

    (5) reemplace *éxito* por *éccito*

5. Oración 5: <u>**Si el valor de las mismas baja abruptamente, se puede incluso perder todo lo invertido.**</u>

    (1) no es necesario hacer correcciones

    (2) reemplace *valor* por *balor*

    (3) cambie *se puede* por *se pueden*

    (4) sustituya *incluso* por *inclusive*

    (5) elimine la coma después de *abruptamente*

Concordancia de los tiempos verbales

La siguiente oración se compone de dos oraciones independientes, por lo que consta de dos sujetos y dos verbos. Fíjese en los verbos de la oración.

INCORRECTO: Si me **habrías avisado, habría venido** sin demora. [potencial compuesto, potencial compuesto]

CORRECTO: Si me **hubieras avisado, habría venido** sin demora. [pretérito pluscuamperfecto de subjuntivo, potencial compuesto]

CORRECTO: Si me **hubieses avisado, habría venido** sin demora. [pretérito pluscuamperfecto de subjuntivo, potencial compuesto]

EJERCICIO 11: CONCORDANCIA DE LOS TIEMPOS VERBALES

Instrucciones: Subraye el tiempo verbal de las opciones en paréntesis que corresponde al sentido de la oración.

1. Si María (fuese, sería) más lista, hablaría de inmediato con su jefe.

2. Te hubiera llamado si me (hubieses, habrías) avisado.

3. Aunque (acudieras, acudías) a la cita, no lo verías.

4. Apenas (hubo, hubiera) entrado, se dirigió a la habitación.

Modificadores inconexos y traspuestos

Otra forma de combinar frases es mediante el uso de *frases modificadoras:* frases que describen o añaden información. Por lo general, la oración bien construida habrá de (1) expresar con claridad el elemento modificado y (2) situar el modificador lo más cerca posible del elemento modificado. Observe la ambigüedad que producen los *modificadores traspuestos* de los ejemplos citados abajo.

AMBIGUO: Llorando amargamente, vimos a Juan salir de la habitación.
CLARO: Vimos a Juan salir de la habitación llorando amargamente.

AMBIGUO: Frío e impasible lo vi cruzar la calle.
CLARO: Lo vi cruzar la calle frío e impasible.

Además de traspuestos, los modificadores también pueden estar inconexos.
Los modificadores inconexos son aquéllos que no modifican a ningún
elemento de la oración.

AMBIGUO: Al pisar los frenos, el auto patinó.
CLARO: Cuando pisé los frenos, el auto patinó.

AMBIGUO: Ya a punto de empezar, llegamos al estadio.
CLARO: Ya a punto de empezar el partido, llegamos al estadio.

EJERCICIO 12: MODIFICADORES INCONEXOS Y TRASPUESTOS
Instrucciones: Subraye la frase modificadora de la oración. Vuelva a redactar la oración que contenga un modificador inconexo o traspuesto.

1. Clavado en la pared, Ricardo vió el letrero de "No fumar".
2. Estando en la ducha, sonó el teléfono.
3. De viaje por Colorado, mi equipaje se perdió en el tren.
4. El perro estaba debajo de la mesa pidiendo comida a todos los
   comensales.

Paralelismo

Se recomienda que los elementos de la oración que desempeñen la misma
función presenten la misma estructura o forma. A este tipo de construcción
en que los elementos de función semejante se construyen de manera
semejante se denomina *paralelismo.*

NO PARALELOS: Prefiere bailar, cantar y ser actriz
PARALELOS: Prefiere bailar, cantar y actuar.

NO PARALELOS: La modelo es alta, delgada y tiene una mirada atractiva.
PARALELOS: La modelo es alta, delgada y atractiva.

EJERCICIO 13: PARALELISMO
Instrucciones: Escriba en el espacio en blanco la letra de la oración mejor
redactada.

_____ 1. (a) Thomas Edison inventó la bombilla eléctrica, inició el
               arte de la cinematografía y el fonógrafo.

        (b) Thomas Edision inventó la bombilla eléctrica, la
               cinematografía y el fonógrafo.

_____ 2. (a) Tener un buen trabajo, vivir sola y divertirse son los
               objetivos de Victoria.

        (b) Tener un buen trabajo, estar viviendo sola y divertirse son
               los objetivos de Victoria.

_____ **3.** **(a)** Prometo que te voy a amar, quererte, y te voy a honrar.

(b) Prometo amarte, quererte y honrarte.

EJERCICIO 14: CONSTRUCCIÓN Y USO

Instrucciones: Lea el párrafo siguiente y verifique si hay errores de concordancia de tiempos verbales, de modificadores inconexos o traspuestos, de falta de paralelismo o de construcción y uso en general. Luego, efectúe las correcciones necesarias o vuelva a redactar las partes subrayadas. Si la frase original es, a su parecer, la mejor versión, elija la opción (1).

(1) Cuando nos poníamos toda la familia a jugar juegos de preguntas y respuestas, nuestros niños más pequeños se sentían dejados de lado, de cinco y seis años. (2) Por ello, decidimos que nuevas preguntas deberían ser escritas por nosotros que los chicos pudieran contestar. (3) Tratamos de hacer preguntas que les parecieran interesantes y motivadoras pero no desalentarlos. (4) Les preguntábamos sobre temas que habían estudiado en el colegio. (5) Otras preguntas eran de temas vistos en los libros que les leíamos.

1. Oración 1: **Cuando nos poníamos toda la familia a jugar juegos de preguntas y respuestas, <u>nuestros niños más pequeños se sentían dejados de lado, de cinco y seis años.</u>**
   - **(1)** nuestros niños más pequeños se sentían dejados de lado, de cinco y seis años.
   - **(2)** sus niños más pequeños se sentían dejados de lado, de cinco y seis años.
   - **(3)** nuestros niños más pequeños, de cinco y seis años, se sentían dejados de lado.
   - **(4)** nuestro niños, de cinco y seis años, más pequeños se sentían dejados de lado.
   - **(5)** nuestros más pequeños, de cinco y seis años, se sintieron dejados de lado.

2. Oración 2: **Por ello, <u>decidimos que nuevas preguntas deberían ser escritas por nosotros</u> que los chicos pudieran contestar.**
   - **(1)** decidimos que nuevas preguntas deberían ser escritas por nosotros
   - **(2)** decidimos que nuevas preguntas serían escritas por nosotros
   - **(3)** decidimos que nuevas preguntas debieran ser escritas por nosotros
   - **(4)** decidimos escribir nuevas preguntas
   - **(5)** escribieron nuevas preguntas

3. Oración 3: **Tratamos de hacer preguntas que les parecieran <u>interesantes y motivadoras pero no desalentarlos.</u>**
   - **(1)** interesantes y motivadoras pero no desalentarlos
   - **(2)** interesantes y motivadoras pero sin desalentarlos
   - **(3)** interesantes, motivadoras y no desalentarlos
   - **(4)** interesantes y motivadoras pero no desalentadoras
   - **(5)** interesantes, motivadoras y no desalentadoras

4. Oraciones 4–5: **Les preguntábamos sobre temas que habían estudiado en el <u>colegio. Otras preguntas eran de temas vistos en los libros</u> que les leíamos.**

   (1) colegio. Otras preguntas eran de temas vistos en los libros
   (2) colegio. Otras preguntas se basaban en temas vistos en los libros
   (3) colegio. Les preguntábamos también acerca de temas vistos en los libros
   (4) colegio o vistos en los libros
   (5) colegio o visto en los libros

3
ORTOGRAFÍA Y PUNTUACIÓN

Cuando leemos, nos valemos de las normas de ortografía y la puntuación para reconocer los vocablos y comprender el sentido del texto escrito. Todos alguna vez hemos leído, o tratado de leer, textos que presentan tantos errores que son incapaces de transmitir su mensaje. En este capítulo se enfocarán aquellos temas que pueden aparecer en la Prueba de Expresión Escrita.

Uso de las mayúsculas

Se escriben siempre con mayúsculas los *nombres propios,* o sea, los nombres específicos de personas, animales, lugares, etc. Escriba en el espacio en blanco un nombre propio y cerciórese de emplear mayúscula.

Nombres comunes (generales)	Nombres propios (específicos)
mujer	*Bette Midler*
calle	_____
país	_____
día feriado	_____
doctor	_____

Otras reglas sobre el uso de las mayúsculas

1. **Los títulos, los nombres de dignidad y los tratamientos, especialmente si están abreviados, se escriben con letra inicial mayúscula, a menos que se empleen en sentido genérico.**

   Ejemplos: Me recomendaron un buen pediatra, el **Dr.** Armando Azcárraga.

   Fui a ver al **doctor** porque tenía una tos que no se me iba.

2. **Se escriben con mayúscula los toponímicos o nombres de lugares específicos; pero no se emplea mayúscula con los gentilicios.**

   Ejemplos: Mi amigo nació en **Rusia;** tiene ciudadanía **rusa.**

   La **Plaza Mayor** de Madrid es preciosa.

   Hoy fui a dar una vuelta por la **plaza.**

3. **Se escribe con mayúscula la letra inicial de un escrito y la que vaya a continuación de un punto. Después de los dos puntos se usa indistintamente mayúscula o minúscula, a no ser que a los dos puntos siga una cita.**

   Ejemplos: Entiéndeme, por favor: **sólo** queríamos hacerte una broma.
   Luego me dije a mí mismo: "**Ya** estoy listo para la prueba. . ."

EJERCICIO 1: REGLAS SOBRE EL USO DE LAS MAYÚSCULAS

Instrucciones: Reescriba las siguientes oraciones, poniendo y eliminando mayúsculas donde sea necesario. El número de errores que hay en cada oración está dado en paréntesis.

1. El alcalde de chestertown solicitó la asistencia del gobernador kelly. (*3 errores*)
2. Nos reuniremos con el Senador el Miércoles, 9 de Agosto, en el Lincoln Center de memphis. (*4 errores*)
3. Siga en dirección Norte hasta la avenida baker, luego doble a la izquierda en el Kennedy Expressway. (*2 errores*)
4. El río ohio es muy bonito. (*1 error*)

Puntuación

Todas las oraciones terminan en punto (.), puntos suspensivos (. . .), signo de interrogación (?) o signo de admiración (!). En el caso de estos dos últimos, la oración también debe llevar al principio signo de interrogación (¿) o de admiración (¡) invertidos. Se habrá, por tanto, de estar atento a la puntuación, cuidando que esté presente y debidamente colocada. El simple hecho de que un grupo de palabras acabe en punto o en signo de interrogación no necesariamente implica que la oración esté completa.

> INCOMPLETO: De la limpieza del garaje.
> COMPLETO: Pedro se encargó de la limpieza del garaje.

La coma

La *coma* se usa en casos específicos. Recuerde que peca tanto el que ponga comas innecesarias como el que deja de ponerlas. Las reglas más importantes en cuanto al uso de la coma son las que se presentan a continuación.

1. **Se usa la coma para separar los elementos de una serie. Generalmente no se pone coma entre el penúltimo y el último elemento de la serie si media entre éstos conjunción.**

   Ejemplos: Estudiamos **matemáticas, geografía, ciencias y literatura.**
   Risa y llanto, nube y sol, ¡cuánto contraste!

2. **En cualquier acotación explicativa intercalada en la oración principal o cualquier construcción que altere el orden normal de la oración.**

   Ejemplos: El perro, **que ya no oye,** salió disparado.
   Federico, **cuando lo oyó venir,** salió de la habitación.

3. **Se usa la coma después de la subordinada, si ésta precede a la oración principal.**

   Ejemplos: **Si me esperas,** te llevo.
   Aunque insistas, no cederé.

4. Van entre comas las siguientes expresiones enfáticas: *finalmente, en efecto, sin embargo, por el contrario, por consiguiente, ahora bien,* y otras semejantes.

Ejemplos: Diremos, **finalmente,** que los acontecimientos se precipitaron y**, en efecto,** el desenlace sobrevino rápidamente.

EJERCICIO 2: EL USO DE LA COMA
Instrucciones: Ponga las comas necesarias al texto de la siguiente carta.

Querida mamá:

Como me queda poco dinero no podré ir a casa en las vacaciones de primavera. Por lo tanto me quedaré aquí en Des Moines estudiando. Debo confesar que aunque no malgasté el dinero tampoco ahorré lo suficiente para el boleto de avión. Así pues espero que lo entiendas. Por último quería pedirte que llamaras a Daniel y Estela y les dijeras que no voy.

Un abrazo,
Delia

El punto y coma

El *punto y coma* indica una pausa mayor que la dada por la coma y menor que la dada por los dos puntos. El punto y coma se suele emplear en los siguientes casos.

1. Para enlazar dos o más oraciones independientes que guardan relación entre sí.

Ejemplo: Siempre que vamos a casa de mis padres, hacemos excursiones al campo; montamos a caballo; nos bañamos en el lago; nos acostamos en la hierba; en fin, lo pasamos de lo más bien.

2. Entre los dos miembros de oraciones coordinadas adversativas y consecutivas extensas.

Ejemplos: Los habitantes del poblado lo buscaron por todo el bosque durante varios días; pero no lograron seguirle la pista.
Ya te han pagado lo que te debían; por lo tanto, ya me podrás pagar lo que me debes.

3. Entre los elementos de una enumeración que ya tienen comas.

Ejemplo: Se aconseja seguir los siguientes pasos: primero, lijar la superficie; segundo, aplicar una capa de pintura protectora; tercero, dejar secar; y, por último, aplicar la pintura.

Los dos puntos

Se emplean los dos puntos en los casos siguientes:

1. En la salutación de cartas.

Ejemplo: Estimada Sra. Ruiz:

2. **Para indicar que lo que sigue es una cita textual.**

   Ejemplo: Entonces dijo: "¿Por qué te quedas ahí parado?"

3. **En la ampliación o desarrollo de una idea.**

   Ejemplo: El mundo es suyo: cuídenlo, quiéranlo.

EJERCICIO 3: REPASO DE PUNTUACIÓN
Instrucciones: Cada oración de abajo presenta un error. Identifíquelo y corríjalo.

1. Para quitar la pintura, necesitarás, un galón de aguarrás, trapos, pincel y máscara protectora
2. Elisa no ha devuelto el vestido a la tienda: porque ha perdido el recibo.
3. Aunque me acueste tarde siempre me despierto a la misma hora.
4. En esta caja están los platos blancos, en la otra, los platos azules.
5. Jimena contestó; "Cumpliré con mi promesa".

Ortografía

Se recomienda al estudiante repasar las reglas de ortografía si se desea obtener un buen rendimiento en la Prueba de Expresión Escrita. Conviene enfocarse tanto en las reglas generales como en las excepciones: la dificultad **b/v** (p. ej.: *baca, vaca*), **c/z/s** (*hacía, hizo, asía*), **c/k/qu** (*cosa, kilo, quiosco*), **g/j** (*giro, jirafa*), **y/i** (*reino, rey*), **ll/y** (*llanta, yanta*), **m/n** (*álbum, germen*), **r/rr** (*río, correr*), **s/x** (*espiral, extraño*); **c/z/p/d + consonante** (*acta, hazle, corrupto, adquirir*); la **h** (*hala, ala*); **palabras juntas y separadas** (*a ver, haber*); acentuación; y otros.

4
CÓMO PREPARARSE PARA LA
<u>PRUEBA DE COMPOSICIÓN</u>

Una composición puede ajustarse a las normas de sintaxis, ortografía y puntuación, con oraciones completas, bien estructuradas y conformes al uso, pero no decir absolutamente nada. Todo buen escrito debe decir algo: ofrecer una explicación, expresar una opinión con argumentos válidos y bien razonados, o describir a alguien o alguna cosa. El proceso de escritura es comparable a un entrenamiento físico: es necesario seguir una serie de pasos hasta alcanzar el nivel deseado. La escritura es asimismo un "ejercicio" mental que nos ayuda a organizar nuestras ideas y expresarlas en el papel.

El proceso de escritura

Se puede dividir el proceso de escritura en cinco etapas:

1. **Pre-escritura.** Ponga su mente a trabajar en la búsqueda de un tema, ya sea mediante diagramas, tablas u otras estrategias organizativas.

2. **Apunte de ideas.** Anote en un borrador las ideas resultantes de las actividades de preescritura.

3. **Revisión.** Escriba un segundo borrador más estructurado. Analice lo que le agrada o desagrada del escrito.

4. **Corrección.** Compruebe la sintaxis, gramática, ortografía y puntuación.

5. **Finalización.** Escriba con un propósito, por ejemplo: recopilar historias familiares, pasar la Prueba de Composición del GED.

Precalentamiento a la escritura

Póngase a pensar en los distintos tipos de escritos que usted redacta a diario: listas (de supermercado, de quehaceres del hogar, de recados, de regalos, de asuntos pendientes, etc.); notas (a miembros de su familia, amigos, maestros); cartas (de negocios, personales, de solicitud de trabajo, a periódicos o revistas); y anotaciones en su diario. ¿Hay otras clases de escritos que usted redacta pero que no se han mencionado en este apartado?

Temas de escritura

El mantenerse informado y escribir acerca de sus experiencias, conversaciones y pensamientos cotidianos le ayudará a acumular recursos que necesitará a la hora de escribir. Veamos algunas sugerencias:

1. Lleve un diario (sucesos del día, experiencias, ideas, sensaciones).
2. Piense en conversaciones que haya tenido con otros (métodos de persuasión).
3. Lea desde el punto de vista del escritor (desarrollo de las ideas, organización de los párrafos y datos implícitos en el contexto).
4. Trate de escribir algo que no haya escrito antes (cartas sorpresa, historias familiares, etc.).

EJERCICIO 1: PRECALENTAMIENTO

1. Escriba una nota a alguien o el texto de una anotación de un diario, que tenga una extensión de cuatro o cinco oraciones.

2. Piense en un día memorable de su vida y escriba unas cuantas líneas describiendo el día o el acontecimiento.

Tema, público y propósito

El *tema* es el asunto sobre el que se escribe. Por ejemplo, si se escribe una carta al casero, el tema podría tratar de "la suba del alquiler", "una extensión del contrato de alquiler" o "un electrodoméstico que necesita arreglo".

Una vez decidido el tema, el escritor ha de determinar su *propósito* u objetivo. ¿Qué está tratando de decir? ¿Qué lo motiva a escribir? ¿Quiere narrar un suceso, describir algo, informar sobre un tema o persuadir a alguien? Cuando escribimos una carta de reclamo a una tienda, nuestro propósito es expresar un problema, comunicar una opinión y proponer una solución.

Su propósito depende también de quién va leer lo que escribe: depende de su *público.* Mientras que los diarios son escritos personales, la mayor parte de los demás tipos de escritos tienen por objetivo el que alguien los lea, como sucede en el caso de la persona que escribe una carta solicitando trabajo al director de personal de una empresa. Una redacción de tipo "ensayo" va dirigida normalmente al público lector en general, de manera tal que todos los que la lean puedan comprenderla.

EJERCICIO 2: TEMA, PÚBLICO Y PROPÓSITO
Instrucciones: Lea este párrafo final de carta e identifique: (1) el tipo de escrito, (2) el tema, (3) el propósito y (4) el lector (o público).

Por está razón, solicito permiso para que Erik pueda faltar a su clase de historia el viernes próximo, esperando que esta ausencia no perjudique su progreso en la misma. Le rogaría asimismo le asignara el día anterior la tarea que le corresponde.

Gracias de antemano.

Preescritura de los párrafos

¿Alguna vez le ha ayudado usted a alguien a mudarse de casa? ¿Ha notado que si se tiene todo empacado, identificado y organizado, la parte que sigue se hace mucho más fácil? Pues lo mismo sucede cuando se escribe. Si se planean y organizan las ideas antes de empezar a escribir, el proceso de escritura en sí es más fácil y el producto final, mejor.

Búsqueda de los párrafos

Una vez identificado el tema, el propósito y el público, se habrán ahora de buscar las ideas que se van a plasmar en el escrito. A este proceso se le conoce como *brainstorm* ("tormenta cerebral" en inglés, es decir, "tormenta de ideas").

Cuando haga *brainstorm*, conviene apuntar rápidamente todas las ideas que le vengan a la mente acerca del tema en cuestión. No se detenga a corregir ni a evaluar sus ideas; no se preocupe de la ortografía ni intente escribir oraciones completas. Un "remolino" de ideas le deberá venir a la mente cuando se ponga a buscar distintas formas de razonar y argumentar su opinión sobre el tema.

Veamos un ejemplo de *brainstorm:*

Tema: ventas de garaje
Oración temática: La organización es fundamental en la preparación de una venta de garaje.

Lista de ideas de *brainstorm:*

clasificar y poner precio a los artículos
limpiar los armarios y el sótano
mantener a los niños del vecindario fuera de mi jardín
pedir mesas prestadas
poner un anuncio en el periódico
hacer carteles y colocarlos

Estructura del párrafo

El *párrafo* es, en sentido estricto, un grupo de oraciones que se escriben sobre un tema o idea principal. Los párrafos están formados por dos componentes muy importantes: la *oración temática* y las *oraciones secundarias.* La oración temática expresa la idea principal del párrafo y aparece normalmente al principio. Las oraciones secundarias respaldan y explican la idea principal, presentando evidencia, ejemplos, razones y argumentos. Los párrafos también pueden tener una *oración de cierre* o conclusión, donde se resume o se vuelve a expresar la idea principal.

En el siguiente ejemplo, podemos observar que la primera oración es la oración temática. Ésta da la pauta que ha de seguir el resto del párrafo. Las oraciones secundarias explican la idea principal y la oración de cierre hace un resumen sin repeticiones.

Las lecciones de karate han contribuido a mejorar notablemente la auto-estima de Juan. Él es un niño de tamaño más bien pequeño y sin muchas inclinaciones atléticas; pero, después de empezar a ver las películas de "Karate Kid", se enamoró de ellas y se empezó a interesar por el karate. Ha estado yendo a un curso desde hace seis meses y se le ve muy contento. A medida que progresa en el curso, va ganando más confianza en sí mismo y parece que se está relacionando mejor con sus compañeros de clase. Juan se siente ahora mucho más seguro de sí mismo y está tratando de conseguir su objetivo: ¡la cinta negra!

Redacción de la oración temática

La oración temática es la más importante del párrafo y se encuentra con frecuencia encabezando el párrafo. La oración temática expresa el propósito del escrito. Se podría comparar la oración temática con una "oraciónsombrilla" bajo la cual todas las oraciones secundarias se cobijan y se corresponden con la idea expresada por la oración temática: *Las lecciones de karate han contribuido a mejorar notablemente la auto-estima de Juan.*

EJERCICIO 3: REDACCIÓN DE LA ORACIÓN TEMÁTICA

Instrucciones: Escriba la oración temática que falta en los párrafos que siguen. Primero, lea las oraciones secundarias y de cierre; luego, redacte la oración.

En los días soleados, tengo mucha energía y me siento bien: cuando hace sol, soy por lo general de lo más sociable y me llevo bien con todos. Cuando llueve, me deprimo y siento un desgano total. Me encanta andar en trineo con mis hijos; por lo que me alegro mucho cuando nieva. Como pueden ver, si no mirara nunca afuera sería una persona más contenta y satisfecha.

Siempre que me meto a la fila para comprar los boletos de entrada vuelvo a recordar esa emoción que he sentido siempre al venir a esta feria año tras año. Cada vez que me monto al caballito del tíovivo me vienen a la memoria tantos recuerdos del pasado. . . ¡Hasta la música sigue igual! Los aromas del dulce de chocolate, el maní y el algodón dulce me recuerdan cómo gastaba mi mensualidad en golosinas en este parque de diversiones. Y, cuando me lleno de valor y me subo a la montaña rusa, incluso hoy me mareo. ¡Hay cosas que no cambian nunca!

Selección y organización de ideas

Es necesario seleccionar las ideas que se van a utilizar en el escrito. ¿Se pueden usar todas las ideas de la lista de *brainstorm* o hay que eliminar algunas? Conviene siempre eliminar las ideas intranscendentes: las ideas que no respaldan la oración temática.

Pero, ¿en qué orden estructurar las ideas? Cada tema y cada párrafo son distintos; por lo que no existe una forma específica de ordenar las ideas. Éstas se pueden ordenar cronológicamente, de menor a mayor importancia, o en cualquier otra secuencia que sirva a la presentación del tema del escrito.

Abajo volvemos a adjuntar la lista de ideas de *brainstorm* de la página XX después de haber eliminado las ideas intranscendentes. Las ideas restantes aparecen numeradas conforme al orden en que el escritor va a presentar sus ideas: el orden es cronológico.

2. clasificar y poner precio a los artículos
1. limpiar los armarios y el sótano
4. pedir mesas prestadas
3. poner un anuncio en el periódico
5. hacer carteles y colocarlos

Redacción del borrador inicial

Ahora usted está listo para redactar un párrafo: un primer borrador. A medida que vaya escribiendo, guíese por su lista numerada de ideas de *brainstorm*. Es lógico que no tiene que seguirla al pie de la letra; pero, si ha confeccionado bien su lista, ya tiene hecha gran parte del trabajo: lo que queda es transformar las ideas de la lista en oraciones secundarias y añadir la oración de cierre.

Tenga presente que está escribiendo un borrador: sus párrafos no tienen necesariamente que salir perfectos al primer intento. Trate inicialmente de plasmar las ideas en el papel; luego puede ir puliendo lo que haya escrito y haciendo las correcciones necesarias. Deje márgenes amplios y espacio entre renglones. No olvide las siguientes características de los párrafos:

1. La primera palabra tiene que estar sangrada.

2. El párrafo contiene una oración temática que expresa la idea principal.

3. El párrafo se compone de varias oraciones que dan apoyo a la idea principal.

EJERCICIO 4: REDACCIÓN DEL BORRADOR INICIAL
Instrucciones: Haga una lista de ideas de *brainstorm* y escriba el borrador de un párrafo. Guarde su redacción.

EJERCICIO 5: PRÁCTICA DEL PROCESO DE ESCRITURA
Instrucciones: Elija dos de los siguientes temas.

1. su auto favorito
2. el músico o el grupo de rock que menos le gusta
3. un amigo o pariente a quien admire

Para cada tema:

- Escriba una oración temática que exprese la idea principal del párrafo.
- Busque ideas mediante *brainstorm* que respalden su oración temática.
- Seleccione y ordene las ideas que quiera usar en el párrafo.
- Escriba un borrador de cada párrafo.

Revisión del borrador

Después de haber preparado el borrador del párrafo, se recomienda dejarlo a un lado por un momento. Piense entonces en lo que usted quería comunicar y lea el párrafo que ha escrito como si usted fuera su público. ¿Se ha desarrollado la idea principal? ¿Es clara la oración temática y está bien argumentada? ¿Hay una oración de cierre? Hágase las siguientes preguntas:

- ¿Qué es lo bueno del párrafo?
- ¿Qué es lo que no me gusta?
- ¿Qué puedo hacer para mejorarlo?

Esta etapa del proceso de escritura se denomina *revisión*. El proceso de revisión es como una "segunda oportunidad": una oportunidad para mudar de lugar palabras y oraciones, agregar ideas, eliminar oraciones superfluas o volverlas a escribir, y clarificar oraciones que se hayan redactado de forma confusa o ambigua. En lugar de volver a copiar su párrafo, haga los cambios necesarios en los espacios que hay entre renglones y en los márgenes de ambos lados. No se preocupe todavía de los errores de puntuación y ortografía: tendrá oportunidad de corregir su trabajo más tarde.

Observe el siguiente borrador de muestra, el cual necesita de algunas correcciones. ¿Qué haría usted para mejorarlo?

El Día de Acción de Gracias es un día para descansar. Mamá y papá, como sacrificados padres que son, se levantan como a las 6:00 A.M. para preparar el pavo y luego se vuelven a acostar. En casa, por lo general, la gente se levanta tarde. Como los tíos y los primos traen el resto de la comida, sólo hay preparaciones de última hora que hacer y así nos queda tiempo para sentarnos a hablar o jugar a las cartas. Los niños corretean por todas partes y casi no nos dejan conversar con tranquilidad. Después de una gran comilona a la 1:00 y de hacer visitas por la tarde, nos sentimos todos agradecidos por el tiempo compartido juntos.

Se podría dar más fuerza al párrafo con estos dos cambios: (1) invirtiendo el orden de la segunda y tercera oraciones y (2) eliminando o rehaciendo la oración: "Los niños corretean por todas partes y casi no nos dejan conversar con tranquilidad". Esta oración no sirve de apoyo a la oración temática: es una idea intranscendente.

EJERCICIO 6: REVISIÓN DEL BORRADOR
Instrucciones: Elija dos de los párrafos que ha escrito. Revíselos, asegurándose de que la idea principal esté expresada con claridad y bien argumentada. No se olvide de guardar su trabajo.

Corrección final del borrador

En esta etapa del proceso de escritura, se realizan las correcciones necesarias según las normas de sintaxis y gramática, puntuación y ortografía. En los capítulos anteriores, usted ha tenido oportunidad de realizar este tipo de corrección; de manera que ya tiene experiencia en lo que respecta a la identificación de errores. En el ejemplo siguiente, observe cómo ha usado las marcas el escritor para indicar las correcciones de forma clara y cuidadosa.

Como una semana antes de la fecha de venta, llamo al

p   *anuncio*

~~P~~eriódico y ~~anunsio~~ todo lo que quiero vender. En casa, todos

garaje

me ayudan a limpiar el ~~garage~~ y dejarlo listo para la venta. El

día anterior, pido mesas prestadas y ya dejo colocados todos

artículos

los ~~articulos~~.

Cuatro tipos de escritura

Tipos de escritura	Propósito
Narrativa	narrar o contar una historia
Descriptiva	describir algo
Informativa	informar o explicar por medio de datos
Persuasiva	convencer al lector que crea o haga algo

Escritura narrativa

El fin de la *escritura narrativa* es contar una historia, por lo general, en orden cronológico. Si el relato no se narra en una secuencia determinada, el lector u oyente no lo comprenderá. Lea el siguiente párrafo y observe que el narrador, un oficial de policía, relata en orden cronológico un caso típico de disputas domésticas.

Uno de los aspectos más difíciles de mi trabajo es responder a llamadas de disputas domésticas. En gran parte de estas disputas tienen lugar actos de violencia: es frecuente el caso del hombre que pega a la mujer o a los niños. Cuando mi colega y yo llegamos al lugar del incidente, lo primero que hacemos es verificar si hay armas de algún tipo. Luego, identificamos rápidamente al agresor. Entonces es cuando intervenimos directamente, tratando siempre de no hacer ningún arresto y aconsejando a todos los miembros de la casa. Si es necesario, mi colega o yo mismo llevamos para fuera de la casa a una de las personas para tratar de calmarla. Como las víctimas suelen tener miedo de presentar denuncia contra los perpetradores, a veces nos vemos obligados a irnos de la casa sin saber si las personas que ahí viven van a estar bien. En fin, es por esto que las llamadas de disputas domésticas son unas de las más frustrantes para los oficiales de policía.

Las palabras que nos ayudan a seguir la secuencia de ideas de un párrafo se denominan *palabras de transición.* Las siguientes palabras son útiles dentro de la escritura narrativa porque indican un orden cronológico.

antes	ahora	después	primeramente	finalmente
anteriormente	durante	luego	primero	por fin
previamente	mientras	entonces	en primer	por último
	mientras tanto	enseguida	lugar	
	entre tanto	seguidamente	segundo	
	cuando	más tarde	en segundo	
		muy pronto	lugar	

Vuelva a leer el párrafo sobre disputas domésticas y subraye las palabras de transición que indican un orden cronológico.

[Respuesta: *cuando, primero, luego, entonces*]

EJERCICIO 7: PRÁCTICA DE ESCRITURA NARRATIVA

Instrucciones: Redacte una párrafo narrativo que contenga una oración temática y presente los sucesos cronológicamente. Sírvase de las palabras de transición para que el lector pueda seguir con facilidad el hilo del relato. Narre una experiencia que recuerde vivamente de su niñez.

Escritura descriptiva

El tipo de escritura que presenta una especie de imagen mental al lector se denomina *escritura descriptiva.* Al realizar una descipción, el autor puede hacer evocar los cinco sentidos: qué aspecto presenta el objeto (forma, color y tamaño), qué sonido emite, qué olor o qué sabor tiene, qué textura presenta al tacto.

Es de suma importancia que la descripción contenga detalles específicos para que al lector le sea posible "imaginarse" lo que se describe. No obstante, evite emplear expresiones cuyo sentido sea vago o ambiguo, así como expresiones trilladas o clisés como *muy, bien, bastante, bueno, malo,* etc. En su lugar, use palabras más específicas que transmitan al lector exactamente aquello que usted quiere expresar. Trate de evitar el lenguaje florido, repetitivo y poco sustancioso.

A continuación ofrecemos una muestra de escritura descriptiva. ¿Qué problemas puede ver en la misma?

> Rich y Heather acaban de tener una niña. Nació el 10 de noviembre y le pusieron el nombre de Meghan. Es una bebita gordita y muy guapa. Nos enviaron unas fotografías de la nena cuando tenía unos cuantos días de vida. Es una niña muy linda.

El párrafo sólo proporciona un mínimo de información general que no nos permite formarnos una imagen más vívida de la niña. Sabemos que Meghan es guapa y gordita, pero desconocemos su color de pelo o de ojos, su tez, su peso al nacer, su estado de salud, a quién se parece y otros detalles más. Observe cómo el párrafo siguiente es más específico y ofrece mayor cantidad de detalles.

> El 10 de noviembre pasado, Rich y Heather tuvieron una bebita preciosa: pelirroja de ojos oscuros y cara redondeada, de nueve libras de peso. Sus padres la llamaron Meghan Brady Marmor y ya nos han enviado fotografías de la niña, la primeriza. En una de las fotos, se la ve a Meghan con un conjunto marrón: ¡Qué ricura! Parece un animalito de peluche. . . como para comérsela a besos. De los cachetes, ni se hable: carnosos y rosados, casi de terciopelo. . . como para pellizcárselos todos. La niña parece ser bien robusta y saludable; igual que la madre cuando era bebita. ¡Quién diría. . .! ¡Cómo pasan los años. . .!

EJERCICIO 8: USAR LA ESCRITURA DESCRIPTIVA

Instrucciones: Desarrolle las siguientes oraciones en párrafos que contengan detalles específicos de interés. ¡Eche a volar la imaginación!

1. He conseguido un buen trabajo
2. Es una película divertida
3. Es un muchacho muy bueno

   Ejemplo: Hemos comprado un auto muy bueno.

   Por fin hemos comprado el auto: una camioneta familiar muy cómoda y espaciosa de color gris metálico y con el interior azul oscuro. Está repleta de opciones: control crucero, radiograbadora con CD, ventanas y seguro automáticos y mucho más.

EJERCICIO 9: ESCRIBIR UN PÁRRAFO DESCRIPTIVO

Instrucciones: Suponga que usted va a ir al aeropuerto a recibir a una vieja amiga de la familia: no se han visto desde que usted tenía cinco años. Escriba un párrafo descriptivo acerca de usted y la ropa que se va a poner para que se le pueda reconocer en el aeropuerto. Incluya detalles específicos para ofrecer al lector una imagen más vívida del relato.

Escritura informativa

La *escritura informativa* presenta datos y no opiniones. Un ejemplo muy común de escritura informativa son las noticias, las cuales presentan información al lector. Entre otros ejemplos comunes de escritura informativa destacan las recetas de cocina y las instrucciones para ensamblar juguetes y muebles.

   Un gran número de escritos tienen por objetivo presentar información para (1) explicar las causas de un efecto o (2) explicar los efectos o consecuencias de una causa. Lea detenidamente el párrafo del *Ejercicio 10* y observe cómo está organizado de acuerdo con la causa y el efecto. El párrafo presenta la causa en la oración temática y los efectos en las oraciones secundarias.

EJERCICIO 10: CAUSA Y EFECTO

Instrucciones: Identifique los seis efectos del divorcio de los Wilson.

   Los Wilson han presentado una demanda de divorcio recientemente. Por esta razón, la casa de la familia se pondrá a la venta y ambas partes habrán de llegar a un acuerdo con respecto a la propiedad familiar. Es muy probable que la Sra. Wilson, que ha trabajado a tiempo parcial durante varios años, busque un trabajo a tiempo completo. Desde la separación, el Sr. Wilson se ha mudado a un apartamento, mientras que la Sra. Wilson y los niños se han ido a vivir con la hermana de ésta. La vida de los Wilson ha cambiado radicalmente en los dos últimos meses.

Palabras de transición entre causa y efecto			
porque puesto que dado que	ya que como consecuentemente	por ello por esta razón si...entonces	por consiguiente por lo tanto

EJERCICIO 11: ESCRITURA INFORMATIVA: CAUSA Y EFECTO

Instrucciones: Elija uno de los siguientes temas y escriba un párrafo que declare las causas o los efectos.

1. Redacte un párrafo explicando por qué usted ha decidido prepararse para el Examen del GED. (El párrafo deberá hablar de las causas.)

2. Redacte un párrafo explicando cómo ha afectado su vida el hecho de estudiar para el Examen del GED. (El párrafo deberá hablar de los efectos.)

Escritura persuasiva

La *escritura persuasiva* expresa una opinión. El propósito del escritor es "vender" al lector un punto de vista particular o un modo de razonar. El escritor persuasivo tiene que ser capaz de expresar una opinión y luego concentrarse en argumentos claros y lógicos.

Declaración de una opinión

¿Cuál de los siguientes párrafos de apertura es más persuasivo?

El aumento de impuestos para la expansión de la facultad comunitaria de la zona ofrece grandes ventajas; pero, al mismo tiempo, existen razones válidas para votar en contra de dicha medida. No será fácil la decisión.

El aumento de impuestos para la expansión de la facultad comunitaria capacitará a los habitantes de la zona a hacer frente a las necesidades del futuro. A pesar de ser costosa, toda mejora que se pueda hacer a la facultad redundará en beneficio de la población; razón por la cual apoyo la propuesta.

El segundo párrafo tiene más fuerza porque expresa un punto de vista definido. El escritor del primer párrafo se vería obligado a hacer un gran esfuerzo por convencer a alguien de votar a favor, o en contra, del aumento de impuestos. El escritor del segundo párrafo adopta una posición clara sobre el tema.

Argumentación

Una vez redactada la oración temática del párrafo persuasivo, habrá que *argumentarla* con razones que la respalden. ¿Por qué la expansión de la facultad comunitaria beneficiaría a la comunidad?

Oración temática: El aumento de impuestos para la expansión de la facultad comunitaria capacitará a los habitantes de la zona a hacer frente a las necesidades del futuro.

Lista de ideas de *brainstorm*:

1. no será necesario salir del pueblo en busca de programas educativos
2. la mayoría de los habitantes no votará a favor de un aumento en los impuestos
3. las nuevas industrias que se trasladen a esta zona requerirán nuevos programas de capacitación
4. las clases ya no dan abasto a la cantidad creciente de alumnos; las matriculaciones están aumentando

Se debe eliminar el apartado 2 porque va en contra de la opinión del escritor en lugar de respaldarla.

EJERCICIO 12: ESCRIBIR PÁRRAFOS PERSUASIVOS

Instrucciones: Escriba un párrafo persuasivo sobre el siguiente tema.

Desde el momento en que una persona anuncia su candidatura a un cargo público, su vida privada pasa a ser del dominio público y sufre el escrutinio de los medios de comunicación. En muchos casos, la vida privada del candidato afecta sus posibilidades de ganar una elección. ¿Pero tiene el público el derecho de enterarse de la vida privada de las figuras políticas?

Técnica de comparación/contraste

La técnica de *comparación/contraste* es de gran utilidad en la organización de ideas en una variedad de párrafos de tipo persuasivo.

Oración temática: Como mascota, es mejor el gato para aquéllos que viven en la ciudad.

Gatos	Perros
usan una bandeja de tierra dentro de la casa	se les tiene que sacar
sirven de compañía sin exigir mucha atención	hay que jugar con ellos frecuentemente
no necesitan mucho espacio	necesitan mucho espacio para correr

El cuadro presenta las ideas del escritor de una forma más organizada. El párrafo que se transcribe abajo se basa en las ideas del cuadro. Subraye las palabras que indican una relación de comparación/contraste entre ideas.

Como mascota, es mejor el gato para aquéllos que viven en la ciudad. Mientras que los gatos pueden hacer sus necesidades en una bandeja de tierra, a los perros hay que sacarlos varias veces al día. Los gatos sirven de compañía y no exigen mucha atención; al contrario, hay que jugar con los perros frecuentemente o, si no, se entristecen. Los gatos no necesitan mucho espacio para correr y jugar, pero los perros sí; además, ocupan mucho espacio en un apartamento de ciudad. El gato es, en definitiva, la mejor opción para las personas que viven en la ciudad y buscan la compañía de una mascota.

[Respuesta: *mejor, mientras, al contrario, pero.*]

EJERCICIO 13: PERSUASIÓN MEDIANTE COMPARACIÓN/ CONTRASTE

Instrucciones: Redacte un párrafo persuasivo empleando la técnica de comparación/contraste. Elija dos estados o ciudades que conozca: determine cuál de los dos estados o ciudades es más agradable para vivir y escriba un párrafo con el objeto de persuadir a otras personas de que usted ha hecho una elección acertada.

Ejemplos de los cuatro tipos de escritura

Escritura narrativa: Cuente una historia sobre:
(1) el día más feliz de su vida (o el más nefasto)
(2) el error más grande de su vida (o la decisión más acertada)

Escritura descriptiva: Describa vívidamente con lenguaje específico:
(1) una habitación de su casa
(2) el aspecto físico de una persona que usted conozca bien

Escritura informativa: Explique con detalle a sus lectores:
(1) la importancia de una nutrición adecuada
(2) cómo reducir los gastos de agua, teléfono o electricidad en el hogar

Escritura persuasiva: Exprese su opinión y arguméntela con razones válidas que respalden una posición a favor o en contra de:
(1) fumar en los lugares públicos
(2) rezar en las escuelas públicas

Escritura de la redacción

Si usted es capaz de redactar bien un párrafo, también será capaz de escribir composiciones más extensas. Hay muchas semejanzas entre un párrafo, que es un trozo de escritura, y una composición entera. Cuando se escribe un párrafo como cuando se escribe una redacción entera, los objetivos son los mismos: expresar una idea principal y tratar sobre el tema durante toda la pieza. La estructura de una redacción completa es también semejante a la de un párrafo.

Párrafo	Redacción
Oración temática	Párrafo introductorio
Oraciones secundarias	Párrafos del cuerpo
Oración de cierre (conclusión)	Párrafo de cierre (conclusión)

Veamos ahora las distintas partes de una redacción.

- El *párrafo introductorio* contiene la exposición de la tesis, que comunica al lector la idea principal, o propósito, de la redacción. La introducción debe examinar también los puntos principales que usted va a presentar para argumentar la tesis.

- La parte principal de la redacción es el *cuerpo*. De la misma forma en que las oraciones secundarias de un párrafo dan apoyo a la oración temática, los párrafos del cuerpo de una redacción dan apoyo a la tesis. Cada uno de los argumentos que se presentan se desarrolla en un párrafo. En los párrafos del cuerpo se pueden emplear las relaciones causa-efecto, la técnica de comparación/contraste o la secuenciación de eventos para organizar las ideas.

- El *párrafo de cierre* o conclusión de la redacción hace una recapitulación de la tesis y otros puntos principales y presenta la conclusión de lo tratado en el escrito. Esta conclusión puede ir acompañada de una sugerencia o recomendación.

Preescritura de la redacción

Lea el siguiente *esquema*. El escritor ha agrupado detalles y ejemplos bajo unos encabezados principales que indican cómo se va a desarrollar en los párrafos cada una de las ideas de apoyo a la tesis.

Párrafo 1: Introducción
Exposición de la tesis: la escuela primaria de nuestra zona necesita más guardias de tránsito en los cruces de calles

Párrafo 2: hay dos intersecciones peligrosas a unas cuantas cuadras de la escuela
A. una en la intersección de la calle Lincoln y la avenida Davis
B. otra en las calles Plum y Morton

Párrafo 3: alrededor del mediodía es cuando la mayor parte de los niños entran y salen de la escuela
A. los niños del jardín de infantes del turno de la mañana salen a las 11:30
B. los alumnos se van a la casa a almorzar almuerzo y regresan después
C. los niños del jardín de infantes del turno de la tarde llegan a las 12:15

Párrafo 4: aumento del tráfico este año a causa del centro comercial
A. situado en la calle Oak, a cuatro cuadras de las escuela
B. más tráfico en general a causa del centro comercial

Párrafo 5: *Conclusión:* Considerando las razones arriba expuestas, recomiendo que el director solicite cuatro guardias más, por lo menos.
A. padres o jubilados
B. la escuela debe ser responsable por la seguridad de los alumnos

Preparación del borrador de la redacción

Una vez esbozados el plan de trabajo y el esquema de los párrafos, procedemos a preparar el *borrador de la redacción*. Todas las etapas previas de preparación a la redacción le ayudarán a escribir el borrador. Deje márgenes amplios y espacio entre renglones para poder hacer cambios más adelante. Cuando escriba el borrador, tenga a mano su plan de trabajo. Básese en las palabras y frases del esquema al redactar las oraciones.

Empiece a desarrollar un proceso propio de escritura cuando tenga que redactar estas piezas más largas. Un gran número de escritores de larga experiencia redacta la introducción y la conclusión después de haber escrito primeramente los párrafos del cuerpo de la obra. No se infringe regla alguna si se comienza con los párrafos del cuerpo, se escribe una conclusión de peso y luego se le agrega una introducción general a la exposición de la tesis.

A continuación, se presenta el borrador de una redacción sobre el tema de los guardias de tránsito para los cruces de calles. La exposición de la tesis aparece en **negrita.** A medida que lea el borrador, observe que el escritor no ha seguido estrictamente su esquema, sino que lo ha usado como una especie de guía, haciendo alteraciones en varios puntos según creía necesario. Usted podrá notar asimismo que, en algunos lugares, es difícil seguir el hilo de pensamiento del escritor. Subraye estas secciones y busque la mejor manera de rehacer estas secciones con mayor claridad.

ESQUEMA

Párrafo 1: Introducción
Tesis: la escuela primaria de nuestra zona necesita más guardias de tránsito en los cruces de calles

Un gran número de padres de alumnos que asisten a la escuela Jefferson y que van a pie a la misma han expresado su preocupación por el tránsito de vehículos que circulan en las calles aledañas al recinto escolar. Si bien es cierto que, a las horas de entrada y salida, se encuentran apostados, en todas las intersecciones circundantes al terreno de la escuela, estudiantes de grados superiores que desempeñan la función de guardias de tránsito, éstos no bastan para subsanar el problema: las intersecciones no circundantes pero aledañas a la escuela, las entradas y salidas a la hora del mediodía y el aumento del tráfico en general causado por la apertura del nuevo centro comercial siguen representando un riesgo para aquellos alumnos que van a clase a pie, sobre todo para los más pequeños. **Urge, por lo tanto, aumentar el número de guardias de tránsito en los cruces de calles aledaños a la escuela Jefferson.**

Párrafo 2: hay dos intersecciones peligrosas a unas cuantas cuadras de la escuela
A. una en la intersección de la calle Lincoln y la avenida Davis
B. otra en las calles Plum y Morton

En primer lugar, se debería contratar a guardias que cubran dos peligrosas intersecciones ubicadas a sólo unas cuadras de la escuela: una de ellas es la intersección de la calle Lincoln y la avenida Davis, donde hay una señal de ceda el paso que los conductores no suelen respetar; la otra es la esquina de las calles Plum y Morton, donde últimamente se han registrado varios accidentes. Necesitamos un guardia de tránsito adulto en cada uno de estos puntos que esté constantemente alerta a la presencia de niños en las intersecciones.

Párrafo 3: alrededor del mediodía es cuando la mayor parte de los niños entran y salen de la escuela

Hacia el mediodía es cuando se observa el mayor movimiento de alumnos que entran y salen de la escuela: por un lado, tenemos a los niños del jardín de infantes del turno de la mañana que salen a las 11:30. De entre éstos,

A. los niños del jardín de infantes del turno de la mañana salen a las 11:30

B. los alumnos se van a la casa a almorzar almuerzo y regresan después

C. los niños del jardín de infantes del turno de la tarde llegan a las 12:15

Párrafo 4: aumento del tráfico este año a causa del centro comercial

A. situado en la calle Oak, a cuatro cuadras de las escuela

B. más tráfico en general a causa del centro comercial

Párrafo 5: *Conclusión:* Considerando las razones arriba expuestas, recomiendo que el director solicite cuatro guardias más, por lo menos.

A. padres o jubilados

B. la escuela debe ser responsable por la seguridad de los alumnos

son muchos —niños de cinco años de edad— que van caminando a sus casas. A esas horas no hay guardias de tránsito en servicio en ninguna de las intersecciones. A las 12:00, por otro lado, tenemos un número elevado de estudiantes que van a sus casas a almorzar y regresan a la escuela alrededor de las 12:45. Por último, los niños del jardín de infantes del turno de la tarde empiezan a llegar entre las 12:00 y las 12:15, de modo que son muy numerosos los niños que cruzan las calles sin la ayuda de un guardia. No obstante, conviene asimismo recalcar que también son numerosos los padres que llevan a sus hijos en auto a la escuela.

Este año se ha producido un aumento notable en el tráfico de la zona por la apertura del nuevo centro comercial de la calle Oak, situado a cuatro cuadras de la escuela. El volumen de tráfico circulante ha crecido substancialmente en todas las arterias del barrio.

Por las razones arriba expuestas, consideramos que el director debería solicitar a la Junta Escolar la inmediata contratación de cuatro guardias más de cruce, por lo menos. Aunque hay padres que se han ofrecido como voluntarios en carácter temporal, instamos al distrito escolar a que tome las medidas necesarias para subsanar los problemas del momento así como garantizar la seguridad del alumnado a largo plazo.

Revisión de la redacción

Antes de proceder a revisar la redacción, conviene despejar la mente por un instante. Interrumpa el proceso de escritura y deje la redacción a un lado momentáneamente. Ahora retome el hilo y analice su escrito de la forma más objetiva posible: léalo como si fuera uno de sus lectores. ¿Qué le dice el texto? Luego, léalo como autor. ¿Qué se puede sustituir, agregar o eliminar, o qué se puede trasponer o rehacer de modo que las ideas sean más claras y den apoyo a lo que quiere comunicar? ¿Cómo se puede mejorar el fraseo de la oración? ¿Qué idea se puede desarrollar un poco más o qué hay de superfluo?. . .

Guía para la revisión de la redacción

❑ ¿Anticipa la introducción los párrafos del cuerpo?

❑ ¿Está expresada la tesis de forma clara y concisa? ¿Es válida la idea?

❑ ¿Están organizados de forma lógica en los párrafos del cuerpo los argumentos que respaldan la tesis?

❑ ¿Podrá comprender el lector cómo las ideas se relacionan entre sí y cómo dan apoyo a la tesis?

❑ ¿Hay ideas intranscendentes o superfluas?

❑ ¿Qué es lo mejor de mi redacción?

❑ ¿Qué es lo que no me agrada de la redacción?

❑ ¿Qué puedo hacer para mejorarla?

Corrección final de la redacción

La *corrección final de la redacción* consiste en buscar errores de forma en su escrito: errores de ortografía, acentuación y puntuación; sintaxis, uso y estilo. Si la forma del texto no está a la altura de su contenido, el lector no podrá apreciar a cabalidad lo que usted ha escrito. Hasta los errores más insignificantes pueden oscurecer el sentido de lo que quiere transmitir o empañar la belleza o el ingenio con que ha plasmado una idea. Hay escritores que, al corregir sus escritos, los leen de atrás para adelante palabra a palabra, para ver si hay errores. También es útil, en muchos casos, leer de atrás para adelante de oración en oración a fin de identificar aquéllas oraciones que hayan quedado incompletas.

EJERCICIO 14: CORRECCIÓN FINAL DE LA REDACCIÓN
Instrucciones: Realice la corrección final de su redacción atendiendo a la ortografía, acentuación, puntuación, sintaxis, uso y estilo. Cerciórese que todas las oraciones tengan sentido completo y preste atención a los siguientes puntos en particular: tiempos verbales, referentes y antecedentes, oraciones compuestas, acentuación, etc.

Redacción del GED

Preguntas más frecuentes acerca de la redacción del GED

• **¿De cuánto tiempo se dispone? ¿Qué extensión debe tener la redacción?**
Se dispone de 45 minutos para escribir una redacción de aproximadamente 200 palabras de extensión. Esta cifra es sólo una referencia: no se le restarán puntos si se excede o no llega a esa cantidad de palabras, siempre que exprese bien sus ideas. Se requiere el uso de bolígrafo, el cual no será proporcionado por los examinadores; se le proveerá, sin embargo, papel borrador. (Recuerde que lo que escriba en su borrador no se calificará.)

- **¿Por qué hay una redacción en el Examen del GED?**
  Tanto en los centros de enseñanza como en los lugares de trabajo se considera que escribir es una destreza importante de la que no puede prescindir ninguna persona adulta. Si se espera que el Examen del GED sea una evaluación de conocimientos y destrezas equivalentes a las adquiridas en una institución de enseñanza secundaria, el examinado o la examinada deberá demostrar que puede escribir.

- **¿Cuál es el tema de la redacción?**
  En la sección de Redacción se le pedirá expresar una opinión o explicar temas generales que toda persona adulta ha de conocer. Se espera de usted que argumente sus afirmaciones con razones válidas y claras y las ilustre con detalles y ejemplos específicos y apropiados. El tema será lo suficientemente amplio como para permitirle a usted enfocar la redacción desde distintos ángulos.

- **¿Cómo se califica la redacción?**
  Todas las redacciones serán leídas y calificadas por lectores capacitados en las normas generales desarrolladas por el Servicio de Pruebas del GED. (Los puntajes se basan en una escala que va del 1 al 6.) Los lectores evaluarán la efectividad general de la redacción: su trabajo puede presentar algunos errores y, aun así, recibir una calificación alta. Para obtener una buena puntuación, usted tiene que ser capaz de escribir un texto organizado, estructurado y coherente que presente argumentos claros y válidos que respalden de forma efectiva la idea central de su redacción. También se habrán de observar las normas de gramática y ortografía.

- **¿Cuáles son las normas generales de puntuación?**
  Presentamos a seguir las distintas puntuaciones y el nivel de rendimiento correspondiente.

  6 El trabajo muestra un plan organizativo claro. El examinado es capaz de argumentar puntos de vista bien razonados con minucia de detalles y ejemplos específicos y pertinentes. El trabajo cautiva el interés del lector y presenta un número mínimo de errores.

  5 El trabajo está bien organizado, con ideas argumentadas de forma convincente; pero el estilo no posee la soltura de un trabajo de puntuación 6. El trabajo ha sido, en sentido amplio, correctamente escrito, aunque presenta algunos errores.

  4 El trabajo evidencia ideas organizadas con argumentos que respaldan en cierta medida sus puntos de vista. Presenta una mayor cantidad de errores, pero éstos no obstaculizan al lector la comprensión del texto.

  3 El trabajo está organizado o desarrollado en cierta medida pero de una forma limitada y poco convincente. Hay vacilaciones en el uso de la lengua y el texto no alcanza a expresar el propósito del autor.

  2 El trabajo carece de un objetivo definido. Está desorganizado y apenas ofrece respaldo a las ideas del autor. Los errores en el uso del idioma son frecuentes y a ratos obstaculizan al lector la comprensión del texto.

1 El trabajo no evidencia ningún objetivo u organización. El autor es incapaz de expresar sus ideas empleando la lengua de forma correcta.

▶ **Nota**: Los trabajos que estén en blanco, sean ilegibles o que hayan desarrollado un tema no asignado no recibirán puntuación. Tampoco se podrá calcular la puntuación conjunta de la Prueba de Expresión Escrita.

• **¿Qué debo estudiar en preparación a la redacción?**
Emplee su tiempo de estudio en aprender, desarrollar o perfeccionar el proceso de escritura y en buscar la mejor manera de aplicarlo durante la prueba. Practique escribiendo redacciones cronometradas y planee cómo va a distribuir su tiempo cuando se examine.

Cómo administrar el tiempo

Si se desea un buen rendimiento el día del examen, se debe adaptar el proceso de escritura al contexto de la prueba. Es imprescindible valerse de una estrategia para poder distribuir el tiempo adecuadamente durante la misma. A continuación presentamos sugerencias sobre cómo abordar la redacción. Piense en la mejor forma de adaptar esta estrategia a su estilo de escritura.

Preescritura (5–10 minutos): Analice el tema: vea las opciones que tiene y las distintas direcciones que puede seguir; luego exponga la tesis de su redacción. Apunte rápidamente ideas que den apoyo a la tesis. Organice su lista de *brainstorm* enumerando las ideas, uniendo con flechas las ideas afines o haciendo un breve esquema.

Borrador (25–30 minutos): El tiempo de que se dispone no basta para escribir un borrador propiamente, que luego se puede desechar; por lo que en la prueba tendrá que proceder a redactar directamente—en tinta—teniendo presente que no podrá pasar a limpio su redacción. En vista de eso, deje márgenes amplios para poder añadir ideas y hacer correcciones. A medida que escriba, trate de no desviarse del plan organizativo general de su redacción.

Revisión y corrección final (5–10 minutos): Lea su redacción de principio a fin. Vea si puede hacer cambios para lograr que sus ideas resulten claras al lector y que el texto sea fluido, sin interrupciones abruptas, divagaciones innecesarias, frases oscuras o palabras superfluas. Cerciórese de que la tesis haya sido expresada con claridad y coherencia en la introducción y de que sus párrafos secundarios sean pertinentes y estén bien estructurados. Luego corrija la ortografía, la puntuación y otros errores de forma.

Temas de muestra

A continuación citamos algunos temas de redacción muy parecidos a los que pueden aparecer en la *Parte 2* de la Prueba de Expresión Escrita. Use los conocimientos adquiridos y administre su tiempo con cuidado. Usted dispone de cuarenta y cinco minutos.

1. ¿Cómo ha cambiado en los últimos veinticinco años el papel que desempeñan los hombres y/o las mujeres dentro de la sociedad? ¿Cómo han afectado a su familia estos cambios?

2. Las cualidades personales como la generosidad, el espíritu de servicio, el buen humor y el egoísmo son algunas de las características que hacen que la persona se dé a querer o a detestar. Identifique una cualidad que usted admire o deteste en una persona y explique cómo le afecta a usted.

3. ¿Cómo afecta a los hijos de parejas divorciadas el que los padres tengan custodia conjunta de los mismos? Describa ya sea los efectos positivos, los efectos negativos, o bien ambos.

4. Para algunos, las fiestas de fin de año son los días más felices del año, una oportunidad de congregarse y pasar momentos agradables con familiares y amigos; para otros, sin embargo, son días de tristeza y soledad. ¿Por qué hay personas que se deprimen en esta época?

5. Como ciudadanos que vivimos en una democracia, nosotros tenemos el derecho al voto; aunque hay muchas personas que no ejercen este derecho. Explique por qué un gran número de ciudadanos no concurre a las urnas en día de elecciones.

6. La frustración y la ira son emociones que todos habremos experimentado en un momento dado. Sin embargo, hay personas que son capaces de reconocer y controlar sus sentimientos; mientras existen otras que dan rienda suelta a sus impulsos e instintos cuando se disgustan, pudiendo llegar incluso a la violencia. ¿Por qué algunas personas se saben controlar mejor que otras?

PRUEBA 2: ESTUDIOS SOCIALES

La Prueba de Estudios Sociales del GED consta de preguntas de opción múltiple. Estas preguntas requieren que usted sepa algunos de los conceptos básicos de estudios sociales que se tratarán en este libro. Sin embargo, la prueba se centra más en su capacidad para reflexionar acerca de estos conceptos. No habrá necesidad de recordar fechas o datos aislados como ocurre en otras pruebas. Más bien, se habrá de leer un pasaje u observar una ilustración y contestar preguntas basadas en los mismos.

Para poder tener un buen rendimiento, será necesario comprender los conceptos básicos de estudios sociales e interpretar bien las ilustraciones y pasajes de lectura. También hará falta demostrar que se comprende lo que se lee, aplicar la información a una nueva situación, analizar las relaciones entre ideas y emitir juicios sobre el material presentado.

¿Cuántas preguntas hay en la prueba?

Hay 64 preguntas de opción múltiple y se dispone de 85 minutos para hacer la prueba. Aproximadamente dos tercios de las preguntas se han de basar en pasajes de lectura de hasta 250 palabras cada una, y el tercio restante en información visual: mapas, cuadros, gráficas o caricaturas de corte político. Fíjese en la Prueba Posterior al final del libro. Ésta ha sido confeccionada en base a la prueba normal del GED.

¿De qué consta la prueba?

La Prueba de Estudios Sociales del GED se puede dividir según las áreas de contenido que aborda y las destrezas que pone a prueba. El contenido de estas pruebas es el siguiente: Ciencias del Comportamiento—20%; Historia de EE.UU.—25%; Ciencias Políticas—20%; Economía—20%; y Geografía—15%. (En Canadá, la distribución es la siguiente: Ciencias del Comportamiento—15%; Historia de Canadá—25%; Ciencias Políticas—20%; Economía—20%; y Geografía—20%.)

Estos conceptos esenciales de estudios sociales se presentan en los capítulos 1 a 5 de esta sección. Sin embargo, cabe recalcar que una pregunta dada puede estar relacionada con varias de las áreas mencionadas. Es difícil estudiar la sociedad o el individuo de manera aislada sin tocar distintas áreas al mismo tiempo. Por ejemplo, una pregunta acerca de la Constitución de EE.UU. puede caer tanto bajo la esfera de las ciencias políticas como de la historia.

Recuerde usted asimismo que lo que se va a poner a prueba es su capacidad para reflexionar sobre determinadas ideas y conceptos. Se le pedirá realizar algo más que la simple búsqueda de una respuesta explícitamente dada dentro de un pasaje. Entre las destrezas de razonamiento que se van a poner a prueba figuran las siguientes: Comprensión de Ideas—20%; Aplicación de Ideas—30%; Análisis de Ideas—30%; y Evaluación de Ideas—20%.

1
CIENCIAS DEL COMPORTAMIENTO

Las ciencias del comportamiento constituyen la rama de los estudios sociales que tiene que ver con el comportamiento de los seres humanos como individuos y como integrantes de sus respectivos grupos y culturas. En la Prueba de Estudios Sociales se harán preguntas sobre tres áreas de las ciencias del comportamiento, a saber: antropología, sociología y psicología.

Aunque cada una de estas áreas se traslapa en cierta forma con las demás, esta sección examina las mismas de modo individual. Dichas ciencias del comportamiento se concentran sobre aspectos específicos de la humanidad: La antropología se pregunta *¿Quiénes son seres humanos?* La sociología indaga *¿A qué grupos pertenecen las personas?* La psicología investiga el difícil problema de *¿Cómo piensan y se comportan las personas?*

Antropología:
¿Quiénes son seres humanos?

¿Alguna vez se ha detenido a pensar en la raza humana en general: quiénes somos, de dónde venimos, en qué nos parecemos y en qué nos diferenciamos? La *antropología* es la ciencia que intenta dar respuesta a estas y otras muchas preguntas sobre los orígenes y las civilizaciones de los seres humanos.

La palabra "antropología" deriva de dos vocablos griegos: *anthropos,* que significa "hombre", y *logos,* que significa "estudio". Lógicamente, por estudio del "hombre" entendemos el estudio del ser humano, mujeres y varones incluidos. La antropología se divide en dos ramas: antropología física y antropología cultural. Los *antropólogos físicos* estudian los antepasados del hombre con el objeto de comprender cómo se han ido adaptando biológicamente los seres humanos a la variedad de ambientes que se encuentran en el mundo. Los *antropólogos culturales* estudian cómo viven las personas en grupos y cómo han desarrollado las herramientas de cultura, como el lenguaje, la religión y la tecnología, para poder sobrevivir. La *cultura* es el comportamiento compartido y aprendido que desarrollan las personas a partir de sus experiencias dentro del grupo.

Las investigaciones en el campo de la antropología han conducido a numerosos y sorprendentes descubrimientos acerca de los seres humanos y de su adaptación al medio ambiente en que viven. Por ejemplo, en 1913 se encontraron en la India unos "niños lobos". Se trataba de dos niños de diez años que vivían con tres lobos y sólo comían alimentos crudos. No hablaban ni sonreían nunca. Evitaban el contacto con los seres humanos pero, sin embargo, permitían que un perro comiera con ellos. Incluso después de haber sido capturados por unos cazadores, nadie pudo enseñar a estos niños ningún tipo de comportamiento humano y fallecieron poco tiempo después.

El antropólogo físico podría hacerse las siguientes preguntas frente a este fenómeno: ¿Cómo lograron unos seres humanos sobrevivir entre lobos? ¿Cómo se adaptó el cuerpo de los niños a la forma de vida de los lobos? ¿Cómo fueron aceptados y criados por estos animales? El antropólogo cultural se preguntaría, en cambio: ¿Cómo pudieron dos niños aprender a vivir con los lobos? ¿Cómo se comunicaban unos seres humanos con estos animales?

Aunque cada uno observa el comportamiento humano desde distintos puntos de vista, tanto el antropólogo físico como el antropólogo cultural formulan y contestan las preguntas que contribuyen a formar nuestro conocimiento general de los seres humanos y sus diversos medio ambientes.

LAS RESPUESTAS DE LOS EJERCICIOS DE ESTE CAPÍTULO EMPIEZAN EN LA PÁGINA 446.

EJERCICIO 1: ANTROPOLOGÍA FÍSICA Y CULTURAL

Instrucciones: Escriba una *F* al lado del tema que estudiaría el antropólogo físico y una *C* al lado del tema que estudiaría el antropólogo cultural.

_____ **1.** fósiles de huesos de personas prehistóricas

_____ **2.** jeroglíficos encontrados en las paredes de una cueva egipcia

_____ **3.** preferencia de las personas por la carne cruda

Cultura

La cultura comprende el conocimiento, las creencias y el comportamiento humano aprendido que comparte un grupo de personas. Abarca la manera en que pensamos, sentimos y nos comportamos según nos vamos adaptando a nuestro medio ambiente. Los seres humanos tienen la capacidad de adaptarse a muchos medios, a los que los animales inferiores no podrían. Esto se debe a que nosotros poseemos la inteligencia y creatividad necesarias para desarrollar una cultura.

De hecho, los seres humanos *deben necesariamente* crear una cultura para poder adaptarse y sobrevivir. Para que pueda seguir existiendo, toda cultura debe satisfacer ciertas necesidades básicas de sus miembros. Estas necesidades, comunes a todas las culturas, reciben el nombre de *universales culturales.* Entre éstas se pueden citar: alimento, abrigo, lenguaje, familia, sistema de creencias, sistema económico y sistema político.

Costumbres

Estudiamos culturas diferentes para poder aumentar nuestro entendimiento de otras gentes del mundo. Estudiamos sus *costumbres,* es decir, las normas de comportamiento que comparten los miembros de una cultura determinada. Las costumbres se basan en los valores que cada cultura considera importantes. Por ejemplo, el comer con cuchillo y tenedor es una costumbre arraigada en nuestra sociedad. En Estados Unidos, la familia, la escuela y la iglesia son instituciones importantes que transmiten la cultura a los jóvenes.

Valores, etnocentrismo y relatividad cultural

Los *valores* son creencias que rigen e influyen en el comportamiento. Por ejemplo, uno de los valores fundamentales del modo de vida estadounidense es la creencia de que todas las personas han sido creadas iguales. Entre estos valores figuran la libertad, la igualdad, la justicia y el individualismo. Al observar otras culturas, los antropólogos ponen cuidado en no juzgar la cultura que estudian según valores propios a ellos mismos. El juzgar a otra cultura en base a valores propios de uno recibe el nombre de *etnocentrismo.* Por ejemplo, el estadounidense que condene los métodos de crianza de los niños en Asia por el mero hecho de que sean diferentes de los nuestros está practicando etnocentrismo. Los antropólogos tratan de estudiar las distintas culturas reconociendo de antemano que cada una de ellas es diferente y, al mismo tiempo, satisfactoria para sus miembros.

Lo contrario al etnocentrismo es la *relatividad cultural,* es decir, el juzgar las culturas en base a valores propios a esas culturas. Al reconocer las diferencias que existen entre las culturas, aumentamos nuestro entendimiento de la variedad de formas en que las personas pueden adaptarse a un medio ambiente determinado.

Sociología: ¿A qué grupos pertenecen las personas?

Las personas pertenecen a muchos grupos distintos. En su caso, puede que usted sea madre o padre de familia, cónyuge, hermana o hermano, o amiga o amigo. También es, lógicamente, estudiante porque está estudiando para el examen del GED. Todos los papeles que desempeña indican su pertenencia a diferentes grupos.

La *sociología* estudia cómo se relacionan los seres humanos entre sí. Las personas desarrollamos relaciones y aprendemos a comportarnos conforme a las creencias y los valores de la sociedad en que vivimos. Los sociólogos definen *grupo* como el conjunto de dos o más personas que se comunican entre sí. Sin embargo, el simple hecho de que unas personas estén congregadas no constituye una relación de grupo. Todas las personas que viajan en un autobús o están en un salón no forman un grupo a menos que exista una relación entre ellas, es decir, a menos que se comuniquen entre sí.

Tipos de grupos

Los sociólogos dividen los grupos en dos categorías según la influencia que ejerza el grupo en los individuos que lo integran. Los *grupos primarios* son los más importantes e inmediatos a una persona. La familia es el más primario de todos los grupos. La mayoría de la gente mantiene una relación estrecha y personal con los demás miembros de su familia. A partir de este grupo, formamos nuestros hábitos, creencias y actitudes. Los amigos íntimos, con quienes se comparten asuntos personales, son también miembros del grupo primario al que pertenecemos, aunque no mantengamos con ellos una relación tan estrecha como con nuestra familia.

Las relaciones de grupo que son menos personales y ejercen menos influencia en el individuo constituyen los *grupos secundarios.* Las personas con quienes trabajamos o los demás estudiantes de un salón de clase son ejemplos de grupos secundarios. La comunicación con nuestros compañeros de trabajo y de clase tiende a ser específica y breve. Estas relaciones son, por lo general, temporales e impersonales. Sin embargo, cuando trabajamos en equipo con las mismas personas durante un cierto período de tiempo, las relaciones con los compañeros de trabajo pueden empezar a asemejarse a las que mantenemos con los amigos íntimos o la familia.

EJERCICIO 2: GRUPO PRIMARIO Y SECUNDARIO

Instrucciones: Escriba una *P* si la situación corresponde a un grupo primario y una *S* si corresponde a un grupo secundario.

_____ 1. estudiantes de la clase de matemáticas

_____ 2. familia

_____ 3. personas de un pueblo de 120 habitantes

Instituciones sociales

Una *institución* es un sistema organizado por la sociedad para satisfacer las necesidades básicas de sus miembros. La función principal de la mayor parte de las instituciones es la de transmitir a los ciudadanos los valores y las costumbres de su cultura. En las sociedades más complejas, las instituciones son de cinco tipos principales: familiares, religiosas, económicas, políticas y educativas. De éstas, las más importantes son las familiares.

La socialización y la familia

La familia es el primer grupo al que pertenecemos. La función más importante de la familia es la reproducción, es decir, la perpetuación de la especie. Para que una sociedad pueda sobrevivir, es necesario que continuamente se sumen a la misma nuevos miembros. Tras el nacimiento de un niño, la familia tiene la responsabilidad de proteger y cuidar de él, y de enseñarle las costumbres y los comportamientos apropiados. Este proceso de enseñanza recibe el nombre de *socialización.*

Los seres humanos deben aprender a ser seres humanos. Los niños lobo que mencionamos en la sección de antropología eran seres humanos biológicamente. Sin embargo, no habían sido nunca socializados como seres humanos y, a consecuencia de esto, jamás se ajustaron a la sociedad humana. Esporádicamente se mencionan en periódicos y revistas casos de personas que se criaron sin haber tenido ningún tipo de contacto con otros seres humanos.

Familia nuclear y extendida

La estructura que adopta la familia depende de las costumbres y los principios de la sociedad. La estructura de la familia estadounidense ha sido tradicionalmente nuclear. La *familia nuclear* se centra alrededor del padre, la madre y los hijos. Otras sociedades se basan en una estructura de familia extendida. En la *familia extendida,* la familia nuclear se extiende al incluir a los abuelos y, en algunos casos, a otros familiares. En la estructura de familia extendida, todos sus miembros adultos son responsables del cuidado y la crianza de los hijos.

EJERCICIO 3: FAMILIA NUCLEAR Y EXTENDIDA

Instrucciones: Escriba una *N* en el espacio en blanco si la situación corresponde a una familia nuclear y una *E* si corresponde a una familia extendida.

_____ **1.** En Japón, India, Irán, Turquía y muchos países de África, la unidad familiar está integrada por tres generaciones que cohabitan en el hogar.

_____ **2.** La cultura dominante de Estados Unidos dicta que, en la mayoría de los casos, la unidad familiar esté integrada por sólo dos generaciones—los padres y los hijos—que cohabitan en el hogar.

_____ **3.** Los indios hopi, navajo e iroqueses exigen que las parejas recién casadas residan con la familia de la esposa.

Estructura social

Muchas sociedades están divididas en categorías llamadas clases sociales. Los miembros de una *clase social* poseen niveles semejantes de prestigio. La *estratificación* se refiere a la forma en que la sociedad se halla dividida en clases. La distribución de las personas en las distintas clases sociales se basa en los valores y comportamientos de la sociedad.

En Estados Unidos, las clases sociales se basan en valores económicos, es decir, en cuánto gana una persona. Las clases alta, media y baja se diferencian por la riqueza y el poder de los individuos que las componen. La clase alta es mucho más rica y poderosa que la clase baja.

La clase social es un ejemplo de *status adscrito* (alcanzado de forma automática), dado que uno nace en ella, pero no es una situación permanente. A medida que uno va subiendo de un nivel más bajo a otro más alto, la nueva clase social se considera como un *status adquirido* (ganado). Hay algunas sociedades que prohíben esta *movilidad social* (cambio de status).

En la India, por ejemplo, la estructura social tradicional consistía en un *sistema de castas*. Las personas nacían dentro de uno de los cinco niveles (o clases) del sistema de castas. Estaba prohibido cambiar de nivel y, por lo tanto, el status atribuido permanecía constante durante la vida de la persona, pese a cualquier intento de superación.

EJERCICIO 4: ESTRATIFICACIÓN SOCIAL

Instrucciones: Lea las siguientes expresiones. Escriba *CL* en el espacio en blanco si la frase se refiere a un sistema de clases y *CA* si se refiere a un sistema de castas.

_____ **1.** promueve la ambición y la autosuperación.

_____ **2.** posee una estructura social estricta.

_____ **3.** ofrece muchas opciones de trabajo.

Psicología: ¿Cómo piensan y se comportan las personas?

La *psicología* o el estudio del comportamiento humano busca dar respuesta a las preguntas relativas a por qué los seres humanos piensan y se comportan de una forma determinada. Tres de los componentes que estudian y analizan los psicólogos son: los procesos de pensamiento y aprendizaje, la personalidad y el ambiente social.

Los procesos de pensamiento y aprendizaje

Dado que las personas tienen que aprender a ser seres humanos, el aprendizaje es la base del comportamiento humano. Según la escuela *behaviorista* de psicología, el **aprendizaje** es un cambio permanente del comportamiento que se produce a causa de experiencias pasadas.

Los psicólogos han identificado varias de las formas que tienen los humanos de aprender. Cada una de estas formas representa un nivel mayor de sofisticación por parte del aprendiz. En el nivel más básico, la persona aprende a responder a un estímulo (un hecho que ocasiona una respuesta o reacción). Esto recibe el nombre de **condicionamiento**. Las formas más sofisticadas de aprendizaje conllevan un razonamiento y una búsqueda de soluciones a problemas.

EJERCICIO 5: TIPOS DE APRENDIZAJE

Instrucciones: Lea las definiciones y aplíquelas a las preguntas que vienen después.

condicionamiento clásico: Tras haber introducido un estímulo repetidas veces, la persona aprende a responder de un modo determinado. Cierto grado de reforzamiento (ya sea por medio de una recompensa o un castigo) también forma parte del proceso de condicionamiento.

condicionamiento operante: El aprendizaje es el resultado de la interacción con el medio ambiente. En el condicionamiento operante no hay un estímulo directo. Las personas hacen cosas porque quieren obtener algo o evitar que se produzca o realice algún efecto.

aprendizaje por tanteo: Con el fin de resolver un problema, se prueban distintas posibilidades hasta que finalmente se llega a la respuesta o se logra el objetivo.

percepción cognoscitiva: El aprendizaje es el resultado de un proceso de razonamiento lógico. La mente capta la información, la reorganiza y la adapta para que se ajuste a una nueva situación.

aprendizaje en laberinto: El aprendizaje requiere una serie de respuestas con el fin de alcanzar el objetivo. Las respuestas se suelen hacer por tanteo, pero el aprendizaje en laberinto requiere también que el individuo siga un proceso de pensamiento lógico para lograr resolver un problema.

1. Una niña llora al despertarse en una habitación oscura. Cuando la oye su padre, va a la habitación, la toma en sus brazos y enciende la luz. La niña deja de llorar. El padre sigue haciendo lo mismo durante varias semanas. Pero una noche, enciende la luz antes de levantar a la bebita en sus brazos y se queda muy sorprendido al observar que la niña deja de llorar. Por consiguiente, el haber encendido la luz ha ocasionado la misma respuesta que si se hubiera levantado a la niña en brazos. Éste es un ejemplo de:
   (1) condicionamiento clásico
   (2) condicionamiento operante
   (3) aprendizaje por tanteo
   (4) percepción cognoscitiva
   (5) aprendizaje en laberinto

2. A un niño le dicen que los pájaros vuelan. Mientras juega en el jardín, el niño ve un avión cruzar el cielo. Basándose en su conocimiento almacenado, el niño le dice a su mamá que ha visto un pájaro. La madre contesta, "No, cariño, es un avión", y le explica las diferencias entre ambos. La próxima vez que el niño vea volar un objeto podrá saber si es un avión o un pájaro. Éste es un ejemplo de:

(**1**) condicionamiento clásico

(**2**) condicionamiento operante

(**3**) aprendizaje por tanteo

(**4**) percepción cognoscitiva

(**5**) aprendizaje en laberinto

Personalidad

La personalidad influye en gran medida en nuestra forma de comportarnos. La *personalidad* puede definirse como los rasgos que presenta la persona en su forma de comportarse, ajustarse y relacionarse con otras personas y el entorno. Dado que no existen en el mundo dos personas que sean exactamente iguales, se puede decir que no es posible duplicar la personalidad. Sin embargo, sí existen semejanzas en el comportamiento de las personas, y son precisamente estas semejanzas las que estudian los psicólogos en su afán de comprender mejor el comportamiento humano.

El estudio de la personalidad es tan complejo que no todos los psicólogos se han puesto de acuerdo en cómo explicar esta faceta del comportamiento humano. En esta sección se describen someramente cuatro teorías en las que se basan los psicólogos para comprender la personalidad: teoría psicoanalítica, teoría de la superioridad y la compensación, teoría de la ansiedad y teoría de la auto-realización.

Teoría psicoanalítica   Sigmund Freud afirmaba que gran parte de la personalidad proviene de instintos y deseos inconscientes y ocultos. Las tres partes que conforman la personalidad son: el *id* (impulso que busca el placer para satisfacer las necesidades de alimento, sexo y autoprotección), el *ego* (un control a la búsqueda de placer del id), y el *superego* (la conciencia). De acuerdo con esta teoría, la personalidad se desarrolla a partir de las experiencias de la niñez.

Teoría de la superioridad y la compensación   Alfred Adler creía que la personalidad se moldea a través de la lucha por la superioridad. La no realización de las personas en su afán de llegar a ser fuertes o poderosas puede acarrear un sentimiento de inferioridad. El estar consciente de la propia debilidad impulsa a la persona a empeñarse en gran manera por superar esta situación. Algunos de los problemas de los adultos se pueden atribuir a sentimientos de inadecuación experimentados durante la niñez.

Teoría de la ansiedad   Karen Horney sostenía que las personas sufren de ansiedad cuando les preocupa no poder llegar a ser aquello que quieren ser. A fin de disminuir su ansiedad, estas personas adoptan comportamientos o adquieren necesidades que les permiten ajustarse. La teoría de la ansiedad explica cómo los adultos desarrollan necesidades neuróticas

—es decir, necesidades aprendidas—para reducir su ansiedad. Por ejemplo, lavarse las manos en exceso puede ser el resultado del énfasis abrumador que ponía uno de los padres sobre la limpieza durante la niñez.

Teoría de la auto-realización   Abraham Maslow creía que la personalidad humana se encuentra motivada a satisfacer ciertas necesidades vitales. Estas necesidades se expresan en forma jerárquica (en rangos por orden de importancia). La pirámide de necesidades de Maslow comprende las siguientes necesidades: *fisiológicas* (supervivencia: alimento, abrigo y vestido), *de seguridad y estabilidad* (deseo de orden y predictibilidad), *de pertenencia a un grupo* (vínculos sociales), *de estima* (reconocimiento y respeto de los demás), y *de auto-realización* (la necesidad humana más importante: satisfacer el potencial propio). Maslow creía que la gran atracción que ejercen las necesidades de orden superior produce una mayor motivación en los seres humanos, y la no satisfacción de tales necesidades acarrea frustración e infelicidad.

Mecanismos de defensa

La compensación se ha descrito anteriormente al explicar la teoría de Adler sobre la personalidad. Las personas compensan sus deficiencias tratando de superarlas con todas sus fuerzas. Los *mecanismos de defensa* son estratagemas que se adoptan para reducir la frustración producida al intentar alcanzar nuestros objetivos. Entre estos mecanismos se pueden citar:

represión: el mantener soterrados pensamientos que, en caso de ser asumidos, podrían suscitar ansiedad

> *Ejemplo:*   A María no le gustan los taladros del dentista, así que muy cómodamente se "olvida" de su cita con el odontólogo.

proyección: el esconder la fuente del conflicto echándoles la culpa a otros

> *Ejemplo:*   Para aprobar matemáticas, Jaime necesita sacarse una A en la prueba. Se siente tentado a copiar pero su conciencia no se lo permite. Entonces, él acusa de haber copiado en la prueba a estudiantes inocentes que han obtenido buenas calificaciones.

desplazamiento: el substituir un objeto u objetivo por otro

> *Ejemplo:*   Rafael se enfada con su jefe, pero teme decírselo abiertamente. En vez de ello, se enreda en una discusión con su esposa apenas llegado a su casa.

racionalización: el atribuir la razón del fracaso a otra cosa

> *Ejemplo:*   Héctor no ha podido clasificarse para integrar el equipo titular de baloncesto, entonces le echa la culpa al entrenador diciendo que éste tiene prejuicios contra él.

formación de reacción: el encubrir por completo un motivo mostrando el comportamiento opuesto

> *Ejemplo:*   Julia siente un odio profundo por su padre, pero da la impresión de que está excesivamente preocupada por la salud y el bienestar de éste.

EJERCICIO 6: MECANISMOS DE DEFENSA

Instrucciones: Vuelva a leer las definiciones de la página 110 y elija la mejor respuesta para cada una de las siguientes situaciones.

1. En la fábula del zorro y las uvas, había un zorro que apetecía un racimo de uvas pero no podía alcanzarlas. Como no pudo comerse las uvas, se marchó diciendo que estaban amargas y que, al fin y al cabo, no valían la pena.
    (1) represión
    (2) proyección
    (3) desplazamiento
    (4) racionalización
    (5) formación de reacción

2. Miguel está disgustado porque su equipo ha perdido el partido y, cuando llega a su casa, le da una patada al perro cuando éste corre a recibirle. El mecanismo de defensa descrito es:
    (1) represión
    (2) proyección
    (3) desplazamiento
    (4) racionalización
    (5) formación de reacción

Ambiente social

Las personas se comportan de forma distinta cuando están solas que cuando están en grupo. El ambiente social influye en gran medida en el comportamiento de las mismas. Los *psicólogos sociales* estudian los efectos que produce el grupo en el individuo y se centran en dos áreas: las actitudes sociales y el comportamiento del grupo.

Las actitudes sociales abarcan las acciones, creencias y sentimientos de las personas hacia los grupos y clases de personas. Al estudiar las actitudes, los psicólogos sociales pueden comprender mejor los procesos de atracción o rechazo entre las personas.

El comportamiento de grupo comprende las distintas formas en que el individuo se comporta dentro del grupo. Un ejemplo de la influencia que ejerce el grupo en el comportamiento del individuo es el grupo paritario de adolescentes. Cuando los niños llegan a cierta edad, el grupo paritario llega a ser más importante para ellos que la propia familia.

Los psicólogos sociales han descubierto que cuando la persona se integra a ciertos tipos de grupos, se vuelve anónima, es decir, pierde su identidad individual y pasa a formar parte de la multitud. Esta "pérdida de identidad" le permite hacer cosas que normalmente no hubiera hecho a nivel individual. Como ejemplos negativos de estos grupos tenemos a las turbas y a los grupos de "vigilantes" (pseudo-policías que toman la ley en sus manos). Como ejemplo positivo se pueden mencionar los grupos de rescate que trabajan en conjunto para prestar ayuda a las víctimas de un terremoto.

2
HISTORIA DE EE.UU.

¿Por qué estudiar el pasado? Estudiamos el pasado porque cada uno de nosotros somos el resultado de quienes nos precedieron. Si comprendemos sus triunfos y sus fracasos, podremos entender mejor los acontecimientos de nuestra sociedad actual y prepararnos mejor para el futuro. La Historia es, en gran medida, un registro de relaciones causa-efecto. Los historiadores estudian estas conexiones que existen entre los sucesos. En este capítulo se incluyen breves *vistas panorámicas* de algunos de los acontecimientos más importantes de la historia de Estados Unidos.

Una nueva nación en un Nuevo Mundo

Exploración y colonización   Las noticias del viaje de Colón a América en 1492 desataron una ola de viajes de exploración por parte de España, Portugal, Francia e Inglaterra durante los siglos XVI y XVII. Todos estos países, junto con otras cuantas naciones europeas, reclamaron para sí distintas regiones del continente americano, y para principios del siglo XVIII la mayoría de éstos ya habían establecido asentamientos coloniales. Los derechos de los americanos nativos (indígenas o indios americanos) fueron ignorados y un gran número de ellos murieron a causa de las enfermedades traídas a América por los europeos o fueron muertos en guerras contra éstos.

Francia fundó una gran colonia en Canadá. Inglaterra poseía trece colonias diseminadas a lo largo de la costa del Atlántico, desde Maine hasta el borde de la Florida española. Los conflictos debidos a otras reclamaciones de tierras en Norteamérica y otros lugares desembocaron en una guerra entre Inglaterra y Francia que se extendió de 1754 a 1763 (conocida en América como la **Guerra Franco-Indígena** puesto que cada uno de los bandos contaba con aliados indios). Con su victoria, Inglaterra asumió el control de la mayor parte de las posesiones francesas en Norteamérica.

El período colonial   Cada una de las colonias inglesas era gobernada por un consejo o un gobernador que actuaba en representación del monarca inglés. Los colonos eran en su mayoría ingleses, pero también había entre ellos holandeses y alemanes así como grupos menos numerosos procedentes de otros países europeos. Tenían distintas costumbres al igual que ideas políticas y religiosas. Había grandes oportunidades económicas, y los abundantes recursos naturales de Norteamérica favorecieron el desarrollo de industrias tales como la construcción de barcos, la minería, el comercio de pieles y la pesca.

A fin de poder solventar los gastos de la Guerra Franco-Indígena, Inglaterra trató de obtener ingresos de América. Los colonos se resistieron alegando que, como no estaban representados en el Parlamento (legislatura británica), el gobierno de Londres no tenía derecho de gravarles con ningún tipo de impuesto. Inglaterra intentó poner en marcha diferentes planes: impuestos sobre las importaciones como el azúcar y el té, un impuesto sobre el timbre y, por último, un conjunto de leyes que los colonos denominaron *Leyes Intolerables*—leyes que el Parlamento había promulgado con la intención de que los colonos acataran todas las leyes británicas—inclusive las leyes impositivas. Los colonos se resistieron.

Revolución e Independencia Las protestas de los colonos condujeron a la resistencia violenta y desembocaron, finalmente, en una guerra entre colonos y soldados británicos. Los representantes de las colonias, reunidos en un Congreso Continental en Philadelphia, aprobaron la *Declaración de Independencia* en 1776. La *Guerra Revolucionaria* duró hasta 1781, año en que las fuerzas americanas bajo el mando de George Washington, con la ayuda de un poderoso contingente enviado por Francia, capturaron a un numeroso ejército británico en Yorktown, Virginia. En un tratado de paz firmado en Versalles dos años después, los británicos reconocieron la independencia de los Estados Unidos de América.

LAS RESPUESTAS DE LOS EJERCICIOS DE ESTE CAPÍTULO
EMPIEZAN EN LA PÁGINA 446.

EJERCICIO 1: UNA NUEVA NACIÓN
Instrucciones: Relacione las causas de la columna izquierda con su efecto correspondiente de la columna derecha.

_____ 1. Inglaterra y Francia reclaman territorios en Norteamérica

_____ 2. Declaración de Independencia

_____ 3. los colonos se niegan a pagar los impuestos británicos

(a) Guerra Revolucionaria

(b) Leyes Intolerables

(c) Guerra Franco-Indígena

Los comienzos de la República

Durante la Guerra Revolucionaria, los americanos establecieron un gobierno bajo los *Artículos de Confederación.* Tras largos años bajo el cetro de los reyes ingleses, los americanos no confiaban en un gobierno central poderoso y delegaron gran parte del poder en los estados individuales. Sin embargo, este hecho ocasionó disputas sobre temas tales como la emisión de dinero, el comercio y la defensa nacional. Conforme a lo estipulado en los Artículos, cada estado tenía el derecho de imprimir su propio papel moneda y el comercio entre estados estaba gravado con impuestos al igual que si fueran importaciones del extranjero. Además, durante la guerra, las tropas estaban mal equipadas y no recibían ningún pago por parte de los estados que las enviaban. Para resolver estos y otros problemas, el Congreso Continental pidió que se convocara una Convención Constituyente para revisar los Artículos de Confederación. Esta Convención, que tuvo lugar en Philadelphia en 1787, fue más allá de lo que se había propuesto originalmente.

La Constitución de EE.UU. Los delegados que enviaron los estados a Philadelphia redactaron una constitución enteramente nueva. En la convención se dieron muchos desacuerdos: respecto a qué tipo de legislatura debía establecerse, cómo se debía contar la población de los estados a efectos impositivos y de representación, la esclavitud, así como una cantidad de asuntos de mucha y poca importancia.

Mediante una serie de concesiones y acuerdos entre los delegados, se redactó el borrador de una constitución. Según ésta, se establecería un legislatura bicameral (de dos cámaras). Cada estado estaría proporcionalmente representado en la Cámara de Representantes según su población. Los estados más grandes tendrían más representantes que los pequeños; pero, en el Senado, cada estado tendría la misma representación: dos senadores. Otra concesión, esta vez sobre el tema de la esclavitud, determinó que los esclavos se contarían cada uno como tres quintos de persona a efectos de impuestos y representación, pero no tendrían el derecho al voto. El comercio de esclavos se aboliría en 1808, pero no se tomó en ese entonces ninguna medida para acabar con la esclavitud.

La campaña por la ratificación Una vez redactada y aprobada por los delegados la Constitución de EE.UU., se inició una vivaz campaña por su ratificación (aprobación) por parte de los estados. El país se dividió en dos bandos básicos: los *Federalistas,* que estaban a favor del fuerte gobierno central que establecía la Constitución, y los *Anti-Federalistas,* que deseaban mantener la soberanía (poder supremo) de los estados. La ratificación fue aprobada y en el mes de marzo de 1779 George Washington fue investido en el cargo como el primer presidente de la nueva nación.

EJERCICIO 2: LOS COMIENZOS DEL GOBIERNO AMERICANO
Instrucciones: Lea las siguientes afirmaciones. Escriba una *V* en el espacio en blanco si la afirmación es verdadera y una *F* si es falsa.

_____ **1.** Despúes de la Revolución, la mayor parte de los poderes gubernamentales eran ostentados por los estados.

_____ **2.** Los Artículos de Confederación eran inadecuados para abordar temas comunes a los trece estados.

_____ **3.** Artículos de Confederación y Constitución son títulos de un mismo documento.

EJERCICIO 3: DISPUTAS, CONCESIONES Y ACUERDOS
Instrucciones: Elija la mejor respuesta para cada una de las siguientes preguntas.

1. Al contar a cada esclavo como sólo tres quintos de persona, se favorecía a los estados del Norte porque
   (1) se limitaba el número de senadores que representaban al Sur.
   (2) se limitaba el número de escaños que tenía el Sur en la Cámara de Representantes.
   (3) se basaba en la cantidad de propiedad a efectos impositivos.
   (4) se evitaba que se extendiera la esclavitud.
   (5) se igualaba el número de representantes que tenían el Norte y el Sur.

2. Hoy en día, gran parte de los conservadores, tanto Demócratas como Republicanos, son fervientes partidarios de los derechos de los estados del país. De haber vivido en la época de la independencia, éstos hubieran sido probablemente partidarios

(1) del anti-federalismo.
(2) del federalismo.
(3) del republicanismo.
(4) de la democracia.
(5) del colonialismo.

La nación se expande

Los Estados Unidos experimentaron un período de gran expansión geográfica entre 1701 y 1850. Durante la presidencia de George Washington fueron admitidas a la Unión Vermont, Kentucky y Tennessee (entre 1791 y 1796); Ohio fue admitida (1802) durante la presidencia de Thomas Jefferson. Con la enorme Compra de Louisiana (1803) se duplicó el tamaño del país: el *Destino Manifiesto* se convirtió en la consigna motriz en pro de que se extendieran las fronteras de EE.UU. hasta el Océano Pacífico.

Relaciones exteriores   En 1812, los Estados Unidos declararon la guerra a Gran Bretaña por su interferencia en el comercio del país y su ayuda a los indios. Gran Bretaña impuso un bloqueo. A pesar de algunas exitosas campañas militares, los Estados Unidos perdieron esta guerra tan impopular. Como resultado de este conflicto, perdieron fuerza los Federalistas pro-británicos, continuó la expansión hacia el oeste, se aceleró el proceso de industrialización a causa del bloqueo británico y surgió un nuevo sentir nacionalista.

El Presidente James Monroe proclamó la llamada *Doctrina Monroe* (1823), según la cual ya no les sería permitido a las naciones europeas colonizar el continente americano y según la cual los Estados Unidos se mantendrían neutrales respecto de los conflictos europeos. La expansión hacia el Oeste proseguía.

La democracia Jacksoniana y la Guerra Mexicana

El *seccionalismo* (diferencias políticas, culturales y económicas entre las distintas regiones del país, principalmente entre el Norte, el Sur y el Oeste) pasó a convertirse en un problema de importancia. El Presidente Andrew Jackson, *populista* que representaba al común de la gente, fue elegido como consecuencia de las diferencias entre facciones y secciones. Jackson se opuso a la creación de un banco nacional y los agricultores y artesanos pasaron a tener más voz en el gobierno. Durante la presidencia de James Polk, los Estados Unidos anexionaron Texas (1845), pero no pudieron comprar el territorio que hoy ocupan New Mexico y California. Las disputas fronterizas llevaron a los Estados Unidos a declarar la guerra a México; el Tratado Guadalupe Hidalgo (1848) puso fin a la guerra y dio como resultado la *Cesión Mexicana.* Los Estados Unidos ganaron extensos territorios que comprendían los actuales estados de California, Utah y Nevada, así como partes de otros cuatro estados.

EXPANSIÓN DE LOS ESTADOS UNIDOS (1783–1853)

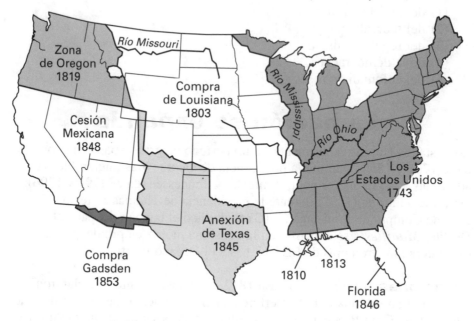

EJERCICIO 4: LA GUERRA DE 1812

Instrucciones: Elija la mejor respuesta para la siguiente pregunta.

¿Qué acontecimiento contribuyó al sentir nacionalista en Estados Unidos después de la Guerra de 1812?

(1) el espíritu del Destino Manifiesto que ardió a principios del siglo XIX
(2) la necesidad de manufacturar los productos dentro del país a causa del bloqueo naval británico
(3) el haber usado a los Federalistas como chivo expiatorio tildándolos de traidores
(4) 1 y 2
(5) 2 y 3

Tiempos de conflictos internos

El seccionalismo persistía; los *aranceles* (impuestos sobre los bienes importados, que eran favorecidos por el Norte más industrializado y opuestos por el Sur y Oeste agrícolas) eran considerados desiguales e injustos. La esclavitud se había convertido en un tema candente. Existían en la época puntos de vista conflictivos acerca de la misma, como la *soberanía popular* (los afectados tenían que determinar qué era lo mejor), la aceptación de la esclavitud donde ya existía con la prohibición de la misma en nuevas áreas, y la creencia de los *abolicionistas* de que la esclavitud era abominable y debía abolirse. La *decisión Dred Scott* (1857) agravó las relaciones entre el

Norte y el Sur cuando la Corte Suprema dictaminó que el esclavo era objeto de propiedad y no podía entablar demanda por su libertad en una corte federal.

La nación va a la guerra   El Presidente Abraham Lincoln prometió restringir la esclavitud a aquellos lugares donde ya existía; no obstante, los estados sureños temían la dominación por parte del Norte. Once estados sureños optaron por separarse de la Unión y formaron los Estados Confederados de América.

La Guerra Civil   La Guerra Civil (1861–1865) se desarrolló en su mayor parte en el Sur. El Norte tenía una mayor población, superiores medios de fabricación, excelentes medios de transporte y mayor cantidad de recursos naturales. El Sur, por su parte, estaba más familiarizado con los sitios en que se libraban las batallas y tenía una gran confianza en sus destacados líderes militares. Lincoln publicó la *Proclamación de Emancipación* (1862), decretando la libertad de los esclavos en los estados que se habían separado. La guerra terminó con la rendición del General Robert E. Lee en 1865. El país se enfrentaba a la enorme tarea de remediar la división entre Norte y Sur, reconstruir el Sur y readmitir el Sur dentro de la Unión.

Reconstrucción   El plan de Lincoln para unir a la nación contemplaba la reinstauración de los derechos de ciudadanía y del status de estado para el Sur; sin embargo, fue asesinado por un simpatizante de los confederados antes de que pudiera llevar a cabo su plan. Lo sucedió Andrew Johnson, natural de Tennessee; pero el Congreso recelaba de él por considerarlo pro-Sur. Se convirtió en el primer presidente de EE.UU. en sufrir *impeachment* (acusación por delito en el desempeño del cargo) o imputación pero no fue condenado ni destituido. La Decimotercera Enmienda a la Constitución (1865) abolió la esclavitud. La Decimocuarta y la Decimoquinta Enmienda (1868 y 1870) garantizaban la ciudadanía y el derecho al voto a los esclavos emancipados. El Congreso exigió a los estados sureños que ratificaran estas enmiendas antes de que pudieran ser readmitidos a la Unión.

EJERCICIO 5: UNA NACIÓN DIVIDIDA
Instrucciones: Elija la mejor respuesta para las siguientes preguntas.

1. El referéndum es un procedimiento político que permite a los votantes aprobar o rechazar una medida propuesta por los mismo votantes o por la legislatura. ¿A cuál de las siguientes soluciones propuestas acerca del tema de la esclavitud se asemeja más este método?
   (1) abolicionismo
   (2) compromiso
   (3) soberanía popular
   (4) secesión
   (5) equilibrio territorial

2. A la decisión Dred Scott se la considera como uno de los acontecimientos decisivos que desencadenaron la Guerra Civil. Los valores
confirmados por la decisión de la Corte Suprema mantenían que
(1) la esclavitud era inhumana.
(2) los estados tenían más derechos que las personas.
(3) los nuevos estados podían permitir la esclavitud.
(4) la esclavitud sólo se podía mantener en el Sur.
(5) los seres humanos podían ser tratados como objetos de propiedad.

EJERCICIO 6: EL VOTO SOBRE LA SECESIÓN

Instrucciones: Basándose en el siguiente mapa, paree el estado de la columna
izquierda con su descripción correspondiente de la columna derecha.

_____ **1.** Virginia

_____ **2.** Texas

_____ **3.** Kentucky

(a) Como "estado fronterizo", permaneció en la
Unión a pesar de ser un estado que permitía
la esclavitud.

(b) Este estado se dividió en dos por el tema de
la secesión, y la parte occidental se mantuvo
fiel a la Unión.

(c) Todo el estado se separó de la Unión aunque
sólo la parte oriental había votado a favor de
ello.

El surgimiento
de un país industrial

Terminada la Guerra Civil, el crecimiento de la industria transformó la economía de la nación. Se empezó a producir en masa una mayor cantidad de
productos a un costo menor y, a finales de siglo, Estados Unidos se convirtió

en un líder industrial en el mundo. Las fábricas y la población de las ciudades crecieron, y la demanda de los consumidores favoreció la expansión de las empresas, la creación de nuevos productos y el establecimiento de nuevas industrias.

Desarrollo de grandes empresas   La industrialización rápida y generalizada provocó el surgimiento de grandes empresas, sobre todo en las industrias del acero, el ferrocarril y el petróleo. Las condiciones de trabajo se deterioraron mientras el gobierno seguía una política de *laissez-faire* (no interferencia) con respecto a las empresas.

Urbanización y cambio social   La urbanización es el proceso de población de ciudades. Las gentes abandonan las áreas rurales y se trasladan a vivir a las ciudades. Antes de la industrialización, una sexta parte de la población estadounidense vivía en ciudades: hacia 1890 había subido a una tercera parte. Las ciudades contaban con centros de ferrocarril para el transporte de pasajeros, provisiones y mercancías. Una oleada de inmigrantes (1870–1900) contribuyó a una abundante oferta de mano de obra.

Trabajo y progresismo   Como la salud, la seguridad y la comodidad de los trabajadores habían sido en gran medida ignorados, se organizaron sindicatos que lidiaran con el empleador. Entre los primeros sindicatos figuran los Caballeros del Trabajo (1869) y la Federación Estadounidense de Trabajo (1881). Otros grupos e individuos lucharon contra la corrupción política e intentaron mejorar la calidad de vida del estadounidense. Entre sus reformas progresivas de finales del siglo XIX y principios del siglo XX se puede mencionar la Ley Antitrust Sherman, que prohibió los monopolios; la Ley Hepburn, que confirió mayor autoridad a la Comisión de Comercio Interestatal para regular los ferrocarriles de la nación; la Ley de Alimentos y Medicamentos Puros, que reglamentó la producción y venta de alimentos y medicamentos; el establecimiento del Departamento de Agricultura de los Estados Unidos (cuyas siglas en inglés son USDA), que comenzó inspeccionando la carne; leyes que regulaban el trabajo de menores; y leyes sobre el salario mínimo y la indemnización por accidentes laborales.

EJERCICIO 7: DESARROLLO DE GRANDES EMPRESAS
Instrucciones: Marque con una cruz las acciones que se refieran a una actividad económica donde *no* intervenga el gobierno.

_____ **1.** La Comisión Federal de Comunicaciones (FCC en inglés) exige el desmembramiento de AT&T en compañías más pequeñas.

_____ **2.** Una compañía grande contrata a trabajadores no cualificados y les paga lo mínimo que dicta el mercado pero no se le entabla juicio por violar la ley del salario mínimo.

_____ **3.** Una compañía de tarjetas de crédito que recarga a sus clientes el interés que quiera.

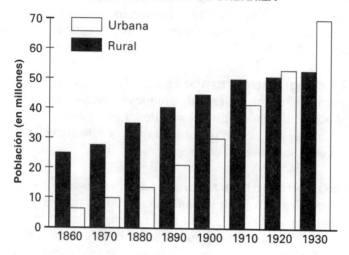

ESTADOS UNIDOS SE URBANIZA

Gráfica de barras. Eje vertical: Población (en millones), de 0 a 70. Leyenda: Urbana (barra blanca), Rural (barra negra). Eje horizontal: décadas de 1860 a 1930.

EJERCICIO 8: ESTADOS UNIDOS SE URBANIZA

Instrucciones: Basándose en la gráfica de arriba, conteste las siguientes preguntas.

1. **(a)** ¿En qué década empezó a ser mayor el número de personas que vivía en áreas urbanas que el que vivía en áreas rurales? _____

   (b) ¿Aproximadamente cuántos millones de personas vivían en áreas urbanas hacia 1930? _____

2. En base a las cifras de la gráfica de barras, Estados Unidos logró probablemente alcanzar la mitad de su población actual de 248 millones de personas (según el censo de 1990) hacia
   (1) la década de 1890.
   (2) el siglo XX.
   (3) la década de 1910.
   (4) la década de 1920.
   (5) la década de 1930.

La transformación en potencia mundial

Su política constante de *aislacionismo* evitó que Estados Unidos se mezclara en asuntos de países extranjeros, pero sus crecientes necesidades industriales exigían la apertura de mercados exteriores para sus productos. Estados Unidos estableció relaciones comerciales con Japón en 1854. Más tarde, el país se unió a las grandes potencias europeas para exigir la apertura de establecimientos comerciales en China. La nación había comprado Alaska (en 1867). A finales del siglo XIX incorporó Hawaii a su ya extenso territorio (anexada en 1893) así como unas cuantas pequeñas islas del Pacífico. La tendencia continua de la nación hacia el *imperialismo* (política que consiste en obtener el control sobre otras regiones o naciones) siguió en aumento durante la década de 1890.

La Guerra Hispano-Estadounidense   Estados Unidos apoyaba a los rebeldes cubanos que se habían rebelado contra España y envió el acorazado Maine para proteger a los ciudadanos estadounidenses en Cuba. Cuando el acorazado explotó por razones desconocidas, Estados Unidos responsabilizó a España del hecho y declaró la guerra a este país en 1898. En un período de cuatro meses, Estados Unidos ganó la guerra y obtuvo el control de Guam, Puerto Rico y Filipinas.

La Primera Guerra Mundial   Los conflictos nacionalistas y las luchas por el poder en Europa empujaron a veintisiete naciones a tomar parte en una guerra mundial que comenzó en 1914. Entre las Potencias Centrales se encontraban Alemania, Austria-Hungría y Turquía. Las Potencias Aliadas las formaban Gran Bretaña, Francia, Rusia e Italia. Estados Unidos intentó permanecer neutral pero se sumó a las Potencias Aliadas después de que Alemania atacara a barcos que transportaban a ciudadanos norteamericanos. Las Potencias Aliadas rechazaron las fuerzas de las Potencias Centrales y los alemanes aceptaron su derrota. Con la firma del Tratado de Versalles (1919), se estableció una Liga de Naciones con el cometido de velar por la paz mundial. Debido a la oposición del Congreso, Estados Unidos no integró dicha liga, hecho que contribuyó al declive de la misma. El país regresó a su política aislacionista, concentrándose en asuntos domésticos.

De la prosperidad a la desesperación   El Presidente Calvin Coolidge era partidario de la poca reglamentación gubernamental, la reducción del gasto público y la disminución de los impuestos. Los "locos años veinte" fueron un período de prosperidad, de arriesgadas inversiones con la esperanza de obtener ganancias sustanciales, de comercio ilegal de licor y de materialismo. En 1929, quebró la bolsa de valores. Enseguida comenzaron a quebrar las empresas y el desempleo se disparó. El Presidente Herbert Hoover trató de controlar la crisis económica, pero su política de no interferencia en las empresas lo condenaba al fracaso desde el inicio. El número de desempleados ascendió a 11 millones. Franklin D. Roosevelt prometió un *New Deal* (o Nuevo Trato) y fue electo a la presidencia.

Los objetivos del *New Deal* eran: ayuda de emergencia, recuperación económica y reformas para evitar que se produjera otra depresión. Nuevos programas y agencias, incluyendo el sistema de seguridad social y la Ley de Recuperación Nacional, transformaron la política del gobierno. El clima económico y emocional del país fue mejorando lentamente, pero la recuperación total sólo se dio con el desencadenamiento de otra guerra mundial.

EJERCICIO 9: ESTADOS UNIDOS SE CONVIERTE EN POTENCIA MUNDIAL

Instrucciones: Elija la mejor respuesta para las siguientes preguntas.

1. ¿Cuál de las siguientes medidas de política exterior recientes es resultado directo de la política imperialista estadounidense anterior?
    (1) el apoyo militar norteamericano a Israel en el Medio Oriente
    (2) el apoyo implícito al apartheid en Sudáfrica por parte de algunas de las grandes empresas estadounidenses

(3) el establecimiento de bases militares estadounidenses en la Bahía Subic en las Filipinas

(4) el estacionamiento de tropas estadounidenses en la antigua Alemania Occidental

(5) el patrullaje de las aguas frente a la costa de Libia por parte de Estados Unidos

2. Durante el período comprendido entre el final de la Guerra Civil y la Guerra Hispano-Estadounidense de 1898, la mayoría de los estadounidenses eran aislacionistas. ¿Cuál sería la causa más probable de este deseo generalizado de sustraerse de los asuntos internacionales?

(1) la falta de información sobre los acontecimientos que ocurrían en el extranjero

(2) el deseo de expandir las fronteras de EE.UU. por el continente, hacia Canadá y México

(3) la desilusión con los aliados extranjeros que se habían rehusado a tomar partido durante la Guerra Civil

(4) la preocupación de la nación con la reconstrucción e industrialización una vez finalizada la Guerra Civil

(5) el resentimiento hacia los nuevos inmigrantes que estaban invadiendo el país

EJERCICIO 10: LA PRIMERA GUERRA MUNDIAL
Instrucciones: Rellene los espacios en blanco y complete el párrafo.

En 1917, Estados Unidos entró en la guerra y se unió al bando de los

(1) _____. Con la firma de (2) _____ en 1919, se puso

oficialmente término a la guerra. El Congreso se opuso a que Estados

Unidos entrara a formar parte de (3) _____. A consecuencia de esto,

Estados Unidos volvió a adoptar su antigua política de (4) _____.

EJERCICIO 11: EL *NEW DEAL*
Instrucciones: Relacione los grupos de la izquierda con la legislación del *New Deal* que estos grupos habrían apoyado.

_____ 1. trabajadores desempleados   (a) Ley de Recuperación Industrial Nacional

_____ 2. los ancianos   (b) Cuerpos de Conservación Civil

_____ 3. los medioambientalistas   (c) Ley de la Seguridad Social

De aislacionista a superpotencia

Debido a su política aislacionista y a la depresión en que estaba sumida, Estados Unidos hizo caso omiso de los conflictos que se producían en los distintos países: el militarismo en aumento de Alemania; la agresión de Japón contra China; la guerra civil española; y la invasión italiana de Etiopía.

La Segunda Guerra Mundial   Tras la invasión alemana de Polonia (1939), Gran Bretaña y Francia declararon la guerra. Italia y Alemania, junto con Japón, formaron las llamadas potencias del Eje. Con el ataque japonés a Pearl Harbor en 1941, Estados Unidos declaró la guerra a Japón y Alemania, y se unió a las fuerzas Aliadas, que integraban Gran Bretaña, la Unión Soviética y Francia. Esta guerra mundial duró seis años y concluyó con la pérdida de millones de vidas y con un costo de miles de millones de dólares. Roosevelt murió un mes antes de que los esfuerzos masivos de los Aliados lograran la rendición de Alemania.

Harry Truman fue electo presidente y estaba firmemente decidido a poner un rápido fin a la guerra contra Japón. Con el lanzamiento de las destructivas bombas atómicas sobre Hiroshima y Nagasaki, Japón se rindió. Finalizada la guerra, el Acuerdo de Yalta estableció la división de Alemania en cuatro zonas controladas por Gran Bretaña, la Unión Soviética, Francia y Estados Unidos. Asimismo se creó una organización mundial con el objetivo de velar por la paz de sus miembros: la Organización de las Naciones Unidas (ONU). Entre las secuelas dejadas por la guerra se puede mencioar el Holocausto (exterminio sistemático de seis millones de judíos).

La Guerra Fría   El Presidente Harry Truman postuló la llamada Doctrina Truman (que apoyaba a los pueblos libres que se oponían a minorías internas armadas o a poderes extranjeros). La contención del comunismo se convirtió en la política de EE.UU. durante los años que duró la llamada Guerra Fría, lucha no militar entre la Unión Soviética y Estados Unidos, junto a sus respectivos aliados. La Guerra Fría se "caldeó" en Corea.

La Guerra de Corea   Después de la Segunda Guerra Mundial, la Unión Soviética y Estados Unidos ocuparon las mitades norte y sur de Corea respectivamente. Hacia 1950, se estableció un gobierno comunista en el Norte y se estacionaron a lo largo de la frontera ejércitos representantes del Norte y del Sur del país. Cuando Corea del Norte cruzó la frontera e invadió Corea del Sur, el Presidente Truman envió tropas norteamericanas y pidió el apoyo de las Naciones Unidas. La lucha continuó hasta 1953, año en que se firmó un tratado y se restableció la línea divisoria entre Corea del Norte y Corea del Sur. Las tensiones no cesaban.

La época de Eisenhower   Mientras seguía su curso la Guerra Fría, Estados Unidos y la Unión Soviética aumentaron sus fuerzas militares y desarrollaron la potente bomba de hidrógeno. Durante la década de 1950, el Senador Joseph McCarthy y otros extremistas anticomunistas llevaron a cabo una campaña de persecución apoyada en el odio y temor desmedidos al comunismo, acusando y arruinando en consecuencia a prominentes figuras del gobierno, el mundo empresarial y el mundo del espectáculo.

Durante el segundo mandato del Presidente Eisenhower, el desarrollo económico y los cambios sociales cobraron impulso. El lanzamiento del primer satélite artificial (Sputnik) por la Unión Soviética motivó a Estados Unidos a entrar en la carrera espacial. El actual movimiento de los derechos civiles se inició como resultado de la decisión de la Corte Suprema de EE.UU. sobre el caso *Brown v. Junta de Educación de Topeka*. Muchas escuelas del Sur se opusieron al dictamen judicial que sostenía que "las instalaciones educativas separadas son inherentemente desiguales". Una ley de 1957 creó la Comisión de Derechos Civiles para que investigara la ilegalidad de ciertos requisitos para el ejercicio del voto.

EJERCICIO 12: LA SEGUNDA GUERRA MUNDIAL
Instrucciones: Escriba una *V* si la expresión es verdadera y una *F* si es falsa.

_____ **1.** La agresión territorial de los países del Eje fue una de las principales causas de la Segunda Guerra Mundial.

_____ **2.** El bombardeo de Pearl Harbor por parte de Japón puso término a la neutralidad de Estados Unidos.

_____ **3.** Las Naciones Unidas es una liga de naciones cuya misión es salvaguardar a sus miembros en caso de guerra.

Las décadas recientes

Kennedy y Johnson   La década de 1960 se inició en medio de prometedoras expectativas. Un joven presidente asumía el poder y alentaba a sus compatriotas a trabajar por un futuro mejor. Al final, esa década acabó convirtiéndose en un turbulento período plagado de divisiones políticas, raciales y sociales. John F. Kennedy, el primer católico elegido a la presidencia, fundó el Cuerpo de Paz y VISTA (siglas en inglés de los Voluntarios al Servicio de América). Kennedy imaginó para EE.UU. una "nueva frontera" de vuelos espaciales tripulados que llevaría a los estadounidenses a aterrizar en la Luna antes de finalizada la década.

En 1961, Kennedy impuso un bloqueo para impedir el paso de barcos soviéticos destinados a Cuba y exigió que se desmantelaran las instalaciones de misiles de la isla. Khrushchev, el primer ministro soviético, cedió a fin de evitar el posible inicio de otra guerra. Kennedy continuó la política de derechos civiles de Eisenhower, mientras el Reverendo Martin Luther King, Jr. encabezaba protestas no violentas. Kennedy fue asesinado en 1963 antes de que muchos de sus programas sociales se convirtieran en realidad.

El Presidente Lyndon B. Johnson juró que continuaría con los programas de Kennedy y logró que el Congreso aprobara leyes de carácter social que sirvieran de base a su visión de una "Gran Sociedad". De entre estas leyes, las más significativas fueron la Ley de Derechos Civiles (1964), que prohibía la discriminación racial en los lugares públicos y allí donde se usaran fondos federales, y la Ley de Derechos de Voto (1965), que protegía el derecho al voto de los estadounidenses africanoamericanos. La participación de Estados Unidos en la Guerra de Vietnam siguió en escalada durante el período de 1963 a 1968 y la controversia pública dividió al país. Hubo protestas en contra de la guerra y Johnson decidió no buscar la reelección.

La época de Nixon La Guerra de Vietnam proseguía. El Presidente Richard M. Nixon había dado órdenes de que se enviaran tropas a Camboya. Paulatinamente luego fue retirando las tropas y terminó negociando una retirada total en 1973. La política de Nixon de ***détente*** o distensión (disminución de las tensiones entre países) contribuyó a la firma con la Unión Soviética del tratado SALT (siglas en inglés de las Conversaciones Estratégicas para la Limitación de Armamentos), el cual establecía límites a los misiles. Nixon visitó la República Popular China (1972) y Estados Unidos se convirtió en una de las principales influencias en el mantenimiento de la paz. Estos logros, sin embargo, se vieron eclipsados por el escándalo de Watergate (1972), que obligó a Nixon a dimitir para así evitar el proceso de *impeachment* o imputación. El Vicepresidente Gerald Ford asumió la presidencia y concluyó el mandato de Nixon.

Carter   Jimmy Carter, un "desconocido" en los medios políticos de Washington, fue electo presidente en 1976 y trató de devolver al pueblo de Estados Unidos la confianza en sus líderes. Tuvo que hacer frente a problemas como la inflación y la subida del precio del petróleo. Sus mayores triunfos fueron su labor de mediación entre Egipto e Israel, que culminó con la firma del tratado de paz entre ambos países, el mejoramiento de las relaciones diplomáticas con China, la firma de un segundo tratado SALT de limitación de armamentos y el traspaso del control del Canal de Panamá. Entre los hechos que opacaron su mandato se destacan la toma de la embajada de Estados Unidos en Irán y el cautiverio de los rehenes estadounidenses. La liberación de los mismos se produjo el mismo día de la toma de posesión del Presidente Ronald Reagan.

Reagan-Bush   El Presidente Ronald Reagan tenía sesenta y nueve años cuando asumió la presidencia del país. Era un conservador muy popular. Bajo su mandato se cortaron o recortaron gran cantidad de programas sociales, cuya sustitución se esperaba viniera de los propios estados, los gobiernos locales y la industria privada. El número de personas que vivían en pobreza y de personas sin casa subió, a la vez que se disparaba el desempleo a niveles no vistos desde la depresión de la década de 1930. Se volcaron en la lucha anticomunista grandes esfuerzos, incluyendo una acumulación militar masiva, al tiempo que se mantenía una política de defensa de línea dura.

Entre los cambios políticos registrados durante la administración del Presidente George Bush (1989–1993) se destacan el colapso del comunismo en la Europa del Este, la Guerra del Golfo Pérsico y el desmembramiento de la Unión Soviética. Estados Unidos sufrió una profunda recesión a principios de la década de 1990, el Producto Interno Bruto (GNP en sus siglas en inglés) bajó y la tasa de desempleo se mantuvo en alza. El punto fuerte de Bush era la política exterior, pero sus oponentes políticos se concentraron en la necesaria recuperación de la economía doméstica.

Clinton   En 1992, se consideraba al Presidente Bill Clinton un neo-demócrata, es decir, un moderado que se alejaba de la idea de un "gobierno a gran escala de impuestos y gastos públicos". Con la promesa de impulsar el cambio, Clinton concentró sus esfuerzos en el déficit federal, la creación de puestos de trabajo, la reforma de las asistencias médica y social, la diversidad (mujeres y minorías en el Gabinete y otros nombramientos), la limitada ayuda económica a Rusia y la intervención en Bosnia.

EJERCICIO 13: LAS DÉCADAS RECIENTES

Instrucciones: Relacione los presidentes con los acontecimientos que tuvieron lugar durante sus correspondientes mandatos.

_____ **1.** John F. Kennedy   **(a)** Escándalo de Watergate

_____ **2.** Lyndon B. Johnson   **(b)** Guerra del Golfo Pérsico

_____ **3.** Richard M. Nixon   **(c)** Crisis de los rehenes en Irán

_____ **4.** Jimmy Carter   **(d)** Crisis de los misiles cubanos

_____ **5.** Ronald Reagan   **(e)** Acumulación militar masiva

_____ **6.** George Bush   **(f)** Ley de Derechos de Voto

3
CIENCIAS POLÍTICAS

El ser humano es un animal social; por ello debe necesariamente vivir en grupo. A fin de poder mantener el orden en la sociedad, se hace menester establecer gobiernos que dicten normas y leyes para satisfacer las necesidades de los individuos que integran la sociedad. Entre las importantes funciones del gobierno se pueden citar: la toma de decisiones, la resolución de conflictos y el proporcionamiento de los servicios necesarios. Los estudiosos de las ciencias políticas analizan la organización y administración del gobierno dentro de la sociedad.

Tipos de sistemas políticos

Existen en el mundo varios tipos de sistemas políticos. Las diferencias entre estos sistemas estriban principalmente en la forma en que los gobiernos derivan y ejercen su autoridad.

dictadura: Un líder único controla en su totalidad los aspectos políticos, sociales y económicos de la vida de un país. Entre los ejemplos históricos se destacan Adolf Hitler (Alemania) y Benito Mussolini (Italia). Entre los ejemplos de la era actual se pueden mencionar el Coronel Muammar Gadhafi (Libia) y Saddam Hussein (Irak).

monarquía: El poder de gobernar lo ostenta la familia real y se transmite a las generaciones subsiguientes. En el pasado, las *monarquías absolutas* tenían la última palabra en el proceso de toma de decisiones del gobierno. Hoy en día, la mayor parte de las monarquías están sujetas a las leyes de una constitución y poseen una autoridad limitada. Ejemplo de ello es la Reina Isabel II de Inglaterra, quien reina en carácter de líder ceremonial, mientras que las decisiones gubernamentales recaen sobre el Parlamento, encabezado por un primer ministro.

democracia: El jefe de gobierno es elegido por el pueblo y las decisiones del líder deben contar con la aprobación del pueblo. En la actualidad existen dos tipos de democracia. En las *democracias puras,* el pueblo toma las decisiones directamente, lo cual no es práctico cuando la población es muy grande. La democracia pura sólo se suele encontrar en pequeños pueblos, por ejemplo, los concejos municipales de vecinos en algunas regiones de New England. En las *democracias representativas,* el pueblo elige representantes que determinan las políticas que se deben seguir y dictan las leyes para toda la población. Estados Unidos es un ejemplo de democracia representativa.

oligarquía: El gobierno se halla depositado en manos de unos cuantos líderes que integran un grupo. Este sistema se asemeja a la dictadura en el hecho de que los funcionarios del gobierno no son elegidos por el pueblo y suelen llegar al poder después de una revolución. Las *juntas gubernativas* son grupos de personas que controlan el gobierno luego de haber tomado el poder mediante una revolución. Entre los ejemplos de nuestro tiempo se pueden citar algunos países comunistas como la antigua Unión Soviética y la República Popular China.

EJERCICIO 1: MÉTODOS PARA OBTENER EL PODER

Instrucciones: A continuación se presenta una lista de formas en que los líderes de un gobierno pueden asumir el poder. Lea las definiciones y aplíquelas a las preguntas que siguen.

ascendencia: El líder viene de una familia que ha gobernado al país por varias generaciones.

derecho divino: El líder aduce que su posición le fue dada por Dios.

conquista: El líder adquiere un territorio por medio de una conquista militar.

revolución: El líder llega al poder tras la deposición del sistema político vigente.

voto popular: El líder es elegido a través de la votación del pueblo al que va a gobernar.

1. Los franceses, inspirados en parte por la revolución de las trece colonias americanas contra Inglaterra, erigieron una república en lugar de la antigua monarquía. El nuevo líder llegó al poder por
    (1) ascendencia.
    (2) derecho divino.
    (3) conquista.
    (4) revolución.
    (5) voto popular.

2. La antigua Checoslovaquia mantuvo su independencia en la década de 1930 hasta que el ejército de Hitler ocupó esta pequeña nación y la obligó a formar parte del Tercer Reich. Hitler adquirió el poder sobre Checoslovaquia por
    (1) ascendencia.
    (2) derecho divino.
    (3) conquista.
    (4) revolución.
    (5) voto popular.

El gobierno federal de EE.UU.

La Constitución de EE.UU. se basa en el concepto de federalismo. En el *federalismo,* la autoridad del gobierno se divide entre los estados y un gobierno central. El gobierno central se divide a su vez en tres poderes: el *legislativo,* que hace las leyes; el *ejecutivo,* que se encarga de llevar a efecto esas leyes; y el *judicial,* responsable de interpretar las leyes. Gracias a esta división, ninguno de los tres poderes del estado tiene la capacidad de dominar a los demás. Cada poder puede ejercitar su autoridad para evitar que cualquiera de los otros dos se vuelva demasiado poderoso.

El poder legislativo: Hacedor de leyes

Las facultades del poder legislativo se enumeran en el Artículo I de la Constitución. La asamblea legislativa de EE.UU., que recibe el nombre de

Congreso, se compone de dos cámaras: la Cámara de Representantes y la Cámara de Senadores o Senado. La Cámara de Representantes se conoce como cámara baja y el Senado como cámara alta, aunque sus poderes son básicamente iguales.

En la Cámara de Representantes, el número de representantes de cada estado se basa en su población relativa a la población total del país. Los estados pequeños tienen menos representantes que los estados más grandes. Para determinar el número de representantes que corresponde a cada estado, se realiza cada diez años un *censo* o contaje de habitantes. En el Senado, cada estado está representado equitativamente por dos senadores. Los representantes son elegidos a través del voto popular y desempeñan su cargo por un período de dos años. Los senadores también son elegidos por votación popular, aunque según la Constitución original eran elegidos por las cámaras legislativas de los estados. Los senadores sirven en su cargo por un período de seis años.

El Congreso de EE.UU. tiene la facultad de

- gravar y recaudar impuestos
- pedir dinero prestado
- regular el comercio
- acuñar moneda
- declarar la guerra
- crear y mantener un ejército y una marina
- ratificar tratados (sólo el Senado)
- imputar al presidente (sólo la Cámara)
- juzgar a un presidente que ha sido imputado (sólo el Senado)
- presentar proyectos de ley además de los impositivos
- presentar un proyecto de ley de rentas o impuestos (sólo la Cámara)
- aprobar los nombramientos del presidente (sólo el Senado)
- admitir nuevos estados a la Unión

Estas facultades reciben el nombre de *facultades enumeradas* porque se enumeran en el Artículo I de la Constitución de Estados Unidos. Además de las facultades enumeradas, la Constitución prevé aquellas facultades no contempladas en su texto. La *cláusula elástica* permite al poder legislativo extender su autoridad para hacer frente a situaciones específicas no previstas por los autores de la Constitución.

EJERCICIO 2: REPRESENTACIÓN LEGISLATIVA

Instrucciones: Elija la mejor respuesta para cada una de las siguientes preguntas.

1. ¿Cuál de los siguientes estados es probable que tenga el menor número de representantes en la Cámara de Representantes?
   (1) Texas
   (2) New York
   (3) Alaska
   (4) California
   (5) Georgia

2. Aunque el estado de New Jersey es más pequeño que Wyoming o Nevada, posee un número mayor de representantes. En base a este hecho, ¿cuál de las siguientes afirmaciones sería la más válida?

(1) La población de New Jersey está decreciendo.
(2) New Jersey es un estado industrial y fundamentalmente urbano.
(3) New Jersey es una estado densamente poblado.
(4) 1 y 2
(5) 2 y 3

EJERCICIO 3: EL PODER LEGISLATIVO

Instrucciones: Escriba una *C* en el espacio en blanco si la acción es ejemplo de una de las facultades enumeradas en la Constitución de Estados Unidos y que se citan en la página 129. Escriba una *E* si es un ejemplo de aplicación de la cláusula elástica.

_____ **1.** El Congreso aprueba sanciones económicas contra el régimen de apartheid de África del Sur.

_____ **2.** El Congreso reforma la estructura impositiva de la nación en 1996.

_____ **3.** El 99° Congreso presenta un proyecto de ley para abolir la edad de jubilación obligatoria de los trabajadores.

El poder ejecutivo: Ejecutor de las leyes

El Artículo II de la Constitución de Estados Unidos enumera las facultades del poder ejecutivo del gobierno de Estados Unidos. El poder ejecutivo lo componen el presidente, el vicepresidente y todas las agencias y departamentos necesarios para administrar y llevar a efecto las leyes del país. Según se describe en el Artículo II de la Constitución de Estados Unidos, el presidente

- es comandante en jefe de las fuerzas armadas
- tiene la facultad de conceder indultos y perdones por ofensas contra los Estados Unidos
- puede nombrar jueces a la Corte Suprema de EE.UU. y embajadores (con la aprobación del Senado)
- puede nominar y nombrar los funcionarios ejecutivos más importantes
- puede vetar (rehusarse a aprobar) los proyectos de ley enviados por el Congreso

La vaguedad con que se expresa la autoridad ejecutiva le ha permitido a cada presidente moldear el cargo conforme a su propia personalidad. Los presidentes "fuertes" han en cierta medida dominado el poder legislativo y han dependido menos del consejo de sus respectivos gabinetes y de la guía del Congreso. Los presidentes fuertes hacen valer con frecuencia su poder de veto. En cambio, los presidentes "débiles" han subordinado el cargo a la legislatura, han dependido más de sus respectivos gabinetes y han sido menos autoritativos. Sin embargo, se puede decir que, en general, la autoridad de la presidencia ha ido en paulatino aumento.

El presidente de la república desempeña su cargo por un período de cuatro años y está limitado a un máximo de dos mandatos. El vicepresidente asume la presidencia en caso de que el presidente quede incapacitado o muera en el desempeño de sus funciones antes del término de su mandato. El presidente y el vicepresidente son electos por votación popular, pero es el colegio electoral el que certifica oficialmente el resultado de la elección popular. El *colegio electoral* está integrado por un grupo de electores de cada estado que, un mes después de la elección general, emiten sus votos para presidente y vice-presidente. Para ser elegido presidente de forma oficial, el candidato debe recibir la mayoría de los votos electorales. El colegio electoral, que se había creado originalmente como organismo de control en caso de una decisión poco sensata de los votantes, es hoy objeto de crítica. Opinan numerosos políticos que esta institución ha perdido su utilidad y debería abolirse.

Por lo general, el candidato que recibe los votos electorales del estado casi siempre ha recibido previamente la mayoría del voto popular de ese estado. Sólo en dos ocasiones ha recibido un candidato la mayoría del voto popular y perdido la elección debido a los votos electorales (las elecciones de 1876 y 1888).

EJERCICIO 4: EL PODER EJECUTIVO
Instrucciones: Elija la mejor respuesta para las siguientes preguntas.

1. ¿Cuál de estos presidentes se ajusta mejor al tipo de presidente "fuerte"?
   (1) el Presidente Madison, estadista que en 1812 declaró la guerra a la Gran Bretaña después de que la demanda popular así lo exigiera
   (2) el Presidente John Adams, quien pensaba que los representantes del gobierno habían de ser "ricos, bien nacidos y capaces"
   (3) el Presidente Thomas Jefferson, quien tuvo reparos acerca de la Compra de Louisiana y se opuso al primer Banco de Estados Unidos basado en el hecho de que no estaban contemplados en la Constitución
   (4) el Presidente James Monroe, quien postuló la llamada Doctrina Monroe siguiendo el consejo de su secretario de estado, John Quincy Adams
   (5) el Presidente Andrew Jackson, quien hizo un uso sin precedentes de su poder de veto y dependió poco de su gabinete y del Congreso a la hora de tomar decisiones

2. Originalmente, el candidato que obtenía el segundo lugar en número de votos recibidos en una elección presidencial pasaba a ser automática-mente el vicepresidente. Este sistema fue posteriormente modificado cuando se fundaron los partidos. Desde entonces los candidatos para presidente y vicepresidente se han postulado juntos en una misma boleta. ¿Cuál de las siguientes razones explica mejor por qué se cambió el sistema de elección del vicepresidente?
   (1) La Constitución requería que los candidatos a la presidencia y vicepresidencia fueran del mismo partido.
   (2) Se atendía mejor a los intereses del estado cuando los candidatos a la presidencia y vicepresidencia eran de diferentes regiones del país.
   (3) Antes de que se modificara el sistema, era más fácil engañar a un candidato para que no se postulara a la presidencia.
   (4) Había muchos candidatos a la presidencia no aptos para el cargo y el nuevo sistema garantizaba la idoneidad de los candidatos.
   (5) El nuevo sistema evitaba que el vicepresidente (que a menudo tenía opiniones políticas opuestas) obstruyera la capacidad de gobernar del presidente.

El poder judicial: Intérprete de las leyes

El Artículo III de la Constitución describe la Corte Suprema de Estados Unidos. La finalidad de la Corte Suprema es la de dictaminar respecto de la constitucionalidad de ciertas leyes aprobadas por el Congreso, el presidente y los mismos estados. La autoridad de decidir si una ley cumple o no con el espíritu de la Constitución se denomina *revisión judicial.*

La Corte Suprema está integrada por nueve magistrados vitalicios (designados de por vida) nombrados por el presidente (con la aprobación del Senado). Encabeza este órgano judicial un *presidente.* El poder judicial del gobierno federal lo componen la Corte Suprema de EE.UU, los once Tribunales de Apelación distribuidos por todo el país y los noventa y tantos Juzgados federales de Distrito. Entre las facultades conferidas a la Corte Suprema se pueden citar la facultad para dictaminar en: casos que atañan a un estado y a ciudadanos de otro estado, controversias entre dos o más estados, casos entre ciudadanos de diferentes estados, casos entre un estado y sus ciudadanos o entre un país extranjero y ciudadanos de EE.UU., conflictos que surjan en alta mar y conflictos sobre patentes y derechos de autor. En el proceso de dictaminación, se llega a una decisión cuando concurre o concuerda en un asunto la mayoría de los magistrados de la Corte Suprema.

EJERCICIO 5: EL PODER JUDICIAL

Instrucciones: Elija la mejor respuesta que complete el siguiente párrafo.

En 1907, el Presidente de la Corte Suprema Charles Evans Hughes escribió: "La Constitución es lo que los Magistrados dicen que es". Esta cita define mejor la facultad de la Corte Suprema de
(1) servir de control y equilibrio de poderes.
(2) ignorar las decisiones del poder legislativo.
(3) estar "por encima de la ley".
(4) revisión judicial.
(5) supremacía judicial.

EJERCICIO 6: DERECHOS ESTATALES VERSUS DERECHOS INDIVIDUALES

A lo largo de la historia de la Corte Suprema de EE.UU., ésta ha tenido que decidir si era necesario preservar y confirmar el sistema federal (incluyendo el apoyo a la autoridad de los estados individuales) o bien confirmar los derechos de los individuos.

Instrucciones: A continuación se citan casos que han sentado un importante precedente legal. Escriba una *I* si el caso representa una victoria para los derechos individuales.

_____ **1.** el caso *Plessy v. Ferguson* (1896), en el que la Corte Suprema confirmó la decisión de una corte inferior de que las instalaciones separadas, pero iguales, para negros y blancos eran correctas y legales

_____ **2.** el caso *Roe v. Wade* (1973), en el que la Corte dictaminó que los estados no podían prohibir el aborto bajo ciertas condiciones durante los seis primeros meses de embarazo

_____ **3.** el caso *Miranda v. Arizona* (1966), en el que la Corte dictaminó que toda persona acusada de un delito debe ser informada de sus derechos o cualquier confesión resultante será inválida

Sistema de control y equilibrio de poderes

Los artífices de la Constitución comprendieron que debía existir un equilibrio entre los tres poderes del gobierno para que ninguno de ellos pudiera dominar a los dos restantes. A fin de evitar que esto suceda, la Constitución de EE.UU. permite a cada poder ciertas acciones que puedan restringir las actividades de los demás. Una de estas restricciones es la capacidad que tiene el presidente para negarse a aprobar, o vetar, cualquier proyecto de ley que le envíe el Congreso.

No obstante, el Congreso aún tiene la posibilidad de aprobar el proyecto de ley y convertirlo en ley si por lo menos dos tercios de sus miembros votan a favor. Este procedimiento se conoce como *invalidación del veto.* Finalmente, si el asunto se presenta ante la Corte Suprema, ésta puede declarar la ley inconstitucional. Esto sucede si los jueces de la Corte Suprema llegan a la conclusión de que la ley contradice los preceptos de la Constitución.

LA PROMULGACIÓN DE UNA LEY

EJERCICIO 7: LA PROMULGACIÓN DE UNA LEY
Instrucciones: Elija la mejor respuesta para la siguiente pregunta.
¿Qué expresión está mejor respaldada por el cuadro anterior?

(1) Los proyectos de ley justificados por la cláusula elástica de la Constitución deben presentarse directamente al presidente.
(2) Antes de enviar al presidente un proyecto de ley, éste deberá ser aprobado de igual manera por ambas cámaras del Congreso.
(3) Es posible que no se den en ninguna de las cámaras maniobras de dilación para obstruir la aprobación de ciertos proyectos de ley.
(4) Todo proyecto de ley presentado al Senado puede ser modificado en la Cámara de Representantes, pero no al revés.
(5) El presidente tiene que firmar todos los proyectos de ley para que se conviertan en ley.

EJERCICIO 8: SISTEMA DE CONTROL Y EQUILIBRIO DE PODERES

Instrucciones: Escriba en la columna I el *poder del estado que ejercita* la facultad descrita a la izquierda. Escriba en la columna II el *poder del estado al que se controla* mediante el ejercicio de dicha facultad.

Facultad	I ¿Qué poder la ejercita?	II ¿A qué poder se controla?
1. nombrar a jueces federales	(a) _____	(b) _____
2. imputar al presidente	(a) _____	(b) _____
3. declarar inconstitucional una ley	(a) _____	(b) _____

Gobiernos estatales y locales

El gobierno estatal

El Artículo IV de la Constitución define el papel que desempeñan los estados. La estructura del gobierno de los estados se asemeja a la del gobierno federal. La autoridad ejecutiva del estado recae en el gobernador. El gobernador, al igual que el presidente, tiene el poder de veto.

El poder legislativo, que hace las leyes, se compone de dos cámaras en todos los estados, excepto en Nebraska. Cada estado tiene su propio sistema de cortes, incluyendo los juzgados, los tribunales de apelación y la corte suprema del estado. Asimismo, cada estado tiene su propia constitución escrita (basada en gran medida en el modelo federal).

La constitución del estado define las facultades y deberes de los funcionarios y de las agencias estatales. Al igual que el sistema federal, los cincuenta estados cuentan con sistemas de control y equilibrio entre los tres poderes.

Los códigos penales y las leyes civiles se establecen en su mayoría mediante legislación estatal. El estado también estipula las leyes referentes a los contratos, las relaciones comerciales, y el matrimonio y divorcio. Otra de las responsabilidades del gobierno estatal es la de asistencia a los gobiernos locales. Las facultades de los municipios—aldeas, pueblos y ciudades—se enumeran y definen en los estatutos aprobados por el estado.

EJERCICIO 9: FACULTADES DEL GOBIERNO ESTATAL

Instrucciones: Escriba una *E* en el espacio en blanco si la facultad compete al gobierno estatal, una *F* si compete al gobierno federal y una *A* si compete a ambos.

_____ 1. facultad del jefe ejecutivo para vetar un proyecto de ley

_____ 2. declaración de guerra contra un país extranjero

_____ 3. estipulación de la edad legal para la consumición de bebidas alcohólicas

El gobierno local

Mientras que la estructura y organización de los gobiernos federal y estatal son muy similares, las de los gobiernos locales, en cambio, pueden ser bastante diferentes. Los gobiernos locales son generalmente de tres tipos:

alcalde-concejo: se elige un alcalde; los concejales representan a los distritos
concejo-administrador: se elige un concejo; se contrata un administrador para supervisar las operaciones
comisión: se eligen comisionados que encabezan los departamentos, como el de policía/bomberos, obras públicas

Los municipios reciben la mayor parte del dinero necesario para poder operar de los impuestos, tarifas, tasas y aranceles.

El sistema político de EE.UU.

La población de votantes manifiesta una amplia gama de posiciones respecto de los temas políticos. Estas posiciones o posturas políticas, agrupadas bajo cinco categorías generales, se pueden representar en una gráfica como segmentos de un espectro. A estos segmentos nos referimos por lo general por medio de etiquetas políticas. Para poder ganar la elección, el partido político debe obtener la mayoría de los votos emitidos. Como la mayoría de los votantes de Estados Unidos ocupan la parte media del espectro, ambos partidos políticos deben atraer para sí a este grupo de votantes a fin de ganar los comicios.

EL CONTINUO POLÍTICO

Mayoría de los estadounidenses

| Radical | Liberal | Moderado | Conservador | Reaccionario |
| De izquierda | Progresivo | Centrista | *Statu quo* | De derecha |

radical: propugna cambios profundos en las leyes y métodos de gobierno
liberal: propugna cambios políticos para poder progresar, sobre todo en lo que atañe al mejoramiento de los aspectos sociales
moderado: cree que se deben evitar medidas y cambios extremos
conservador: apoya el orden social existente y propugna sólo cambios graduales
reaccionario: se resiste al cambio y propugna el retorno a políticas anteriores

EJERCICIO 10: EL ESPECTRO POLÍTICO

Instrucciones: Identifique a qué sistema político se refieren las siguientes citas.

El bilingüismo en Estados Unidos es un tema que ha suscitado diversas y controvertidas opiniones y en razón de ello ha dividido a la población del país. Gran parte de los estadounidenses se hallan alarmados por el acelerado ritmo con que el país se está convirtiendo en una nación bilingüe, con el inglés y el español como idiomas primario y secundario respectivamente. Con relación a las crecientes concesiones hechas a la minoría hispano-parlante, los estadounidenses abrigan distintos pareceres.

1. "Es mejor que aceptemos el hecho de que la población estadounidense de origen hispano está y se ha de quedar aquí y que contribuyen de forma significativa al nivel de vida del país. En lugar de criticarlos por hablar en su idioma nativo, el gobierno debería mejorar los programas bilingües para que los hispanos puedan aprender el inglés con más facilidad". Esta opinión se diría que es más bien:

   (1) radical (2) liberal (3) moderada (4) conservadora (5) reaccionaria

2. "El inglés ha sido y será siempre el idioma oficial del país. Yo opino que antes de concederles la ciudadanía a los hispanos o de darles empleo, se les debería exigir que pasaran una prueba de inglés". Esta opinión se diría que es más bien:

   (1) radical (2) liberal (3) moderada (4) conservadora (5) reaccionaria

3. "A menos que se cambien inmediatamente las leyes que tratan a los mexicanos como ciudadanos de segunda clase sólo por no poder hablar el idioma, a partir de mañana, los mexicanos deberían dejar de recoger lechugas, lavar platos, y fregar pisos, es decir, dejar de hacer los trabajos sucios mal pagados que los demás estadounidenses no quieren hacer". Esta opinión se diría que es más bien:

   (1) radical (2) liberal (3) moderada (4) conservadora (5) reaccionaria

Partidos políticos

Los *partidos políticos* son grupos que tienen por objetivo influenciar la política del país. Para cumplir con su cometido, buscan que sus candidatos sean elegidos a los cargos públicos. Si bien la Constitución de EE.UU. no contempla la existencia de partidos políticos, éstos cumplen funciones de gran utilidad dentro de nuestra democracia. Los partidos políticos definen los temas a tratar y proponen posibles soluciones a los problemas que afectan al gobierno. También actúan como otra forma de control dentro de nuestro sistema gubernamental de control y equilibrio de poderes, vigilando las políticas del partido que se encuentra en el poder. Los partidos habilitan a los ciudadanos a participar en el aparato gubernamental y hacen más manejable el número de candidatos que se postulan a los cargos públicos.

Durante más de un siglo, han existido dos partidos políticos importantes en Estados Unidos: los demócratas y los republicanos. Las diferencias entre el partido demócrata y el partido republicano tienden a centrarse en temas domésticos, económicos y sociales, así como en política exterior. Sin embargo, estos dos partidos discrepan fundamentalmente en lo que atañe al papel que debe desempeñar el gobierno en cuanto a la resolución de problemas.

En general, el partido demócrata propugna un gobierno federal fuerte a expensas de los derechos soberanos de los estados; aboga por la regulación gubernamental de las grandes empresas; apoya a los sindicatos laborales; y defiende los derechos de los menos afortunados y de las minorías. Por otro lado, el partido republicano, es por lo general partidario de una autoridad mayor de los estados a expensas del gobierno federal; aboga por la libre empresa; apoya el control de los sindicatos; y cree que se debe mantener el statu quo (mantener las cosas como están). Se dan lógicamente excepciones a estas generalidades; y en los últimos años, la distinción entre los dos partidos se ha vuelto cada vez más borrosa.

EJERCICIO 11: LOS PARTIDOS POLÍTICOS

Instrucciones: Escriba una *D* en el espacio en blanco si la expresión se aplica en términos generales a la filosofía del partido demócrata y una *R* si se aplica a la del partido republicano.

_____ **1.** Está a favor de que los gobiernos estatales y locales resuelvan sus propios problemas.

_____ **2.** Apoya la existencia de sindicatos y el derecho a la huelga de sus miembros.

_____ **3.** Aboga por que se destinen grandes sumas de dinero al bienestar social y otros servicios sociales.

Grupos de presión

Una vez elegidos los funcionarios públicos, actúa sobre ellos la presión constante proveniente de los individuos, empresas, agencias gubernamentales y otros que conforman su electorado. Los *grupos de presión* son grupos organizados no asociados a un partido político específico que buscan de forma activa influenciar la opinión, política y acción públicas. Este intento de ejercer influencia en la legislación recibe el nombre de *cabildeo*. Los miembros de los grupos de presión están atentos a los proyectos de ley que puedan afectar al grupo o grupos que representan. Los Comités de Acción Política, conocidos como PACs por sus siglas en inglés, buscan ejercer una influencia directa sobre los funcionarios públicos.

El proceso electoral

Tanto el partido demócrata como el republicano cuenta con una central nacional y personal apropiado. Cada cuatro años, tiene lugar una convención nacional con el objeto de nominar un candidato presidencial, el cual debe obtener una mayoría de delegados ya sea en las elecciones primarias o en los caucus que preceden a la convención o bien en la misma convención. Las *elecciones primarias* permiten a los miembros de un partido expresar su preferencia por tal o cual candidato para que se presente a la elección general. En la mayoría de las elecciones primarias, los candidatos deben recibir una *pluralidad de votos* (mayor cantidad de votos que la de cualquier otro candidato) para ganar. Las primarias pueden ser cerradas o abiertas. En las *primarias abiertas,* los votantes no tienen que declarar a qué partido están afiliados. En las *primarias cerradas,* los votantes deben declarar si son demócratas, republicanos o de otra afiliación. Los *caucus* son mítines a nivel local dentro de un estado donde los miembros del partido se congregan y votan por sus candidatos preferidos.

Para la convención, cada estado envía un número determinado de delegados, que son representantes a nivel local y estatal, a fin de que participen en la selección del candidato del partido. Una vez finalizado un foro de una semana de duración, durante el que se discuten asuntos y se pronuncian discursos, los delegados realizan una votación para elegir al candidato del partido y aprobar la plataforma del partido. La *plataforma* es una declaración formal de la postura que adopta el partido respecto a los distintos temas.

Después de que se llevan a cabo las campañas políticas de los candidatos, se realiza la elección general. En la elección general, el ganador tiene que recibir la *mayoría de los votos* emitidos por el colegio electoral. El candidato puede ganar la elección sin haber obtenido la mayoría del voto popular, pero sí tiene que recibir la mayoría de los votos del colegio electoral. Si no se produce esta mayoría, la elección se decide en la Cámara de Representantes. Ya electos, los funcionarios públicos tienen una obligación para con su *electorado,* es decir, el grupo de personas que los han elegido para desempeñar el cargo.

EJERCICIO 12: LA ELECCIÓN DEL PRESIDENTE

Instrucciones: Relacione los términos de la izquierda con su correspondiente definición.

_____ 1. primarias

_____ 2. plataforma

_____ 3. electorado

(a) declaración de la postura de un partido respecto de los diferentes temas

(b) personas a quienes representa un funcionario público

(c) elección llevada a cabo por el partido para escoger un candidato para la elección general

EJERCICIO 13: EL PROCESO ELECTORAL

Instrucciones: Elija la mejor respuesta para la siguiente pregunta.

En base a la definición de elecciones primarias cerradas y si se desea que los resultados de las elecciones sean válidos, ¿cuál de las siguientes prácticas se debe llevar a cabo?

(1) Los demócratas y los republicanos pueden votar en la eleción primaria que deseen.

(2) Los votantes deben declarar su afiliación política (republicana o demócrata) y votar en las primarias correspondientes.

(3) Los votantes no tienen que declarar si son republicanos o demócratas cuando votan en las primarias.

(4) Los votantes pueden saltarse las primarias y votar solamente en la elección general.

(5) Los votantes no deberían tener derecho a votar en las primarias; las primarias sólo son para los miembros asiduos del partido a nivel local y estatal.

4
ECONOMÍA

La supervivencia del ser humano consiste en algo más que en la satisfacción de las necesidades básicas de alimento, abrigo y vestido. Los *economistas* estudian la forma en que la sociedad satisface con recursos limitados sus ilimitadas necesidades materiales. Esta limitación en los recursos obliga a las personas a elegir las necesidades que desean satisfacer.

La sociedad también se ve obligada a realizar esta elección. Cada sociedad debe contestar tres preguntas básicas a la hora de determinar el tipo de sistema económico con el cual pretende operar. Estas preguntas son, a saber:

- ¿Qué se ha de producir?
- ¿Cómo se ha de producir?
- ¿Cómo se ha de distribuir lo producido (el producto)?

A fin de dar respuesta a estas preguntas, cada gobierno debe identificar primero sus objetivos y valores y luego determinar qué recursos tiene disponibles para producir lo que necesita la sociedad.

Factores de producción

Los economistas han identificado tres factores vitales de producción: recursos naturales, capital y trabajo.

Los *recursos naturales* son las materias primas que se necesitan para producir los bienes. Se necesitan árboles para poder producir productos de madera y papel. Sólo se pueden fabricar automóviles si se dispone de minas de hierro para producir el acero necesario. El *capital,* en el sentido empleado aquí, es todo equipo, fábrica o máquina que se utiliza para producir otros bienes o para proveer servicios. El capital se puede definir también como el dinero invertido en una empresa dada. Tanto una máquina de coser como un aserradero son ejemplos de capital. El *trabajo* se refiere al esfuerzo humano que realiza la labor. Son personas las que dirigen las líneas de montaje, siembran las cosechas, construyen los edificios, manejan los camiones y venden las mercancías.

La historia nos enseña que, por muy cuidadosa y eficiente que sea una economía en la administración de los factores de producción, éstos seguirán siendo escasos en comparación con las demandas cada vez mayores que hace la sociedad de los mismos.

LAS RESPUESTAS DE LOS EJERCICIOS DE ESTE CAPÍTULO EMPIEZAN EN LA PÁGINA 450.

EJERCICIO 1: FACTORES DE PRODUCCIÓN

Instrucciones: Escriba una *N* si el factor de producción se refiere a los recursos naturales, una *C* si se refiere al capital y una *T* si se refiere al trabajo.

_____ **1.** las herramientas que usa un fontanero (plomero) para ejercer su oficio

_____ **2.** los diamantes que se extraen de las minas de Sudáfrica

_____ **3.** los agricultores que plantan la cosecha de maíz de primavera

La economía y el gobierno

El sistema de gobierno de una nación determina por lo general el tipo de sistema económico en el que ha de operar esa nación. Por ejemplo, el sistema de gobierno de EE.UU. se basa en el principio de la libertad individual. Esta creencia en la importancia de la libertad individual contribuyó en gran medida al establecimiento del capitalismo como la forma económica en la que opera la economía estadounidense.

Capitalismo

El *capitalismo* es un sistema económico basado en la propiedad privada de los recursos de producción. Las decisiones de inversión son realizadas por los individuos o las corporaciones, y no por el gobierno. La producción, la distribución y los precios de los bienes y servicios se determinan a través de la competencia en un mercado libre. El gobierno interviene solamente cuando es necesario proteger el interés público.

Socialismo

En el *socialismo,* las industrias y los servicios más importantes están en manos del gobierno y son propiedad cooperativa. Estas industrias, que pueden ser de siderúrgicas (de producción de acero), bancarias y financieras, de transporte público, o de la salud, son controladas por el gobierno con la finalidad de poder ofrecer oportunidades iguales para todos.

En las economías socialistas, la propiedad privada está permitida; sin embargo, los propietarios de empresas, junto con el gobierno, deciden qué bienes y servicios se habrán de producir, cómo producirlos y para quién. La economía de Suecia es de tipo socialista.

Comunismo

Existe un tercer orden económico que no admite en absoluto que ni la propiedad ni los medios de producción estén bajo control privado. En el *comunismo,* el gobierno controla la propiedad y distribuye los bienes de la sociedad de acuerdo con el "bien común". El gobierno decide qué bienes y servicios se han de producir y quiénes los han de recibir. Entre los ejemplos más destacados están las economías de la República Popular China (antes de las recientes reformas), Cuba y la antigua Unión Soviética.

Ninguno de estos tres sistemas políticos existe en forma pura. Es decir, no existe en el mundo moderno una economía que sea entera y exclusivamente capitalista, socialista o comunista. En la práctica, cada sistema económico incorpora algunos aspectos de los demás sistemas. Para describir la economía estadounidense, se usa el término *economía mixta*, dado que existe cierta reglamentación gubernamental de la empresa privada. Por ejemplo, la Administración de Alimentos y Medicamentos (FDA en inglés) se asegura de que cualquier medicina o medicamento nuevo que se comercialice en Estados Unidos haya sido debidamente probado antes de venderse al público.

EJERCICIO 2: LOS SISTEMAS ECONÓMICOS Y LOS GOBIERNOS

Instrucciones: Elija la mejor respuesta que complete las siguientes afirmaciones.

1. La cita "En economía, el gobierno que gobierna menos gobierna mejor" se aplica mejor al sistema económico de
   (1) capitalismo.
   (2) socialismo.
   (3) comunismo.

CONTINUO DE SISTEMAS ECONÓMICOS

MERCADO (Capitalismo   Socialismo   Comunismo) **CONTROL**

2. Según el continuo de sistemas económicos, ¿cuál de las siguientes conclusiones podría sacarse?
   (1) El comunismo es un ejemplo patente de sistema de mercado.
   (2) El capitalismo es un ejemplo patente de sistema de control.
   (3) El socialismo es lo opuesto al capitalismo.
   (4) El capitalismo es lo opuesto al comunismo.
   (5) El capitalismo es mejor que cualquiera de los otros sistemas representados.

La oferta y la demanda

La base del capitalismo estadounidense es la oferta y la demanda. La *oferta* es la cantidad de bienes y servicios disponibles a la venta a todos los precios posibles. La *demanda* es el deseo de comprar un producto o servicio y la capacidad de costearlos.

Los productores o proveedores entran al mercado con el fin de obtener una ganancia. En razón de ello, suministran bienes y servicios a un precio determinado. Asimismo, deben éstos fijar los precios de manera tal que cubran sus costos de producción y les dejen una ganancia. Los consumidores que quieren y pueden comprar esos bienes y servicios crean una demanda.

La producción (oferta) de un bien al igual que su precio dependen del costo de producción y de la demanda del mercado. En general, los productores persiguen los precios más altos posibles para llevar al máximo sus ganancias. Los consumidores, por su parte, persiguen los precios más bajos posibles para poder retener más dinero en sus bolsillos. Estos objetivos opuestos de productores y consumidores tienen un efecto importante en los precios del mercado.

Precio y oferta:
Punto de vista del productor

En términos generales, cuanto más alto sea el precio, mayor será el número de compañías que ofrezcan un producto o servicio. Un bien o servicio, fijado a un precio alto y que produzca una ganancia sustancial podrá atraer a muchos productores que habrán de competir entre sí por una parte del mercado. Un buen ejemplo de relación entre precio y oferta es el fenómeno de los zapatos para correr. Los consumidores, tanto adultos como adolescentes, pagan precios más altos por marcas como Nike y Reebok que el que pagarían por otras marcas. Debido a esto, entraron en el mercado varios competidores (aumentando la oferta) con la esperanza de obtener ganancias con este tipo de producto. Sin embargo, cuando compiten muchos productores en el mercado, la oferta es superior a la demanda porque los compradores no pueden, o no quieren, comprar todos los bienes ofrecidos a la venta. A consecuencia de esto, se produce un excedente y se bajan los precios.

Precio y oferta:
Punto de vista del consumidor

Desde el punto de vista del consumidor, cuanto más alto sea el precio, menor será la demanda; cuanto menor sea el precio, mayor será la demanda. Si el precio de los zapatos para correr suben demasiado, los consumidores pueden dejar de comprarlos y conformarse con marcas poco conocidas. Por otra parte, cuando el precio de un artículo baja demasiado y la demanda de los consumidores excede la capacidad del productor de proveer el producto, se produce una escasez de oferta. A consecuencia de esto, los precios suben y, en casos extremos, es necesario racionar el producto. Racionar significa restringir la cantidad de un artículo que se pone a la venta.

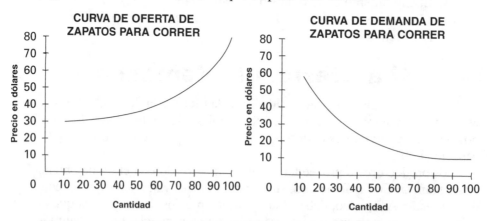

Como se podrá observar en la gráfica de la izquierda, a medida que sube el precio de los zapatos para correr, aumenta también la cantidad ofrecida. La gráfica de la derecha muestra que a medida que baja el precio de los zapatos para correr, sube la cantidad en demanda.

Oferta y equilibrio

Para producir la cantidad exacta que los consumidores están dispuestos a comprar, los productores deben determinar en qué punto la oferta es igual a la demanda. Los economistas llaman a éste el ***punto de equilibrio.*** El equilibrio se produce en el punto del intersección de las curvas de la oferta y la demanda. Éste establece el precio del mercado de un producto o servicio. Cuando el precio es más alto que el punto de equilibrio, la demanda baja y hay una mayor cantidad de un producto o servicio de lo que la gente desea comprar. A esto se le llama ***excedente.*** Cuando el precio cae por debajo del punto de equilibrio, la demanda aumenta, excediendo la oferta, y se produce una ***escasez*** del producto o servicio.

EJERCICIO 3: OFERTA, DEMANDA Y EQUILIBRIO

Instrucciones: Estudie la gráfica y conteste las siguientes preguntas o afirmaciones.

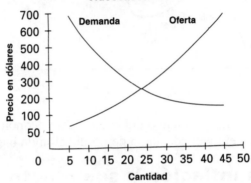

1. Según la gráfica, el precio del mercado de estas videocaseteras será de unos
   (1) 500 dólares.
   (2) 400 dólares.
   (3) 300 dólares.
   (4) 250 dólares.
   (5) 200 dólares.

2. Si el precio del mercado de las videocaseteras bajara a 150 dólares, ¿cuál sería el resultado más probable?
   (1) La demanda disminuiría.
   (2) La oferta permanecería igual.
   (3) La demanda aumentaría.
   (4) Los productores no podrían satisfacer la demanda.
   (5) La oferta escasearía.

Crecimiento económico

El crecimiento económico es uno de los objetivos principales de todo sistema económico. En una economía en crecimiento, hay una capacidad cada vez mayor para producir más bienes y servicios. Durante períodos de gran crecimiento económico, le es posible al consumidor comprar cantidades cada vez mayores de estos bienes y servicios. El crecimiento de una economía debe producirse a un ritmo constante y controlable.

Este proceso se puede comparar con el inflar de un globo. Si se infla muy rápido, puede explotar; si se infla muy despacio, puede que nunca alcance su máxima capacidad. Del mismo modo, la economía estadounidense tiene que crecer de manera constante, o de lo contrario se pueden presentar problemas. El siguiente diagrama ilustra lo que los economistas llaman *ciclo económico*.

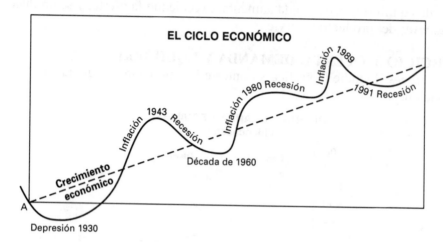

EL CICLO ECONÓMICO

La línea A representa el objetivo del crecimiento económico, lo que los economistas creen es el nivel adecuado de producción de bienes y servicios.

La inflación y sus efectos

Cuando hay un exceso de dinero y crédito disponibles pero pocos bienes para satisfacer la demanda, el dólar pierde su valor y suben los precios de los bienes. Se inicia entonces un período de inflación en el país. (Observe cómo la línea se curva hacia arriba.)

Para que el consumidor pueda soportar el aumento del costo de los bienes, su salario deberá subir. Para que los productores puedan costear el aumento de los salarios, deberán producir más bienes y cobrar precios más altos por los mismos. La reacción en cadena por la que un alza en los salarios provoca un alza en los precios recibe el nombre de *espiral inflacionaria*. Para que disminuya la inflación, la demanda tiene que bajar y el crédito se debe restringir. Sin embargo, uno de los resultados que acarrea el tratar de frenar una alta inflación es la recesión económica.

La deflación y sus efectos

Cuando el dinero y crédito disponibles escasean y hay más bienes que los necesarios para satisfacer la demanda, el dólar aumenta de valor y hace que baje el precio de los bienes. Bajo estas circunstancias, la economía entra en un período de deflación. Como hay bienes que no se venden, disminuyen las ganancias de los productores. La caída de las ganancias lleva al paro forzoso y a los despidos. Si no se corrige la situación, se acaba produciendo una recesión. Si la recesión es prolongada, puede dar paso a una depresión. Estados Unidos atravesó por esta situación durante la llamada Gran Depresión de los años 30.

Medida del crecimiento económico

Los *indicadores económicos* son estadísticas que muestran a los expertos de la economía cómo se está desempeñando la misma. Entre las estadísticas económicas más usadas se destacan las transacciones de la bolsa de valores, los porcentajes de desempleo, el número de casas nuevas empezadas y el producto interno bruto (GNP por sus siglas en inglés).

El *GNP,* una de las medidas más importantes del crecimiento económico, representa el valor total de los bienes y servicios producidos en un año. Los economistas miden el GNP en dólares corrientes y luego vuelven a medirlo en dólares constantes. Los *dólares corrientes* indican el valor actual en dólares de los bienes. Los *dólares constantes* tienen en cuenta el cambio de los precios a lo largo de los años a causa de la inflación. Al medir el GNP de la nación, los economistas miden los dólares corrientes en base a los dólares constantes durante un año dado. Durante los últimos años, los economistas han usado 1987 como el año base con el que comparar los dólares corrientes del GNP.

El dinero y la política monetaria

El *dinero* es el instrumento (o medio) de cambio aceptado por una sociedad para el pago de bienes y servicios. Los haberes monetarios u oferta monetaria de la nación consisten principalmente de monedas, billetes y depósitos de cuentas corrientes y de ahorro. El U.S. Federal Reserve Board (Junta de Gobernadores de la Reserva Federal de Estados Unidos) es responsable de establecer la *política monetaria* de la nación, es decir, de regular la oferta monetaria y crediticia (de crédito) de la nación con el fin de mantener el equilibrio de la economía. A través del sistema bancario de la nación, la Reserva Federal controla la disponibilidad de crédito para los consumidores de dos formas principales: determinando el coeficiente de reserva y estableciendo la tasa de redescuento.

El coeficiente de reserva

Todas las instituciones crediticias—bancos y sociedades de ahorro y préstamo—están obligadas a guardar una cierta cantidad de sus depósitos. Esta cantidad que no se puede dar en préstamo se denomina coeficiente de reserva. La mayoría de los bancos son miembros del Sistema de la Reserva Federal (o Fed, como se conoce en este país). Al controlar el *coeficiente de reserva,* el Fed determina la cantidad de dinero que los bancos pueden dar en préstamo.

La tasa de redescuento

Otro medio con que cuenta la Reserva Federal para influir en la economía de la nación es la *tasa de redescuento.* La tasa de redescuento es la tasa de interés que cobra la Reserva Federal a los bancos que son miembros de la misma cuando piden dinero prestado. Los bancos ganan al cobrar una tasa de interés más alta en los préstamos que conceden que los intereses que pagan a los que depositan dinero en las cuentas corrientes y de ahorro.

Con el fin de disponer de una mayor cantidad de dinero para satisfacer la demanda, los bancos piden prestado al Sistema de la Reserva Federal. Luego, los bancos prestan ese dinero a sus clientes (prestatarios) a una tasa más elevada. La Reserva Federal ajusta la tasa de redescuento para controlar la oferta monetaria. Por ejemplo, si la tasa de redescuento es del 5 por ciento, los bancos comerciales pueden dar prestado ese dinero al 10 por ciento. En razón de ello, podemos apreciar el impacto que un cambio en la tasa de redescuento puede tener en la disponibilidad de crédito en la economía de Estados Unidos.

EJERCICIO 4: EL DINERO Y LA POLÍTICA MONETARIA

Instrucciones: Encierre en círculo la *V* si la afirmación es verdadera, o la *F* si la afirmación es falsa.

V F **1.** El sistema bancario contribuye a aumentar el poder adquisitivo (de compra) gracias a los bancos que, después de apartar las reservas necesarias, dan en préstamo fondos provenientes del dinero depositado.

V F **2.** La mayor parte de los bancos pertenecen al Sistema de la Reserva Federal.

V F **3.** La tasa preferencial es el interés que la Reserva Federal cobra a los bancos miembros cuando piden dinero prestado.

El gobierno y la política fiscal

Mientras que la Reserva Federal ejerce en la economía una influencia directa sobre la oferta monetaria y crediticia, el gobierno, por su parte, a través de su *política fiscal,* también afecta de manera indirecta la situación económica de la nación. Al establecer la política fiscal, el presidente propone al Congreso un presupuesto anual. El Congreso, al determinar qué programas son necesarios, debe asimismo considerar cómo se han de financiar esos programas. Elevar los impuestos es la forma más sencilla y común.

Los consumidores y las empresas pagan impuestos al gobierno. El gobierno, a su vez, emplea el dinero para sufragar programas de utilidad para los ciudadanos y para el país, como la construcción de autopistas, el programa espacial y el ejército. Al decidir si debe subir o bajar los impuestos y si debe aumentar o disminuir el gasto público, el gobierno controla una gran parte de la oferta monetaria.

Si el gobierno gasta menos de lo que recauda con los impuestos, se produce un *superávit presupuestario.* Si el gobierno gasta más de lo que recauda, se produce un *déficit presupuestario.* El *presupuesto equilibrado* es aquel que se da cuando los ingresos procedentes de los impuestos son iguales al dinero empleado en los diferentes programas.

EJERCICIO 5: POLÍTICA MONETARIA Y FISCAL

Instrucciones: Encierre en círculo la opción correcta de dentro del paréntesis.

1. En períodos de recesión, el presidente y el Congreso deben (aumentar / disminuir) el gasto público y (elevar / bajar) los impuestos para poner más dinero en circulación.

2. En períodos inflacionarios, la Reserva Federal debe (aumentar / disminuir) el dinero circulante (elevando / bajando) la tasa de redescuento y (aumentando / disminuyendo) el coeficiente de reserva.

5
GEOGRAFÍA

Los **geógrafos** estudian las características físicas de la Tierra y las formas en que los seres humanos se han adaptado a las mismas. Al investigar las distintas superficies y regiones de la Tierra, los geógrafos se sirven de dos herramientas básicas. Una de ellas es el **globo terráqueo,** el cual es una representación esférica de la Tierra que muestra los continentes, los países y las vías fluviales en su proporción real. Sin embargo, los globos terráqueos no son muy portátiles, razón por la cual los cartógrafos confeccionan **mapas,** que son una representación plana de las regiones de la Tierra.

Mapas

Existen numerosos tipos de mapas. Entre ellos, se pueden citar:

mapas topográficos: muestran las características físicas del terreno (colinas, montañas, llanuras) de un área determinada
mapas políticos: muestran los límites entre países o estados
mapas demográficos: ilustran la distribución de la población de un área determinada
mapas meteorológicos y climatológicos: muestran las condiciones de tiempo actuales o pronosticadas y los climas.

Estos y otros tipos de mapas pueden representar tanto una zona pequeña como el mundo entero.

Símbolos y claves

A fin de facilitar la lectura de los mapas, los **cartógrafos** se valen de **símbolos** y de una nota explicativa, o **clave,** que indica lo que representan los símbolos. Por ejemplo, en los mapas políticos, la estrella representa por lo general la capital del estado o la nación. En los mapas demográficos, el número de habitantes de una ciudad determinada se indica a menudo según el tamaño del punto que sitúa la ciudad. (Los puntos más grandes representan ciudades de mayor población; los puntos más pequeños, ciudades de menor población.)

Es frecuente encontrar en la clave una escala en millas o kilómetros. En la escala del mapa puede haber una nota al pie que diga "Una pulgada representa 50 millas". En la siguiente página se ofrece un ejemplo de escala. Usted puede medir las distancias ya sea con una regla o una tira de papel que tenga el borde recto.

EJERCICIO 1: MEDIR DISTANCIAS

Instrucciones: Estudie el mapa y conteste las siguientes preguntas.

1. Según el mapa, ¿qué distancia hay aproximadamente entre Denver y San Francisco? _____

2. ¿Qué distancia hay aproximadamente entre la costa oeste de California y el límite este de Colorado? _____

Longitud y latitud

La *línea del ecuador* o simplemente ecuador es una línea imaginaria equidistante de los polos que circunda la Tierra y la divide en dos mitades o *hemisferios.* A la mitad que queda al norte del ecuador se le denomina Hemisferio Norte; a la mitad sur, Hemisferio Sur. Norteamérica, Centroamérica y una pequeña parte de Sudamérica están situadas en el Hemisferio Norte.

La distancia que hay desde un punto de la superficie de la tierra al ecuador se mide en los mapas y globos terráqueos en grados de *latitud.* Los *paralelos* o líneas de latitud son líneas imaginarias paralelas al ecuador que miden en grados las distancias al norte o al sur del ecuador. El ecuador está situado a 0 grados (0°) de latitud, el Polo Norte a 90 grados de latitud norte y el Polo Sur a 90 grados de latitud sur. La mayor parte del territorio de Estados Unidos continental está ubicada entre los 25 y 50 grados de latitud norte.

Los *meridianos* o líneas de *longitud* son líneas imaginarias que miden en grados las distancias al este y al oeste del primer meridiano. El *primer meridiano* es una línea imaginaria que va de polo a polo atravesando la ciudad de Greenwich, Inglaterra, y que divide la Tierra en los Hemisferios Este y Oeste. El primer meridiano está ubicado a 0 grados de longitud. Hay 180 grados al este del primer meridiano y 180 grados al oeste del mismo, los que suman un total de 360 grados de circunferencia terrestre. La mayor parte de Estados Unidos, incluyendo Alaska y Hawaii, se encuentra entre los 65 y 125 grados de longitud oeste.

Las líneas de latitud y longitud se intersectan en puntos llamados *coordenadas geográficas.* Para localizar un lugar en particular en un globo terráqueo o en un mapa, hay que encontrar el punto donde se cruzan las dos líneas. Los grados de latitud y longitud nos dan la posición. Por ejemplo, en el siguiente diagrama de coordenadas geográficas, la isla de Madagascar, ubicada en la costa sureste de África, está situada aproximadamente a 20 grados de latitud sur y 45 grados de longitud este.

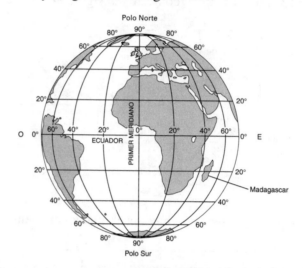

En base a las coordenadas geográficas, ¿en qué continente se encuentra un punto situado a 50° de latitud norte y 0° de longitud?

[Respuesta: *Europa.* El punto en que la línea de 50° de latitud norte se cruza con la línea de 0° de longitud es el continente europeo; Europa está situada directamente al norte de África.]

Husos horarios

El *huso horario* es una región geográfica que se rige por la misma hora. Con el objeto de establecer los husos horarios para todo el planeta, los geógrafos han dividido la Tierra en 24 secciones, una para cada hora del día. Como la Tierra tiene 360 grados, esto significa que 15 grados (360 dividido entre 24) equivalen a una hora del día. En los 48 estados contiguos (adyacentes) de Estados Unidos, hay cuatro husos horarios: Este, Centro, Montaña y Pacífico, tal como lo señala el siguiente mapa.

HUSOS HORARIOS DE ESTADOS UNIDOS

EJERCICIO 2: HUSOS HORARIOS

Instrucciones: Elija la mejor respuesta para las siguientes preguntas.

1. Según el mapa, ¿qué hora es en Los Ángeles cuando es medianoche en Philadelphia, Pennsylvania?
   (1) 9:00 A.M.
   (2) 9:00 P.M.
   (3) 3:00 P.M.
   (4) 3:00 A.M.
   (5) 2:00 A.M.

2. Las líneas que delimitan los cuatro husos horarios son irregulares. Indiana, exceptuando una sección minúscula del noroeste, cae dentro del huso horario del Este. ¿Cuál de las siguientes explicaciones es la más razonable sobre por qué el noroeste de Indiana está dentro del huso horario del Centro?
   (1) Los habitantes del noroeste de Indiana decidieron mediante una votación ser incluidos en el huso horario del Centro.
   (2) Los husos horarios se tienen que dividir uniformemente. A fin de lograr una división uniforme en Estados Unidos, parte de Indiana fue colocada en el huso horario del Centro.
   (3) El oeste de Kentucky y el oeste de Tennessee, los estados que se encuentran al sur de Indiana, están ubicados en el huso horario del Centro; por lo tanto, el noroeste de Indiana tenía que seguir la misma regla.
   (4) Antiguamente el noroeste de Indiana formaba parte del noreste de Illinois, razón por la cual la región tiene un huso horario diferente del resto del estado.
   (5) Al noroeste de Indiana se le considera como parte del área metropolitana de Chicago; por lo tanto, debido a razones económicas está ubicada en el mismo huso horario que Chicago.

Topografía y clima

Los geógrafos dividen el terreno en cuatro accidentes geográficos generales: llanuras, montañas, colinas y mesetas. Estos accidentes geográficos se definen por su forma y *elevación* (distancia por encima del *nivel del mar).*

Las *llanuras* son típicamente superficies planas o ligeramente onduladas (por lo general, a poca altitud). Las *colinas* son elevaciones de menos de 1,000 pies con laderas no muy pronunciadas que culminan en cimas chatas o redondeadas. Las *mesetas* son amplias extensiones de terreno llano situadas generalmente a cierta altitud. Las *montañas* son elevaciones de más de 1,000 pies con laderas pronunciadas en todos los costados y cimas puntiagudas o redondeadas.

Las regiones de las llanuras disfrutan de un clima uniforme que se caracteriza por un tiempo caluroso y seco durante el verano y temperaturas muy frías durante el invierno. Dado que las llanuras son terrenos planos, no cuentan con una barrera contra el aire frío que sopla durante el invierno. Las colinas y las mesetas por lo general presentan las mismas características climáticas que las llanuras circundantes, aunque pueden ser más frías dependiendo de su altura. Las montañas suelen servir de límite entre las

distintas regiones climáticas. Las laderas más bajas de las montañas normalmente comparten el clima de los alrededores, pero a medida que aumenta la
altura, el aire se enfría. Las montañas más altas están cubiertas de nieve porque
el aire que las rodea nunca se eleva por encima del punto de congelación.

Los cartógrafos ilustran las diferentes alturas y formas de las extensiones
de terreno por medio de **curvas de nivel,** que muestran la altitud en pies o
metros. Cuanto más cerca estén las líneas de nivel, mayor es la inclinación.
Seguidamente se ofrece un plano topográfico donde se pueden apreciar las
curvas de nivel.

PLANO TOPOGRÁFICO

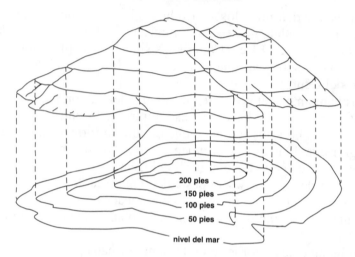

¿Cómo debería clasificarse este accidente geográfico: colina, llanura, montaña
o meseta?

[Respuesta: Dada la altitud inferior a 1,000 pies y dada su cima redondeada,
el accidente geográfico se ajusta a la descripción de colina.]

EJERCICIO 3: TOPOGRAFÍA DE EE.UU.

Instrucciones: Elija la mejor respuesta para las siguientes preguntas.

1. En base a su ubicación, ¿cuál de las siguientes ciudades de Estados
   Unidos tiene la mayor altitud?
   (1) Detroit
   (2) Boston
   (3) Denver
   (4) Chicago
   (5) Memphis

2. Las tierras bajas son propensas a sufrir inundaciones. Las tierras que se
   encuentran por debajo del nivel del mar actúan como un tazón donde se
   acumula el agua. ¿Cuál de las siguientes ciudades se ajusta mejor a esta
   descripción?
   (1) Las Vegas
   (2) New York
   (3) New Orleans
   (4) Atlanta
   (5) Phoenix

EJERCICIO 4: EL SUBCONTINENTE INDIO

Instrucciones: Estudie el mapa y conteste las siguientes preguntas.

EL SUBCONTINENTE INDIO

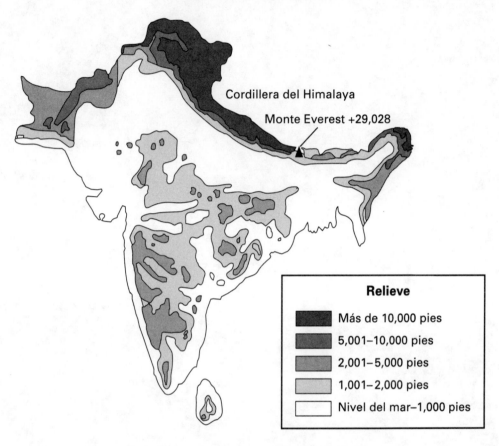

Cordillera del Himalaya

Monte Everest +29,028

Relieve

Más de 10,000 pies

5,001–10,000 pies

2,001–5,000 pies

1,001–2,000 pies

Nivel del mar–1,000 pies

1. ¿Cuál es el punto más alto de la Cordillera del Himalaya?
   (**1**) 6,000 pies
   (**2**) 10,300 pies
   (**3**) 19,861 pies
   (**4**) 29,028 pies
   (**5**) 33,411 pies

2. Se puede decir que, en general, la mayor parte del terreno representado
   en el mapa se encuentra a una altitud
   (**1**) de más de 10,000 pies.
   (**2**) de 5,000 a 10,000 pies.
   (**3**) de 2,000 a 5,000 pies.
   (**4**) de 1,000 a 2,000 pies.
   (**5**) comprendida entre el nivel del mar y los 1,000 pies.

PRUEBA 3: CIENCIAS

La Prueba de Ciencias del GED consta de preguntas de opción múltiple que
requieren un conocimiento de los conceptos básicos de ciencias. La prueba se
centra en su capacidad de reflexionar sobre estos conceptos. No se le pedirá
que recuerde hechos aislados, sino que se habrá de leer un pasaje u observar
una ilustración y contestar la pregunta basándose en los mismos. Para poder
tener un buen rendimiento, será necesaria una comprensión de los conceptos
básicos de ciencias y la capacidad de interpretar ilustraciones y pasajes de
lectura. También hará falta demostrar que se comprende lo que se lee, aplicar
la información a una nueva situación, analizar las relaciones entre ideas y
emitir juicios sobre el material presentado.

¿Cuántas preguntas hay en la prueba?

Hay 66 preguntas de opción múltiple y se dispone de 95 minutos para hacer
la prueba. Aproximadamente dos tercios de las preguntas se han de basar en
pasajes de lectura de hasta 250 palabras cada uno, y el tercio restante en
información visual: diagramas, cuadros o gráficas. Fíjese en la Prueba
Posterior del final del libro. Ésta ha sido confeccionada en base a una prueba
normal del GED.

¿De qué consta la prueba?

La Prueba de Ciencias del GED se puede dividir según las áreas de
contenido que aborda y las destrezas que pone a prueba. El contenido de
estas pruebas es el siguiente: Ciencias Biológicas (Biología)—50%; y
Ciencias Físicas (Ciencias de la Tierra, Química y Física)—50%. Sin
embargo, cabe recalcar que una pregunta dada puede estar relacionada con
varias de las áreas mencionadas. Por ejemplo, una pregunta acerca de la
contaminación atmosférica puede caer tanto bajo la esfera de la biología
como de la química.

Recuerde usted asimismo que lo que se va a poner a prueba es su
capacidad para reflexionar sobre determinadas ideas y conceptos. Se le pedirá
realizar algo más que la simple búsqueda de una respuesta explícitamente
dada dentro de un pasaje. Entre las destrezas de razonamiento que se van a
poner a prueba figuran las siguientes: Comprensión de Ideas—20%;
Aplicación de Ideas—30%; Análisis de Ideas—30%; y Evaluación de
Ideas—20%.

1
BIOLOGÍA: EL ESTUDIO DE LOS SERES VIVOS

La ciencia que estudia las diversas formas de vida es la *biología*. El interés de los biólogos radica en cómo crecen, cambian y se relacionan los seres vivos entre sí y con su medio ambiente. Todos los seres vivos reaccionan ante un estímulo, se alimentan y crecen, eliminan desechos y se reproducen. Comencemos con la unidad básica de la vida: la célula.

La célula, base de la vida

La *célula* es la unidad más pequeña de materia viva capaz de llevar a cabo las actividades vitales. Las células, "componentes básicos" de todo organismo, fueron observadas por primera vez en 1665 por Robert Hooke, con la ayuda de un microscopio rudimentario. Las células varían ampliamente en tamaño y aspecto. Sin embargo, es el número de células que posee un organismo y no el tamaño de las mismas, lo que determina el tamaño de ese organismo. Las células de un ser humano y de una ballena tienen el mismo tamaño. La ballena es más grande porque su código genético dicta que se produzca un número mayor de células. Una célula "promedio" mide unos 10 micrómetros (0.00004 pulgadas) de diámetro. Esto significa que una hilera de 25,000 células típicas alineadas unas tras otras mediría solamente una pulgada.

Tipos de células

Hay dos tipos de célula: *célula vegetal* y *célula animal.* La célula vegetal está recubierta por una *pared celular* que la protege, mientras que la célula animal carece de ella. Asimismo, la célula vegetal contiene *cloroplastos,* estructuras activas en el proceso de elaboración de alimentos, mientras que las células animales no poseen estas estructuras. Tanto las células vegetales como las células animales están envueltas por una muy delicada estructura que la limita, la *membrana celular.* La membrana celular preserva la célula al actuar como barrera entre ésta y el medio externo, al ayudar a mantener su forma y al regular el tráfico molecular que entra y sale de la célula.

En la siguiente ilustración se pueden apreciar las diferencias que hay entre la célula vegetal y la célula animal.

ESTRUCTURA DE LA CÉLULA

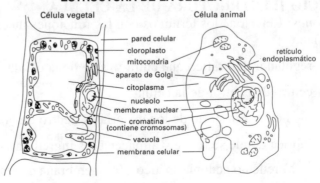

Célula vegetal — Célula animal

pared celular
cloroplasto
mitocondria
aparato de Golgi
citoplasma
nucleolo
membrana nuclear
cromatina (contiene cromosomas)
vacuola
membrana celular

retículo endoplasmático

Estructura de la célula

Contenido dentro de los límites de la membrana celular se encuentra el *protoplasma,* sustancia gelatinosa y componente más abundante de la célula. El protoplasma que se halla entre la membrana nuclear y la membrana celular recibe el nombre de *citoplasma.* La célula es una estructura altamente especializada y compleja que cuenta con sus propios centro de control, sistema de transporte, centrales eléctricas, fábricas para la producción de los materiales necesarios y hasta un esquema o receta química de reproducción.

Gran parte de los *orgánulos* (órganos diminutos) que realizan estas funciones están situados dentro del citoplasma. El *retículo endoplasmático,* semejante a un intrincado sistema de túneles, actúa como una red de transporte de materiales de una parte a otra de la célula o de la célula al medio externo. Las centrales eléctricas de la célula son las *mitocondrias,* donde se genera la energía necesaria para la actividad celular. Las mitocondrias abundan en células altamente activas que producen energía para los procesos vitales fundamentales. Por ejemplo, se han contado más de 1,000 mitocondrias en una sola célula de hígado.

Ubicado a un lado del núcleo, semejando un grupo de membranas en forma de plato apiladas, el *aparato de Golgi* desempeña la función de una planta de empacado, donde se reúnen las proteínas y los carbohidratos y se los encierra dentro de un saco membranoso. En las células de las glándulas, el aparato de Golgi se encarga de liberar las hormonas de las glándulas al interior del cuerpo.

De entre todas las estructuras que contiene la célula, la más importante es el *núcleo,* el cual es el centro de control de la célula. El núcleo está rodeado por una *membrana nuclear* doble. Los poros de la membrana nuclear permiten el paso de las moléculas entre el citoplasma y el núcleo. Dentro del núcleo se encuentran los cromosomas y los nucleolos. Cada *cromosoma* posee varios cientos de genes, los cuales contienen *ADN,* ácido molecular que transmite instrucciones sobre cómo se ha de desarrollar el organismo. Si se consideran los cromosomas como la "receta química" de la célula, los *genes* vendrían a ser los distintos ingredientes.

El *nucleolo* es rico en *ARN,* ácido esencial para la actividad química de la célula. El nucleolo presenta secciones de cromosomas que se cree son importantes en la fabricación de proteínas.

> LAS RESPUESTAS DE LOS EJERCICIOS DE ESTE
> CAPÍTULO EMPIEZAN EN LA PÁGINA 452.

EJERCICIO 1: ESTRUCTURA DE LA CÉLULA

Instrucciones: Relacione los términos con las funciones mecánicas que desempeñan.

_____ **1.** regulador del tráfico que entra y sale de la célula

_____ **2.** centro de control de la célula

_____ **3.** medio de transporte de los materiales dentro de la célula

_____ **4.** fábrica donde se reúne y almacena los ingredientes del ARN

(a) núcleo   **(b)** retículo endoplasmático   **(c)** membrana celular   **(d)** nucleolo

EJERCICIO 2: LAS CÉLULAS

Instrucciones: Elija la mejor respuesta para las siguientes preguntas.

1. La finalidad principal del pasaje es señalar que
   - (1) todos los seres vivos se componen de células.
   - (2) el núcleo es el centro de control de la célula.
   - (3) hay diferencias entre la célula animal y vegetal.
   - (4) la célula es una estructura altamente organizada y compleja que posee subsistemas propios.
   - (5) el aparato de Golgi actúa como una planta de empacado de la célula.

2. En las células vegetales, los cloroplastos tienen parte activa en los procesos químicos necesarios para la elaboración de alimentos. Las células animales carecen de cloroplastos. Basándonos en este hecho, podemos llegar a la conclusión de que
   - (1) las células vegetales son más complejas que las células animales.
   - (2) las células vegetales producen reacciones químicas, pero no las células animales.
   - (3) las células animales se alimentan de células vegetales.
   - (4) las células animales son más complejas que las células vegetales.
   - (5) los animales obtienen sus alimentos de fuentes externas.

3. Según el pasaje, las mitocondrias son las centrales eléctricas que generan la energía necesaria para los procesos vitales fundamentales de la célula animal y que, además, son responsables de la respiración celular. ¿Qué parte de la célula vegetal desempeña una función similar?
   - (1) pared celular
   - (2) núcleo
   - (3) nucleolo
   - (4) cromosoma
   - (5) cloroplasto

Las células y el transporte activo

Todas las células disponen de una membrana que permite de manera selectiva la entrada y salida de ciertas moléculas hacia dentro y fuera de la célula. El movimiento de moléculas que se realiza a través de la célula sin que ésta haga ningún esfuerzo se lleva a cabo gracias a la difusión. La *difusión* es el movimiento de moléculas desde un área de alta concentración a un área de baja concentración. Las moléculas en vibración se impulsan mutuamente al chocar entre sí. Es mediante este proceso que el olor puede llenar una habitación de gran tamaño en un corto período de tiempo. La difusión es importante en organismos superiores como el cuerpo humano. Por ejemplo, el oxígeno sale de unas bolsas de aire que hay en los pulmones, pasa a través de las membranas celulares, y llega a la sangre por medio de la difusión.

El citoplasma de las células contiene numerosas sustancias en distintos grados de concentración. Estas concentraciones difieren notablemente de las del fluido que circunda la célula. Estas diferencias son esenciales: tal es así que la célula puede llegar a morir si las diferencias no se mantienen. Dada la oportunidad, la difusión eliminaría con rapidez estas diferencias de importancia crítica. Por lo tanto, la célula debe ser capaz de anular, y a veces invertir, el proceso de difusión. Esto se logra mediante el llamado transporte activo. En el *transporte activo,* la célula desplaza materiales desde un área de baja concentración a un área de alta concentración. La realización de este trabajo, sin embargo, requiere energía.

EJERCICIO 3: LAS CÉLULAS Y EL TRANSPORTE ACTIVO

Instrucciones: Escriba en los espacios en blanco las palabras que faltan para completar las oraciones.

1. La difusión es el desplazamiento de las moléculas de un área de

   _____ concentración a un área de

   _____ concentración.

2. En el transporte activo, los materiales se desplazan de un área de

   _____ concentración a un área de

   _____ concentración.

EJERCICIO 4: DIFUSIÓN Y ÓSMOSIS

Instrucciones: Elija la mejor respuesta para las siguientes preguntas.

1. En el cuerpo humano, el proceso de difusión
   (1) permite la concentración de materiales donde necesite el cuerpo, almacenando los mismos.
   (2) regula la circulación de la sangre.
   (3) permite una distribución uniforme de sustancias por todas las células del cuerpo.
   (4) funciona mejor en los casos de enfermedad grave.
   (5) desempeña un papel preponderante en el funcionamiento del cuerpo.

2. En el proceso llamado *ósmosis,* el agua de una solución es capaz de desplazarse a través de una membrana celular desde una región de concentración más baja a otra de concentración más alta con el fin de mantener el equilibrio a ambos lados de la membrana. Si la solución salina (de sal) del plasma sanguíneo que rodea los glóbulos rojos de la sangre es más concentrada que la solución que hay dentro de las células, ¿qué es lo más probable que ocurra?
   (1) El agua saldrá de la célula y pasará al plasma sanguíneo.
   (2) El agua saldrá del plasma sanguíneo y pasará a la célula.
   (3) La célula se encogerá debido a la pérdida de agua.
   (4) 1 y 2
   (5) 1 y 3

Mitosis: División de la célula

Todo organismo tiene la capacidad de crecer. A medida que crece la célula, llega un momento en que no le es ya posible a su membrana celular proporcionar el oxígeno y los nutrientes que necesita el interior de la célula ni se les hace ya posible a los desechos abandonar la misma. Además, el núcleo sólo es capaz de controlar cierta cantidad de citoplasma. Por lo tanto, cuando la célula alcanza su tamaño límite, habrá de dividirse o sufrir el proceso llamado mitosis.

La *mitosis* es el proceso mediante el cual las células se reproducen por división celular. En los organismos multicelulares, la mitosis tiene como consecuencia el crecimiento y el mantenimiento de los tejidos. En los organismos unicelulares, la mitosis produce dos nuevos organismos independientes y genéticamente idénticos. La mitosis se puede dividir en cuatro etapas o fases, como se podrá apreciar a continuación.

Etapa 1: Profase

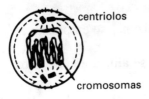

El material genético del núcleo se duplica. Luego, al iniciarse la profase, desaparecen la membrana nuclear y el nucleolo. El material genético, que antes no se podía observar con facilidad, se organiza y se hace ahora evidente en forma de corpúsculos filiformes alargados: los *cromosomas.* Aparecen después, en los polos (extremos opuestos) de la célula los *centriolos* y comienzan a formarse entre ellos pequeñas fibras.

Etapa 2: Metafase

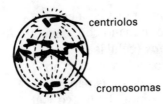

Las fibras del *huso* se adhieren al material genético que está en el centro de los cromosomas *(centrómeros).* Los cromosomas, ahora bastante gruesos y visibles, comienzan a alinearse en el ecuador de la célula.

Etapa 3: Anafase

Los centrómeros se dividen y los pares duplicados de cromosomas se separan. Los pares separados se repelen mutuamente y se desplazan hacia los polos de la célula.

Etapa 4: Telofase

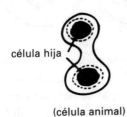

(célula animal)

La telofase comienza cuando los cromosomas llegan a los polos. En la telofase, los núcleos se vuelven a formar, los cromosomas se empiezan a desorganizar y a volverse menos visibles y la célula se parte, dando origen a dos nuevas células. Las células hijas son genética y físicamente idénticas a la célula madre, excepto en lo que respecta al tamaño.

En los organismos unicelulares, la división de la célula produce dos nuevos individuos. En los organismos complejos (que poseen más de una célula), las nuevas células hijas forman un subsistema de la célula madre. En muchos organismos, la reproducción celular alcanza su máxima actividad durante la etapa de crecimiento del organismo. A medida que envejece el organismo, el proceso se limita a la sustitución de células viejas o dañadas.

EJERCICIO 5: MITOSIS

Instrucciones: Relacione las fases de la mitosis con su descripción correpondiente.

_____ **1.** profase   **(a)** los cromosomas se organizan y se empiezan a distinguir

_____ **2.** metafase   **(b)** el material cromosómico se alinea en el centro de la célula

_____ **3.** anafase   **(c)** la célula se divide y forman dos nuevas células

_____ **4.** telofase   **(d)** pares de cromosomas se mueven a polos opuestos

La meiosis: División reproductiva celular

Cada organismo tiene un número de *cromosomas* característico a ese organismo. Por ejemplo, todas las células del cuerpo humano contienen cuarenta y seis cromosomas, exceptuando los *gametos* (células reproductoras). Las células reproductoras (espermatozoide y huevo) no pueden tener el mismo número de cromosomas que el de otras partes del cuerpo. Si así fuera, la descendencia resultante de la unión del huevo y el espermatozoide tendría después de la división de la célula dos veces la cantidad normal de material genético. En los animales, esto ocasionaría la muerte del embrión en su primera etapa de desarrollo. Con el objeto de evitar que esto suceda, las células sexuales sufren el proceso llamado meiosis.

En la *meiosis,* la célula madre pasa por dos tipos especiales de división celular que culminan en la producción de cuatro gametos. Cada gameto posee la mitad de cromosomas que la célula progenitora (que les ha dado origen). Las dos etapas de la meiosis se ilustran a continuación.

MEIOSIS I

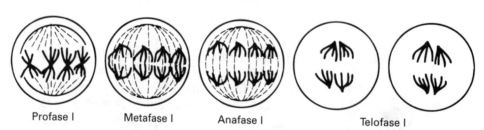

Profase I   Metafase I   Anafase I   Telofase I

Los pares de cromosomas se unen e intercambian genes. Este proceso, llamado *sobrecruzamiento* o *crossing-over,* asegura la recombinación del material genético. Más tarde, el par se separa y un miembro de cada par se desplaza a una nueva célula. Durante la telofase I, el citoplasma se divide y se forman dos células hijas. Cada célula hija recibe el nombre de *célula haploide,* la cual es una célula que contiene la mitad de cromosomas que la célula progenitora.

MEIOSIS II

| Profase II | Metafase II | Anafase II | Telofase II (Cuatro células haploides) |

(NOTA: Aquí sólo se muestra una célula hija resultante de la meiosis I).

En la Meiosis II el material cromosómico se combina, se separa y se desplaza a las nuevas células, dando origen a cuatro células reproductoras. En los seres humanos, al unirse durante la fertilización dos células haploides (un espermatozoide y un huevo, conteniendo cada uno veintitrés cromosomas), éstas forman una *célula diploide,* es decir, una célula que contiene cuarenta y seis cromosomas. La célula fertilizada posee cuarenta y seis cromosomas, o veintitrés pares: la mitad proveniente de la madre y la otra del padre.

EJERCICIO 6: MEIOSIS
Instrucciones: Enumere las etapas de meiosis según el orden en que se llevan a cabo.

_____ Dos células nuevas se dividen, formando cuatro células reproductoras.

_____ Los pares de cromosomas se unen.

_____ Los pares de cromosomas se separan y cada uno se mueve a una nueva célula.

_____ Los cromosomas intercambian genes.

EJERCICIO 7: DIVISIÓN CELULAR
Instrucciones: Elija la mejor respuesta para las siguientes preguntas.

1. El método de reproducción que produce mayor variedad en la descendencia es la
   (1) reproducción asexual (no sexual).
   (2) reproducción mutante.
   (3) reproducción sexual.
   (4) clonación.
   (5) reproducción celular.

2. El cáncer es una condición en la que las células que no desempeñan ninguna función en el cuerpo invaden a las células saludables. Basándonos en este hecho, podemos llegar a la conclusión de que las células cancerosas malignas
   (1) no se reproducen por mitosis.
   (2) se dividen por meiosis.
   (3) se dividen de forma más impredecible que las células normales.
   (4) se dividen con menos frecuencia que las células benignas.
   (5) son parásitas y no se reproducen mediante la división.

Genética y herencia

La **herencia** es el término que se utiliza para referirse a la transmisión de rasgos biológicos de padres a hijos. La **genética** estudia cómo se transmiten estos rasgos biológicos. Los **genetistas,** es decir, los científicos que estudian la herencia, han descubierto que la información hereditaria de un organismo se transmite a través de los cromosomas del núcleo celular.

Los **genes** predeterminan todos nuestros rasgos hereditarios. Por cada rasgo, cada ser humano recibe dos genes: uno de la madre y otro del padre. Los genes pueden ser **dominantes** o **recesivos.** El gen dominante, en caso de estar presente, aparecerá siempre en la descendencia. Por ejemplo, como el color de ojo marrón es un rasgo dominante, el 90 por ciento de los seres humanos tienen ojos marrones. Si se heredan dos genes dominantes, el rasgo resultante será una combinación de las dos características heredadas.

La reproducción sexual asegura que la descendencia esté compuesta por material genético procedente de ambos padres. Este material genético se vuelve a mezclar completamente con cada fertilización, de modo que, a excepción de los gemelos idénticos, no hay dos hijos de unos mismos padres que sean genéticamente iguales.

Género y mutaciones

El que una madre engendre un niño o una niña viene determinado por los cromosomas "X" e "Y". Cada persona recibe dos cromosomas sexuales: uno procedente del espermatozoide del padre y uno del óvulo de la madre. Los óvulos contienen un único cromosoma "X". El espermatozoide masculino puede contener tanto un cromosoma "X" como un cromosoma "Y". Si se unen dos cromosomas "X", el resultado será una hembra. Si el espermatozoide que llega al óvulo tiene un cromosoma "Y", se engendrará un varón. El espermatozoide es, por consiguiente, el portador del cromosoma que determina el **género** de la descendencia.

A veces suele darse un error en la constitución genética de un cromosoma durante la duplicación de la célula. Este cambio en los genes se denomina **mutación** y puede transmitirse a la descendencia. Dos de las mutaciones que se dan en los seres humanos son el síndrome de Down, el cual ocasiona daños cerebrales, y la distrofia muscular, enfermedad que produce atrofia en los músculos.

EJERCICIO 8: GENÉTICA Y HERENCIA
Instrucciones: Analice el diagrama y elija la mejor respuesta para las preguntas que siguen.

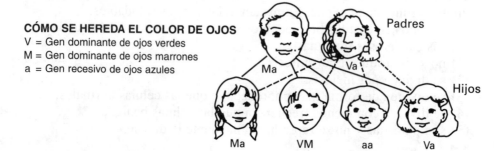

CÓMO SE HEREDA EL COLOR DE OJOS
V = Gen dominante de ojos verdes
M = Gen dominante de ojos marrones
a = Gen recesivo de ojos azules

1. Según el diagrama, ¿qué porcentaje de los hijos de esta pareja es probable que salgan con ojos azules?
    (1) 75 por ciento
    (2) 50 por ciento
    (3) 0 por ciento
    (4) 25 por ciento
    (5) 100 por ciento

La *Pregunta 2* no está basada en el diagrama anterior.

2. La familia Jones ha tenido cuatro hijas. El quinto hijo ha sido niño. Este cambio se debe a
    (1) los cursos de parto que han hecho los padres.
    (2) haber observado cuidadosamente los ciclos de fertilidad.
    (3) la contribución del padre con un cromosoma "Y".
    (4) la contribución de la madre con un cromosoma "X".
    (5) que finalmente se ha cumplido la "ley de los promedios".

Crecimiento, energía y seres vivos

Entre las características que distinguen a los seres vivos de los no vivos se hallan la capacidad de crecimiento, el consumo de alimentos y la liberación de energía para la realización de la actividad celular. El ciclo del nitrógeno, la fotosíntesis y la respiración celular son importantes procesos biológicos que intervienen en estas funciones.

El ciclo del nitrógeno

El *nitrógeno,* que constituye cerca del 80 por ciento de la atmósfera terrestre, es un ingrediente esencial para el tejido vivo. Tanto los seres humanos como los demás animales dependen de las plantas como fuente de nitrógeno. Las plantas no pueden fabricar nitrógeno por sí mismas, de modo que para obtenerlo se valen de otros organismos. Sin embargo, son muy pocos los organismos que pueden utilizar el nitrógeno de la atmósfera, en razón de lo cual lo deben combinar con otros elementos para formar *nitratos* que se puedan usar. Las plantas absorben estos nitratos para fabricar *aminoácidos,* los cuales son componentes esenciales de la proteína que necesitan las células vivas. Los aminoácidos se utilizan para la producción de proteínas y ácidos nucleicos que absorben los seres humanos.

La transformación del nitrógeno libre de la atmósfera en una forma compuesta se denomina *fijación del nitrógeno.* Este proceso se lleva a cabo gracias a ciertas bacterias—microorganismos y descomponedores—que habitan en el suelo. Estos microorganismos viven en sacos especiales, llamados *nódulos,* en las raíces de las leguminosas (plantas como la alfalfa, la arveja o guisante y el frijol o judía). Los microorganismos producen *nitrogenasa,* enzima esencial para la fijación del nitrógeno. Los científicos son de la opinión de que todo el nitrógeno de la atmósfera terrestre se ha fijado y liberado repetidas veces. Es probable que, en un momento dado, sólo hubiera en nuestro planeta unas cuantas libras de nitrogenasa. No obstante, esta pequeña cantidad es suficiente para sustentar toda la vida de la Tierra.

EJERCICIO 9: EL CICLO DEL NITRÓGENO

Instrucciones: Elija la mejor respuesta para las siguientes preguntas.

1. La *simbiosis* es la relación que existe entre dos organismos diferentes que viven juntos para beneficio mutuo. Se puede decir que son simbióticos, por ejemplo, los microorganismos que residen en los nódulos de las leguminosas. Otros ejemplos de relación simbiótica sería(n)

    (1) las bacterias que sólo habitan en el estómago de los animales ungulados facilitándoles la digestión.

    (2) las abejas que construyen sus panales en las cuevas, proporcionando así una fuente de alimento para los osos.

    (3) las hormigas soldado que viven y trabajan juntas en colonias.

    (4) la tenia que vive en el intestino humano.

    (5) los animales de carroña, como los buitres, que se alimentan de los despojos de animales muertos.

2. ¿Cuál de los siguientes métodos agrícolas ilustra mejor el proceso de fijación del nitrógeno?

    (1) el alternamiento o rotación de una plantación de algodón con una de remolacha

    (2) la irrigación de la tierra con métodos más modernos

    (3) el uso de equipos más avanzados para arar la tierra

    (4) el alternamiento o rotación de una plantación de algodón con una de soja

    (5) el uso de aviones para fumigar las cosechas con insecticidas

La fotosíntesis

Las plantas pueden vivir sin los seres humanos, pero los seres humanos no podemos vivir sin las plantas. Éstas proporcionan el oxígeno que necesitamos para respirar y los nutrientes que necesitamos para nuestro desarrollo. Las plantas verdes son autosuficientes porque son capaces de producir su propio alimento, mientras que los seres humanos y los animales inferiores deben obtener el alimento necesario para su subsistencia.

La *fotosíntesis* es el proceso de producción de alimentos mediante el cual las plantas verdes convierten la energía de la luz que reciben del Sol en energía química utilizable. La fotosíntesis puede entenderse como un proceso que comprende varios pasos. El primer paso se da con la captación de la energía por parte de la planta. En la mayoría de las plantas, el proceso de la fotosíntesis se lleva a cabo dentro de los *cloroplastos,* donde se encuentran moléculas de clorofila que absorben la luz solar. La *clorofila* es la sustancia que les da a las plantas su característico color verde. Con la energía que la clorofila libera a partir de la luz solar, las plantas dividen el agua en sus dos componentes: oxígeno e hidrógeno. El oxígeno es liberado en la atmósfera mientras que el hidrógeno se vuelve a combinar con el dióxido de carbono produciendo moléculas de carbohidratos (una forma de almidón) en la planta.

EJERCICIO 10: LA FOTOSÍNTESIS

Instrucciones: Elija la mejor respuesta para las siguientes preguntas.

1. ¿A cuáles de las siguientes conclusiones podemos llegar respecto de las plantas y de los procesos fotosintéticos?

    (1) Las plantas que no tienen clorofila deben valerse de un proceso distinto a la fotosíntesis para producir la energía que necesitan.

(2) Las plantas usan la fotosíntesis para producir energía porque es el método más sencillo que hay disponible.

(3) Las plantas que no se valen del proceso de fotosíntesis son parásitas y deben obtener su alimento de otra fuente.

(4) 1 y 2

(5) 1 y 3

La *Pregunta 2* está basada en la información contenida en el siguiente pasaje.

En algunas plantas, las hojas tienen secciones en las que la clorofila no está presente y otras donde sí está presente. Como ejemplo de esto citaremos a la planta coleus, cuyas hojas presentan llamativos colores. En un experimento en el que se ha eliminado el pigmento (color) de las hojas del coleus, una solución de yodo podrá identificar los lugares donde el almidón está presente al hacer que esas secciones de la hoja adquieran un color marrón.

2. ¿Qué cree ha de suceder con la hoja de coleus en un experimento de este tipo?

(1) Las secciones que cambien su color a marrón serán aquellas que inicialmente eran de color verde.

(2) Ninguna sección de la hoja cambiará su color a marrón.

(3) Las secciones que cambien su color a marrón serán aquéllas que inicialmente no eran de color verde.

(4) Toda la hoja cambiará su color a marrón.

(5) Sólo la mitad de la hoja cambiará su color a marrón.

La respiración celular

La *respiración celular* es una serie compleja de reacciones químicas mediante las cuales la célula elimina la energía atrapada dentro de las moléculas de glucosa. La *glucosa,* que es una forma de azúcar, es el producto final del proceso de fotosíntesis. Por lo tanto, la respiración celular es el proceso inverso a la fotosíntesis. Durante la respiración celular, las células (de las plantas o los animales) descomponen la glucosa a fin de liberar energía para la realización de la actividad celular. Como la energía no puede flotar libremente en la célula, es empacada y almacenada. La respiración celular se lleva a cabo en tres etapas, comenzando con la descomposición de la molécula de glucosa y terminando con la obtención de la energía necesaria para que la célula pueda realizar su actividad. La energía que no se usa se libera en forma de calor.

EJERCICIO 11: LA RESPIRACIÓN CELULAR

Instrucciones: Elija la mejor respuesta para las siguientes preguntas.

1. Basándonos en la información sobre la respiración celular, podemos inferir que

(1) en las plantas, la fotosíntesis debe preceder siempre a la respiración celular.

(2) no existe ninguna relación entre la fotosíntesis y la respiración celular.

(3) la fotosíntesis y la respiración comparten muchos procesos.

(4) la respiración celular sólo tiene lugar en la célula animal.

(5) las plantas no realizan ninguna actividad celular.

2. El ritmo de la respiración celular en los seres humanos se puede medir por la cantidad de dióxido de carbono exhalado. ¿Cuál de las siguientes afirmaciones cree usted ha de ser verdadera acerca del ritmo de respiración celular de un grupo de estudiantes de la misma edad, altura y peso?

(1) Los africanos tendrán un ritmo de respiración celular más alto que los asiáticos.

(2) Los niños tendrán un ritmo de respiración celular más alto que las niñas.

(3) Las niñas tendrán un ritmo de respiración celular más alto que los niños.

(4) Los atletas tienden a tener ritmos de respiración celular más altos que los que no son atletas.

(5) Los que no son atletas tendrán un ritmo de respiración celular más alto que los atletas.

3. Si usted se pusiera a medir la cantidad de dióxido de carbono exhalado, ¿cuál de las siguientes poblaciones sería más efectiva para probar la hipótesis que usted escogió en el ejemplo precedente?

(1) grupo de estudiantes inmediatamente después de despertarse

(2) grupo de estudiantes después de realizar un ejercicio físico intenso

(3) un estudiante en reposo y otro estudiante después de un ejercicio físico intenso

(4) la mitad de los estudiantes en reposo y la otra mitad después de un ejercicio físico intenso

(5) un cuarto de los estudiantes en reposo y un cuarto de los mismos después de un ejercicio físico intenso

Diversidad de la vida

La tarea de establecer categorías para agrupar los diversos y numerosos tipos de seres vivos se ha facilitado gracias a la creación de un sistema de clasificación.

Clasificación de los organismos

El sistema de clasificación de los seres vivos es una jerarquía que va de lo general a lo específico. Se van haciendo grupos y dentro de ellos subgrupos, es decir que, a medida que se va bajando en el sistema de clasificación, se van proporcionando cada vez más detalles acerca del organismo que se clasifica. El *reino* es el grupo más amplio. Dentro de cada reino, los organismos que son más similares se agrupan en *filos*. Dentro de cada *filo* se encuentran las *clases*. A las clases siguen los *órdenes, familias, géneros* y *especies.* La clasificación del ser humano *(Homo sapiens)* se ilustra en el cuadro siguiente.

TAXONOMÍA DE LA CLASIFICACIÓN DEL SER HUMANO

Categoría	Taxón	Características
Reino	Animalia	Es multicelular; incapaz de fabricar su propio alimento; pero capaz de moverse.
Filo	Cordata	Tiene notocordio (espina dorsal) y cordón nervioso hueco.
Clase	Mamíferos	Tiene pelo o pelaje; la hembra amamanta sus crías con leche que segrega.
Orden	Primate	Tiene dedos aplanados para poder asir, visión aguda y pobre sentido del olfato.
Familia	Homínidos	Camina con dos pies; tiene cara aplanada, ojos en parte frontal y visión en color.
Género	Homo	Tiene niñez prolongada, cerebro grande y capacidad de hablar.
Especie	Sapiens	Tiene poco pelo corporal, frente alta y mentón prominente.

EJERCICIO 12: CLASIFICACIÓN DE LOS ORGANISMOS

Instrucciones: Lea las definiciones y aplíquelas a las preguntas que siguen. A continuación se da una lista de los cinco reinos por orden de jerarquía (de inferior a superior) en que están clasificados los organismos vivos.

reino de los moneras: organismo unicelular simple y móvil que carece de orgánulos; hay algunos que pueden producir su propio alimento (ejemplo: las bacterias)

reino de los protistas: organismos unicelulares y móviles que poseen una estructura celular más compleja que la de los moneras (ejemplo: los paramecios)

reino de los hongos: multicelular; carece de clorofila; no tiene movilidad; obtiene su alimento de otros organismos (ejemplo: las setas)

reino de las plantas: multicelular; tiene clorofila; produce su propio alimento; no tiene movilidad (ejemplo: los musgos)

reino de los animales: multicelular; capaz de moverse por sí mismo y obtener su propio alimento (ejemplo: las aves)

1. El estreptococo es un organismo unicelular que no posee orgánulos y que presenta la forma de una serie de cadenas. Causa la inflamación de la garganta cuando invade esta región del cuerpo. ¿En qué reino clasificaría a este organismo?

    (1) moneras   **(2)** protistas   **(3)** hongos   **(4)** plantas   **(5)** animales

2. El moho es un parásito que crece en el pan, el queso y otros alimentos orgánicos. Carece de clorofila y obtiene los nutrientes de su huésped. ¿En qué reino lo clasificaría?
   (1) moneras
   (2) protistas
   (3) hongos
   (4) plantas
   (5) animales

La evolución y la selección natural

Todas las culturas humanas han tratado de explicar el origen de la humanidad. En muchas de estas culturas, la teoría de la Creación Divina o *creacionismo* es la más difundida en lo que respecta al origen de la Tierra y de sus criaturas. Esta teoría o creencia mantiene que tanto el mundo como las diversas formas de vida que en él habitan fueron creadas por un ser supremo, y que todas las especies creadas no han sufrido cambio alguno desde sus orígenes.

Existe, por otro lado, una explicación científica de gran aceptación: la teoría de la evolución o *evolucionismo.* Propuesta en 1859 por Charles Darwin en su libro *El origen de las especies,* esta teoría mantiene que todas las formas de vida se han ido desarrollando gradualmente (a lo largo de 600 millones de años) a partir de antepasados diferentes y, a menudo, más simples. Estas formas de vida se fueron adaptando con el correr de los años según las necesidades de su medio ambiente. Por lo tanto, todas las líneas de descendencia se remontan a un organismo ancestral común.

A medida que las crías fueron diferenciándose de sus padres, fueron apareciendo generaciones con características cada vez menos similares. Finalmente, se acabaron formando nuevas especies a partir de estas diferentes crías puesto que las nuevas características que éstas presentaban se podían heredar. Estas nuevas características se explican mediante la llamada *selección natural* ("ley del más fuerte"). Las especies que se adaptaron mejor a las condiciones en que vivían fueron las que lograron sobrevivir y reproducirse; en cambio, las que no pudieron adaptarse, perecieron.

EJERCICIO 13: LA EVOLUCIÓN Y LA SELECCIÓN NATURAL
Instrucciones: Elija la mejor respuesta para las siguientes preguntas.

1. Un miembro poco común del reino animal es el ornitorrinco, animal que presenta numerosas características de ave, mamífero y reptil. Este animal, originario de Australia y Tasmania, posee un pico parecido al de un pato, tiene patas palmeadas y con uñas, y el cuerpo cubierto por un pelaje espeso. Además, pone huevos de los que nacen las crías. ¿Cuál de las siguientes hipótesis relativas a la teoría de la evolución de Darwin se puede aplicar al ornitorrinco?
   (1) El ornitorrinco es el resultado del apareamiento entre tres clases distintas de animales.
   (2) El ornitorrinco es el miembro viviente más antiguo de una familia de mamíferos.
   (3) El ornitorrinco se desarrolló independientemente en un medio ambiente cerrado durante la etapa inicial de la evolución de los mamíferos.

(4) El ornitorrinco no estuvo sujeto a las influencias que se describen en la teoría de Darwin.

(5) Los mamíferos se originaron en Australia y Tasmania hace cientos de millones de años.

La *Pregunta 2* se refiere al siguiente pasaje.

Los mamíferos se clasifican en dos grupos: los **placentarios** (que tienen una placenta que alimenta al feto) y los **marsupiales** (que poseen una bolsa en la que guardan y alimentan a sus crías). La mayor parte de los marsupiales del planeta se encuentran en el continente australiano y las islas cercanas, donde vivieron pocos mamíferos placentarios durante la etapa inicial de la vida de los continentes.

2. En base a la información dada arriba sobre las diferencias entre los marsupiales y los mamíferos placentarios, se puede inferir que
   (1) los marsupiales son biológicamente menos avanzados que los mamíferos placentarios.
   (2) los mamíferos placentarios son más primitivos que los marsupiales.
   (3) los marsupiales no pueden sobrevivir fuera de Australia y de Norteamérica.
   (4) los marsupiales son las formas de vida más antiguas de la Tierra.
   (5) los marsupiales descienden de los reptiles.

3. ¿Cuál de los siguientes mamíferos exhibe una mejor adaptación física a las condiciones del medio ambiente?
   (1) vaca
   (2) león
   (3) ratón
   (4) foca
   (5) oso

La ecología y los ecosistemas

La ciencia de la *ecología* se ocupa de las relaciones que establecen los organismos vivos entre sí y con su medio ambiente no viviente. El ecologista estudia las relaciones que se dan entre los organismos que integran un medio ambiente y ese medio ambiente. Cuando el medio ambiente es autosuficiente, recibe el nombre de *ecosistema*. Los productores fotosintéticos, los consumidores, los descomponedores y su medio ambiente constituyen un ecosistema.

En un ecosistema típico, los *productores primarios* son las plantas verdes que obtienen su energía del Sol. Por ejemplo, los conejos (*consumidores primarios*) se alimentan de las plantas; los zorros (*consumidores secundarios*) se comen a los conejos; los buitres (*consumidores terciarios* o de tercer nivel) se alimentan de los restos de animales muertos que dejan los zorros; las bacterias y los hongos (*descomponedores*) se nutren de las sobras que deja el buitre y proporcionan los nitratos necesarios para las plantas verdes.

El *equilibrio ecológico* de una comunidad es delicado. La desaparición de un elemento clave puede destruir un sistema, a veces de forma permanente. El siguiente pasaje describe un desequilibrio ocurrido en un determinado ecosistema.

EJERCICIO 14: LA ECOLOGÍA Y LOS ECOSISTEMAS

Instrucciones Lea el pasaje y escriba en el espacio en blanco el elemento que corresponde al ecosistema descrito.

A fines del siglo XIX, un grupo de rancheros se trasladó a la Meseta Kaibad, ubicada en el norte de Arizona. Llegaban a esa zona atraídos por las vastas áreas de pastoreo y la buena calidad de los pastos así como por la abundancia de ciervos para la caza. Por temor a que el puma que habitaba la región devorara el ganado y los ciervos, los rancheros iniciaron una campaña para erradicar a este felino de la meseta. Con éxito lograron su propósito y el puma desapareció de la región a los pocos años.

Sin embargo, el logro de los rancheros tuvo catastróficas consecuencias ecológicas. La creciente población de ciervos, junto con las manadas de ganado vacuno que pastaban en la tierra, acabaron denudándola. Muy pronto, copiosas lluvias causaron una erosión importante y la tierra útil se redujo a una fracción de su antigua extensión. Este problema se ha presentado en repetidas ocasiones cada vez que los seres humanos han intentado manipular un ecosistema sin considerar las posibles consecuencias.

1. productor primario: _____

2. consumidores primarios: _____ y

   _____

3. consumidor secundario: _____

4. La erradicación de _____ provocó un aumento

   en la población de animales que se alimentan de pasto, como

   _____ y _____, lo cual

   condujo a la _____ de la tierra y posteriormente

   a su _____ debido a copiosas lluvias.

2
CIENCIAS DE LA TIERRA: EL ESTUDIO DE LA TIERRA

Las *ciencias de la Tierra* tienen por objeto el estudio del planeta Tierra, su origen y desarrollo. Se diferencian de las ciencias de la vida en el hecho de que centran su interés en los objetos no vivientes en lugar de los seres vivientes. Las ciencias de la Tierra constituyen un campo muy amplio que abarca temas relativos a la astronomía, la geología, la meteorología y la oceanografía.

Astronomía: El estudio de los cuerpos celestes

Por lo general, todo estudio acerca de la Tierra se basa, en su etapa inicial, en la astronomía. Los *astrónomos* estudian el tamaño, los movimientos y la composición de los cuerpos celestes. A través de la observación de las estrellas, los planetas, los cometas y demás cuerpos del espacio sideral, los astrónomos intentan comprender cómo se creó nuestro planeta y cómo fue evolucionando. Se ha postulado un gran número de importantes teorías para explicar el origen de la Tierra y el universo en que se encuentra. Entre estas teorías se pueden citar la teoría del *big bang* y la teoría de la pulsación.

Las teorías del *big bang* y de la pulsación

De acuerdo con la *teoría del big bang,* es decir, "de la gran explosión", un "huevo cósmico" constituido por polvo y gases que contenía toda la materia del universo explotó entre 15 y 20 mil millones de años atrás. Así se crearon los átomos, los elementos y los cuerpos celestes básicos. Se trata ésta de una teoría ampliamente aceptada porque explica la aparente expansión del universo y los vestigios de radiación presentes en el espacio exterior. El desarrollo de la *teoría de la pulsación* constituyó un refinamiento de la teoría del *big bang.* Según esta teoría, el universo se ha de expandir hasta alcanzar un límite determinado y entonces comenzará a contraerse. Esta contracción proseguirá hasta que se vuelva a dar el llamado huevo cósmico, el cual volverá a explotar en otro *"big bang"* provocando de esta manera una nueva expansión del universo.

Las estrellas y las galaxias

La teoría del *big bang* también explica cómo se forman las *estrellas.* De acuerdo con los defensores de esta teoría, la energía procedente de la explosión fue tan poderosa que ocasionó que una materia más ligera que el aire permaneciera suspendida en el espacio. Con el tiempo, se empezó a ejercer la fuerza de la gravedad y la materia se aglomeró junto con el helio y los gases de hidrógeno en formaciones oscuras semejantes a nubes. La materia gaseosa se empezó a comprimir y el choque de las partículas comprimidas produjo calor. Se formaron estrellas cuando la temperatura llegó a 15 millones de grados centígrados, que es la temperatura a la que se inician las reacciones nucleares.

La vida de una estrella oscila desde unos cientos de miles de años hasta miles de millones de años. La mayoría de las estrellas terminan por consumir sus existencias de hidrógeno, se contraen a un tamaño más pequeño y luego estallan. La explosión produce nubes de polvo y gas. Algunas de estas estrellas terminan contrayéndose y forman *agujeros negros,* es decir, estrellas de diminuto tamaño que poseen campos gravitacionales tan fuertes que ni la luz puede escaparse de ellas.

Gran parte de las estrellas existen en vastas formaciones llamadas *galaxias.* Se cree que existen cientos de millones de galaxias en el universo. Hay galaxias muy distantes cuyas estrellas están agrupadas de manera tan compacta que sólo se pueden ver como una masa borrosa de luz sin poder distinguir las estrellas individuales.

Nuestra galaxia, la *Vía Láctea,* es una galaxia espiral al igual que el 80 por ciento de todas las galaxias. La Vía Láctea está compuesta por 100 mil millones de estrellas, por lo menos, y la materia suficiente para crear millones de soles más. En la siguiente ilustración se puede apreciar la galaxia de la Vía Láctea.

GALAXIA DE LA VÍA LÁCTEA

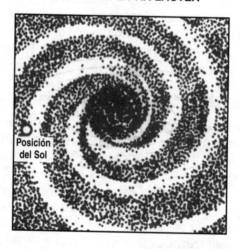

Posición
del Sol

LAS RESPUESTAS DE LOS EJERCICIOS DE ESTE CAPÍTULO
EMPIEZAN EN LA PÁGINA 454.

EJERCICIO 1: ESTRELLAS Y GALAXIAS

Instrucciones: Enumere las etapas de formación de las estrellas en el orden correcto. El 1 corresponde a la primera etapa y el 4 a la última.

_____ El calor se produce al chocar las moléculas.

_____ Se alcanza una temperatura de quince millones de grados y se emite una luz visible.

_____ El polvo y el gas se mueven por el universo.

_____ El gas y el polvo se comprimen a causa de las fuerzas gravitacionales.

El Sol y el sistema solar

A pesar de la importancia que tiene el *Sol* por ser la estrella central de nuestro *sistema solar*, en realidad no es más que una estrella "promedio" al compararla con otras de nuestra galaxia. Es promedio en cuanto a su edad (de 4 a 5 mil millones de años), tamaño (860,000 millas de diámetro), e intensidad de calor (la temperatura de la superficie es de 6,000 grados centígrados).

También forman parte de nuestro sistema solar los nueve *planetas*—siete de los cuales tienen uno o más satélites (lunas)—y 1,600 *asteroides* de gran tamaño ubicados entre Marte y Júpiter. Los *planetas interiores* (Mercurio, Venus, Tierra y Marte) son pequeños y de alta densidad y cuentan con un número reducido de satélites. Los *planetas exteriores* (Júpiter, Saturno, Urano y Neptuno) son gigantes gaseosos que tienen muchas lunas. Plutón está tan lejos que lo único que se puede afirmar de él es que no guarda semejanza a los demás planetas exteriores.

Se cree que los planetas eran en sus orígenes aglomeraciones de materia contenidas dentro de la nube de polvo de la que se formó el Sol. Estas aglomeraciones eran demasiado pequeñas como para llegar a reunir las condiciones necesarias para convertirse en estrellas. A diferencia de lo sucedido con las estrellas, se enfriaron y se convirtieron en los planetas que conocemos hoy. Nuestras sondas espaciales han llegado a todos los planetas, excepto los más alejados, y parece ser que la Tierra es el único astro (cuerpo celeste) habitado de nuestro sistema solar. La siguiente ilustración presenta un diagrama de nuestro sistema solar.

NUESTRO SISTEMA SOLAR

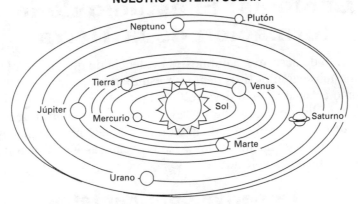

EJERCICIO 2: EL SISTEMA SOLAR

Instrucciones: Elija la mejor respuesta para la siguiente pregunta.

En astronomía, el llamado "problema Goldilocks" (en que uno de los planetas vecinos a la Tierra es demasiado caliente como para permitir la existencia de la vida y el otro es demasiado frío como para que pueda existir vida) se aplica a dos planetas. ¿Cuáles son?

(1) Plutón y Neptuno
(2) Marte y Saturno
(3) Mercurio y Venus
(4) Venus y Marte
(5) Júpiter y Urano

EJERCICIO 3: LOS PLANETAS

Instrucciones: Basándose en la información de la tabla, escriba en el espacio en blanco el nombre del planeta que corresponda para completar la afirmación.

Planeta	Duración del año	Duración del día	Número de satélites	Distancia al Sol (millas)
Mercurio	88 días	58 días	0	36 millones
Venus	225 días	243 días	0	67 millones
Tierra	365.26 días	23.9 horas	1	93 millones
Marte	686.98 días	24.6 horas	2	142 millones

1. La duración del día es aproximadamente igual en

   _____ y_____.

2. De los planetas de la lista, una persona "envejecería" más rápido en

   _____.

3. El tiempo que tarda Marte en girar alrededor del Sol es poco más de tres veces superior al que tarda _____.

Geología: El estudio de la formación de la Tierra

El acaecimiento de desastres naturales es evidencia de que la Tierra está sujeta a continuos cambios. Los *geólogos* estudian las características de la Tierra y cómo éstas afectan al desarrollo del planeta. En este siglo, los geólogos han realizado importantes y revolucionarios descubrimientos, entre los que se cuenta la formulación de la teoría de la tectónica de placas, que explica el desarrollo de las montañas y fosas oceánicas y el acaecimiento de terremotos y erupciones volcánicas.

La deriva continental y la tectónica de placas

Desde hace mucho tiempo, los científicos han observado que los contornos de África y Sudamérica hacen pensar que estos continentes pudieron haber estado unidos en el pasado. Partiendo de esta información, los geólogos han formulado la teoría de la *deriva continental,* según la cual los siete continentes actuales formaron hace millones de años parte de un supercontinente. Luego se dividieron y se separaron formando las extensiones de tierra que hoy se conocen como los siete continentes.

A pesar de que los continentes semejan piezas que encajan de un rompecabezas, los científicos no han logrado explicar por qué se separaron.

La teoría de la *tectónica de placas,* postulada en la década del 60, ofrecía una explicación a este fenómeno. Según esta teoría, la Tierra está formada por la corteza, el manto, el núcleo externo y el núcleo interno, como se presenta en la siguiente ilustración.

ESTRUCTURA DE LA TIERRA

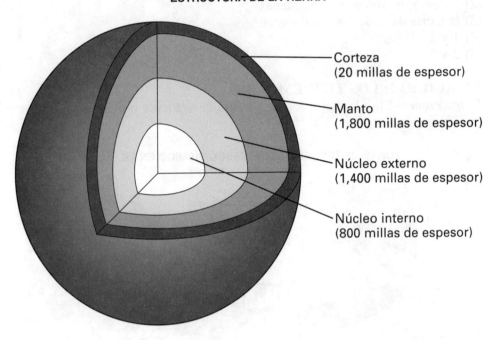

Corteza
(20 millas de espesor)

Manto
(1,800 millas de espesor)

Núcleo externo
(1,400 millas de espesor)

Núcleo interno
(800 millas de espesor)

La corteza y el manto superior se componen de unas veinte *placas.* Estas placas semejan platos que flotan en la superficie del agua de un inmenso estanque. Se desplazan con gran lentitud: entre media pulgada y cuatro pulgadas por año aproximadamente. Los continentes y el fondo oceánico se encuentran unidos a la superficie de estas placas. A medida que las placas lentamente se desplazan, transportan con ellas a los continentes. Los geólogos creen que las placas se mueven porque son arrastradas por las corrientes de roca parcialmente fundida que hay en el manto superior.

Este movimiento de las placas ofrece una serie de explicaciones. Cuando dos placas colisionan, una de las placas se apila encima de la otra, formando una *montaña.* Cuando una de las placas se introduce por debajo de la otra y desciende hacia el manto, se produce una *fosa.* Los *volcanes* se forman cuando el calor acumulado bajo la superficie de la Tierra funde el material de la placa que se introdujo en la fosa y envía la roca fundida a la superficie. Los *terremotos* se producen debido al movimiento y la ruptura de las rocas de la superficie al deslizarse una placa sobre otra.

Las vibraciones generadas por el deslizamiento de las placas reciben el nombre de *ondas sísmicas.* La intensidad de estas ondas se mide mediante un dispositivo llamado *sismógrafo* y luego se compara a la escala de Richter. Los terremotos que registran más de 4.5 en la escala de Richter se consideran potencialmente peligrosos.

EJERCICIO 4: LA TECTÓNICA DE PLACAS

Instrucciones: Elija la mejor respuesta para la siguiente pregunta.

Según el pasaje, ¿a cuál de estos casos ofrece explicación la teoría de la tectónica de placas?
(1) la fuerza gravitacional de la Tierra
(2) terremotos, volcanes y montañas
(3) la teoría de la deriva continental
(4) 1 y 2
(5) 2 y 3

EJERCICIO 5: LOS TERREMOTOS

Instrucciones: Elija la mejor respuesta para la siguiente pregunta basándose en el mapa de abajo.

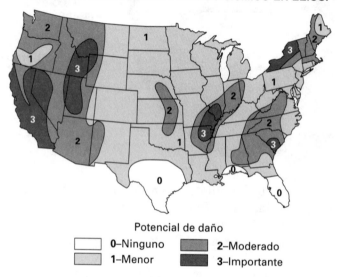

ZONAS DE TERREMOTOS Y RIESGO SÍSMICO EN EE.UU.

Potencial de daño

0–Ninguno **2**–Moderado
1–Menor **3**–Importante

¿A cuál de las siguientes afirmaciones sobre los terremotos respalda el mapa?
(1) California es el único estado donde se pueden esperar daños importantes causados por terremotos.
(2) Texas y Florida son los dos únicos estados que no tienen que preocuparse por los terremotos.
(3) El potencial para que se produzca un terremoto de tipo moderado a importante es mayor en la costa oeste.
(4) La mayor parte del territorio continental de Estados Unidos no está afectada por los terremotos.
(5) Los terremotos son los fenómenos más peligrosos de la Tierra.

EJERCICIO 6: DERIVA CONTINENTAL

Instrucciones: Lea el siguiente pasaje y elija la mejor respuesta para la pregunta que sigue.

La Isla de Ascensión es una pequeña isla volcánica ubicada en el Atlántico Sur, a medio camino entre África y Sudamérica.

Es un lugar de desove de tortugas marinas muy conocido. Se tratan éstas de tortugas verdes gigantes que cada año nadan unas 2,000 millas desde la costa de Sudamérica a la Isla de Ascensión donde depositan sus huevos. Este fenómeno ha intrigado a los científicos durante muchos años.

¿Cuál de las siguientes hipótesis geológicas explica mejor el comportamiento de las tortugas gigantes de mar?
(1) La Isla de Ascensión es el único lugar del mundo donde pueden sobrevivir los huevos de tortuga.
(2) Los depredadores, como los caimanes que viven en las costas de Sudamérica, devoran los huevos de tortuga, obligando así a las tortugas a migrar.
(3) La Isla de Ascensión ha sido el lugar de desove de estas tortugas desde hace millones de años, antes de que los continentes de África y Sudamérica se separaran.
(4) 1 y 2
(5) 2 y 3

Tiempo geológico

Para usted, cincuenta años puede que sea un tiempo considerable. Sin embargo, para la geología, cincuenta años no es mucho, dado que el tiempo geológico se remonta a casi 5 mil millones de años en el pasado, que es cuando los geólogos creen se formó la Tierra. El concepto que tenemos nosotros de *tiempo absoluto*—tiempo no influenciado por arbitrarios puntos de referencia humanos—se lo debemos a la geología. Los geólogos son capaces de fijar determinados períodos de tiempo al estudiar las rocas que se encuentran en la corteza terrestre. Estas rocas sirven de registros del tiempo.

Las rocas que se hallan en la corteza pueden ser de tres tipos, clasificados según su origen: Las *rocas ígneas* se forman al enfriarse y endurecerse la roca fundida (magma). Justo debajo de las rocas ígneas, se encuentran las *rocas metamórficas,* las cuales han sufrido transformaciones debido a la alta presión y temperatura que reina dentro de la corteza. Las rocas que se metamorfizan son sobre todo las ígneas. Las *rocas sedimentarias* se forman de partículas sólidas que el viento, el agua y el hielo depositan cerca de la superficie. En las rocas sedimentarias, las capas o *estratos* más viejos se encuentran en la parte inferior mientras que los más jóvenes se ubican en la parte superior.

Instrumentos para medir el tiempo

¿Cómo se puede determinar qué rocas son más antiguas que otras? Por medio de la *medición radiométrica,* los geólogos miden el grado de descomposición radiactiva de los minerales presentes en la roca. A lo largo del siglo pasado, los científicos han observado que las sustancias radiactivas se transforman, es decir, se descomponen con el tiempo, formando sustancias no radiactivas. Este método es válido para materias de hasta 50,000 años de edad. La datación radiométrica se aplica bien a muestras de rocas ígneas y sedimentarias porque mide la radiactividad de los minerales creados al formarse la roca. Sin embargo, en el caso de las rocas metamórficas resulta difícil precisar la edad de la roca de origen y la edad del metamorfismo.

El principio de la *sucesión fáunica* también se utiliza para determinar la edad de las rocas sedimentarias. Los geólogos examinan los tipos de *fósiles* animales encontrados en las capas de roca sedimentaria. Las rocas ígneas y metamórficas raramente contienen fósiles. Los científicos han descubierto que ciertas capas de roca contienen determinadas clases de fósiles, no importa de qué parte del mundo provenga la roca. Es más, los científicos han descubierto que ciertos fósiles se hallan siempre en estratos más inferiores que otros, lo cual indica la existencia de una secuencia en la evolución de los organismos.

EJERCICIO 7: MEDICIÓN DEL TIEMPO GEOLÓGICO

Instrucciones: Elija la mejor respuesta para las siguientes preguntas.

1. En base a la información del pasaje anterior, ¿qué afirmación describe correctamente la ubicación de los tres tipos de roca?
   - (1) Las rocas ígneas están en la superficie, las metamórficas en el medio y las sedimentarias en el fondo.
   - (2) Las rocas sedimentarias están en la superficie, las metamórficas en el medio y las ígneas en el fondo.
   - (3) Las rocas metamórficas están en la superficie, las sedimentarias en el medio y las ígneas en el fondo.
   - (4) Las rocas ígneas están en la superficie, las sedimentarias en el medio y las metamórficas en el fondo.
   - (5) Las rocas sedimentarias están en la superficie, las ígneas en el medio y las metamórficas en el fondo.

2. Los fósiles de trilobites se encuentran a una profundidad de 18 metros en un estrato de roca determinado mientras que los fósiles de coral se encuentran a 14 metros de profundidad. ¿Cuál de las siguientes afirmaciones acerca de estos organismos es probable que sea verdadera?
   - (1) Los fósiles de coral son más antiguos que los de trilobites.
   - (2) Los corales y los trilobites tienen la misma edad.
   - (3) Los corales y los trilobites comparten los mismos ancestros.
   - (4) Los trilobites son más avanzados que los corales.
   - (5) Los trilobites son más antiguos que los corales.

Minerales y rocas

Los minerales son los componentes básicos de las rocas. El *mineral* es un sólido natural e inorgánico que tiene una composición y estructura específicas. Todas las muestras de un mineral dado comparten ciertas propiedades físicas. Entre las propiedades físicas de los minerales se pueden citar la estructura cristalina, la dureza, el color, el brillo y la tenacidad (resistencia que oponen a la rotura).

Más del 95 por ciento de la corteza terrestre se compone de minerales formados a partir de los elementos oxígeno y silicio. En el cuadro siguiente se observan los ocho elementos principales, así como su peso y volumen respecto al peso y volumen de la corteza.

Elemento	Porcentaje de la masa de la corteza (peso)	Porcentaje del volumen de la corteza (espacio)
Oxígeno	46.71	94.24
Silicio	27.69	0.51
Aluminio	8.07	0.44
Hierro	5.05	0.37
Calcio	3.65	1.04
Sodio	2.75	1.21
Potasio	2.58	1.85
Magnesio	2.08	0.27

EJERCICIO 8: MINERALES Y ROCAS

Instrucciones: Elija la mejor respuesta para las siguientes preguntas.

1. Según la información de la tabla, ¿qué elemento representa una porción menor del peso de la corteza pero ocupa un espacio más de tres veces superior que el silicio, uno de los principales componentes de la corteza?
   (1) sodio
   (2) calcio
   (3) potasio
   (4) magnesio
   (5) hierro

2. ¿Cuál de las siguientes afirmaciones explica mejor por qué el oxígeno, que es un gas, es el componente principal de la corteza terrestre?
   (1) El oxígeno es responsable de que el peso de la corteza terrestre sea liviano.
   (2) El oxígeno es el elemento más abundante del mundo.
   (3) El oxígeno se encuentra en las plantas y las plantas constituyen una parte importante de la corteza terrestre.
   (4) El oxígeno es necesario para sustentar la vida en la Tierra.
   (5) El oxígeno es capaz de combinarse con la mayor parte de los elementos de la corteza terrestre.

Una Tierra cambiante

La *erosión* es el desgaste de la superficie de la Tierra causado por la gravedad, el viento, el hielo y el agua. La erosión se ha venido produciendo a lo largo del tiempo y continuará produciéndose mientras exista tierra seca. La *fuerza de la gravedad* impulsa a los materiales de la superficie a que se desplacen hacia abajo. Los movimientos descendentes en superficies inclinadas pueden ser rápidos o muy lentos y pueden involucrar los materiales de la superficie exclusivamente o también el lecho de rocas que se halla debajo.

Las casas que se construyen en las colinas pueden contribuir a los movimientos del suelo porque el peso de las casas se suma a la fuerza gravitacional. El *viento* contribuye al proceso de erosión al transportar material de la superficie de un sitio a otro.

Los *glaciares* son enormes masas de hielo que suelen desplazarse lentamente sobre el terreno arrastrando y transportando rocas y tierra. Al pasar por valles de ríos, los glaciares aumentan la profundidad de éstos. Los glaciares de montaña, sumados a la fuerza de la gravedad, producen avalanchas que causan enormes daños erosivos.

De todos los agentes erosivos, las corrientes de agua son los más potentes. Los ríos, sumados a la fuerza de la gravedad, son agentes erosivos verdaderamente devastadores. La acción de los ríos al fluir contra el terreno ha creado desfiladeros de proporciones tan grandes como las del Gran Cañón del Colorado. A medida que los ríos erosionan el terreno, van transportando depósitos. Los *deltas* se forman en la desembocadura de los ríos que vierten sus aguas en lagos o mares. La tierra transportada por estos ríos y depositada en la desembocadura es la más rica y fértil de todas las tierras de cultivo. Los ríos Nilo y Mississippi han formado deltas que se destacan por la riqueza de su tierra, haciendo de las mismas, regiones extremamente propicias para la agricultura.

EJERCICIO 9: UNA TIERRA CAMBIANTE
Instrucciones: Elija la mejor respuesta para la siguiente pregunta.

¿Cuál de los siguientes procedimientos usados por los agricultores no está directamente relacionado con la prevención de la erosión?
(1) plantar hierba en barrancos para que sirvan de relleno
(2) plantar las cosechas en hileras alternas (cultivo en franjas)
(3) arar siguiendo las curvas de nivel alrededor de una colina
(4) plantar nuevos árboles que sustituyan a los que se destruyen
(5) plantar más semillas de las necesarias para obtener una cosecha mayor

Oceanografía: El estudio de los océanos de la Tierra

Vista desde el espacio, la Tierra semeja una gran esfera azul. Una de las principales razones por la que nuestro planeta presenta este color es el agua, que cubre cerca del 71 por ciento de la superficie terrestre. Los científicos que se dedican al estudio de las grandes masas de agua se llaman *oceanógrafos.* Inventos como el sonar (dispositivo submarino para la localización de objetos), los submarinos para la navegación subacuática y las cámaras de control remoto han sido de gran utilidad en la exploración de los mares.

En sus estudios, los oceanógrafos han hecho numerosos descubrimientos que les han servido para comprender y explicar una serie de fenómenos. Por ejemplo, la teoría de la tectónica de placas se ha visto aun más fuertemente corroborada con el hallazgo de que la dorsal que circunda al planeta yace debajo del océano, la *dorsal oceánica.* Esta dorsal se extiende alrededor del globo terrestre como si fuera la costura de una pelota de béisbol. Se han fotografiado numerosas aberturas a lo largo de esta dorsal. La evidencia que presentan estas fotografías sirve de base a la teoría de que el magma presiona y sube hasta salir por la cresta de las dorsales. De esta manera, empuja y separa las placas oceánicas; luego se enfría y forma al endurecerse nuevas rocas que pasan a integrar la placa oceánica.

El origen de los océanos

Los oceanógrafos no han podido establecer con certeza cómo se originaron los océanos. Muchos creen que se formaron a partir de la eliminación del agua que formaba parte de las rocas del interior de la Tierra. La evidencia que presentan algunas de las rocas sedimentarias más antiguas sugiere que los sedimentos iniciales que dieron origen a estas rocas estaban depositados en agua. Lo que sí saben los científicos es que el volumen de agua que cubre la Tierra está afectado por la formación de glaciares y el deshielo de enormes bloques de hielo que cubren la superficie de la Tierra. La gráfica siguiente ilustra el cambio registrado en el nivel del mar durante los últimos 20,000 años. (Los glaciares cubrían gran parte de la Tierra hace 20,000 años.)

EJERCICIO 10: CAMBIOS EN EL NIVEL DEL MAR
Instrucciones: Elija la mejor respuesta para la pregunta que sigue.

CAMBIOS EN EL NIVEL DEL MAR DURANTE LOS ÚLTIMOS 20,000 AÑOS

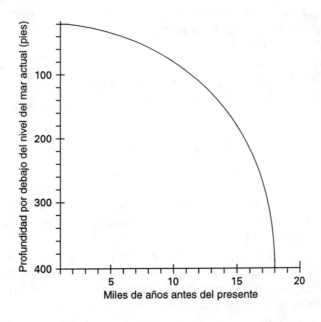

Según la gráfica, el nivel del mar de la Tierra estaba al mínimo hace aproximadamente
(1) 1,000 años.
(2) 5,000 años.
(3) 10,000 años.
(4) 15,000 años.
(5) 18,000 años.

EJERCICIO 11: EL ORIGEN DE LOS MARES

Instrucciones: Elija la mejor respuesta para las siguientes preguntas.

DISTRIBUCIÓN DEL AGUA EN LA TIERRA	
Tipo de agua	**% relativo de abundancia**
Agua de mar	86.5
Lagos, ríos	0.03
Hielo continental	1.3
Vapor de agua en la atmósfera	0.001
Agua en sedimentos y rocas sedimentarias	12.2

1. ¿Cuál de éstas es la fuente que produce la menor cantidad de agua en la Tierra?
   (1) agua de mar
   (2) ríos y lagos
   (3) hielo continental
   (4) vapor de agua en la atmósfera
   (5) agua en sedimentos y rocas sedimentarias

2. La presencia del 12 por ciento de agua en sedimentos y rocas sedimentarias sirve de apoyo a la teoría
   (1) de la deriva continental.
   (2) de la tectónica de placas.
   (3) de cómo el nivel del mar de la Tierra ha aumentado con los años.
   (4) del origen de los océanos.
   (5) de la sucesión fáunica.

Las mareas

Uno de los fenómenos marítimos fácilmente observables es el de las mareas. Las *mareas* son movimientos de ascenso y descenso de la superficie del agua del mar y de grandes lagos producidos por la atracción gravitacional del Sol y de la Luna sobre la Tierra. La Luna es el causante principal de las mareas debido a su cercanía a la Tierra.

Cuando la Luna se encuentra directamente encima, el océano que está debajo tiende a hincharse, produciendo la marea. En el lado opuesto de la Tierra, los océanos experimentan un abultamiento menor. Al dar un giro completo sobre su eje cada veinticuatro horas, la Tierra sufre dos mareas altas y dos mareas bajas. La posición de la Luna relativa al Sol y la Tierra determina el período y altura de las mareas. Las *mareas vivas* tienen una intensidad mayor que la marea promedio. Las *mareas muertas* tienen una intensidad menor que la marea promedio. En la ilustración del ejercicio siguiente se puede observar una marea viva y una marea muerta.

EJERCICIO 12: LAS MAREAS

Instrucciones: Elija la mejor respuesta para las siguientes preguntas.

MAREAS VIVAS Y MUERTAS

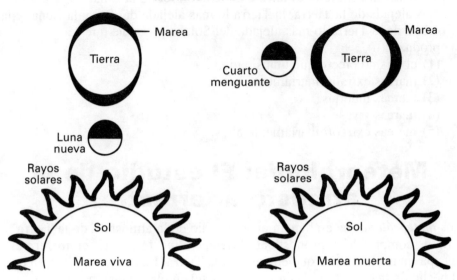

1. Las mareas vivas son mareas que tienen una intensidad mayor que la marea promedio. ¿Durante qué dos fases de la Luna la atracción gravitacional de la Luna junto con la del Sol es probable que sea mayor y que produzca una marea viva?

   A. cuarto menguante: cuando la Luna se encuentra del lado izquierdo de la Tierra, como se muestra en la ilustración
   B. luna llena: cuando la Tierra se encuentra entre el Sol y la Luna
   C. cuarto creciente: cuando la Luna se encuentra del lado derecho de la Tierra
   D. luna nueva: cuando la Luna se encuentra entre la Tierra y el Sol

   (1) A y B
   (2) A y C
   (3) A y D
   (4) B y C
   (5) B y D

La *Pregunta 2* se basa en la siguiente explicación:

   Sicigia es el nombre que recibe el raro fenómeno de alineación del Sol, la Luna y la Tierra y que origina unas mareas extraordinariamente altas. Este fenómeno se produjo durante el período comprendido entre el 30 de diciembre de 1986 y el 4 de enero de 1987 e hizo que se agravaran las rigurosas tormentas que se habían desatado a lo largo de la costa atlántica. Durante este período de cinco días se dieron tres acontecimientos coincidentes.

   A. La órbita de la Luna se situó más cerca que nunca de la Tierra (a unas 223,000 millas en lugar de a 240,000 millas).
   B. La Luna se situó directamente entre la Tierra y el Sol, dando lugar a una luna nueva.
   C. La órbita de la Tierra se situó más cerca que nunca del Sol (a 91.5 millones de millas en lugar de a 93 millones de millas).

2. Si se dieran condiciones tales en que la órbita de la Luna estuviera lo más alejada de la Tierra, la Tierra lo más alejada del Sol y la Luna, y la órbita de la Tierra lo más alejada del Sol, es probable que se produzca(n)

(1) el mismo efecto que una sicigia.

(2) mareas extraordinariamente bajas.

(3) mareas muertas.

(4) mareas vivas.

(5) mareas extraordinariamente altas.

Meteorología: El estudio de la atmósfera terrestre

Los *meteorólogos* se embarcan en el estudio de la atmósfera de la Tierra a fin de comprender y pronosticar el tiempo atmosférico. La *atmósfera* es la capa invisible de aire que envuelve a la Tierra. Los científicos creen que el hecho de que exista vida en la Tierra y no en otros planetas vecinos como Marte y Venus se debe principalmente a nuestra atmósfera. La atmósfera no es una masa de aire homogénea que rodea a la Tierra, sino que está compuesta por varias capas de aire localizadas a determinados niveles de altitud.

Los meteorólogos han identificado cuatro capas o estratos en la atmósfera terrestre, a saber (en orden ascendente): troposfera, estratosfera, ionosfera y exosfera. La *troposfera* es la capa más cercana a la Tierra. Se extiende desde la superficie de la Tierra hasta una altura de siete a diez millas. En esta capa tienen lugar los fenómenos meteorológicos de la Tierra y, además, se encuentran en ella casi todas las nubes. La *tropopausa* es el límite donde termina la troposfera y comienza la estratosfera. La *estratosfera* empieza entre las siete y diez millas de altura y se extiende unas treinta millas hacia arriba. Es una capa uniforme de aire con mínimo movimiento vertical del aire. Los aviones se desplazan en esta capa porque es generalmente suave y de buena visibilidad.

Por encima de la estratosfera se halla la *ionosfera* la cual se extiende unas 300 millas. El aire de la ionosfera es extremadamente fino y las partículas de aire están electrificadas. A través de la ionosfera, las ondas de radio se transmiten a grandes distancias por toda la Tierra. La *exosfera* es la capa más alta de la atmósfera. Se caracteriza por el calor extremo que reina en la misma durante el día, cuando inciden sobre ella los rayos directos del Sol y por el frío extremo durante la noche, cuando se encuentra escudada de esos rayos directos del Sol.

EJERCICIO 13: CAPAS DE LA ATMÓSFERA TERRESTRE

Instrucciones: Lea el pasaje y analice el diagrama; luego elija la mejor respuesta para las preguntas que siguen.

A distintas altitudes de la atmósfera terrestre se pueden observar distintos fenómenos. Además, los científicos pueden aplicar distintas tecnologías para explorar y comprender la Tierra y las regiones del espacio exterior.

1. Las nubes noctilucas, nubes especta-
   culares que sólo se pueden ver al
   anochecer, aparecen poco tiempo
   después de ponerse el Sol. ¿A qué nivel
   atmosférico son visibles estas nubes?
   (1) exosfera
   (2) troposfera
   (3) estratosfera
   (4) ionosfera
   (5) tropopausa

2. Las ondas de radio de la capa "D" que
   se transmiten por todo el mundo se
   pueden encontrar en
   (1) la sección más alta de la
       estratosfera.
   (2) la sección más baja de la
       estratosfera.
   (3) la sección más baja de la
       ionosfera.
   (4) la sección más alta de la
       ionosfera.
   (5) la sección más alta de la
       troposfera.

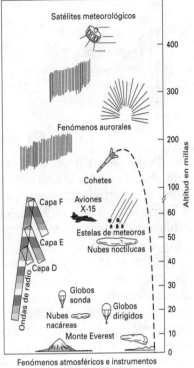

Fenómenos atmosféricos e instrumentos
de observación

3. La ilustración sugiere que la cumbre
   del Monte Everest
   (1) se encuentra algunas veces oculta
       por las nubes.
   (2) se extiende más allá de la
       tropopausa.
   (3) se encuentra en la troposfera.
   (4) 1 y 2
   (5) 1 y 3

EJERCICIO 14: EL OZONO EN LA ATMÓSFERA

Instrucciones: Lea el pasaje y elija la mejor respuesta para la pregunta que
sigue.

El *ozono* es un gas tóxico, corrosivo y de olor penetrante
que se forma en la atmósfera cuando los rayos solares
ultravioleta ionizan los átomos de oxígeno. El ozono es
beneficioso para el planeta porque absorbe los rayos
ultravioleta, evitando que estas letales longitudes de onda
alcancen la superficie de la Tierra. Sin embargo, en los
niveles más bajos de la atmósfera terrestre, sobre todo en las
áreas urbanas, el ozono se puede formar mediante una
reacción química entre el calor solar y el humo del escape de
los automóviles. Esta forma de ozono, que es el ingrediente
principal del *smog*, es dañina para los seres humanos y
puede dificultar la respiración.

La forma dañina de ozono que se puede observar como *smog* se forma en la
(1) exosfera.
(2) troposfera.
(3) estratosfera.
(4) ionosfera.
(5) tropopausa.

El ciclo del agua

Para poder pronosticar el tiempo, los meteorólogos tienen que considerar no sólo el aire que nos rodea sino también cómo éste interactúa con el agua que cubre la superficie terrestre. La atmósfera y la **hidrosfera** (la parte acuosa de la Tierra) dan origen al llamado **ciclo del agua.** Gracias a este ciclo, podemos explicar el fenómeno de precipitación, importante elemento de nuestro tiempo atmosférico.

El Sol es un eslabón clave dentro de la cadena de acontecimientos que conforman el ciclo del agua. El Sol irradia calor, el cual es responsable de que diariamente se evaporen en el aire millones de toneladas de agua procedentes de océanos, lagos, ríos y arroyos del planeta. A medida que se eleva, este aire húmedo empieza a enfriarse de forma paulatina. Finalmente, se enfría tanto que la **humedad** (vapor de agua presente en el aire) llega al 100 por ciento. En este punto, el vapor de agua se condensa y comienzan a formarse las nubes. Dependiendo de la temperatura y de otras condiciones, el agua empieza a precipitarse en forma de lluvia o nieve cuando a las nubes no les es ya posible contener toda esa cantidad de agua. La lluvia o la nieve posteriormente desagua en el océano y el ciclo una vez más se completa. En la siguiente ilustración se puede observar el ciclo del agua.

EL CICLO DEL AGUA

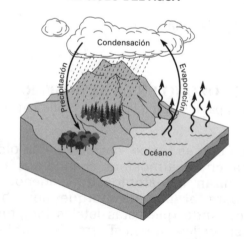

EJERCICIO 15: EL CICLO DEL AGUA:

Instrucciones: Enumere de 1 a 5 (primera a última) las siguientes etapas del ciclo del agua según el orden que corresponda.

_____ La lluvia o la nieve devuelve el agua al océano.

_____ Se produce una condensación y se forman las nubes.

_____ El Sol irradia calor.

_____ Se produce una precipitación en forma de lluvia o nieve.

_____ El agua se evapora y pasa a la atmósfera.

EJERCICIO 16: HUMEDAD

Instrucciones: Lea el pasaje y conteste las preguntas que siguen.

La *humedad* es la cantidad de vapor de agua presente en el aire en un momento dado. En temperaturas cálidas, el aire puede contener mayor volumen de humedad que en temperaturas frías. La *humedad relativa* es la cantidad de vapor de agua presente en el aire en un momento dado expresada como el porcentaje de la cantidad total de vapor de agua que el aire es capaz de contener. Por ejemplo, a 86 grados Fahrenheit, el aire puede contener un máximo de 30.4 gramos de agua por metro cúbico. Si el aire a esa misma temperatura sólo contiene 15.2 gramos de agua, la humedad relativa es del 50 por ciento. Cuando se alcanza el punto en que el aire se satura (excede la cantidad de vapor de agua que puede contener), se elimina dicho vapor de agua en forma de condensación (rocío) o de precipitación.

1. Si el aire a 61 grados contiene su máxima cantidad de humedad posible y la temperatura baja de repente a 45 grados, ¿qué es lo más probable que ocurra?
   (1) El aire se saturaría con el vapor de agua
   (2) Se produciría una precipitación en forma de lluvia.
   (3) Se produciría una precipitación en forma de granizo.
   (4) 1 y 2
   (5) 1 y 3

2. En numerosas regiones del país, cuando la temperatura está por debajo del punto de congelación, la humedad relativa interior de las casas disminuye con la calefacción. Los muebles y la piel se resecan y aumenta la electricidad estática. Por razones de salud, los doctores recomiendan el uso de humidificadores. ¿Cuál de las siguientes afirmaciones explica mejor la falta de humedad en el aire del interior de las casas?
   (1) Baja la cantidad de vapor de agua en el aire.
   (2) Se evapora el vapor de agua en el aire.
   (3) La cantidad de vapor de agua presente en el aire a temperaturas más bajas es menor que la cantidad de vapor que puede contener el aire calentado del interior.
   (4) 1 y 2
   (5) 2 y 3

Masas de aire, frentes y tiempo atmosférico

Otro elemento clave a la hora de determinar el tiempo atmosférico terrestre son las masas de aire. Las masas de aire frías tienden a ser inestables y turbulentas y a moverse con más rapidez que las masas de aire caliente. Las nubes que se forman de masas de aire frío son los *cúmulos,* nubes densas semejantes a copos de algodón. En tiempo cálido, cuando las masas de aire frío producen precipitaciones, hay probabilidades que estas precipitaciones se den en forma de tormenta. Las masas de aire calientes son normalmente estables y el viento que las acompaña es constante. Las nubes que se forman de masas de aire caliente son los *estratos,* nubes uniformes en forma de capas situadas a baja altura que en tiempo cálido producen precipitaciones en forma de llovizna.

Los *frentes* se forman cuando chocan dos masas de aire y se forma un límite entre las mismas. Esto afecta el tiempo atmosférico de la región localizada debajo de estos frentes, que pueden ser débiles o fuertes. Los frentes fuertes, por lo general, producen precipitaciones. Cuando el aire frío actúa como un arado y hace retroceder al aire caliente, se forma un *frente frío.* Si el aire frío retrocede y el aire caliente es el que lo empuja, se forma un *frente cálido.* A veces, el límite entre las dos masas de aire no se desplaza y el frente se vuelve estacionario. Los *frentes estacionarios* producen condiciones similares a las que producen los frentes cálidos. Sin embargo, la precipitación resultante suele ser más moderada y de mayor duración.

EJERCICIO 17: MASAS DE AIRE, FRENTES Y TIEMPO ATMOSFÉRICO

Instrucciones: Elija la mejor respuesta para las siguientes preguntas.

1. ¿Cuál de los siguientes cambios de tiempo podría producirse si una fuerte masa de aire caliente desplazara a una masa de aire frío?
   (1) Podrían formarse cúmulos, empezar a soplar el viento en ráfagas y producirse tormentas.
   (2) Podrían formarse estratos, empezar a soplar el viento de forma constante y producirse lloviznas.
   (3) Podrían formarse estratos, empezar a soplar el viento de forma turbulenta y producirse tormentas.
   (4) Podrían formarse cúmulos, empezar a soplar el viento de forma constante y producirse tormentas.
   (5) El cielo permanecería despejado y no habría viento ni precipitaciones.

2. En base al pasaje anterior, ¿cuál de los siguientes puntos *no guarda relación alguna* con la acción de los frentes responsables de los cambios en el tiempo?
   (1) la temperatura de la masa de aire
   (2) la velocidad a que se desplaza la masa de aire
   (3) la fuerza de la masa de aire
   (4) la estabilidad de los vientos que acompañan a la masa de aire
   (5) la dirección en que se desplaza la masa de aire

3
QUÍMICA:
EL ESTUDIO DE LA MATERIA

La *química* es la rama de la ciencia que estudia la naturaleza, composición, estructura y cambios de la materia. *Materia* es cualquier sustancia que ocupa espacio y tiene masa. Una silla, un pupitre, una mesa al igual que el aire que respiramos están compuestos de materia. La materia existe en cuatro estados: sólido, líquido, gaseoso y de plasma. El plasma es un gas ionizado del que se compone el Sol.

El átomo, base de la materia

En química, el *átomo* es la estructura básica de la materia. Es la partícula más pequeña de un elemento que posee las propiedades de ese elemento. El *elemento* es una sustancia que se da en la naturaleza y que no se puede descomponer en otra sustancia más simple. En la naturaleza se dan casi 100 sustancias fundamentales conocidas como elementos. Los seres humanos también han producido sintéticamente algunos elementos. Los átomos se agrupan en moléculas. La *molécula* es la parte más pequeña de un compuesto que puede existir por sí misma. Una molécula consta de dos o más átomos químicamente unidos.

A principios del siglo XIX, sólo se conocía la existencia de unos cuantos elementos. Según la teoría de John Dalton, el átomo no se puede crear, destruir o dividir; además, todos los átomos de un mismo elemento son iguales. Ésta se llegó a conocer como *teoría atómica.* Posteriormente, los físicos descubrieron que el núcleo de un átomo puede dividirse si se lo bombardea con neutrones, proceso que se conoce como *fisión nuclear.*

Dmitri Mendeleyev, químico ruso, creó la llamada *tabla periódica* mediante la que calculó el peso atómico de los distintos elementos. Los elementos se identifican mediante símbolos tomados en su mayor parte de las letras del nombre en latín de dichos elementos. Los pesos de todos los demás elementos se basan en el peso (masa) del hidrógeno, el elemento más ligero que se conoce. Al hidrógeno se le adjudicó la *masa atómica* 1 y se le asignó el *número atómico* 1. El átomo de oxígeno, gas muy abundante en la Tierra, posee una masa 16 veces mayor que el átomo de hidrógeno; por lo tanto, al oxígeno se le dio peso atómico de 16. El oxígeno es el octavo elemento más ligero y se le ha asignado el número atómico 8. Los descubrimientos de Dalton y Mendeleyev fueron los más importantes en el campo de la química desde los realizados por Lavoiser, químico francés que identificó el oxígeno como elemento clave en la combustión. En la página 195 se ilustra un ejemplo de la tabla periódica.

Estructura atómica

Desde los tiempos de Dalton, los científicos han realizado grandes avances en su conocimiento de los átomos. Por ejemplo, se sabe que el átomo se compone de un núcleo rodeado por uno o más electrones. El *núcleo,* situado en el centro del átomo, está formado por protones y neutrones. El *protón* es una partícula de carga positiva. El *número atómico* de un elemento viene determinado por el número de protones presentes en el núcleo. Como el hidrógeno tiene un solo protón en su núcleo, se le ha asignado el número atómico 1. El *neutrón* posee una masa casi igual a la de un protón, pero carece de carga. El núcleo tiene una carga positiva que viene determinada por el número de protones que contiene. El núcleo proporciona el número másico (de masa) de un elemento.

El *electrón* es una partícula de carga negativa. Los electrones ocupan una órbita, o capa, que rodea al núcleo. En cada capa hay un número fijo de electrones. Lo que distingue a un elemento de otro es su número de capas. Cuanto mayor sea el número de capas con electrones en movimiento que tenga un elemento, mayor será su número atómico. En la siguiente ilustración se observa la estructura del átomo.

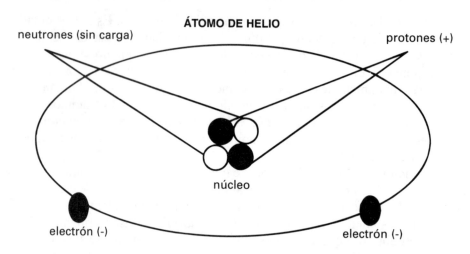

ÁTOMO DE HELIO

neutrones (sin carga)   protones (+)

núcleo

electrón (-)   electrón (-)

LAS RESPUESTAS DE LOS EJERCICIOS DE ESTE CAPÍTULO EMPIEZAN EN LA PÁGINA 456.

EJERCICIO 1: ESTRUCTURA ATÓMICA

Instrucciones: Relacione los términos de la derecha con su descripción y escriba en el espacio en blanco la letra correspondiente.

_____ **1.** el segundo elemento más ligero; contiene dos protones en su núcleo

_____ **2.** partícula de carga negativa

_____ **3.** parte del átomo que determina la masa del elemento

_____ **4.** partícula sin carga

_____ **5.** partícula de carga positiva

_____ **6.** elemento que contiene ocho protones en su núcleo

(a) oxígeno

(b) neutrón

(c) protón

(d) helio

(e) electrón

(f) núcleo

EJERCICIO 2: ENERGÍA NUCLEAR

Instrucciones: Lea el pasaje y elija la mejor respuesta para las preguntas que siguen. (Refiérase a la tabla periódica de la página 195.)

La energía nuclear se puede liberar de dos formas: por fisión o por fusión. En la **fisión nuclear** se produce la escisión del núcleo de un elemento químico pesado al ser bombardeado con neutrones. En la **fusión nuclear** se produce la unión de dos núcleos de un elemento a alta temperatura y presión, formándose así el núcleo de un elemento nuevo y más pesado.

1. En base a la información del pasaje y a las masas atómicas que se indican en la tabla periódica, la energía procedente de la fusión nuclear se liberará cuando
   (1) los núcleos del uranio se fusionen formando plutonio.
   (2) los núcleos del hidrógeno se fusionen formando oxígeno.
   (3) los núcleos del oxígeno se fusionen formando helio.
   (4) los núcleos del hidrógeno se fusionen formando helio.
   (5) los núcleos del helio se fusionen formando hidrógeno.

2. ¿En la escisión del núcleo de qué elemento se liberará energía procedente de la fisión nuclear?
   (1) plutonio
   (2) hidrógeno
   (3) oxígeno
   (4) 1 y 2
   (5) 1 y 3

EJERCICIO 3: ELEMENTOS ISOTÓPICOS

Instrucciones: Lea el pasaje y la tabla y elija la mejor respuesta para las preguntas que siguen.

A veces, el número de neutrones que contiene el átomo de un elemento puede variar. Este hecho puede afectar el número másico de ese elemento. Por ejemplo, el carbono tiene seis protones en su núcleo, pero también puede tener un mínimo de seis y un máximo de siete neutrones en su núcleo. Los elementos cuyo núcleo posee un número variable de neutrones en su núcleo se dice que son **isotópicos**. Así, por ejemplo, existen dos isótopos de carbono, carbono 12 y carbono 13, los cuales tienen propiedades químicas diferentes. El más común de estos isótopos es el carbono 12.

Elemento	Número atómico	Número másico
Hidrógeno	1	1.01
Helio	2	4.00
Litio	3	6.94
Berilio	4	9.01
Boro	5	10.81

1. El único elemento de la tabla anterior que puede tener un isótopo de número másico 6 y cuyos dos núcleos pueden fusionarse y formar carbono 12 sería el
   (1) hidrógeno.
   (2) helio.
   (3) litio.
   (4) berilio.
   (5) boro.

2. El deuterio y el tritio son dos isótopos de número másico 2 y 3 respectivamente. De estos dos isótopos, el tritio es especialmente radiactivo. En base a la tabla anterior, se podría inferir que estos elementos utilizados en la fusión nuclear son formas diferentes de
   (1) hidrógeno.
   (2) helio.
   (3) litio.
   (4) berilio.
   (5) boro.

Los elementos y la periodicidad

La *tabla periódica* (que se aprecia en la página siguiente) organiza los elementos en base a sus propiedades atómicas y físicas. Esta tabla relaciona las propiedades de los elementos con sus números atómicos. Los elementos de una misma fila tienen el mismo número de capas que contienen un número variable de electrones. Los elementos de la misma columna tienen el mismo número de electrones en la capa más externa.

Al clasificar los elementos de acuerdo con sus propiedades físicas, los científicos consideran el color, olor, sabor, densidad, punto de ebullición, solubilidad (capacidad de disolverse), maleabilidad (capacidad de deformarse al ser golpeado) y dureza. En base a estas propiedades, han surgido los tres grupos amplios que han empleado los químicos para clasificar todos los elementos: metales, no metales y metaloides (o semimetales).

Los *metales* conducen bien el calor y la electricidad, se funden a altas temperaturas y tienen alta densidad y brillo. Entre los metales se pueden citar el sodio, el oro y el aluminio. Los *no metales* se funden a bajas temperaturas, tienen poco brillo, son menos densos que los metales y no son buenos conductores del calor y la electricidad. Entre los no metales se pueden mencionar el carbono, el azufre y el oxígeno. Los *metaloides* o *semimetales* tienen propiedades tanto de los metales como de los no metales.

Según la ley periódica, a medida que aumenta el número atómico de los elementos de una columna, las propiedades similares ocurren con mayor regularidad y en mayor grado. Por ejemplo, los elementos con números atómicos 3, 11 y 19 (litio, sodio y potasio respectivamente) son metales químicamente activos. En muchos casos, cuanto mayor es el número atómico, mayor es el grado en que se dan ciertas propiedades. Mientras el segundo miembro de este grupo, el sodio, es químicamente activo, el rubidio, que es el cuarto miembro, es tan altamente activo que arde con sólo entrar en contacto con el aire.

TABLA PERIÓDICA DE ELEMENTOS

Leyenda:

Número atómico — **6**
Símbolo — **C**
Nombre — Carbono
Número másico (número de protones y neutrones) — 12

1 (IA)	2 (IIA)	3	4	5	6	7	8	9	10	11	12	13	14	15	16	17	18
1 **H** Hidrógeno 1																	2 **He** Helio 4
3 **Li** Litio 7	4 **Be** Berilio 9											5 **B** Boro 11	6 **C** Carbono 12	7 **N** Nitrógeno 14	8 **O** Oxígeno 16	9 **F** Flúor 19	10 **Ne** Neón 20
11 **Na** Sodio 23	12 **Mg** Magnesio 24											13 **Al** Aluminio 27	14 **Si** Silicio 28	15 **P** Fósforo 31	16 **S** Azufre 32	17 **Cl** Cloro 35	18 **Ar** Argón 40
19 **K** Potasio 39	20 **Ca** Calcio 40	21 **Sc** Escandio 45	22 **Ti** Titanio 48	23 **V** Vanadio 51	24 **Cr** Cromo 52	25 **Mn** Manganeso 55	26 **Fe** Hierro 56	27 **Co** Cobalto 59	28 **Ni** Níquel 59	29 **Cu** Cobre 64	30 **Zn** Zinc 65	31 **Ga** Galio 70	32 **Ge** Germanio 73	33 **As** Arsénico 75	34 **Se** Selenio 79	35 **Br** Bromo 80	36 **Kr** Criptón 84
37 **Rb** Rubidio 85	38 **Sr** Estroncio 88	39 **Y** Itrio 89	40 **Zr** Circonio 91	41 **Nb** Niobio 93	42 **Mo** Molibdeno 96	43 **Tc** Tecnecio 98	44 **Ru** Rutenio 101	45 **Rh** Rodio 103	46 **Pd** Paladio 106	47 **Ag** Plata 108	48 **Cd** Cadmio 112	49 **In** Indio 115	50 **Sn** Estaño 119	51 **Sb** Antinomio 122	52 **Te** Telurio 128	53 **I** Yodo 127	54 **Xe** Xenón 131
55 **Cs** Cesio 133	56 **Ba** Bario 137	57 **La** Lantano 139	72 **Hf** Hafnio 178	73 **Ta** Tantalio 181	74 **W** Volframio 184	75 **Re** Renio 186	76 **Os** Osmio 190	77 **Ir** Iridio 192	78 **Pt** Platino 195	79 **Au** Oro 197	80 **Hg** Mercurio 201	81 **Tl** Talio 204	82 **Pb** Plomo 207	83 **Bi** Bismuto 209	84 **Po** Polonio 209	85 **At** Astato 210	86 **Rn** Radón 222
87 **Fr** Francio 223	88 **Ra** Radio 226	89 **Ac** Actinio 227	104 **Unq** Uniluadio 260	105 **Unp** Unilpentio 262	106 **Unh** Unilhexio 263	107 **Uns** Unilheptio 262	108 **Uno** Uniloctio 265	109 **Une** Unilenio 266	110 **Uun** Unununio								

Elementos Terrestres Raros

Lantánidos

58 **Ce** Cerio 140	59 **Pr** Praseodimio 141	60 **Nd** Neodimio 144	61 **Pm** Prometio 145	62 **Sm** Samario 150	63 **Eu** Europio 152	64 **Gd** Gadolinio 157	65 **Tb** Terbio 159	66 **Dy** Disprosio 163	67 **Ho** Holmio 165	68 **Er** Erbio 167	69 **Tm** Tulio 169	70 **Yb** Iterbio 173	71 **Lu** Lutecio 175

Actínidos

90 **Th** Torio 232	91 **Pa** Protoactinio 231	92 **U** Uranio 238	93 **Np** Neptunio 237	94 **Pu** Plutonio 244	95 **Am** Americio 243	96 **Cm** Curio 247	97 **Bk** Berkelio 247	98 **Cf** Californio 251	99 **Es** Einstenio 252	100 **Fm** Fermio 257	101 **Md** Mendelevio 258	102 **No** Nobelio 259	103 **Lr** Laurencio 260

EJERCICIO 4: LOS ELEMENTOS Y LA PERIODICIDAD

Instrucciones: Elija la mejor respuesta para las siguientes preguntas.

1. Los metales cobre, plata y oro pertenecen al mismo grupo (columna) y tienen los números atómicos 29, 47 y 79 respectivamente. De acuerdo con el principio de la ley periódica, ¿de qué propiedad física tendría el oro el grado más alto de entre estos tres metales?
   (1) valor
   (2) rareza
   (3) volatilidad
   (4) maleabilidad
   (5) escasez

2. El radón está en el mismo grupo que el helio, el neón, el argón, el criptón y el xenón. ¿Cuál de los siguientes hechos le ayudaría a determinar que el radón tiene una densidad mayor que cualquiera de los demás elementos del mismo grupo?
   (1) El radón se encuentra en el suelo mientras que los otros no.
   (2) El radón tiene un número atómico más alto que los demás elementos de su grupo.
   (3) El radón puede causar problemas de salud a aquéllos que habitan en áreas donde se encuentran grandes concentraciones del mismo en el suelo.
   (4) 1 y 2
   (5) 2 y 3

Los elementos y las reacciones químicas

En toda reacción química hay dos componentes: reactante y producto. *Reactante* es la sustancia o sustancias que participa(n) en la reacción. El *producto* es la sustancia o sustancias que resulta(n) de la reacción. Las reacciones químicas pueden ser *reacciones de combinación,* en las que dos elementos o sustancias se combinan, o *reacciones de descomposición,* en las que un elemento o sustancia se descompone.

Las reacciones químicas se representan en forma de *ecuaciones químicas.* Las fórmulas químicas usan símbolos para representar los elementos e indican el número de átomos de cada elemento de una sustancia. Por ejemplo, para representar la reacción química que produce agua, escribiríamos:

$$2H_2 + O_2 \rightarrow 2H_2O$$

Cuando leemos una ecuación química, el número de mayor tamaño expresa cuántas moléculas (estructuras que contienen más de un átomo) hay presentes. Cuando sólo hay presente una molécula o átomo, el número 1 no se escribe. El subíndice de tamaño menor indica cuántos átomos de un elemento determinado están presentes en cada molécula.

La ecuación del agua expresa que dos moléculas de gas hidrógeno (H_2) se combinan con una molécula de oxígeno (O_2) formando dos moléculas de agua (H_2O). Obsérvese que una molécula de hidrógeno (H_2) contiene dos átomos de hidrógeno, y una molécula de oxígeno (O_2) contiene dos átomos de oxígeno. Cada molécula de agua (H_2O) contiene dos átomos de hidrógeno y un átomo de oxígeno.

La reacción química en la que un átomo de carbono se une con dos átomos de oxígeno para formar dióxido de carbono se escribiría:

$$C + O_2 \rightarrow CO_2$$

Esta ecuación expresa que una molécula de carbono se combina con una molécula de oxígeno (dos átomos de oxígeno) formando una molécula de dióxido de carbono (CO_2).

Todas las reacciones químicas están gobernadas por la *ley de la conservación de la materia.* Esta ley mantiene que la materia no se puede crear ni destruir en una reacción química. Las ecuaciones químicas cumplen con esta ley: sus dos miembros situados a ambos lados de la flecha presentan el mismo número de átomos para todos los elementos de la reacción. Por ejemplo, cuando el gas metano (CH_4) se quema con oxígeno se produce la siguiente reacción química:

$$CH_4 + 2O_2 \rightarrow CO_2 + 2H_2O$$

El gas metano se quema con oxígeno obteniéndose dióxido de carbono y vapor de agua; o más específicamente una molécula de dióxido de carbono y dos moléculas de agua. Obsérvese que la reacción se inicia con un átomo de carbono (C) y termina con cuatro átomos de hidrógeno ($2H_2 = 2 \times 2 = 4$). La reacción comienza asimismo con cuatro átomos de oxígeno ($2O_2 = 2 \times 2 = 4$) y termina con 4 átomos de oxígeno ($O_2 + 2O = 4$). Cuando el número de átomos de cada elemento es igual en ambos lados de la ecuación, decimos que la ecuación está *equilibrada* o *ajustada.*

EJERCICIO 5: ECUACIONES EQUILIBRADAS

Instrucciones: Indique si las siguientes ecuaciones son equilibradas *(E)* o desequilibradas *(D).*

_____ 1. $N_2 + O_2 \rightarrow 2NO$

_____ 2. $Fe + HCl \rightarrow FeCl_3 + H_2$

_____ 3. $2H + O \rightarrow H_2O$

EJERCICIO 6: REACCIONES QUÍMICAS

Instrucciones: Elija la mejor respuesta para las siguientes preguntas.

1. La reacción química que da a las bebidas carbonadas (sodas, refrescos, o gaseosas) su efervescencia es la de disolver una molécula de dióxido de carbono en una molécula de agua. ¿Cuál de las siguientes ecuaciones químicas representa este proceso?
   (1) $CO_3 + H_2O \rightarrow H_2CO_4$
   (2) $CO_2 + H_2O \rightarrow H_2CO_3$
   (3) $CO + H_2O \rightarrow H_2CO_2$
   (4) $CO_2 + H_2O \rightarrow H_2CO_2$
   (5) $CO + 2H_2O \rightarrow H_4CO_2$

2. Los reactantes y productos de una reacción química
   (1) siempre duplican su masa.
   (2) deben equilibrarse siempre.
   (3) nunca se igualan en masa.
   (4) necesitan siempre un catalizador.
   (5) deben triplicarse para poder alcanzar el equilibrio.

La *Pregunta 3* se refiere al siguiente pasaje.

Los **cambios físicos** no producen sustancias nuevas. Por ejemplo, cuando serramos madera o disolvemos sal en agua no cambiamos la composición química de las sustancias. Sin embargo, cuando se produce un **cambio químico,** se forma una nueva sustancia. Entre los cambios químicos más comunes se pueden citar la quema de la madera y la oxidación del metal en los automóviles.

En un experimento sobre cambios físicos y químicos, se añaden 10 g de sulfato de cobre a 100 ml de agua. Se calienta la solución a fuego lento y se agita. Después de que la solución se haya enfriado, se coloca un trozo de papel de aluminio en la solución de sulfato de cobre. Pasadas 24 horas, la solución ha cambiado de color, de azul oscuro a un azul muy claro, y el aluminio ha adquirido una gruesa capa de cobre.

3. ¿Con cuál de los siguientes datos se podría probar que se ha producido un cambio químico?
   (1) el haber calentado la solución de sulfato de cobre
   (2) el haber agitado la solución
   (3) el haber transcurrido 24 horas
   (4) el haber adquirido el aluminio una capa de cobre
   (5) el que el aluminio se pudiera romper

Elementos en combinación

Los *compuestos* se forman cuando dos o más elementos se combinan en una reacción química. El producto resultante tiene propiedades distintas a las de los elementos componentes. Una vez formados, los compuestos sólo se pueden descomponer en sustancias simples por medio de una acción química. Por ejemplo, el agua, que es el compuesto más conocido, está formada por dos átomos de hidrógeno y un átomo de oxígeno. Cuando se somete el agua a temperaturas extremas, se puede reducir a sus elementos componentes— hidrógeno y oxígeno—perdiéndose así su característica de líquido.

Las *mezclas* son sustancias que se forman cuando dos o más elementos o compuestos se mezclan en diferentes proporciones. El producto resultante retiene las propiedades de los elementos que se combinan. En la mayor parte de las mezclas los ingredientes que se combinan se pueden separar con facilidad. Por ejemplo, la pólvora es una mezcla de carbón, azufre y nitrato de potasio (un compuesto de potasio y nitrógeno). Al mezclarse los tres ingredientes, forman la pólvora, sustancia altamente explosiva. Estos tres ingredientes se pueden identificar en esta mezcla por sus diferentes colores.

Cuando en un líquido se disuelve un sólido, un líquido, o una sustancia gaseosa, se obtiene una *solución* homogénea. La sustancia que se disuelve en el líquido se llama *soluto.* El líquido donde se disuelve la sustancia se llama *solvente o disolvente.* Una solución acuosa utiliza agua como solvente. Una tintura tiene por solvente alcohol, como sucede con la tintura antiséptica de yodo. Algunas veces, se forman soluciones al disolverse una sustancia en un gas o en un sólido.

Cuando los metales se combinan en distintas proporciones suelen formar *aleaciones.* En una aleación, cada metal se disuelve en el otro a altas temperaturas. Ejemplos comunes de aleaciones son el latón (cobre y zinc), el bronce (cobre, estaño y otros elementos), y el acero (hierro, carbono y otros elementos). Se obtiene una *amalgama* cuando se disuelve un metal en mercurio, un metal líquido. Las amalgamas se usan principalmente para hacer empastes dentales.

EJERCICIO 7: TIPOS DE SUSTANCIAS

Instrucciones: Elija la mejor respuesta para las siguientes preguntas.

1. La sal común o cloruro de sodio—una de las sustancias más comunes presentes en la naturaleza—se puede clasificar mejor como
   (1) compuesto.   (4) aleación.
   (2) mezcla.   (5) amalgama.
   (3) solución.

2. El aire está compuesto por nitrógeno (78 por ciento), oxígeno (21 por ciento), argón (0.93 por ciento), dióxido de carbono (0.03 por ciento), y otros gases (0.04 por ciento). El aire se puede clasificar mejor como
   (1) compuesto.   (4) aleación.
   (2) mezcla.   (5) amalgama.
   (3) solución.

Enlaces químicos

Cuando se forman los compuestos, se crea un enlace entre dos o más elementos. El *enlace* es la fuerza que une dos átomos, dos *iones* (partículas eléctricamente cargadas), dos moléculas, o una combinación de éstos. El enlace puede ser el resultado tanto de la transferencia de electrones entre átomos como del compartir electrones entre átomos.

Cuando se transfieren electrones de un átomo a otro, se crea un *enlace iónico.* En el siguiente ejemplo, se forma un enlace iónico cuando un electrón de un átomo de sodio se transfiere a la capa más externa de un átomo de cloro. El resultado es el compuesto conocido como sal común.

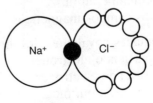

ÁTOMOS DE SODIO Y CLORO   CLORURO DE SODIO

● = electrón de Na
○ = electrón de Cl

El electrón de Na se ha transferido al átomo de Cl.

En el ejemplo anterior, tanto el sodio como el cloro son eléctricamente neutros (carecen de carga); sin embargo, cuando el átomo de sodio pierde su electrón, se carga positivamente. Las cargas opuestas se atraen, creando un enlace. Los compuestos iónicos, como la sal común, tienen típicamente puntos elevados de fusión y ebullición, son inflamables, conducen la electricidad cuando están disueltos en agua y son sólidos a temperatura ambiente.

Cuando dos o más átomos de elementos diferentes comparten electrones para formar una molécula, se crea un *enlace covalente.* Por ejemplo, dos átomos de hidrógeno se enlazan a un átomo de oxígeno y forman el compuesto conocido como agua.

MOLÉCULA DE AGUA

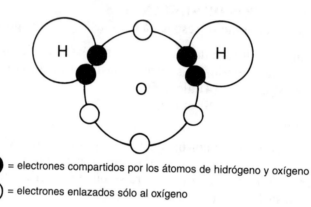

● = electrones compartidos por los átomos de hidrógeno y oxígeno

○ = electrones enlazados sólo al oxígeno

En el enlace covalente, la capa más externa del elemento que tenga el número mayor de electrones se llena a su máxima capacidad con ocho electrones. Una vez que el elemento que se combina obtiene ocho electrones en su anillo exterior, no se podrá combinar con ningún otro elemento. Los compuestos covalentes, como el agua, tienen por lo general puntos bajos de fusión y ebullición, no son inflamables, tienen mala conductividad y existen en forma de gases y líquidos.

EJERCICIO 8: COMPUESTOS Y ENLACES QUÍMICOS

Instrucciones: Elija la mejor respuesta para las siguientes preguntas.

1. En los enlaces iónicos, los átomos se mantienen unidos
   (1) compartiendo electrones.
   (2) transfiriendo electrones.
   (3) por atracción química.
   (4) por la temperatura.
   (5) por los campos magnéticos.

2. En los enlaces covalentes, los átomos se mantienen unidos
   (1) compartiendo electrones.
   (2) transfiriendo electrones.
   (3) por atracción química.
   (4) por la temperatura.
   (5) por los campos magnéticos.

Ácidos, bases y sales

Muchos de los compuestos resultantes de enlaces iónicos y covalentes se clasifican en ácidos o bases. Los *ácidos* son compuestos covalentes que producen iones de hidrógeno al disolverse en agua. Los ácidos tienen un sabor agrio, siendo los más comunes : el ácido acético (el componente principal del vinagre), el ácido cítrico (presente en las frutas cítricas), el ácido láctico (que se encuentra en la leche) y el ácido clorhídrico (componente del ácido estomacal que se emplea en la digestión).

Las *bases* son compuestos que forman iones de hidróxido al ser disueltos en agua. Las bases son capaces de tomar un protón de un ácido o de ceder a un ácido un par de electrones no compartidos. Se puede calificar a las bases de alcalinas, porque se disuelven en agua y son resbalosas al tacto. Muchos de los hidróxidos son bases. Los agentes que se usan en la limpieza casera, como el amoníaco, el bórax, la lejía y los detergentes son ejemplos de bases comunes.

Cuando un ácido se combina con una base, se forma una *sal* y se desprende agua porque el metal presente en la base reemplaza al hidrógeno contenido en el ácido. Los ácidos y bases inorgánicos, así como las sales inorgánicas pueden conducir la electricidad cuando se disuelven en agua. Los químicos aplican la *prueba del papel tornasol* a una sustancia para determinar si es un ácido o una base. Los ácidos hacen que el papel tornasol azul se vuelva rojo, y las bases hacen que el papel tornasol rojo se vuelva azul.

EJERCICIO 9: ÁCIDOS, BASES Y SALES

Instrucciones: Lea el pasaje y estudie la escala; luego elija la mejor respuesta para las preguntas que siguen.

La designación **pH** (potencial de formación de ion Hidrógeno) es un valor mediante el cual se clasifican algunas sustancias de acuerdo con su acidez o alcalinidad. La **escala de pH** va de 0 a 14, donde el valor 7 corresponde a una solución neutra. La escala de pH se ilustra a continuación.

ESCALA DE pH

1. Según la escala de pH, el ácido acético, un ácido muy suave, es probable que se encuentre entre los valores
   (1) 7 y 8.
   (2) 0 y 1.
   (3) 2 y 3.
   (4) 4 y 5.
   (5) 10 y 1.

2. En base a la escala de pH, el valor para el agua sería
   (1) entre 0 y 1.
   (2) entre 3 y 4.
   (3) 7.
   (4) 14.
   (5) entre 5 y 6.

3. ¿Cuál de los siguientes puntos se puede usar para probar que una sustancia es un ácido?
   (1) La sustancia tiene un pH superior a 7.
   (2) La sustancia es agria o cáustica.
   (3) La sustancia neutraliza una base y forma sal y agua.
   (4) 1 y 2
   (5) 3 y 3

EJERCICIO 10: LA BATERÍA DE AUTOMÓVIL

Instrucciones: Lea el pasaje y conteste las preguntas que siguen.

Los ácidos, las bases y las sales inorgánicas (las que se obtienen de seres no vivientes) son conductores muy efectivos de la electricidad. La batería común de automóvil es un ejemplo de corriente eléctrica generada mediante la reacción química entre un ácido y un metal. En las baterías de automóvil, el plomo puro (pitón negativo) y el dióxido de plomo (pitón positivo) se sumergen en ácido sulfúrico (conductor). Periódicamente se añade agua destilada para mantener el nivel adecuado de ácido sulfúrico. El plomo puro pierde dos electrones cuando reacciona con el ácido sulfúrico —el ácido transforma el plomo a dióxido de plomo. Al mismo tiempo, el pitón positivo que contiene dióxido de plomo gana dos electrones y transforma el ácido sulfúrico en que está inmerso en sulfato de plomo (que es una sal) y agua. La corriente que hace que el auto pueda arrancar es el resultado del flujo de electrones del plomo al dióxido de plomo a través del ácido sulfúrico y hasta el interruptor de arranque, completando así el circuito. A continuación se ofrece un diagrama de una batería de automóvil.

BATERÍA DE AUTOMÓVIL

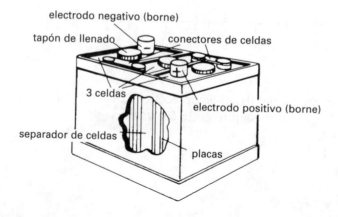

1. Los *electrolitos* son compuestos inorgánicos que conducen la corriente eléctrica cuando se disuelven en agua. ¿Cuál es el electrolito en el ejemplo precedente?
   (1) dióxido de plomo
   (2) ácido sulfúrico
   (3) agua destilada
   (4) 1 y 2
   (5) 2 y 3

2. Las sustancias *se oxidan* cuando pierden electrones. En el ejemplo anterior, ¿cuál de los siguientes compuestos está oxidado?
   (1) plomo
   (2) dióxido de plomo
   (3) sulfato de plomo
   (4) agua
   (5) ácido sulfúrico

3. Las sustancias que se oxidan se denominan *agentes oxidantes* mientras que las sustancias que reducen a otras sustancias se denominan *agentes reductores.* En el ejemplo anterior, los agentes oxidantes y reductores son respectivamente
   (1) el dióxido de plomo y el agua.
   (2) el ácido sulfúrico y el dióxido de plomo.
   (3) el plomo y el ácido sulfúrico.
   (4) el sulfato de plomo y el dióxido de plomo.
   (5) el ácido sulfúrico y el agua.

4. ¿Cuál de las siguientes afirmaciones son válidas cuando una batería se descarga y deja de generar corriente?
   (1) El ácido sulfúrico ya no puede oxidar el plomo.
   (2) El dióxido de plomo ya no puede reducir el ácido sulfúrico.
   (3) La batería se ha quedado sin ácido sulfúrico.
   (4) 1 y 2
   (5) 1 y 3

Velocidad de reacción, catalizadores y equilibrio

Las reacciones químicas se producen a distintas velocidades según las condiciones en que se realicen. El azúcar se disuelve con más rapidez en agua caliente que en agua fría. El fósforo blanco arde al entrar en contacto con el aire. Se puede aumentar o disminuir la velocidad de reacciones como éstas introduciendo otra sustancia en la reacción. Los *catalizadores* son sustancias que aumentan la velocidad de las reacciones químicas sin sufrir ellos ninguna alteración química. Hay catalizadores que producen el efecto contrario. Los catalizadores negativos disminuyen la velocidad de la reacción química. Los catalizadores negativos suelen ser inhibidores, como sucede con los productos químicos que se utilizan de base en la pintura de los autos para retardar el proceso de oxidación.

Un conjunto dado de reactantes puede reaccionar y formar más de un producto. Los productos resultantes suelen reaccionar y formar los reactantes iniciales. Cuando la velocidad de la reacción inicial se equilibra con la reacción inversa, se produce un *equilibrio químico.* Por ejemplo, el monóxido de carbono procedente del escape de los automóviles entra en la atmósfera y reacciona con el oxígeno para formar dióxido de carbono. El dióxido de carbono se descompone mediante la luz solar formando el reactante inicial, monóxido de carbono. Esta reacción representa un equilibrio químico porque la reacción se revierte por sí sola. Este tipo de reacciones químicas dan origen a un ciclo.

EJERCICIO 11: VELOCIDAD DE REACCIÓN, CATALIZADORES Y EQUILIBRIO

Instrucciones: Elija la mejor respuesta para las siguientes preguntas.

1. La lipasa es una enzima producida por el hígado que ayuda a la digestión de las grasas acelerando la velocidad con que los lípidos (grasas) se convierten en ácidos grasos y glicerol. Basándonos en esta descripción, podemos concluir que una enzima es
   (1) un producto de una reacción química.
   (2) un catalizador negativo.
   (3) un catalizador biológico.
   (4) 1 y 2
   (5) 1 y 3

2. ¿Cuál de los siguientes procesos sirve para ilustrar el equilibrio químico?
   (1) enlace
   (2) fotosíntesis
   (3) respiración
   (4) 1 y 2
   (5) 2 y 3

4
FÍSICA: EL ESTUDIO DEL COMPORTAMIENTO DE LA MATERIA

La *física* estudia las fuerzas que hacen que la materia se comporte de una forma dada en nuestro mundo. El campo de la física es tan amplio que no se pueden comprender a cabalidad las otras ramas de la ciencia sin conocer las leyes básicas de la física. Las *fuerzas* son evidencia de la presencia de *energía* (o capacidad para realizar un trabajo) en un medio determinado. El área de la física que se ocupa de las fuerzas, la energía y el efecto que tienen en los cuerpos se denomina *mecánica*.

La mecánica

La mecánica fue una de las primeras ciencias en desarrollarse. Aristóteles, filósofo y científico de la Grecia Antigua, postuló que los cuerpos pesados caen con más rapidez que los más livianos. A comienzos del siglo XVII, un científico y matemático italiano llamado Galileo probó la falsedad de esta teoría cuando dejó caer desde lo alto de la Torre de Pisa objetos de diferentes pesos. Sin embargo, no se comprendía cabalmente la fuerza que actuaba sobre los objetos, hasta que el británico Sir Isaac Newton formuló las leyes de la gravedad y el movimiento que explicaban cómo actúan las diferentes fuerzas sobre los objetos.

La fuerza gravitacional

La existencia de la fuerza gravitacional o fuerza de la gravedad, la fuerza de la naturaleza que se experimenta con más frecuencia, fue postulada por primera vez por Newton cuando observó cómo caía una manzana de un árbol. Newton desarrolló la *ley de la gravitación universal,* según la cual todos los cuerpos que tienen masa ejercen una fuerza de atracción sobre cualquier otro cuerpo que tenga masa en el universo. La intensidad de la fuerza dependerá de las masas de los objetos y de la distancia que exista entre ellos. (La *masa* es la medida de la cantidad de materia que hay en un objeto). De esta manera, la manzana que caía al suelo sirve para ilustrar la fuerza gravitacional (atracción) de la Tierra, que es más grande, sobre la manzana, que es más pequeña. Esta ley explica también cómo los planetas, atraídos por el Sol, que es mucho más grande, permanecen en sus órbitas al girar alrededor del mismo.

Las tres leyes del movimiento de Newton

Según la *ley de la inercia,* un cuerpo permanece en reposo o continúa en estado de movimiento uniforme a menos que una fuerza actúe sobre el mismo. Por ejemplo, cuando una persona va conduciendo un automóvil y aprieta los frenos bruscamente, su cuerpo sigue desplazándose hacia adelante. Esto se debe a que el cuerpo de esta persona tiene tendencia a permanecer en el mismo estado de movimiento uniforme (movimiento hacia adelante en este caso). Cuando se aplicaron los frenos al automóvil, se alteró este movimiento uniforme.

La **ley de la fuerza aplicada** expresa que el cambio de velocidad y dirección de un cuerpo es proporcional a la cantidad de fuerza aplicada sobre el mismo. Por ejemplo, las aspas de un molino de viento que giran impulsadas por la fuerza del viento aumentarán su velocidad según la velocidad y dirección del viento que las impulsa.

La **ley de acción y reacción** afirma que por cada acción se produce una fuerza de reacción de igual intensidad pero de sentido contrario. Por ejemplo, el cañón de una pistola retrocede al salir disparada la bala.

LAS RESPUESTAS DE LOS EJERCICIOS DE ESTE CAPÍTULO EMPIEZAN EN LA PÁGINA 458.

EJERCICIO 1: LAS LEYES DE LA FUERZA Y EL MOVIMIENTO

Instrucciones: Escriba en el espacio en blanco una *G* si el ejemplo ilustra la ley de la gravitación universal, *I* si se aplica a la ley de la inercia, *FA* si se aplica a la ley de fuerza aplicada y *AR* si se aplica a la ley de acción y reacción de Newton.

_____ 1. Un avión baja los alerones de sus alas al aterrizar. Los alerones crean una resistencia al avance que es una fuerza que reduce la elevación y ayuda a que el avión disminuya su velocidad.

_____ 2. Un cohete sale propulsado hacia arriba por las potentes fuerzas de descarga descendente de los gases de escape.

_____ 3. Una bala disparada al aire termina cayendo a la tierra.

_____ 4. El péndulo de un reloj de péndulo, una vez puesto en movimiento continúa oscilando y, por lo tanto, regulando la marcha del reloj.

EJERCICIO 2: LA FUERZA GRAVITACIONAL

Instrucciones: Lea el párrafo y conteste la pregunta que sigue.

Un astronauta se pesa antes del lanzamiento. Cuando se pesa al llegar a la Luna, ve que su peso es sólo una fracción de su peso inicial. Ya rumbo a Júpiter observa que su peso ha aumentado varias veces con respecto a su peso inicial.

Los cambios de peso se pueden explicar mejor por

(1) la cantidad de fuerza que ejercía cada planeta al pesarse el astronauta.
(2) la distancia al Sol de los planetas donde se pesaba.
(3) los cambios en la presión atmosférica en los distintos astros.
(4) la cantidad de calorías consumidas durante el vuelo.
(5) el tiempo transcurrido entre pesajes.

Trabajo, energía y potencia

En física, se realiza *trabajo* cuando una fuerza desplaza un objeto sobre el cual está actuando. Por ejemplo, una persona que levanta un peso de 50 libras a una altura de un pie del suelo está realizando un trabajo. Para que se realice un trabajo, el movimiento del objeto debe hacerse en la misma dirección de la fuerza, en este caso en línea vertical. El trabajo se puede expresar como la unidad de fuerza multiplicada por la unidad de distancia y se puede representar con la siguiente expresión: $T = F \times D$.

El trabajo realizado es entonces la cantidad de fuerza aplicada multiplicada por la distancia recorrida. En el ejemplo anterior, se realizan 50 libras-pie de trabajo cuando se levantan cincuenta libras de peso a un pie de altura: 50 lb x 1 pie = 50 libras-pie.

Para hacer un trabajo se requiere energía. En el ejemplo de arriba, se ilustra la energía muscular como un cuerpo capaz de realizar un trabajo. La *energía cinética* es la energía que posee un cuerpo en movimiento, como por ejemplo un tren que se desplaza.

La *energía potencial* es la energía que los cuerpos almacenan o que se encuentra disponible para ser usada por los mismos. Por ejemplo, el carbón tiene una energía potencial que sólo se libera al quemarse. Una roca ubicada en lo alto de una colina tiene energía potencial; después de ser empujada colina abajo, su energía potencial se convierte en energía cinética.

Potencia es la velocidad a la que se realiza el trabajo. La potencia se mide normalmente en caballos de fuerza, equivaliendo un caballo de fuerza a 550 libras-pie por segundo o 33,000 libras-pie por minuto.

La ley de la conservación de la energía

La *ley de la conservación de la energía* afirma que toda la energía del universo se conserva. La capacidad que tiene la energía para realizar un trabajo se puede transformar de un tipo a otro, pero no se puede perder. Para ilustrar este principio se da el siguiente ejemplo de energía generada por una cascada.

El agua posee una *energía potencial*. Al desplazarse a gran velocidad en movimiento descendente arrastrada por la fuerza gravitacional, la energía potencial se transforma en *energía cinética*. La energía cinética de la cascada se puede aprovechar para accionar una turbina, la cual es un motor rotativo, creando de esta manera *energía rotativa*. Esta energía rotativa es suficiente para generar *energía eléctrica*, que a su vez se convierte en *energía luminosa* y *energía calorífica*, que se usan en las casas. La energía potencial inicial se transformó en cuatro formas distintas de energía.

EJERCICIO 3: FORMAS DE ENERGÍA

Instrucciones: Escriba una *C* en el espacio en blanco si el ejemplo indica energía cinética y *P* si indica energía potencial.

_____ **1.** un viento fuerte del oeste que sopla por toda la región

_____ **2.** un cartucho de dinamita sin explotar

EJERCICIO 4: TIPOS DE ENERGÍA

Instrucciones: Más abajo se definen cinco tipos de energía que pueden realizar un trabajo. Lea las definiciones y aplíquelas a las preguntas que siguen después.

energía nuclear: producida por la fisión de un átomo o la fusión de dos o más átomos

energía química: producida por la reacción de dos o más sustancias al combinarse

energía eléctrica: producida por una corriente eléctrica

energía solar: producida por el calor solar

energía vaporífica: producida por la presión del vapor

1. La energía producida por la fisión del núcleo de uranio 235 que se usa para generar electricidad es
   (1) energía nuclear.
   (2) energía química.
   (3) energía eléctrica.
   (4) energía solar.
   (5) energía vaporífica.

2. La energía producida por la combustión de la mezcla de gasolina y aire que impulsa a los automóviles es
   (1) energía nuclear.
   (2) energía química.
   (3) energía eléctrica.
   (4) energía solar.
   (5) energía vaporífica.

Máquinas simples

Una *máquina* es un artefacto que transmite fuerza o la multiplica. Se apoya en el principio de la aplicación de una fuerza pequeña a lo largo de una gran distancia para vencer una gran resistencia. La carretilla, la pata de cabra, la polea y el plano inclinado son máquinas simples. Las máquinas complejas están formadas por dos o más máquinas simples. La *palanca* es una máquina simple que se usa para realizar el trabajo de levantar un gran peso. La palanca es una barra rígida que puede girar alrededor de un punto fijo llamado *punto de apoyo*. Gracias a la palanca, un peso de mil libras, por ejemplo, se puede levantar con un esfuerzo (fuerza) relativamente pequeño.

LA PALANCA: UNA MÁQUINA SIMPLE

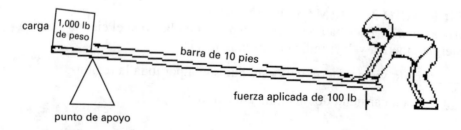

carga | 1,000 lb de peso

barra de 10 pies

fuerza aplicada de 100 lb

punto de apoyo

La ilustración de la página anterior indica que se necesitan 100 libras (lb) de fuerza para que una persona pueda levantar un peso de 1,000 libras situado a 1 pie del punto de apoyo cuando la barra de la palanca mide 10 pies de largo. Esto se puede expresar de la siguiente forma:

$$1,000 \text{ libras (lb)} \times 1 \text{ pies} = 100 \text{ libras (lb)} \times 10 \text{ pies}$$

En este caso, una fuerza relativamente pequeña (100 lb) aplicada a gran distancia del objeto (10 pies) es capaz de vencer una gran resistencia (1,000 lb). De acuerdo con este principio, cuanto mayor sea la distancia entre el punto de apoyo y la fuerza aplicada, menor será la fuerza necesaria para realizar el trabajo.

EJERCICIO 5: MÁQUINAS SIMPLES

Instrucciones: Elija la mejor respuesta para la siguiente pregunta.

Según el principio de que una fuerza pequeña aplicada a una gran distancia puede vencer una gran resistencia, ¿qué es probable que ocurra si se aumentara la longitud de la palanca de la ilustración a 20 pies y se mantuviera el mismo peso en el extremo de la barra?

(1) El esfuerzo para levantar el peso aumentaría a 150 libras de fuerza aplicada.
(2) El esfuerzo para levantar el peso seguiría siendo de 100 libras de fuerza aplicada.
(3) El esfuerzo se reduciría a la mitad, es decir, a 50 libras de fuerza aplicada.
(4) La resistencia que ofrece el peso se duplicaría.
(5) La resistencia que ofrece el peso se triplicaría.

La naturaleza del calor y la energía

Hoy sabemos que el *calor,* el cual es el resultado del movimiento aleatorio de las moléculas, no es más que energía. Una de las teorías físicas que ha contribuido en mayor medida a la comprensión del fenómeno del calor es la teoría cinética, teoría básica que explica cómo pueden existir los diferentes estados de la materia.

La teoría cinética de la materia

Según la *teoría cinética de la materia,* ésta puede existir en tres estados: sólido, líquido o gaseoso. El *plasma,* que constituye un cuarto estado, es un gas ionizado. El Sol, por ejemplo, está compuesto por plasma. La forma, o fase, de la materia está determinada por el movimiento de sus moléculas.

Los *sólidos* se componen de átomos o moléculas que poseen un movimiento limitado. Estos átomos o moléculas están en contacto directo entre sí, dejando de esta manera un espacio mínimo o nulo como para permitir un movimiento aleatorio. Las fuerzas de atracción de las partículas mantienen al sólido intacto y le proporcionan su forma y estructura definidas.

En los *líquidos,* los átomos o moléculas individuales pueden moverse y adoptar nuevas posiciones, proporcionando a esta forma de materia su fluidez. Las fuerzas de cohesión mantienen los líquidos intactos.

Los *gases* son sustancias donde los átomos o moléculas se encuentran en constante movimiento aleatorio. El movimiento, o energía cinética, aumenta al incrementarse la temperatura. A las moléculas no les es posible permanecer unidas; y esta propiedad proporciona a los gases la capacidad para fluir o expandirse hasta llenar el recipiente en que se colocan.

El calor, la temperatura y los estados de la materia

El estado de la materia depende de su contenido calorífico (de calor). La *temperatura* es la medida de la intensidad del calor. El cambio de la materia de un estado a otro implica la adición o sustracción de una cierta cantidad de calor por gramo de sustancia. Por ejemplo, a 32 grados Fahrenheit, el agua (líquido) se convierte en hielo (sólido). Por encima de los 32 grados Fahrenheit, el hielo (sólido) se convierte en agua (líquido). Por encima de los 212 grados Fahrenheit (punto de ebullición del agua), ésta (líquido) se convierte en vapor (gas). Las impurezas presentes en el agua pueden afectar su punto de congelación.

Ciertos materiales se expanden cuando se eleva su temperatura y se contraen cuando se baja la misma. Los líquidos se expanden de forma más perceptible que los sólidos, pero los gases se expanden incluso más. El termómetro de mercurio se basa en este principio.

La temperatura se puede medir en grados centígrados o en grados Fahrenheit. En la escala de grados centígrados (o grados Celsio), 0 grados representa el punto de congelación del agua, y 100 grados el punto de ebullición. En la escala Fahrenheit, 32 grados representa el punto de congelación del agua, y 212 grados el punto de ebullición. Mientras que la temperatura se mide en grados mediante un termómetro, el calor se mide en calorías o en BTU (siglas en inglés de la Unidad Térmica Británica). Una *caloría* es la cantidad de calor necesaria para aumentar en un grado centígrado la temperatura de un gramo de agua. BTU es la cantidad de calor necesaria para aumentar en un grado Fahrenheit la temperatura de una libra de agua.

EJERCICIO 6: TEORÍA CINÉTICA DE LA MATERIA

Instrucciones: Escriba una *V* en el espacio en blanco si la afirmación es verdadera y una *F* si es falsa.

_____ **1.** En los sólidos la estructura molecular es más rígida que en los gases.

_____ **2.** Un aumento en la temperatura hace que disminuya el movimiento molecular de un gas.

_____ **3.** Las moléculas de los líquidos que se mueven pasándose unas a otras proporcionan a los mismos su fluidez.

EJERCICIO 7: CALOR Y TEMPERATURA

Instrucciones: Lea el pasaje y conteste la pregunta que sigue.

Los distintos materiales se expanden a distintos grados de cambio de temperatura y en distintos porcentajes de su longitud, volumen o superficie. Cuando un material, como el asfalto que se usa en la construcción de carreteras, reacciona a los cambios de temperatura, se pandea (encorva) y se forman los baches. Ésta es una de las razones por las que se está extendiendo cada vez más el uso del hormigón armado (o concreto reforzado) en la construcción de carreteras y edificios altos de apartamentos.

El uso extendido del hormigón armado en la construcción sugiere que
(1) el hormigón y el acero se expanden y se contraen casi a la misma temperatura.
(2) el hormigón armado se expande a temperaturas mucho más altas que el asfalto ordinario y no se pandea.
(3) el hormigón armado no se expande ni se contrae en absoluto.
(4) 1 y 2
(5) 2 y 3

La naturaleza de las ondas

Una *onda* es una perturbación periódica o armónica en el espacio o a través de otro medio (agua, por ejemplo) por el que se transmite energía. El agua, el sonido y la luz se propagan en ondas. La iluminación que proporciona una lámpara proviene de las ondas de luz (que son una forma de ondas electromagnéticas); la música que emana de un equipo estereofónico proviene de las ondas de sonido; la energía para conservar los alimentos y calentarlos proviene de las ondas electromagnéticas; la energía para transmitir señales a un televisor proviene de las ondas de radio (otra forma de onda electromagnética); y la energía que proporciona a una cama de agua su movimiento sedante proviene de las ondas de agua.

Tipos de ondas y propiedades

Las ondas transmiten energía de diferentes formas; y todas las fases de la materia transmiten ondas. Como ejemplo de sólidos que transmiten *energía ondulatoria* (de ondas) se destacan los terremotos, que se producen cuando las rocas sometidas a presión se fracturan o se deslizan y cambian de posición. Las ondas que se sienten y se ven en el agua son ejemplos de un líquido que transmite energía ondulatoria. Los gases también transmiten energía ondulatoria, como sucede en el caso de una explosión, en que se generan ondas de calor, sonido y luz.

Las *ondas longitudinales* son aquéllas donde las partículas del medio vibran (se mueven en vaivén) en la misma dirección en que se propaga la onda. Como ejemplo de onda longitudinal se puede citar la onda sonora (de sonido) que se produce, por ejemplo, cuando se golpea un diapasón. En las *ondas transversales,* las partículas del medio vibran en dirección perpendicular a la dirección de propagación de la onda. Para ilustrar este tipo de onda tenemos el ejemplo de una piedra que se arroja a un estanque de aguas tranquilas. Asismismo, la luz se desplaza en ondas transversales.

La *cresta* es el punto de desplazamiento más alto de una onda, denominándose *seno* el punto de desplazamiento más bajo. Las crestas y los senos son observables a simple vista en las olas de agua. La *longitud de onda* se define como la distancia entre dos crestas de onda sucesivas o dos senos de onda sucesivos. La *frecuencia* de onda es el número de crestas de onda que pasan por un punto dado cada segundo. Por consiguiente, cuanto más corta sea la longitud de onda, mayor será la frecuencia. De hecho, la *velocidad de la onda* es igual a la longitud de onda multiplicada por la frecuencia.

ONDA SONORA

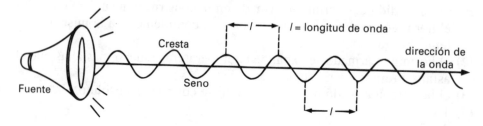

Ondas sonoras

Las *ondas sonoras,* como se puede apreciar arriba, son ondas longitudinales. Los tonos musicales se oyen cuando la onda tiene una frecuencia determinada. Cuanto menor sea la frecuencia, menor será el tono. Por ejemplo, la frecuencia de un altavoz de graves es menor que la de un *tweeter,* o altavoz de alta frecuencia.

La onda sonora es una onda de compresión. Se origina de una fuente como, por ejemplo, un altavoz de bocina. El altavoz vibra, comprimiendo el aire que hay frente al mismo y, como si fuera un resorte, lo empuja. A medida que pasa la onda, comprime las moléculas de aire. La sensación de que se oye se produce cuando estas ondas llegan al tímpano del oído. Las ondas sonoras se pueden propagar a través de sólidos, líquidos y gases. Incluso el cuerpo humano puede servir de medio para las ondas sonoras. Las *ondas ultrasónicas,* que son ondas de tono muy agudo, se emplean en la medicina moderna.

EJERCICIO 8: TIPOS DE ONDAS
Instrucciones: Escriba en el espacio en blanco una *L* si la afirmación se aplica a una onda longitudinal y una *T* si se aplica a una onda transversal.

_____ **1.** onda que se observa cuando se ata una cuerda larga por uno de sus extremos y se agita el extremo libre

_____ **2.** zumbido que se oye cuando una flecha sale disparada de un arco

_____ **3.** las olas que aparecen en la superficie del océano

EJERCICIO 9: PROPIEDADES DE LAS ONDAS
Instrucciones: Observe la ilustración y conteste la pregunta que sigue.

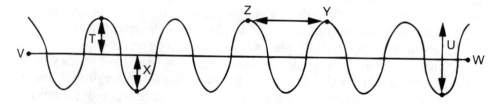

En la ilustración de la página anterior, ¿qué puntos se pueden usar para medir la longitud de onda?

(1) T e Y

(2) X e Y

(3) Z e Y

(4) V y W

(5) T, X y U

La naturaleza de la luz

Los físicos definen la *luz* como una forma de energía electromagnética que estimula las células sensoriales de la retina del ojo humano y produce la percepción de la visión. La energía electromagnética puede expresarse en rangos de longitud de onda a lo largo de un continuo, o espectro. La luz ocupa el centro del espectro electromagnético, que se extiende desde un extremo bajo (rayos gamma) a un extremo alto (ondas de radio). Los otros rayos que ocupan sectores del espectro electromagnético son los rayos X, los rayos ultravioleta y los rayos infrarrojos. Los rayos ultravioleta son invisibles y son los principales responsables del bronceado y de las quemaduras de la piel. Los objetos que irradian calor, como el Sol o los radiadores, emiten rayos infrarrojos que sólo se pueden detectar por medio de ciertos instrumentos muy sensibles.

EL ESPECTRO ELECTROMAGNÉTICO

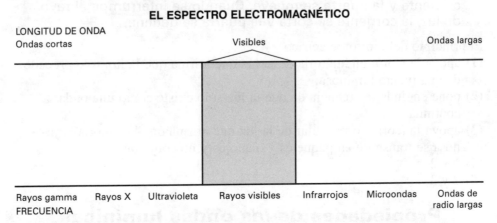

LONGITUD DE ONDA
Ondas cortas   Visibles   Ondas largas

Rayos gamma   Rayos X   Ultravioleta   Rayos visibles   Infrarrojos   Microondas   Ondas de radio largas
FRECUENCIA

El ojo humano reconoce como *colores* los rayos visibles del espectro. Por orden, estos colores son rojo, anaranjado, amarillo, azul, añil y violeta. Las longitudes de onda más cortas que podemos ver son las que llamamos violeta; las más largas son las que llamamos rojas.

Se han postulado dos teorías acerca de la naturaleza de la luz. Estas teorías, aparentemente contradictorias, se centran en realidad en diferentes propiedades de la luz. Según la *teoría ondulatoria* de la luz, la luz es energía luminosa emitida por una fuente de luz y se desplaza por el espacio en forma de onda transversal. Según la *teoría corpuscular* de la luz, la energía luminosa se radia (transmite) y se absorbe en forma de paquetes diminutos, o manojos, y no como ondas continuas. Los átomos y las moléculas son capaces de emitir y absorber la energía luminosa en cantidades específicas.

EJERCICIO 10: EL PRINCIPIO FOTOELÉCTRICO

Instrucciones: Lea el pasaje y conteste la pregunta que sigue.

El ojo eléctrico, o célula fotoeléctrica, es un mecanismo utilizado para abrir y cerrar puertas de garajes mediante la activación o interrupción de un rayo de luz. El principio del ojo eléctrico se basa en el llamado efecto fotoeléctrico. El efecto fotoeléctrico se produce cuando un rayo de luz incide sobre ciertos metales, expulsando electrones del metal y produciendo una corriente eléctrica.

El ojo eléctrico funciona de la siguiente manera: la luz que entra en el interior de una bombilla cubierta por una capa de una sustancia activa hace que se emitan electrones. Estos electrones son atraídos por un electrodo cargado positivamente situado en el centro de la bombilla, a modo de filamento. Cuando los electrones (partículas cargadas negativamente) son atraídos hacia las partículas cargadas positivamente del electrodo, se produce una corriente eléctrica. Se ha observado que los electrones sólo se liberan cuando se alcanza una determinada energía luminosa. La corriente puede controlarse entonces mediante cambios en la intensidad de la luz. Parece ser que los electrones sólo son capaces de absorber una cierta cantidad de luz en un momento dado. Cuando la luz da en el ojo eléctrico, se establece una corriente y la puerta se mueve. Cuando se interrumpe el rayo de luz, la corriente se corta y la puerta se detiene.

El principio del ojo fotoeléctrico
(1) apoya la teoría ondulatoria de la luz que afirma que la luz sólo procede de una fuente luminosa.
(2) pone en duda la creencia de que la luz sólo existe como una onda continua.
(3) apoya la teoría corpuscular de la luz que afirma que la energía luminosa se transmite en paquetes y manojos y no como ondas.
(4) 1 y 2
(5) 2 y 3

Propiedades de las ondas lumínicas

A continuación se presentan en forma resumida las propiedades de las ondas lumínicas (de luz):

reflexión: retorno angular de una onda lumínica que ocurre cuando incide sobre una superficie brillosa (ejemplo: la luz que rebota en un espejo)

refracción: cambio de dirección de las ondas lumínicas al pasar de un medio a otro (ejemplo: un palo sumergido en un vaso de agua que da la impresión de estar partido)

difracción: desviación de las ondas lumínicas según sus longitudes de onda al pasar cerca del borde de un obstáculo o a través de una pequeña abertura (ejemplo: el "arco iris" que se observa en un disco compacto al sujetarlo de lado contra luz blanca) *interferencia:* alteración del brillo de los rayos lumínicos que se produce cuando interfieren entre sí, ya sea reforzándose o anulándose mutuamente (ejemplo: al juntar los dedos pulgar e índice y mirar a través de la abertura a una luz brillante)

polarización: restricción de las ondas lumínicas a un plano determinado, ya sea horizontal o vertical (ejemplo: el efecto atenuante de los lentes polarizados)

EJERCICIO 11: PROPIEDADES DE LAS ONDAS LUMÍNICAS
Instrucciones: Aplique a las preguntas siguientes las definiciones de los cinco cambios que pueden sufrir las ondas de luz.

1. Una moneda que descansa en el fondo de una piscina estará realmente ubicada en un punto diferente de dónde el ojo percibe que está. Los rayos lumínicos procedentes de la moneda cambian de dirección al pasar del agua al aire. Esto demuestra la existencia de
   (1) reflexión.
   (2) refracción.
   (3) difracción.
   (4) interferencia.
   (5) polarización.

2. Los rayos lumínicos que inciden en una pieza brillosa de cromo parecen rebotar en su superficie. Esto demuestra la existencia de
   (1) reflexión.
   (2) refracción.
   (3) difracción.
   (4) interferencia.
   (5) polarización.

La naturaleza de la electricidad

La electricidad es otra de las formas de energía invisibles, pero vitales, de cuya importancia y presencia no nos solemos siempre percatar. Cuanto más urbanizados nos volvemos, más dependemos de la electricidad. La energía nuclear, a pesar de sus peligros potenciales, ha emergido como una fuente importante para la generación de energía eléctrica. Los físicos definen *electricidad* como la forma de energía que resulta del flujo de electrones libres—electrones débilmente enlazados a los átomos. La electricidad está íntimamente relacionada con la fuerza de atracción, es decir, el magnetismo.

El magnetismo y las cargas eléctricas

Los puntos de atracción ubicados en los extremos opuestos de un imán se denominan *polos.* Los imanes tienen un polo norte y un polo sur (también llamados positivo y negativo). Los polos opuestos de dos imanes distintos se atraen entre sí. Asimismo los polos iguales (dos polos norte o dos polos sur) se repelen. Al espacio que rodea al imán y donde actúan sus fuerzas de atracción se le llama *campo magnético.* Son pocos los materiales tanto naturales como artificiales que se pueden magnetizar (imantar): hierro, acero, níquel, cobalto y algunas aleaciones. A continuación se ofrece el diagrama de un imán.

IMÁN Y LÍNEAS DE FUERZA

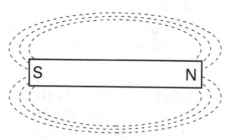

Líneas de fuerza magnéticas

Todas las sustancias magnéticas contienen *dominios,* es decir, grupos de moléculas que poseen fuerzas de atracción. Antes de magnetizada una sustancia, estos dominios se hallan distribuidos al azar de modo tal que el campo de un dominio es anulado por el campo de otro. Cuando se magnetiza una sustancia, los dominios se alinean paralelamente a las líneas de fuerza, con todos los polos norte orientados en la misma dirección. Esto ocasiona que se convierta en imán permanente aquellos materiales que tengan los dominios demasiado débiles como para volver a desorganizarse.

En la mayoría de los elementos, los átomos poseen un ligero campo magnético debido a que sus electrones se encuentran girando constantemente. Sin embargo, los campos se anulan entre sí porque los átomos giran y ruedan en direcciones diferentes. En los imanes, grupos enteros de átomos se alinean en una dirección y se aumentan mutuamente el efecto magnético en lugar de anularlo. Estas concentraciones magnéticas reciben el nombre de **dominios magnéticos.**

ÁTOMOS DE HIERRO IMANTADOS Y SIN IMANTAR

La electricidad estática y el magnetismo

La *electricidad estática* es una carga eléctrica estacionaria producida por la fricción de dos objetos, uno cargado positivamente y otro cargado negativamente. La electricidad estática se basa en el mismo principio que el magnetismo. El roce de los zapatos contra la alfombra hace que nuestro cuerpo se electrice. La sacudida que sentimos se produce cuando nuestro cuerpo negativamente cargado es neutralizado por la carga positiva del objeto que tocamos. Una vez realizado el contacto, nuestro cuerpo deja de estar cargado. La electricidad estática se almacena y no se mueve. El objeto cargado debe ponerse en contacto con otro objeto que tenga una carga opuesta para que se produzca una descarga eléctrica.

EJERCICIO 12: ELECTRICIDAD Y MAGNETISMO

Instrucciones: Elija la mejor respuesta para las preguntas que siguen. La primera pregunta está basada en el párrafo que se da a continuación.

La misma Tierra está rodeada por un campo magnético. Esto puede deberse a fuertes corrientes eléctricas presentes en el núcleo de la Tierra y a la rotación del planeta. El polo norte magnético está situado en Canadá; el polo sur magnético se encuentra ubicado casi en el punto opuesto, cerca de la Antártida. La fuerte atracción magnética que ejercen estos polos tienden a alinear la aguja de las brújulas en dirección norte-sur.

1. En base al pasaje anterior, los compases indican la dirección porque
   (1) toda la Tierra actúa como un imán.
   (2) los chinos descubrieron los polos magnéticos.
   (3) los griegos descubrieron los polos magnéticos.
   (4) existen vastos depósitos de hierro en Canadá.
   (5) la atracción magnética de la Tierra está aumentando.

2. ¿Cuál de los siguientes objetos sería atraído a cualquiera de los polos de un imán?
   (1) un trozo de aluminio
   (2) un trozo de latón
   (3) un trozo de estaño
   (4) un trozo de cobalto sin magnetizar
   (5) un trozo de cobalto magnetizado

Corrientes eléctricas

Los primeros científicos que realizaron experimentos con las cargas eléctricas descubrieron que estas cargas pueden desplazarse fácilmente a través de ciertos materiales llamados *conductores* (como los metales, las soluciones de sal, los ácidos y los gases calientes). Otros materiales (como el caucho), que no conducen las cargas en absoluto, se denominan *aislantes.*

Una carga eléctrica en movimiento crea una *corriente eléctrica.* En un conductor sólido, como el cable de alambre, la corriente se da como un flujo de electrones en movimiento. En un líquido o un gas, la corriente puede estar formada por átomos, o iones, positivamente o negativamente cargados.

Se puede comparar la corriente eléctrica que circula a través de un conductor sólido al caudal de agua que pasa por una tubería. La corriente eléctrica se desplaza lentamente, aproximadamente a una centésima de pulgada por segundo. Las luces se encienden de forma instantánea al accionar el interruptor porque los cables están siempre llenos de electrones, de la misma forma que las tuberías de agua están siempre llenas de agua.

Electroimanes

El *electroimán* consiste en un componente central de material magnético blando y un hilo conductor arrollado al componente central. Cuando se enciende un interruptor o se oprime un botón, se hace pasar a través del hilo conductor una corriente eléctrica para imantar el componente central. El dispositivo adquiere entonces la facultad de atraer objetos de hierro. Cuando se apaga el interruptor, se corta la atracción. Los electroimanes se emplean en los aparatos de radio y en los timbres de las puertas.

EJERCICIO 13: CONDUCTORES Y AISLANTES
Instrucciones: Escriba una *C* si el material es conductor eléctrico y una *A* si es aislante.

_____ **1.** cuero

_____ **2.** plata

_____ **3.** madera

_____ **4.** agua salada

_____ **5.** plástico

EJERCICIO 14: ELECTROIMANES
Instrucciones: Elija la mejor respuesta para la siguiente pregunta.

No sería recomendable colocar un aparato de radio que tenga un electro-imán potente cerca de los instrumentos de navegación de un avión o un barco porque
(1) el aparato de radio no funcionaría a causa de las interferencias eléctricas.
(2) el aparato de radio no se podría oír claramente a causa de la electricidad estática.
(3) la precisión de la brújula se vería afectada por el campo magnético creado por el electroimán del aparato de radio.
(4) el electroimán del aparato de radio haría que los instrumentos de navegación funcionaran mal.
(5) el aparato de radio consumiría mucha energía eléctrica, ocasionando la descarga del sistema eléctrico del barco o del avión.

PRUEBA 4: ARTE Y LITERATURA

La Prueba de Arte y Literatura del GED consta de fragmentos de prosa de aproximadamente 200 a 400 palabras, fragmentos de poesía de unos 8 a 25 versos, así como extractos de obras dramáticas. Cada pasaje viene seguido de preguntas de opción múltiple donde se le pedirá interpretar selecciones de literatura popular, literatura clásica y comentarios sobre arte y literatura. Para ello se habrá de comprender lo que se lee, aplicar la información a una nueva situación y analizar los elementos de estilo y estructura de los varios pasajes.

¿Cuántas preguntas hay en la prueba?

Hay 45 preguntas de opción múltiple y se dispone de 65 minutos para hacer la prueba. Cada pasaje de la prueba de literatura viene encabezado por una pregunta guía, cuyo objetivo principal es dirigir al estudiante en su lectura del fragmento. Refiérase a la Prueba Posterior del libro como ejemplo.

¿De qué consta la prueba?

La Prueba de Arte y Literatura del GED se puede dividir según las áreas de contenido que aborda y las destrezas que pone a prueba. El contenido de estas pruebas es el siguiente: Literatura Popular—50%; Literatura Clásica—25%; y Comentarios sobre Arte y Literatura—25%. Recuerde usted asimismo que lo que se va a poner a prueba es su capacidad para reflexionar sobre determinadas ideas y conceptos. Entre las destrezas de razonamiento que se van a poner a prueba figuran las siguientes: Comprensión de Ideas (Comprensión Literal e Inferencial)—60%; Aplicación de Ideas—15%; y Análisis de Ideas—25%.

1
LA NARRATIVA DE FICCIÓN

Los pasajes de *narrativa de ficción* que se presentan en las Pruebas de Arte y Literatura han sido extraídos de novelas o cuentos cortos y suelen describir personas y sucesos imaginarios que imitan la vida real. Las novelas y los cuentos cortos se escriben, por lo general, en *prosa*—lenguaje del habla cotidiana—y comparten técnicas y artificios literarios comunes. A pesar de compartir una serie de elementos propios de la narrativa de ficción, existen tres diferencias básicas entre la novela y el cuento corto.

La novela y el cuento corto

La *novela* es un relato de extensión considerable. El *novelista,* por lo general, escribe sobre una diversidad de personajes y sobre los sucesos que tienen lugar en sus vidas. El novelista hábil es capaz de fundir a los personajes, sus aventuras y sus problemas dentro de una trama principal.

El *cuento corto* también trata de personajes, lugares o acontecimientos imaginarios; pero, como su nombre lo indica, es menos extenso que la novela. Además de esto, los cuentos cortos se suelen centrar en un número menor de personajes así como en un único suceso. Al limitar su enfoque, el *cuentista* produce un solo efecto. El buen escritor va directamente al grano y desarrolla rápidamente unos personajes y sucesos verosímiles dentro de un espacio reducido que dispone para crear su obra de arte. Edgar Allan Poe, uno de los primeros y mejores escritores estadounidenses de cuentos cortos, opinaba que el cuento corto debía ser leído de una sentada, es decir, en horas y no en los días o semanas que puede llevar la lectura de una novela.

Aunque las novelas y los cuentos cortos se desarrollan en torno a personajes ficticios, los sucesos de la narración se basan a veces en hechos de la vida real. Éste suele ser el caso de las novelas históricas. Por ejemplo, *Lo que el viento se llevó,* una de las novelas más populares de este siglo, relata los acontecimientos acaecidos durante la Guerra Civil estadounidense.

Los elementos básicos de la narrativa de ficción se ilustran en el siguiente rompecabezas.

ELEMENTOS BÁSICOS DE LA NARRATIVA DE FICCIÓN
Novela y cuento corto

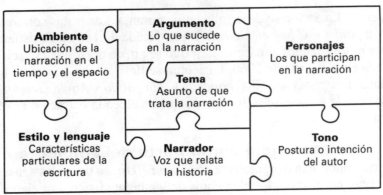

Ambiente
Ubicación de la narración en el tiempo y el espacio

Argumento
Lo que sucede en la narración

Personajes
Los que participan en la narración

Tema
Asunto de que trata la narración

Estilo y lenguaje
Características particulares de la escritura

Narrador
Voz que relata la historia

Tono
Postura o intención del autor

Ambiente: Ubicación de la narración en el tiempo y el espacio

El *ambiente* de un cuento corto o de una novela comprende el tiempo, el lugar, las circunstancias y la atmósfera en que se lleva a cabo la acción. Algunos autores son muy explícitos en lo que al ambiente respecta e informan desde el principio de la obra cuándo y dónde se desarrolla la narración:

> *Ejemplos:* Llegó a caballo a St. Louis en el ardor de un mediodía del mes de agosto de 1875.
>
> El vehículo completó su órbita antes de aterrizar en la superficie de la Luna. Era el año 2021 de nuestra era.

Inferir el tiempo y el lugar

En muchos relatos, el tiempo y el lugar no están dados de forma explícita. El lector ha de leer entre líneas o buscar pistas que hagan referencia a un determinado lugar en el tiempo y el espacio. Lea el siguiente párrafo e intente inferir el ambiente. Subraye todas las pistas que sugieran el *tiempo* (cuándo se desarrolla la acción) y el *lugar* (dónde se desarrolla la acción).

> James ensilló el poni y condujo a la recién adquirida mascota hasta el costado del porche. Luego se detuvo y ató las riendas al tractor y le puso un gran lazo rojo a la brida.
>
> Ayer había comprado la montura, las riendas y la brida en unos grandes almacenes que hay en Helena. Había planeado esta sorpresa con mucho cuidado.
>
> El sol apenas había salido cuando Angie, descalza y todavía vestida en camisón, salió por la vieja puerta de tela metálica y pudo oír cómo su padre decía: "¡Feliz décimo cumpleaños, mi amor!"

1. ¿La acción se desarrolla en una ciudad o en una granja? ¿Qué detalles nos lo indican?
2. ¿La acción se desarrolla en la década de 1860 o en la década de 1960? ¿Qué detalles nos lo indican?
3. ¿La acción se desarrolla a primera hora en la mañana o al caer la tarde? ¿Qué detalles nos lo indican?
4. ¿La acción se desarrolla en Montana o en New Jersey? ¿Qué detalles nos lo indican?

[Respuestas: La acción se desarrolla en una granja. Las pistas son *tractor, ensilló al poni* y *que hay en Helena.* En la década de 1860 no existían los tractores ni los grandes almacenes, así que se puede decir que la acción se desarrolla en la década de 1960. La acción se lleva a cabo a primera hora en la mañana. Las pistas son *El sol apenas había salido* y *Angie, descalza y todavía vestida en camisón.* El lugar en que se ubica la narración es Montana (Helena)].

La atmósfera como parte del ambiente

Una parte importante del ambiente es la *atmósfera,* es decir, las sensaciones y emociones asociadas a los elementos del ambiente físico. Por ejemplo, si el relato se inicia en un ambiente de noche tormentosa de rayos y truenos, con un castillo y un hombre que avanza hacia la puerta, el autor está creando una atmósfera de misterio y suspenso. Sin embargo, si el inicio de la historia se sitúa en un ambiente mañanero con niños que juegan alegremente en los columpios, la atmósfera es de bullicio y desenfado.

LAS RESPUESTAS A LOS EJERCICIOS DE ESTE CAPÍTULO EMPIEZAN EN LA PÁGINA 460.

EJERCICIO 1: LA ATMÓSFERA COMO PARTE DEL AMBIENTE

Instrucciones: Lea el pasaje e indique qué elementos ayudan a crear una atmósfera de miedo.

¿CÓMO SE SIENTE ESTE HOMBRE?

"Tengo que esconderme" —se dijo a sí mismo. Su pecho palpitaba mientras esperaba agazapado en la esquina oscura del vestíbulo. Estaba cansado de correr y huir. Si no encontraba un lugar para esconderse, no tendría más remedio que entregarse. Un auto de la policía pasó como un silbido bajo la lluvia mientras su sirena sonaba cada vez más fuerte. "Me están buscando por todas partes. . ." Se acercó sigilosamente a la puerta y miró por el cristal lleno de vaho entrecerrando los ojos. Se quedó agarrotado cuando la sirena elevó su tono y acabó disipándose en la distancia.

"Sí, tengo que esconderme, ¿pero dónde?"

Apretó los dientes. Entonces, un repentino movimiento en la calle atrajo su atención. . .

—RICHARD WRIGHT: *El hombre que vivía escondido.* (Fragmento)

Personajes: Los que participan en la narración

Los *personajes* de las novelas y los cuentos cortos son, por lo general, ficticios. Cada escritor utiliza una variedad de recursos para dar vida a personajes ficticios que parezcan reales y creíbles. Entre los métodos de que se puede valer el escritor en la creación de sus personajes figuran los citados a continuación. La obra puede: describir el personaje y narrar sus acciones, revelar la forma de expresarse que tiene el personaje, revelar lo que otros personajes dicen acerca de ese personaje y revelar los pensamientos íntimos del personaje.

El diálogo como recurso para la creación de personajes

El *diálogo* es la conversación que se entabla entre los personajes de un relato. El escritor emplea la raya larga (—) para indicar que la cita inserida entre las rayas son palabras textuales del personaje. El poder citar lo que dice el personaje permite al escritor revelar la actitud, los sentimientos y la verdadera personalidad del personaje a través del personaje mismo y no por medio de una descripción por parte del autor. La raya larga se utiliza en este tipo de discurso, llamado ***discurso directo*** porque cita lo dicho por el personaje sin parafrasearlo, es decir, sin emplear un ***discurso indirecto.*** Por lo general, el autor anuncia o señala la transición de narración a discurso directo o viceversa mediante acotaciones del tipo "dijo él", "repuso ella", "contestó", etc. En las siguientes oraciones se puede apreciar la diferencia entre el discurso indirecto (paráfrasis o relato de lo dicho por un personaje) y el directo (reproducción literal de lo pronunciado por el personaje).

Discurso indirecto: Ella me dijo que me llamaría para hacer una cita.
Discurso directo: —Te llamaré para hacer una cita —dijo ella.

En conversaciones más extensas, se suelen omitir las acotaciones del tipo "dijo él" o "preguntó ella" en cada intervención de los personajes. Obsérvese en el fragmento que sigue que a los interlocutores se los identifica sólo una vez al principio del diálogo:

—¿En qué le puedo servir? —preguntó solícito el vendedor de autos.
—Estoy buscando un auto usado, pero a un precio bien económico —repuso Jill.
—¡Estoy seguro de que encontraremos algo dentro de su presupuesto! Venga por aquí, por favor. Le mostraré nuestros modelos más nuevos. Tenemos unos que son una belleza. . .
—Pero. . . recuerde que no tengo mucho dinero: sólo unos cuantos cientos de dólares.
—Pues, venga por este lado y le muestro algunos de nuestros modelos más antiguos y accesibles".

Argumento: Lo que sucede en la narración

Los sucesos que se llevan a cabo en una narración forman el ***argumento*** (o ***trama***) del relato. Los sucesos se producen en orden cronológico, es decir que siguen una secuencia temporal lógica. A modo de práctica, ordene cronológicamente los acontecimientos del argumento que se citan abajo numerándolos del 1 al 5. Observe la relación causa-efecto entre los mismos.

_____ **a.** Luego, mientras me informaba sobre el asunto, se puso a la venta una pequeña tienda de artesanías y decidimos poner manos a la obra.

_____ **b.** Durante muchos años, mis hermanas y yo habíamos hablado sobre la posibilidad de montar nuestro propio negocio.

_____ **c.** Enseguida nos pusimos en contacto con un agente inmobiliario para ver cómo se podía comprar la tienda.

_____ **d.** Toda la familia estuvo presente observando con orgullo a los trabajadores fuera de la tienda mientras levantaban un letrero que decía "Agujas y alfileres".

_____ **e.** Con eso en mente, me puse primero a leer artículos sobre cómo establecer una "empresa familiar", pues estábamos considerando la idea de abrir una tienda en una de nuestras casas.

[Respuesta: **a.** 3, **b.** 1, **c.** 4, **d.** 5, **e.** 2]

Las escenas retrospectivas como parte del argumento

Hay autores que prefieren presentar los acontecimientos fuera de su orden cronológico normal. Una de las técnicas más utilizadas en este tipo de presentación es la llamada *escena retrospectiva (o "flashback").* Por ejemplo, tanto en una novela como en una película se puede presentar una voz que dice: "Todo comenzó hace quince años, cuando la pareja se conoció. . ." El relato pasa entonces a otra escena, quince años antes. Los eventos progresan en secuencia temporal hasta que, hacia el final de la historia, los personajes regresan al tiempo y lugar de la escena inicial.

Partes del argumento

Los acontecimientos que conforman el argumento se pueden agrupar y clasificar según la función que desempeñan en el relato. En el diagrama siguiente se ilustran las cuatro partes básicas en que se divide el argumento: presentación, nudo, clímax y desenlace.

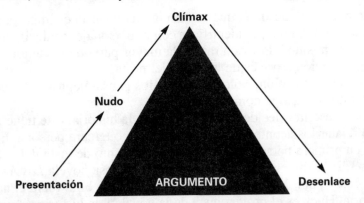

La *presentación* se refiere a la información básica que "allana el terreno" al relato. El *nudo,* o conflicto entre fuerzas o personajes opuestos, es el motor del argumento. La mayoría de los cuentos y novelas se desenvuelven en torno a uno de los siguientes tipos de conflictos:

El individuo contra sí mismo: luchas internas que se libran dentro del personaje cuando trata de decidir qué paso dar: cambiar de trabajo, divorciarse, tener hijos, confesarle a alguien la verdad sobre algo

El individuo contra otro: desavenencias entre personajes

El individuo contra la sociedad: luchas contra las reglas, convenciones o presiones que surgen de la convivencia social

El individuo contra la naturaleza y otras fuerzas: luchas contra las fuerzas que escapan al control del personaje, como los terremotos u otros desastres naturales, o fuerzas abstractas como las fuerzas del mal.

Otro de los elementos que integran el argumento es el *clímax,* o punto de mayor intensidad dentro de la trama. El clímax de la historia se produce cuando el conflicto alcanza su punto culminante. Por ejemplo, el clímax de muchas novelas del Oeste se da cuando el héroe y el villano se enfrentan cara a cara en un duelo con pistolas. El clímax no se produce siempre al final del relato, pero se suele dar en la última parte. Todos los sucesos y conflictos relacionados con los personajes deben aflorar y ser puestos en evidencia antes de que puedan alcanzar el clímax. Las novelas de misterio presentan un clímax muy obvio. Todas las piezas encajan para dar respuesta a la pregunta de "¿Quién lo hizo?" Inmediatamente después del clímax, se unen todos los cabos sueltos y el lector se entera del resultado del conflicto, conocido como *desenlace* (que, por lo general, suele coincidir con el final de la historia).

Narrador: Voz que relata la historia

Cuando usted lee una obra de ficción, pregúntese a sí mismo desde qué perspectiva, o con qué punto de vista, se está relatando la historia. En otras palabras, pregúntese quién es el *narrador,* es decir, la voz que realiza la narración. El autor tiene a su disposición una amplia variedad de formas para realizar el relato. Por ejemplo, si tuviéramos que escribir un relato sobre un juego de baloncesto, podríamos elegir entre distintos puntos de vista: el entrenador, un aficionado, un jugador del equipo puntero o un jugador reserva.

El punto de vista desde el que se cuenta una historia es importante porque el lector se tiene que identificar con el personaje, es decir, "ponerse en el lugar del mismo". Por esta razón, la mayor parte de los autores realizan la narración a través de los ojos del protagonista: el personaje a quien más afecta la acción. Sólo se revelan los pensamientos del mismo cuando el autor lo escoge como narrador.

Cuando el escritor decide quién va a narrar la historia, éste tiene la opción de relatar los acontecimientos en primera o tercera persona. En la narración en primera persona, se habla desde el punto de vista del "yo" y el narrador se dirige directamente al lector. En la famosa novela *Las Aventuras de Huckleberry Finn,* Mark Twain optó por que Huck Finn fuera el narrador de la historia. Huck es el protagonista de la novela y la historia se cuenta a través de sus palabras.

En la narración en tercera persona, la historia se cuenta por medio de un "observador", es decir una persona "de fuera" que no participa en la acción. El narrador utiliza la tercera persona para referirse al protagonista. Este punto de vista puede presentar distintos matices, dependiendo de cuánto quiere el autor que sepan los lectores y el protagonista.

El siguiente fragmento ha sido extraído de un cuento corto de Ernest Hemingway, "La vida corta y feliz de Francis Macomber". Hemingway relata las actividades del cazador y los pensamientos del león cuando le disparan. Se puede ver que la narración está hecha en tercera persona porque Hemingway usa *él* para referirse a Macomber y al león.

EJERCICIO 2: IDENTIFICAR AL NARRADOR

Instrucciones: Subraye todos los nombres (v. gr.: Macomber) y pronombres (v. gr.: él, su o ellos), que representan a personas. Encierre en círculo los nombres o pronombres que se refieran al león. Los dos primeros ejercicios fueron contestados a modo de ejemplo.

¿CÓMO SE SIENTE EL LEÓN?

Macomber salió por la curvada abertura lateral del asiento delantero y puso los pies en el suelo. El león estaba todavía allí mirando majestuosa y fríamente hacia el objeto del que sólo veía la silueta, y cuyo volumen era como el de un enorme rinoceronte. El viento no llevaba hasta sus fosas nasales el olor de hombre y tenía los ojos fijos en aquella forma, moviendo un poco su enorme cabeza de un lado a otro.

Luego, mientras miraba hacia aquel objeto, sin temor alguno, pero dudando antes de decidirse a bajar a beber a la ribera con una cosa semejante frente a él, vio destacarse del conjunto la figura de un hombre, y dando vuelta rápidamente, corrió a acogerse al abrigo de los árboles. En aquel momento, oyó un estampido seco y sintió el golpe de una sólida bala 30–36 de 150 gramos, que le mordía el flanco y la ardiente y repugnante brecha abierta en su estómago. Trotó, sintiendo las patas pesadas, y con su enorme panza herida, corrió por entre los árboles a buscar refugio en las altas hierbas. Nuevamente, el estampido volvió a alcanzarlo y pasó a su lado desgarrando el aire. Luego estalló una vez más y entonces sintió el golpe en sus costillas inferiores y la boca se le llenó de pronto de sangre caliente y espumosa. Galopó hacia los altos pastos donde podría ocultarse aplastado contra el suelo y lograr que esa cosa se acercara para saltarle encima y cazar al hombre que la llevaba.

Tema: Asunto de que trata la narración

Detrás de toda obra escrita o cinematográfica yace la intención del escritor o el director. En la mayoría de los casos, el creador de una obra determinada quiere que ésta transmita un significado a su público. La idea principal, o *tema,* puede ser una tesis sobre la vida, un punto de vista sobre un tema social, el abordaje o análisis de un problema antiguo a partir de una nueva perspectiva, o bien la expresión de opiniones ya sea positivas o negativas sobre la naturaleza humana.

Tanto en las obras de ficción que han tenido éxito, como en las películas de resultado eficaz, raramente se expresa el tema de forma directa. Éste es más bien un mensaje tácito que se implica o sugiere. Se espera por tanto que el lector o espectador capte e interprete el sentido en base a los elementos presentados. Por ejemplo, desde principios de los años 50, muchos de los escritores de ciencia ficción y de los directores de cine nos han presentado historias acerca de extraterrestres venidos a nuestro planeta. Uno de los más típicos argumentos es el de los extraterrestres que intentan apoderarse de la Tierra. Por lo general, hay un ser humano que encabeza una rebelión contra los invasores. El tema, en este caso, es el temor a lo desconocido.

EJECICIO 3: DEDUCIR EL TEMA

Instrucciones: Lea el pasaje y elija la mejor respuesta para cada una de las respuestas que siguen.

¿QUÉ PREOCUPA A LA SRTA. STRANGEWORTH?

Después de pensarlo durante un minuto, ella optó por escribir otra carta, quizás dirigida a la Sra. Harper, como continuación de las que ya había enviado por correo. Esta vez eligió una hoja de color verde y escribió apresuradamente: ¿SE HA ENTERADO YA DE QUÉ SE REÍAN TODOS CUANDO SE FUE USTED DEL CLUB DE BRIDGE EL JUEVES? ¿O ES QUE LA ESPOSA ES SIEMPRE LA ÚLTIMA EN ENTERARSE?

A la Srta. Strangeworth no le interesaban nunca los hechos: sus cartas trataban más bien de asuntos que giraban en torno a sospechas. El Sr. Lewis no hubiera imaginado nunca que su nieto podría estar robando pequeñas cantidades de dinero de la caja registradora de la tienda si no hubiese recibido una de las cartas de la Srta. Strangeworth. La Srta. Chandler, la bibliotecaria, y los padres de Linda Stewart seguirían viviendo sus vidas sin ningún tipo de sospecha, sin haber sabido nunca que el mal estaba acechando muy cerca, si la Srta. Strangeworth no les hubiera mandado sendas cartas abriéndoles los ojos. La Srta. Strangeworth habría quedado genuinamente horrorizada si *en verdad* hubiera habido algo entre Linda Stewart y el hijo de Harris, pero siempre que el mal anduviera sin control por el mundo, era el deber de la Srta. Strangeworth el mantener al pueblo alerta.

—SHIRLEY JACKSON: *La posibilidad de mal.* (Fragmento)

1. En este pasaje, el nudo o conflicto está dado por la Srta. Strageworth y
   (1) la naturaleza.
   (2) el Sr. Harper.
   (3) ella misma.
   (4) la sociedad.
   (5) un mal imaginario.

2. Elija entre las siguientes afirmaciones aquélla que exprese mejor el tema del pasaje.
   (1) Es deber de los ciudadanos el juzgar la conducta de los demás.
   (2) Lo que la gente desconoce no puede hacerles daño.
   (3) Sea cual fuere la intención, hay personas que hacen sufrir a otras.
   (4) No es importante tener conocimiento de todos los hechos cuando se hace una acusación.
   (5) No se debe pertenecer a una organización si se tiene algo que ocultar.

Tono y estilo

Tono: Postura o intención del autor

El *tono* de una novela o de un cuento corto es la actitud general que el autor transmite al tema. Cuando oímos a alguien hablar, podemos deducir la actitud de esa persona según el tono de su voz. El tono nos indica si la persona está siendo sarcástica, si habla con seriedad o bien si pretende ser cómica. Cuando se lee, es necesario inferir el tono del autor.

La elección que hace el autor en su utilización de las palabras y las frases es un reflejo de su actitud. ¿Qué tono presenta el párrafo siguiente? Describa con varios adjetivos el tono de este pasaje.

Nuestro primer hijo, "Matt el Comilón", era un bebé desenfrenado, enorme y constantemente hambriento. A medida que iba creciendo, parecía que los demás niños eran enanos a su lado. ¡Su primera palabra fue *torta* y su primer paso lo dio en dirección al refrigerador! ¡Cómo le gustaba comer a ese niño!

[Respuesta: Por ejemplo: El tono utilizado por el escritor en este fragmento es divertido, jocoso, cómico, desenfadado, nostálgico o burlón. El autor es un padre de familia que realiza una visión retrospectiva de su hijo, el cual tenía unos hábitos alimenticios memorables. El tono no es de tristeza ni de resentimiento, sino de alegre rememoración de experiencias cariñosas y al mismo tiempo humorísticas de la niñez de "Matt el Comilón".]

EJERCICIO 4: TONO Y PERSONAJES

Instrucciones: Lea el pasaje y conteste las preguntas que siguen.

¿CUÁL ES EL TONO DEL AUTOR?

El doctor le había dicho a la mamá de Julian que tenía que perder veinte libras para bajar su presión arterial; así que los miércoles por la noche Julian tenía que llevarla en autobús al centro de la ciudad para que asistiera a unas clases de reducción de peso. La clase de reducción estaba diseñada para mujeres mayores de 50 años que pesaran de 165 a 200 libras. Su madre era una de las más esbeltas, pero afirmaba que las señoras no tienen que decir ni su edad ni su peso. Ella nunca tomaba el autobús sola por la noche desde que habían sido integrados; y, como la clase de reducción era uno de sus pocos placeres, necesarios para su salud y, además, *gratis,* decía que lo menos que podía hacer Julian era llevarla, considerando todo lo que ella había hecho por él. A Julian no le gustaba considerar todo lo que ella había hecho por él, pero todos los miércoles por la noche se preparaba y la llevaba.

—FLANNERY O'CONNOR: *Todo lo que se eleva tiene que converger.* (Fragmento)

1. "Ella. . . decía que lo menos que podía hacer Julian era llevarla, considerando todo lo que ella había hecho por él. A Julian no le gustaba considerar todo lo que ella había hecho por él, pero todos los miércoles por la noche se preparaba y la llevaba". Si el autor leyera estas líneas, ¿con qué tono de voz lo haría?
   (1) amable y tolerante
   (2) enojado y amargo
   (3) trágico y deprimido
   (4) sarcástico y divertido
   (5) dulce y resignado

2. La actitud que manifiesta el autor hacia personas como la madre de Julian parece decirnos que las personas de este tipo
   (1) son ridículas y hay que burlarse de ellas.
   (2) deben ser respetadas por sus ideales.
   (3) deben ser toleradas y dignas de simpatía.
   (4) poseen una opinión completamente errónea de la vida.
   (5) son moralmente superiores a las demás personas.

Estilo y lenguaje: Características peculiares de la escritura

El *estilo* se refiere al modo único y particular que tiene cada autor de expresarse, de hacer uso del lenguaje: la elección de vocablos que realiza, la manera en que construye y distribuye las oraciones, etc. Según su estilo, el autor puede preferir oraciones largas y complejas, o valerse de un lenguaje más corriente y cotidiano, o bien emplear un lenguaje dialectal.

Tipos de estilo

Los autores que se han convertido en clásicos de la literatura deben su fama tanto a su estilo como a sus temas y personajes. Por ejemplo, Hemingway es conocido por su estilo terso y lacónico. A Charles Dickens, por su parte, se lo conoce por un estilo narrativo caracterizado por oraciones largas y vívidas descripciones. Edgar Allan Poe empleaba oraciones cortas, utilizaba la repetición y usaba en abundancia los guiones, los signos de interjección y la tipografía cursiva para inyectar emoción e intriga a sus historias. En su conocido cuento "El corazón delator", Poe comienza el relato como sigue: "¡Es verdad! ¡He estado y estoy, nervioso, muy, muy nervioso! Pero, ¿por qué dices que estoy loco?. . ."

EJERCICIO 5: IDENTIFICAR EL ESTILO DEL AUTOR

Instrucciones: Lea el pasaje y subraye todas las descripciones e imágenes que evocan los sentidos: vista, olfato, gusto, tacto y, en particular, el oído.

¿QUÉ IMÁGENES TRATA DE PLASMAR EL ESCRITOR?

El chirrido de ruedas de carreta que lanzó la soprano castigó mis oídos. El sol que se filtraba por las persianas llenó la habitación de una sulfurosa luz. No sabía por cuánto tiempo había dormido, pero sentí un leve temblor de agotamiento.

La cama gemela que había junto a la mía estaba vacía y sin hacer.

A las siete había oído cómo mi madre se levantaba, se ponía rápidamente la ropa y salía en puntillas de la habitación. Luego pude oír el zumbido del exprimidor de naranjas que venía de la planta baja, y sentir el olor a café y tocino que se colaba por debajo de la puerta. Luego, el agua del fregadero salió del grifo y los platos tintinearon cuando mi madre los secó y los puso en el armario.

Luego, la puerta principal se abrió y se cerró. Luego se abrió y se cerró la puerta del garaje; el motor del auto hizo brum-brum y, avanzando con un crujir de grava, se perdió en la distancia.

—SYLVIA PLATH: *La campana de cristal.* (Fragmento)

Figuras retóricas y elementos de estilo

Las *figuras retóricas* son recursos de que se vale la lengua para hacer más efectivo o expresivo el mensaje que desea comunicar. Su interpretación no puede ser literal. Aunque pasan desapercibidas, las figuras retóricas se oyen continuamente en el lenguaje diario. En las obras de ficción, se usa un lenguaje figurativo para crear imágenes vívidas y descripciones originales. Existen numerosos tipos de figura retórica. En literatura, especialmente en poesía, se pueden encontrar figuras retóricas como el símil, la metáfora y la personificación. Veamos brevemente en qué consiste cada una de éstas:

El *símil* es una comparación que indica una semejanza entre dos cosas diferentes. El símil realiza la comparación por medio de las siguientes expresiones: *como, así, cual, igual que, más/menos que, parecer, semejar, etc.*

Ejemplos: Su cabello *relucía* como una madeja de hilos de oro.
Ella es *más* fría *que* el hielo.
Bill estaba furioso *cual* toro embravecido.

La *metáfora* es una comparación que omite esos nexos entre los elementos que se comparan (*como, cual, así, etc.*). La metáfora da a entender que una cosa es otra.

Ejemplos: Era un volcán de pasiones a punto de estallar.
Sus labios escarlatas de púrpura maldita.

La *personificación* atribuye rasgos o cualidades humanas a animales o cosas.

Ejemplos: El sol me sonrió.
Las hojas despertaron y dieron la bienvenida a la nueva estación.

Cómo leer las obras de ficción por su cuenta

Aunque el análisis de cada uno de los elementos de ficción contribuye a la comprensión del texto, es el *todo*, no las *partes*, lo que hace a una obra de arte. Las sugerencias que damos a continuación le servirán de guía en su lectura de obras de literatura.

GUÍA PARA LA LECTURA DE OBRAS DE FICCIÓN

Cuando se lee una obra, conviene hacerse las siguientes preguntas:

- ¿Dónde se ambienta la obra?
- ¿Cómo es la atmósfera?
- ¿Quiénes son los personajes?
- ¿Se nombra o se describe a los personajes?
- ¿Cuál es el argumento?
- ¿Dónde está el nudo?
- ¿Quién realiza la narración?
- ¿Qué elementos de la obra indican el tema?
- ¿Cómo es el estilo del autor?
- ¿Qué tono emplea el autor?

La ficción en prosa: Comentario

A veces resulta útil leer las críticas literarias de obras de ficción. La **crítica** es el arte de evaluar y analizar una obra de arte o de literatura. El **crítico** es una persona que expresa una opinión o hace un comentario sobre una obra de arte o de literatura.

Los críticos literarios analizan un trabajo determinado en lo que se refiere al ambiente, el argumento, los personajes, el tema, el tono, así como el estilo y el lenguaje. Ellos leen obras de ficción y de no ficción, al igual que piezas dramáticas y se preguntan, por ejemplo: "¿Cómo creó la historia el autor?" u "¿Obtuvo el autor un resultado feliz?"

Los críticos escriben comentarios generales sobre obras de ficción y no ficción en columnas de periódicos o revistas. También comentan películas de cine, programas de televisión, representaciones teatrales, exposiciones de arte, conciertos en vivo o grabados, y obras de ballet.

Aproximadamente la cuarta parte de las preguntas de la Prueba de Arte y Literatura tiene que ver con comentarios. El **comentario** es un juicio *acerca de* una obra de arte o de literatura: opiniones, análisis y críticas.

EJERCICIO 6: COMENTARIOS SOBRE FICCIÓN

Instrucciones: A continuación se presenta la crítica de una novela que habla un poco sobre la autora y su carrera, los acontecimientos principales del argumento del libro y la opinión del crítico acerca del libro. Lea la crítica y conteste las preguntas que siguen.

La historia se repite
Anne Whitehouse
Crítica de *La última habitación* de Elean Thomas
Virago/Trafalgar Square, edición en rústica, $13.95

La última habitación, primera novela de la escritora jamaiquina Elean Thomas, trata de dos generaciones de madres e hijas. Valerie Barton, apodada Putus, ("que significa dulce y especial"), es hija única en quien sus padres han depositado toda su esperanza. Como dice su madre: "Tú va sé la que va rompé la cadena de la clavitú pá siempre". Pero el padre de Putus muere, su madre se vuelve a casar y la niña es enviada a otro sitio. Ésta entabla amistad con un hombre mayor y queda embarazada. Es tan joven e ingenua que no se da cuenta de que esta situación representa el final de sus sueños. La historia se repite cuando Putus abandona a su propia hija, Icylane, en Jamaica, para ir junto a un hombre en Inglaterra con el que se va a casar. Transcurren dieciocho años. La historia continúa con Icy, que ahora es funcionaria del estado y va a Inglaterra en busca de la madre que la abandonó y que, según dicen, está enferma. A lo largo de la novela, la Srta. Thomas hace un uso generoso del dialecto de la isla adjuntándose en el libro un glosario de expresiones jamaiquinas. El hilo del relato se resiente un tanto con la ruptura algo desconcertante entre las historias de Putus e Icy: uno preferiría seguir la vida de Putus como mujer joven en lugar de volver a ella unas décadas después, cuando apenas quedan vestigios de su orgullo y su ira. Con todo, *La última habitación* es una novela conmovedora de esperanza y desilusión, de expectativas y fracaso.

1. ¿Qué opina el crítico del relato?
   (1) El lenguaje dialectal no es muy inteligible.
   (2) El enfoque debió haber quedado en Putus.
   (3) Icy es el mejor personaje del libro.
   (4) Los personajes deberían quedarse en Jamaica.
   (5) El hilo del relato se resiente porque se ambienta en Inglaterra.

2. ¿Qué afirmación expresa mejor la opinión del crítico acerca de la autora?
   (1) Es una buena narradora.
   (2) Es una escritora novicia.
   (3) Su escritura es algo confusa.
   (4) No conoce bien Jamaica.
   (5) No conoce bien Inglaterra.

3. ¿Dentro de qué categoría encajaría *La última habitación*?
   (1) escritura humorística
   (2) detectives y misterios
   (3) ciencia ficción
   (4) drama de la vida real
   (5) romance desenfadado

2
LA POESÍA

La *poesía* expresa ideas y emociones de una forma más concisa, controlada y estructurada, seleccionando aquellas expresiones y construcciones que sean más eficaces para la comunicación del mensaje de la obra. La poesía es un texto comprimido y compacto. La *imaginería* (conjunto de imágenes verbales que evocan los cinco sentidos) y las *figuras retóricas* permiten que el poeta exprese sus ideas con economía de palabras.

En algunos poemas hay **rima,** es decir, repetición de un sonido final en dos o más palabras, como *luna* y *cuna*. La **musicalidad** y el **ritmo** ("compás") avivan los sentidos y suscitan pensamientos. Todas estas características de la poesía hacen de ella un género literario bien diferenciado en la mayoría de los casos. En la Prueba de Arte y Literatura, se habrá de demostrar que se comprende el sentido de los poemas que se presenten. Los examinados habrán de leer e interpretar el poema para poder contestar las preguntas que siguen.

> **LAS RESPUESTAS DE LOS EJERCICIOS DE ESTE CAPÍTULO EMPIEZAN EN LA PÁGINA 461.**

EJERCICIO 1: INTERPRETAR DOS POEMAS

Instrucciones: Lea cada uno de los poemas y conteste las preguntas que siguen.

¿QUÉ DICEN LOS POETAS Y CÓMO LO DICEN?
Ah, cuando de ti estaba enamorado

Ah, cuando de ti estaba enamorado,
    Entonces era hombre limpio y valiente,
Y por millas en derredor quedaban maravillados
    ¡Qué honesto fui y qué decente!

Y ahora que la fascinación se ha ido,
    Y que todo se ha borrado,
Y por millas en derredor dicen que se ha oído
    Que a mi antigua forma he regresado.

                    —A.E. HOUSEMAN

Soneto

Un soneto me manda a hacer Violante,
en mi vida me he visto en tal aprieto;
catorce versos dicen que es soneto;
burla burlando, van los tres delante.

Yo pensé que no hallara consonante,
y estoy en la mitad de otro cuarteto;
mas si me veo en el primer terceto,
no hay cosa en los cuartetos que me espante.

Por el primer terceto voy entrando,
y aun parece que entré con pie derecho,
pues fin con este verso le estoy dando.

Ya estoy en el segundo, y aun sospecho
que estoy los trece versos acabando.
contad si son catorce, y ya está hecho.

—LOPE DE VEGA

1. El tema del primer poema se centra en
   (1) la separación.
   (2) un amor no correspondido.
   (3) la belleza.
   (4) el amor romántico.
   (5) el amor al prójimo.

2. En el segundo poema hay sobre todo
   (1) personificación.
   (2) imágenes.
   (3) rima.
   (4) símiles.
   (5) metáforas.

GUÍA PARA LA LECTURA DE POESÍA

1. Fijarse en el título para ver si ofrece alguna indicación de lo que trata el poema.

2. Leer el poema de principio a fin para captar las ideas generales y la atmósfera.

3. Preguntarse: ¿De qué trata el poema? ¿Qué quiere comunicar el poeta? ¿Qué dice el poema? ¿Cuál es el tema principal?

4. Releer el poema guiándose por la puntuación. (Hacer pausa donde haya coma o punto, y no al final de cada verso).

5. Observar cómo están agrupados y estructurados los versos y si éstos se repiten. ¿Qué desea recalcar el poeta con la repetición de ciertas palabras o versos?

6. Analizar el lenguaje utilizado y la preferencia del poeta por expresiones, comparaciones, imágenes y figuras retóricas poco comunes.

7. Leer el poema en voz alta para que se pueda oír, sobre todo si hay rima.

8. Resumir en propias palabras lo que dice el poema para comprender el tono y el tema del poema.

La forma de la poesía

La estructura y la forma que presenta la poesía es una de las principales caractertísticas que la distinguen de otros géneros literarios. Un gran número de poetas suele preferir un formato altamente estructurado en el que dan vida a sus ideas haciendo uso de rimas, ritmo y estrofas. Las *estrofas* son conjuntos de versos que expresan una idea. La inserción de una nueva estrofa indica, generalmente, que se está presentando una nueva idea en el poema. Es frecuente encontrar un espacio en blanco que separe a las mismas. El siguiente poema de Gustavo Adolfo Bécquer contiene tres estrofas:

estrofa 1

Del salón en el ángulo oscuro,
de su dueño tal vez olvidada,
silenciosa y cubierta de polvo,
veíase el arpa.

estrofa 2

¡Cuánta nota dormía en sus cuerdas
como el pájaro duerme en las ramas,
esperando la mano de nieve
que sabe arrancarlas!

estrofa 3

¡Ay! Pensé; ¡cuántas veces el genio
así duerme en el fondo del alma
y una voz como Lázaro espera
que le diga "Levántate y anda!"

Cada estrofa se compone a su vez de versos. El *verso* es la unidad mínima en que se puede dividir un poema. El conjunto de versos estructurados y ordenados según un patrón conforman el poema. Muchas de las letras de canciones que conocemos fueron en un principio poemas independientes a los que se puso música. Un ejemplo es "El himno de batalla de la república" de Julia Ward Howe. El término *verso libre* se refiere a los versos que no tienen un patrón rítmico regular y que normalmente carecen de rima. Gran parte de la poesía contemporánea se compone en verso libre.

Uso de mayúsculas y puntuación

En la poesía, al igual que en la prosa, la coma o el punto y coma quiere decir "haga una pausa". El punto significa "pare". Si el poema emplea mayúsculas y puntuación, tenemos entonces en manos oraciones completas. En este caso, se deberá leer el poema atendiendo al principio y fin de la oración y no al principio y fin de los versos. A veces, se habrán de leer dos o más líneas seguidas. Por ejemplo, en el poema "Historia" que se ofrece a continuación, los versos 2 a 4 se leen "El sol de la mañana extendía sus lanzas sobre el piso de linóleo". En poesía, el uso de las mayúsculas puede variar: se puede tanto utilizar la mayúscula al inicio de cada verso como también poner palabras en mayúscula para que se destaquen.

EJERCICIO 2: LA FORMA DE LA POESÍA

Instrucciones: Lea en voz alta el poema de la página siguiente, y conteste las preguntas que siguen. Observe el uso de las mayúsculas y la puntuación.

HISTORIA

Abuela encendió la estufa.
El sol de la mañana
extendía sus lanzas
Sobre el piso de linóleo.
Envuelta en un mantón,
Sus ojitos
Con sueño,
Cortó las papas,
Machacó los chiles
Con un mortero
Que trajeron de Guadalajara.

Después de que
el abuelo se fuera a trabajar,
Ella echó agua
En el sendero que sus hijos
pavimentaron
Y a la sombra
De una lila de la China,
Desenterró
Su caja de puros secreta
De monedas
Y billetes, los contó
En inglés,
Y luego en español,
Y luego los enterró en otro lugar.
Más tarde, al volver
Del mercado,
Donde nadie la podía ver,
Ella sacó
Pimientos y remolacha, tallos
De espárragos
De su blusa,
Chocolates diminutos

Que tenía debajo de un pañuelo
estampado,
Y sonrió.
Eso fue en los años 50,
Y abuela tenía unos 50 años
Con su rostro marcado
De cortar uvas
Y de poner ciruelas en cajas.
Yo recuerdo que por dentro
Estaba llena de lombrices
Sus brazos hinchados como bultos
De pequeños tumores—
Su segundo hijo
Se cayó de una escalera
Y se convirtió en polvo.
Y aun así no sé
Las penas
Que la llevaban a rezar
En la oscuridad del closet,
Las ganas de llorar que sentía
Por la noche
Cuando tocaba
La floja piel
De vientre y pechos.
Yo no sé por qué
Su rostro se ilumina
O qué hay detrás de ese
resplandor,
Sólo las historias
Que la sacaron
De Taxco a San Joaquín,
De Delano a Westside,
Los lugares
Donde todos comenzamos.

—GARY SOTO

1. Hay once versos en la primera estrofa. ¿Cuántas oraciones hay? (Observe los puntos).

2. ¿En qué estrofa se la ve más feliz a la abuela? Escriba la palabra clave que comunica esta atmósfera.

3. ¿Quién es el narrador del poema?

La musicalidad en la poesía

La poesía se vale de una gran cantidad de recursos, como la rima, el ritmo y la aliteración para comunicar su mensaje a su público. A los bebés como a los niños pequeños, por lo general, se los inicia en la literatura de su idioma nativo por medio de las canciones de cuna o rimas infantiles. La *rima* es la repetición, presente en dos o más palabras, de un sonido vocálico acentuado y de las sílabas que siguen a ese sonido.

Ejemplo: La princesa está triste. . . ¿Qué tendrá la *princesa*?
Los suspiros se escapan de su boca de *fresa*.

Al igual que la elección de palabras, así también el ritmo o "compás" de un poema produce un efecto deseado. En poesía, el ***ritmo*** es la sucesión de sonidos que alternan entre débiles y fuertes o entre cortos y largos. Si el ritmo es regular, es decir, si sigue un orden estricto, se dice que la ***métrica*** del poema es regular.

La repetición de sonidos dentro de un mismo verso, normalmente al comienzo de las palabras, se denomina ***aliteración***. "Los suspiros se escapan de su boca de fresa" es un ejemplo de aliteración. Las canciones de cuna presentan por lo general mucha aliteración, al igual que los mensajes publicitarios, los que suelen incorporar con frecuencia esta técnica.

EJERCICIO 3: LA MUSICALIDAD EN LA POESÍA

Instrucciones: Lea el poema y conteste las preguntas que siguen. Preste atención (1) al ritmo, (2) la repetición de estrofas y versos y (3) la aliteración de los sonidos indicados por las letras *c, ch, s* y *d*.

Coco, cacao,
cacho, cachaza,
¡upa, mi negro,
que el sol abrasa!

5 Negrón, negrito,
ciruela y pasa,
salga y despierte,
que el sol abrasa,

diga despierto
10 lo que le pasa. . .
Ya nadie duerme,
ni está en la casa:

Coco, cacao,
cacho, cachaza,
15 ¡upa, mi negro,
que el sol abrasa!

—Nicolás Guillén

1. Cite dos o más ejemplos de aliteración:

   (1) _____

   (2) _____

2. La mitad de los versos del poema riman. ¿Podría usted identificar las palabras que riman y explicar los sonidos que tienen en común las mismas?

3. Determine el patrón rítmico a que obedece el poema. ¿Observa usted alguna relación entre la rima y el hecho de que los versos sean pares o impares?

Vocablos que imitan sonidos

Gran parte de la poesía se escribe para ser leída en voz alta. A medida que el poeta escribe las palabras, es consciente del sonido del poema. Hay muchos poetas que usan "palabras-sonidos" para hacer resaltar una imagen o el mensaje de su obra. La ***onomatopeya*** es un recurso de la lengua que consiste en imitar el sonido de una cosa con la palabra que representa a esa cosa. Entre las palabras que imitan sonidos se pueden citar: ronronear, tintinear, miau, tictac, zumbar, pumba, etc.

EJERCICIO 4: VOCABLOS QUE IMITAN SONIDOS

Instrucciones: Lea el poema XXXII del escritor vanguardista César Vallejo y conteste las preguntas que siguen.

> 999 calorías
> Rumbbb. . . Trrraprrr rrach. . . chaz
> Serpentínica *u* del bizcochero
> engirafada al tímpano.
>
> Quién como los hielos. Pero no.
> Quién como lo que va ni más ni menos.
> Quién como el justo medio.
>
> 1,000 calorías.
> Azulea y ríe su gran cachaza
> el firmamento gringo. Baja
> el sol empavado y le alborota los cascos
> al más frío.
>
> Remeda al cuco. Rooooooooeeeeis. . .
> tierno autocarril, móvil de sed,
> que corre hasta la playa.
>
> Aire, aire! Hielo!
> Si al menos el calor (————————— Mejor
>   no digo nada.
>
> Y hasta la misma pluma
> con que escribo por último se troncha.
>
> Treinta y tres trillones trescientos treinta
> y tres calorías

1. Busque dos ejemplos de aliteración y uno de repetición.

2. "Rumbbb. . . Trrraprrr rrach. . . chaz" y "Rooooooooeeeeis. . ." son ejemplos de:
   (1) aliteración
   (2) repetición
   (3) onomatopeya
   (4) personificación
   (5) rima

Interpretar el sentido

Cuando tratemos de interpretar un poema, conviene "reescribirlo", es decir, parafrasearlo con nuestras palabras. En muchos casos habrá que sustituir palabras o modificar oraciones para expresar el texto del poema de una forma que sea más fácil de comprender. Al parafrasear la obra, es importante determinar el propósito fundamental del poeta. En razón de ello, debemos hacernos preguntas como: *¿Por qué emplea el poeta esta comparación?* o *¿Por qué dice esto el poeta?*

Lea el poema "El vals de mi papá" de Theodore Roethke que se transcribe abajo. Luego vuelva a leerlo nuevamente, una estrofa a la vez. Escriba con sus palabras una oración o dos que resuma lo expresado en cada estrofa. Después de que haya escrito su interpretación, lea la interpretación que se ofrece al final del poema: la suya podrá o no estar de acuerdo con la interpretación del libro.

El vals de mi papá

El olor a whisky de tu aliento
Bien podía marear a un chiquillo;
Pero yo me aferré impasible:
Ese vals no fue sencillo.

Retozamos hasta que las ollas
De los estantes de cocina cayeron;
El disgusto que tenía mi madre
Se podía ver en su ceño.

Tenía un nudillo aporreado
La mano que mi muñeca sujetaba;
Y en cada paso trastabillado
Mi oreja con la hebilla chocaba.

Palmeabas en mi cabeza el compás
Sucias de tierra tus manos,
Me llevaste a mi cama al ritmo del vals
De tu camisa fuertemente agarrado.

Interpretación de la estrofa 1: Un hombre recuerda a su padre. Es posible que su padre hubiera estado bebiendo antes de empezar a bailar con su hijo.

Interpretación de la estrofa 2: El hijo recuerda que bailaron desaforados por la cocina mientras su madre observaba con desaprobación.

Interpretación de la estrofa 3: El hijo recuerda que era lo suficientemente pequeño como para notar el nudillo aporreado de su padre y para acordarse del dolor que sentía cada vez que su oreja chocaba contra la hebilla del cinturón del padre cuando éste se tambaleaba.

Interpretación de la estrofa 4: Su padre estaba sucio porque había estado trabajando; sus manos estaban todavía sucias mientras bailaban. El hijo estaba asido de su padre mientras bailaban el vals.

EJERCICIO 5: INFERIR EL SENTIDO

Instrucciones: Indique en los espacios en blanco el número de verso y las palabras clave que sirven de apoyo a las inferencias realizadas, después de leer el poema, "Fuerza", en la página que sigue.

Inferencias	Número de verso	Palabras clave
1. El hombre es el padre.	_____	_____
2. El hombre era una persona muy atlética.	_____	_____
3. El hombre es ahora un anciano.	_____	_____

Fuerza

Esa mano derecha tan fuerte que
antes equilibraba a nuestros
niños cerca del cielo,
una vez movió pacas de
5 heno todos los meses de agosto,
una vez lanzó juegos de béisbol
perfectos los domingos,
una vez acarició con ternura

mis cabellos rojizos . . .
10 Esa mano
ahora se arquea crudamente para
agarrar a una caña de bambú y
ahora tiembla mientras tú
inclinas con reverencia tu cuerpo
15 para rezar y dar gracias por los años
de esa mano derecha tan fuerte.

Deducir el clima

El *"mood"* o *clima* juega un papel muy importante en poesía. Cuando un poeta crea un poema, las palabras que utiliza ayudan a presentar una disposición de ánimo general. El clima puede ser de humor y desenfado o sombrío y serio. En algunos casos, puede ir cambiando dentro de un mismo poema. Lea la letra de la canción del musical *Cats*. A medida que vaya leyendo, identifique el clima de cada sección. Encierre en un círculo la palabra que describe con mayor precisión el clima de cada estrofa.

Recuerdos

Medianoche, ni un ruido en el pavimento.
¿Ha perdido la luna su memoria?
Ella sonríe a solas.
En la luz del farol las hojas marchitas
    se amontonan a mis pies
Y el viento comienza a gemir.

1. (a) optimismo
   (b) soledad
   (c) ansiedad

Recuerdos. Sola a la luz de la luna
Puedo sonreír al recordar los viejos tiempos.
Qué hermosa era yo entonces.
Recuerdo aquel tiempo en que
    sabía lo que era la felicidad,
Deja que vivan otra vez los recuerdos. . .

2. (a) nostalgia
   (b) humor
   (c) temor

Luz del día. Tengo que esperar a que salga el sol
Tengo que pensar en una nueva vida
Y no tengo que ceder.
Cuando llegue el alba
    esta noche será también un recuerdo
Y un nuevo día habrá de comenzar. . .

3. (a) depresión
   (b) sarcasmo
   (c) esperanza

Tócame. Es tan fácil dejarme
Sola con el recuerdo
De mis días al sol.
Si me tocas comprenderás
    lo que es la felicidad.
Mira, ha comenzado un nuevo día.

4. (a) lamentación
   (b) alegría
   (c) confusión

[Respuestas: **1. (b)** soledad (la luna sonríe a solas y el viento empieza a gemir); **2. (a)** nostalgia (el gato sonríe y recuerda); **3. (c)** esperanza (la luz del día y un nuevo día); **4. (b)** alegría (ha comenzado un nuevo día)]

El lenguaje de la poesía
Imaginería

Los poetas confían en la capacidad de los lectores de crear imágenes o instantáneas en sus mentes con las palabras que leen en la página. Por esta razón, el poeta debe elegir la palabra precisa para transmitir un pensamiento. Cuando un poema evoca los sentidos y permite que nos imaginemos una escena, se dice que el poema es rico en *imaginería* poética.

> *Ejemplo:* Las pesadas gotas de lluvia golpeaban el capó del auto haciendo un estrepitoso ruido como si fueran miles de tachuelas las que caían del cielo.

¿Puede "ver" las gotas de lluvia y "oír" el ruido metálico que hacen al golpear el auto?

Personificación

La *personificación* es una figura retórica que consiste en atribuir cualidades o capacidades humanas a animales o cosas. Expresado de otra manera, mediante la personificación, un objeto inanimado cobra "vida" al adquirir atributos humanos. Carl Sandburg se valió de la personificación para inmortalizar la ciudad de Chicago en su famoso poema del mismo nombre. Observe que se dirige a la ciudad como si fuera una persona. Éstos son los primeros versos:

Chicago

Carnicero porcino para el mundo,
Hacedor de herramientas, apilador de trigo,
Jugador con ferrocarriles y manipulador de fletes de la nación;
Tempestuosa, tosca, bulliciosa,
Ciudad de anchas espaldas:

Los sobrenombres que Sandburg da a la ciudad en los tres primeros versos hacen referencia al comercio y a la industria por los que Chicago era conocida. Chicago es personificada—convertida en ser humano—cuando el poeta se refiere a la ciudad como "tempestuosa, tosca, bulliciosa/Ciudad de anchas espaldas".

En el siguiente poema, subraye todos los ejemplos de personificación. ¿Cómo se personifica la ciudad?

Ciudad de acero

Los cielos de agosto aceptan
tu eructo de desperdicios
y las cenizas son excretadas
muy por encima de la joven hierba
que bordea tímidamente
tus venas de cemento,
latiendo para mantener el agitado ritmo
de días que expiran demasiado pronto.
Tu estructura envejece, tu respiración disminuye,
y tú sigues siendo
un cuerpo
sin alma.

[Respuesta: Subrayar: *eructo, excretadas, tímidamente, venas, latiendo, expiran, envejece, respiración,* y *cuerpo sin alma.* El poeta escribe como si la ciudad tuviera una fisiología humana.]

EJERCICIO 6: LENGUAJE POÉTICO

Instrucciones: Escriba *imaginería* si el verso evoca una imagen o *personificación* si atribuye una cualidad humana a un objeto inanimado.

Verso 1: Medianoche, ni un ruido en el pavimento. _____

Verso 2: ¿Ha perdido la luna su memoria? _____

Verso 3: Ella [*la luna*] sonríe a solas. _____

El símil y la metáfora

El *símil* es una comparación que muestra una semejanza entre dos cosas diferentes. El símil se vale de expresiones que conectan los dos elementos de la comparación: *como, así, cual, igual que, más/menos que, tanto como,* etc. En este poema titulado "Designio", el poeta Robert Frost hace uso del símil. Subraye los cuatro símiles del poema.

Designio

Encontré una araña con hoyuelos, gorda y blanca,
En un *heal-all* blanco[1], sujetando una polilla
Como un trozo blanco de tela satinada rígida—
Variados personajes de muerte y sufrimiento
Mezclados y listos para comenzar bien la mañana,
Como los ingredientes de un brebaje de brujas—
Una araña de nieve, una flor como la espuma,
Y alas muertas llevadas como una cometa de papel.
¿Qué culpa tenía la flor de ser blanca,
ese inocente *heal-all* al borde del camino?
¿Qué llevó a la afín araña a esas alturas,
y luego condujo hacia allí en la noche a la blanca polilla?
¿Qué otra cosa sino el designio de las tinieblas?—
Si el designio gobernara algo tan pequeño.

[1] El heal-all es una planta.

[Respuesta: Símiles: "una polilla/Como un trozo blanco de tela satinada rígida"; "Como los ingredientes de un brebaje de brujas"; "una flor como la espuma"; y "alas muertas llevadas como una cometa de papel".]

La *metáfora* es una comparación implícita o sugerida entre dos cosas distintas. En la metáfora no aparacen expresiones conectoras entre los dos elementos que se comparan (*como, cual, así, igual que, más/menos que o tanto como,* etc.). La metáfora da a entender que una cosa es otra.

Ejemplo: El día era una página de diario en blanco a la espera de que alguien la rellenara.

Esta metáfora presenta la imagen de un papel en blanco—el día—listo para empezar sus actividades cotidianas. El día es una página de diario que aún está por ser escrita.

En esta estrofa inicial de "Una día de verano indio en la pradera" de Vachel Lindsay hay tres metáforas. ¿Cuáles son?

El sol es una cazadora joven,   El sol es una muchacha india,
Un júbilo rojo, rojo es el sol.   De la tribu de los illinois

[Respuesta: El poeta compara el sol con una cazadora, con el júbilo y con una muchacha india. El lector obtiene distintas imágenes del sol con las que se puede hacer una idea de cómo es la pradera.]

EJERCICIO 7: MÁS PRÁCTICA DE INTERPRETACIÓN DE POEMAS

¿QUÉ DICE LA POETISA SOBRE LA MUERTE?

Como no podía detenerme para la Muerte

1

Como no podía detenerme para la
    Muerte,
Ella se detuvo amablemente para
    mí;
El carruaje fue sólo para nosotros
Y la Inmortalidad.

2

Nos movimos lentamente, ella no
    tenía prisa,
Y yo tuve que dejar a un lado
Mi trabajo, y también mi tiempo
    libre,
Por cortesía.

3

Pasamos la escuela donde unos
    niños jugaban
A la lucha libre en un círculo;
Pasamos los campos de grano
    observador,
Pasamos el sol que se ponía.

4

Hicimos una pausa frente a una
    casa que parecía
Un bulto hinchado en la tierra;
El techo apenas se veía,
La cornisa no era más que un
    montículo.

5

Desde entonces han pasados siglos;
    pero cada uno
Parece más corto que el día
En que supuse que las cabezas de
    los caballos
Se dirigían hacia la eternidad.

—Emily Dickinson

1. Empareje la estrofa con las imágenes de la derecha escribiendo la letra correspondiente en el espacio dado.

_____ **Estrofa 1**   (a) imágenes del patio de una escuela, una granja, el campo, una puesta de sol

_____ **Estrofa 2**   (b) la narradora va en un carruaje con otras dos personas

_____ **Estrofa 3**   (c) un viaje lento cuando la narradora acepta su destino

_____ **Estrofa 4**   (d) la narradora recuerda el día del paseo en el carruaje, cientos de años atrás

_____ **Estrofa 5**   (e) el carruaje se detiene en un cementerio

2. Al escribir con mayúscula *Muerte* e *Inmortalidad*, la poetisa quiere dar a entender que
   (1) la muerte es un tema de gran importancia.
   (2) éstas son preocupaciones fundamentales en la vida de una persona.
   (3) éstos son los personajes del poema.
   (4) las dos palabras se oponen y una lucha contra la otra.
   (5) éstos son dos conceptos inexplicables a los que la gente debe hacer frente.

3. De la última estrofa, se podría inferir que la narradora del poema
   (1) sabe cuándo va a morir.
   (2) siente que el tiempo transcurre con demasiada lentitud.
   (3) nunca mira atrás hacia el pasado.
   (4) disfruta los paseos en carruaje.
   (5) cree en la vida eterna.

Acerca de la poesía: Comentario

Más abajo se puede apreciar un ejemplo de crítica de una colección de poemas. El comentario fue escrito por un crítico literario que se dedica a evaluar libros de poesía. Usted podrá también tener la oportunidad de leer críticas de poesía en una revista literaria o la sección de literatura de un periódico o revista.

¿CUÁL ES LA OPINIÓN DEL CRÍTICO?

Secretos susurrados de Ann Fox Chandonnet, Denise Lassaw,
Eleanor Limmer y Joanne Townsend
Sedna Press, $10
Crítica de Stephen C. Levi

Secretos susurrados es un libro que se ha hecho esperar y la espera bien ha valido la pena. De hecho, es inesperadamente refrescante. Permítanme que les explique. Sedna Press, como se menciona en el prefacio, deriva su nombre de Sedna, la diosa esquimal, cuyo padre le cortó los dedos y luego dejó que se hundiera en el mar. Ella creó allí toda la vida marina de la que vivían los esquimales, así como todas las tempestades del mar. Por lo tanto, era creadora y destructora al mismo tiempo.

Con este sello editorial y un grupo de cuatro poetisas, yo me estaba preparando para hacer frente a una colección de poesías de diatriba y desprecio hacia los hombres escritas por mujeres amargadas. Me llevé, sin embargo, una agradable sorpresa. Vistos como una unidad, los poemas forman una lanza de opiniones que puja hacia adelante con un tema único: la propiedad que tiene la mujer sobre sí misma a través del conocimiento y la aceptación de su persona y de todo lo que la rodea. Dicho de una forma más simple, los poemas comunican el mensaje de que la riqueza espiritual se logra conociéndose uno a sí mismo y comprendiendo que las hondas y las flechas de la mala fortuna suelen a menudo ser regalos que nos fortalecen.

Es más, las cuatro mujeres presentan su punto de vista de forma separada. Cada poetisa aporta su propia y especial dirección en cuanto a cuestiones filosóficas y, al mismo tiempo, sigue una trayectoria paralela a las inclinaciones de las tres restantes. El resultado final es una colección sólida que presenta su mensaje con lucidez y claridad.

EJERCICIO 8: CRÍTICA DE UN POEMA

Instrucciones: Elija la mejor respuesta para cada una de las preguntas.

1. ¿Con cuál de las siguientes expresiones estaría de acuerdo el crítico?
   (1) La poesía femenina es casi siempre objetiva.
   (2) Las dificultades nos fortalecen para hacer frente a la vida.
   (3) Las editoriales necesitan tener sellos interesantes.
   (4) Conviene que las poetisas escriban siempre en grupo.
   (5) La diosa Sedna no es el tema de un poema.

2. El crítico afirma que *Secretos susurrados* "es un libro que se ha hecho esperar y la espera bien ha valido la pena". ¿De qué otra forma se puede expresar lo mismo?
   (1) El tiempo que se empleó en escribir el libro se hace evidente en la excelencia de lo escrito.
   (2) Las escritoras tardaron mucho tiempo en escribir el libro.
   (3) Los lectores tuvieron que esperar mucho tiempo para poder leer el libro.
   (4) El libro sería mejor si se hubiera publicado antes.
   (5) El hecho de tener que esperar hizo que las expectativas fueran muy altas.

3
<u>EL TEATRO</u>

El *teatro* es el género literario que se escribe con la intención de ser representado en escena por actores que desempeñan el papel de los personajes. En muchos casos, el teatro trata de imitar la vida porque los actores se enfrentan a situaciones y problemas de la vida real.

Los requisitos necesarios para poder leer una obra de teatro en el examen del GED son similares a los que se necesitan para leer ficción en prosa o poesía. En líneas generales, no es difícil leer una pieza teatral; sin embargo, el lector tiene que ser capaz de "visualizar" la acción que se está desarrollando en la obra. Por ello, deberá leerla con cuidado para inferir el ambiente, los personajes y el tema. Las acotaciones, que van entre corchetes, no se deben leer en voz alta. Son instrucciones para los actores y, además, explican lo que está sucediendo en el escenario a medida que hablan los actores.

Diferencias entre el teatro y otros géneros literarios

Aunque el teatro coincide en diversos aspectos con la poesía y la narrativa de ficción, cada uno de estos géneros literarios tiene su modo particular de tratar un tema determinado. A continuación se ilustran las diferencias que se pueden dar en el tratamiento que dan los distintos géneros a un mismo tema; en este caso, una propuesta de matrimonio.

Prosa: La joven pareja, Juan y María, se fueron a dar un paseo en barco a medianoche por el río Mississippi. Juan le entregó a María un anillo de diamante y ella aceptó su propuesta de matrimonio.

Poesía: Amantes a la luz de luna
A bordo del *Delta Expreso*
Intercambiaron anillo y promesas
Y lo sellaron todo con un beso.

Teatro: [*Juan y María se encuentran a bordo del* Delta Expreso *haciendo un crucero de medianoche.*]

JUAN: [*Abrazando a María.*] Te amo. [*Él le entrega un paquete a ella.*]

MARÍA: [*Sorprendida..*] ¿Qué es esto?

JUAN: Es un símbolo de nuestro futuro juntos. . . si aceptas casarte conmigo el mes que viene.

MARÍA: [*Abre el paquete y ve el anillo de diamante.*] ¡Ay, Juan!

JUAN: [*Colocando el anillo en el dedo de María.*] No te lo quites nunca.

MARÍA: No. . . [*Nerviosa.*] digo, ¡sí!. . . Quiero decir, no; no me lo quitaré nunca. . . Sí, sí me casaré contigo. [*Se besan.*]

Diálogo

En las obras teatrales, al igual que en los demás géneros literarios, el *diálogo* es la conversación que entablan los personajes. Cuando se lee el diálogo de una novela o un cuento corto, es a veces difícil identificar quién está hablando porque no siempre se identifica a los interlocutores. Sin embargo, en las obras de teatro hay siempre pistas que le ayudan a llevar la cuenta de quién está hablando.

1ª indicación: Se identifica siempre en cada línea al personaje que habla. El nombre del personaje seguido de dos puntos (:) nos informa quién es el interlocutor. Cuando sólo hablan dos personas, es fácil seguir la obra, pero cuando la acción se desarrolla con tres o más personajes, se hace necesario leer con más cuidado y estar atento a cada intervención para identificar al hablante.

2ª indicación: Se usan signos de puntuación al comienzo y al final de lo que dice un personaje. Observe estos signos, en particular los de interrogación (¿?) y de exclamación (¡!). El autor dramático se vale de los signos de puntuación para indicar el volumen de voz, el tono y el sentimiento del pasaje. La raya larga (—) y los puntos suspensivos (. . .) se emplean también para indicar pausas. La raya larga marca una ruptura en el hilo del pensamiento, mientras que los puntos suspensivos indican una pausa en la oración o una interrupción debido a la intervención de otro personaje.

3ª indicación: Un espacio entre líneas de diálogo indica quién está hablando. Además del punto y aparte, el espacio en blanco nos ayuda a visualizar mejor cuándo interviene cada personaje.

> **LAS RESPUESTAS A LOS EJERCICIOS DE ESTE CAPÍTULO EMPIEZAN EN LA PÁGINA 462.**

EJERCICIO 1: DIÁLOGO Y PUNTUACIÓN

Instrucciones: Lea el diálogo atendiendo a la puntuación. Luego conteste las preguntas que siguen.

> [*La escena se inicia en un salón del siglo XIX. Catherine, la hija de Victoria y de Edward, entra con una taza de té.*]
>
> CATHERINE: ¿Quieren té y. . .
>
> EDWARD: Ahora no. ¿No ves que estamos hablando?
>
> VICTORIA: ¡Tú estás hablando; pero yo no!
>
> EDWARD: Uh, andas algo irritada, ¿no?
>
> VICTORIA: No, aburrida nada más: de ti. . .
>
> CATHERINE: [*Entre dientes.*] Me voy. [*Sale.*]

Complete cada oración con el nombre del personaje que corresponda.

1. Catherine interrumpe a _____.

2. _____ se comporta de manera grosera con Catherine.

3. Victoria está molesta con _____.

EJERCICIO 2: DEDUCIR EL CLIMA DE UN DIÁLOGO

Instrucciones: Elija la mejor respuesta para la siguiente pregunta.

El clima de esta escena se puede decir que es de
(1) tensión.
(2) felicidad.
(3) suspenso.
(4) nostalgia.
(5) comicidad.

Acotaciones

Las *acotaciones* son explicaciones que se usan para asistir a los actores y al director en su interpretación de la intención y el propósito del autor. Las acotaciones también son de gran utilidad para el lector, quien gracias a ellas puede seguir más fácilmente la acción que se desarrolla en la obra. En la breve escena citada anteriormente, se mencionan las siguientes acotaciones: "[*La escena se inicia en un salón del siglo XIX. Catherine, la hija de Victoria y de Edward, entra con una taza de té.*]"; "[*Entre dientes.*]" y "[*Sale.*]". Observe que el autor de la obra introduce acotaciones tanto entre el diálogo como dentro del mismo. Las acotaciones indican al lector quién es Catherine y por qué se va. El extracto de la obra que se presenta más adelante en este capítulo requiere que se siga tanto la acción como el texto.

Del concepto a la puesta en escena

En la Grecia Antigua se representaban las obras teatrales en anfiteatros construidos en laderas de colinas adonde acudía el público. Hoy, tenemos a nuestra disposición una gran variedad de opciones: ver la telvisión, ir al cine o asistir a producciones en vivo. Si se desea apreciar a cabalidad una obra de teatro, una película de cine o de televisión, es de gran utilidad conocer cómo ha creado su obra el escritor (llamado *autor dramático* o *dramaturgo*). Las obras teatrales se escriben en la mayoría de los casos con la intención de ser representadas ante un público antes que leídas por un lector. En la puesta en escena de una pieza teatral participa un gran número de personas de distintas especialidades y talentos: diseñadores de vestuario, decoradores de escena, maquillistas y muchos más.

Cuando los autores (también llamados *guionistas*) escriben un guión, visualizan su trabajo final como una representación. El productor o realizador, que se encarga de financiar la producción, elige al director que va a presentar de manera efectiva la materia prima: el guión. El director elige a los actores y las actrices que le parezcan adecuados a los personajes que ha creado el escritor.

Estructura de la obra teatral

Una obra o pieza teatral se divide en *actos;* y los actos, a su vez, se dividen en *escenas.* Las escenas muestran la acción que se desarrolla en un lugar determinado entre los personajes.

En las obras del teatro clásico, el principio se denomina *prólogo* y el final *epílogo.* Como las primeras representaciones carecían de decorados, uno de los actores aparecía en escena y presentaba la obra explicando el lugar donde se ambientaba así como una parte del argumento. También recitaba un poema resumen o hablaba al final de la obra. Aunque el prólogo y el epílogo ya no son tan frecuentes en el teatro contemporáneo, algunas de las películas de televisión y de cine los usan para ayudar a la audiencia a que entienda la trama.

William Shakespeare, gran escritor de la literatura universal, desarrolló y refinó la estructura de la obra del teatro inglés y le dio la forma que conocemos hoy. Shakespeare presentaba el argumento en cinco actos, los que a su vez se subdividían en escenas numeradas. En el diagrama siguiente se observa cómo se relacionan estos actos con los elementos correspondientes de un argumento tradicional.

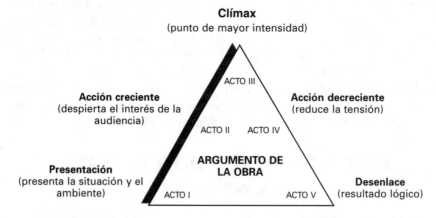

Elementos de la obra teatral

El argumento, el ambiente, los personajes y el tema son elementos que también se aplican al género teatral. El argumento de la obra de teatro está rigurosamente estructurado: al igual que un cuento corto, tiene una *presentación* que informa a la audiencia acerca de la situación y el ambiente. La *acción creciente* la componen todos los acontecimientos que crean suspenso y despiertan el interés de la audiencia. Todos estos sucesos y conflictos conducen al *clímax,* es decir, al punto culminante o de mayor intensidad de la obra. La *acción decreciente* puede ser breve. El final, o *desenlace,* es consecuencia lógica del argumento. Del mismo modo que en la narrativa de ficción, el desenlace ata todos los cabos de la trama que habían quedado sueltos .

Personajes

Dado que los *personajes* de una obra de teatro cobran vida a través de los actores que los representan frente a un público, no se desarrollan de la misma forma que los personajes de las novelas y los cuentos. ¿Cómo se puede leer un personaje? Uno de los métodos sería mediante un análisis del lenguaje del personaje y de sus acciones así como de los motivos que subyacen a esas acciones.

Diálogo y comunicación no verbal

En el teatro, las personalidades se revelan con lo que dicen los personajes. La obra teatral deposita en el *diálogo* una responsabilidad para expresar lo que quiere el autor mayor que la que deposita la narrativa de ficción. En el teatro, el personaje se revela también mediante las *comunicaciones no verbales* del actor: gestos, expresión facial y vestuario.

Motivación

En la obra de teatro, el comportamiento del personaje es producto de su *motivación,* es decir, las razones o causas que impulsan al personaje a actuar de una forma determinada. Los actores que desempeñan un papel se preguntan, *¿Cuál es mi motivación? ¿Qué razones tiene mi personaje para actuar de esta forma?* Más abajo se ofrece el extracto de una obra que trata de la relación entre una madre y su hija. Las dos mujeres están inmersas en una conversación en la que se revelan datos acerca de su personalidad, pasado y conflictos. Si se desea inferir el clima, el carácter y la forma, se deberá basar el análisis en la comprensión que se tenga del diálogo.

EJERCICIO 3: COMPRENDER EL PERSONAJE

Instrucciones: Lea el pasaje y conteste las preguntas que siguen.

¿QUÉ PERSONALIDAD TIENEN LOS PERSONAJES?

MAMA: Nunca nada de lo yo hice te satisfizo, y me gustaría saber por qué.

JESSIE: Eso no es cierto.

MAMA: Y quiero saber por qué has vivido aquí todo este tiempo sintiéndote disconforme con todo lo que hacía.

JESSIE: Tú no tienes la menor idea de lo que yo siento.

MAMA: ¿Cómo podría saberlo? Vives tan alejada de la realidad, Jessie.

JESSIE: ¿Tan alejada de la realidad?

MAMA: ¿Cómo son las cosas donde tú estás? ¿Dice allí la gente siempre lo correcto y consiguen lo que quieren, o qué?

JESSIE: ¿Qué dices?

MAMA: ¿Para qué lees el periódico? ¿Por qué no te pones el suéter que yo te he hecho? ¿Te acuerdas lo bonita que era antes, o soy sólo una vieja ahora? ¿Ves las estrellas cuándo te da tu pataleta, o qué? ¿Cómo te caíste del caballo, de verdad? ¿Por qué te dejó Cecil? ¿Dónde has puesto mis lentes viejos?

JESSIE: Están en el cajón de abajo de tu vestidor en una caja vieja de leche de magnesia. Cecil me dejó porque me hizo escoger entre él y el cigarrillo.

MAMA: Jessie, yo sé bien que él no era así de tonto.

JESSIE: Nunca entendí por qué él lo odiada tanto cuando te hace sentir tan bien. Fumar es lo único que conozco que es siempre aquello que tú esperas. Exactamente igual que la última vez y siempre está allí cuando lo quieres y es muy tranquilizante.

MAMA: Tus pataletas le hacían sentirse muy mal y tú lo sabes.

JESSIE: Di síncopes, no pataletas. Síncopes.

MAMA: Es lo mismo. Un síncope en el hospital es una pataleta en la casa.

JESSIE: No le molestaban a él en absoluto. Excepto que se sentía responsable por ellos. Fue idea suya ir a montar a caballo ese día. Era su idea que yo podría hacer lo que quería si me lo proponía. Me caí del caballo porque no supe cómo agarrarme a él. Cecil se fue prácticamente por la misma razón.

—MARSHA NORMAN: *Buenas Noches, Madre* (Fragmento)

1. La relación entre madre e hija parece estar afectada por
   (1) la dependencia que tiene Jessie de su madre.
   (2) la dependencia que tiene Mama de Jessie.
   (3) la falta de comunicación.
   (4) el resentimiento que tiene Jessie hacia su madre.
   (5) el odio que siente Mama por Cecil, el marido de su hija.

2. Se puede afirmar que Mama
   (1) es comprensiva.
   (2) es vengativa.
   (3) apoya a su hija.
   (4) es crítica de su hija.
   (5) es egoísta.

3. El clima que impera en este extracto es de
   (1) desesperación.
   (2) felicidad.
   (3) suspenso.
   (4) tensión.
   (5) duda.

EJERCICIO 4: APOYAR DATOS E INFERENCIAS

Instrucciones: Más abajo se citan datos e inferencias sobre la personalidad de Jessie. Escriba en el espacio en blanco las palabras clave del pasaje que respaldan cada dato o inferencia.

1. Jessie está separada de Cecil. _____

   _____

2. Jessie se siente confusa acerca de qué quiere saber su madre. _____

   _____

3. Mama no se cree la historia de Jessie sobre cómo se cayó del caballo.

   _____

   _____

EJERCICIO 5: INTERPRETAR UNA ESCENA DE UNA OBRA

Instrucciones: Lea el pasaje y conteste las preguntas que siguen.

¿DE QUÉ PROBLEMA HABLAN ALICE Y GENE?

ALICE: Yo hago mucho por mis hijos pero no espero que algún día me lo retribuyan. [*Gene camina de un lado a otro, pensando y dejando marcas en la hierba.*] Estoy segura de que podemos encontrar un ama de llaves permanente. Él puede permitirse el lujo.

GENE: Él nunca estará de acuerdo.

ALICE: Es eso o buscarle un hogar. [*Gene frunce el ceño.*] A los padres de Sidney les gusta el lugar donde están ahora. Además, hay que admitirlo, está empezando a chochear. Tarde o temprano habrá que pensar en conseguir un poder notarial; quizá habrá que internarle en una institución.

GENE: Todo esto es tan desagradable.

ALICE: [*Sonriendo.*] Sí, mi querido Gene, como muchas cosas de la vida.

GENE: Oye, no trates de hacerme parecer como si fuera un blandengue, un. . . [*No puede encontrar la palabra.*] Yo sé que la vida es difícil.

ALICE: Sí, ya veo que lo sabes. Tú has tenido que sufrir momentos muy difíciles, pero te esfuerzas como un troyano por negarlo, por hacer creer que no pasó lo que pasó. [*Después de un momento, sin discutir.*] Él me echó de la casa y me dijo que no quería verme nunca más. Por muchos años, le destrozó el corazón a nuestra madre con esto. Era malo e incapaz de querer a nadie. Te pegaba cuando eras pequeño. . . Tú le has despreciado y le has tenido miedo durante toda tu vida de adulto.

GENE: [*Interrumpiendo.*] Con todo, sigue siendo mi padre y un hombre. Y lo que le sucede a él me horroriza como hombre.

ALICE: Tenemos un problema práctico entre manos.

GENE: No es tan simple como todo lo demás.

ALICE: Para mí sí lo es. No entiendo por qué estás dejando envolver este asunto con esta niebla mística. Mañana voy a hablar con él sobre el ama de llaves después de la sesión con el abogado. [*Gene reacciona pero no dice nada.*] Deja que me encargue del asunto. Él puede visitarnos y nosotros podemos turnarnos para ir a visitarle. Yo me encargaré de hacer el trabajo sucio; pero cuando él acuda a ti, no cedas.

GENE: No puedo decirte lo avergonzado que me siento. . . de no poder decir con los brazos abiertos, "Papá, vente a vivir conmigo. . . te quiero, papá, y quiero cuidar de ti". . . Necesito quererle. Siempre he querido quererle. [*Deja caer los brazos y se aleja sin rumbo.*]

—ROBERT ANDERSON: *Nunca le canté a mi padre.* (Fragmento)

1. Alice y Gene son
   (1) esposo y esposa.
   (2) enfermera y doctor.
   (3) hermana y hermano.
   (4) amigos íntimos.
   (5) madre e hijo.

2. ¿Con qué afirmación estaría de acuerdo Alice?
   (1) Los hijos deben cuidar de sus padres en la ancianidad.
   (2) Los hogares de ancianos son para personas que no tienen hijos.
   (3) Lo mejor para los ancianos sería quedarse viviendo en sus propias casas.
   (4) Los hijos deben conseguir un poder notarial antes de confinar a los padres en una institución.
   (5) Los padres ancianos no deben esperar que sus hijos cuiden de ellos.

3. Gene manifiesta todas las emociones siguientes excepto
   (1) depresión.
   (2) alivio.
   (3) disgusto.
   (4) vergüenza.
   (5) frustración.

4. Lo último que dice Gene revela
   (1) aceptación del amor de su padre.
   (2) enfado hacia la actitud de Alice.
   (3) entusiasmo por visitar a su padre y decirle que quiere cuidar de él.
   (4) culpabilidad por no poder querer a su padre.
   (5) que no está capacitado para tomar decisiones que afectan a su futuro.

EJERCICIO 6: LEER LA CRÍTICA DE UNA PELÍCULA

Instrucciones: En la Prueba de lectura de Arte y Literatura, es posible que tenga que contestar algunas preguntas acerca de un comentario sobre una película de cine o una pieza teatral. Lea la crítica que se ofrece a continuación y conteste las preguntas que siguen.

¿QUÉ IMAGEN DE HOLLYWOOD PINTA *EL ÚLTIMO DE LOS MAGNATES?*
Crítica de cine de *El último de los magnates*

F. Scott Fitzgerald, autor de *El Gran Gatsby,* ha sido llamado el "Poeta de la era del jazz", los locos años 20. Pero él también tenía algo importante que decir acerca de la Era Dorada de Hollywood, los años 30. Y justamente lo dijo en su último
5 libro, *El último de los magnates.*

En su libro, Fitzgerald pinta a Hollywood como una especie de ciudad-empresa y a los directores de estudios

como reyes absolutos. El crítico Edmund Wilson ha dicho de *El último de los magnates* que es el mejor libro jamás escrito
10 sobre la industria cinematográfica.

De alguna forma, el director Elia Kazan y Harold Pinter (quien escribió el guión) han logrado convertir *El último de los magnates* en una película fascinante y mesurada. No ha tenido que ser ésta una labor fácil. Fitzgerald murió en 1940
15 dejando sólo seis capítulos acabados de *El último de los magnates.* Dejó, sin embargo, algunas notas sobre posibles finales para su obra y puede que el que eligieron Pinter y Kazan no sea del agrado de todos.

El año es 1933; el lugar, un gran estudio de Hollywood,
20 como la famosa MGM. Monroe Stahr (Robert De Niro) es el jefe de producción del estudio. Para crear a Stahr, Fitzgerald se basó en el fallecido Irving Thalberg, el creativo "Niño Maravilla" de la MGM. Al igual que Thalberg, Stahr es el dinamismo personificado: controla todas las etapas de la
25 película; indica a los actores cómo actuar, a los guionistas cómo escribir, y al dueño del estudio (Robert Mitchum) cómo llevar el negocio.

Pero Stahr es un ser humano imperfecto que ve la vida como si fuera una película y a las personas como si fueran
30 sombras. Él trata incluso de incluir en el reparto a Kathleen (Ingrid Boulting), la mujer que ama, como la reencarnación de su esposa muerta. Pero la vida real se interpone continua-mente en sus planes. Los actores se niegan a desempeñar los papeles que él ha elegido para ellos. Los escritores a quien
35 trata como niños están listos a ir a la huelga. A su jefe le molesta su arrogancia y busca la forma de deshacerse de él.

El último de los magnates no va a congeniar con los defensores de la máquina hollywoodiana, pero sí les va a gustar a los fanáticos de Fitzgerald. Es una obra que rinde
40 homenaje a la obra de este escritor y a sus últimos y difíciles años como guionista en Hollywood.

1. Las líneas 11–13 que dicen que ". . . Elia Kazan y Harold Pinter. . . han logrado convertir *El último de los magnates* en una película fascinante y mesurada" ilustran la actitud del escritor hacia Kazan y Pinter. Esta actitud es de
   (1) ridículo.
   (2) admiración.
   (3) envidia.
   (4) indiferencia.
   (5) aversión.

2. Las líneas 28–30 dan apoyo a la idea de que Stahr
   (1) es un hombre con imperfecciones de carácter.
   (2) es como Irving Thalberg, el "Niño Maravilla".
   (3) es un hombre dinámico y considerado.
   (4) trata a los escritores como si fueran niños.
   (5) está al frente de todos los aspectos de la producción. ⟶

3. Al afirmar que "*El último de los magnates* no va a congeniar con los defensores de la máquina hollywoodiana", el crítico implica que la película

(1) será impopular con la mayoría de los críticos de cine.
(2) tendrá éxito y generará altos ingresos.
(3) no ganará premios cinematográficos.
(4) ofenderá a los descendientes de Fitzgerald.
(5) ofenderá a los productores de películas de Hollywood.

ESCRIBA UNA CRÍTICA DE CINE

Los artistas: Lea los créditos.

1. Director(a):

2. Actores/Actrices

(protagonistas)

(actores secundarios)

3. Escritor y compositor de la música:

La película propiamente

4. En un párrafo o dos, diga cuál es el argumento de la película.

5. ¿La actuación del reparto es creíble?

6. ¿Qué le gusta de la película?

7. ¿Qué le disgusta de la película y querría que se mejorase?

8. ¿Cuál es el mensaje o tema de la película?

9. ¿A quiénes probablemente gustará más esta película?

10. Califique esta película en una escala de 0 a 5 (donde 0 es mala y 5 excelente).

4
LITERATURA DE NO FICCIÓN

Cada vez que leemos el periódico o artículos de revistas como *People, Newsweek, Sports Illustrated, Ebony* o *Better Homes and Gardens,* estamos leyendo literatura de no ficción. Los artículos o los libros que explican cómo ponerse a dieta, raspar la pintura de muebles o comprar un automóvil también entran dentro de este campo. La *literatura de no ficción* es literatura basada no en datos ficticios sino en información factual. El autor, en este caso, escribe acerca de personas, acontecimientos e ideas reales con la finalidad de informar, instruir, entretener, examinar, persuadir, analizar o sentar algo por escrito.

Subgéneros de la literatura de no ficción

La literatura de no ficción engloba una extensa variedad de subgéneros y aborda todos los temas concebibles. A fin de organizar una gama tan amplia de material, las bibliotecas utilizan el sistema decimal de Dewey o el sistema de la Biblioteca del Congreso para clasificar los libros. Entre los subgéneros de literatura de no ficción se pueden citar las biografías, autobiografías, artículos, ensayos, discursos y otros. En este capítulo se explica brevemente cada subgénero y se ilustra con un ejemplo.

La biografía

La *biografía,* categoría popular dentro de la literatura de no ficción, es una semblanza, es decir, un relato de la historia de la vida de un individuo o grupo de individuos. Se han escrito biografías de personajes históricos y políticos, figuras célebres del mundo del deporte y del espectáculo, escritores famosos y otros. El biógrafo hace una relación de los acontecimientos importantes de la vida de una persona y da su opinión acerca de los mismos. La finalidad de la biografía suele ser tanto la de entretener como la de educar. Las biografías se han escrito tradicionalmente después de la muerte de una persona, a modo de homenaje. Hoy, sin embargo, el volumen de biografías que se publican en vida de la persona sigue en constante aumento.

LAS RESPUESTAS DE LOS EJERCICIOS DE ESTE CAPÍTULO EMPIEZAN EN LA PÁGINA 463.

EJERCICIO 1: BIOGRAFÍA
Instrucciones: Lea este bosquejo biográfico de un famoso ensayista y conteste las preguntas que siguen.

¿QUIÉN ERA HENRY DAVID THOREAU?

Henry David Thoreau nació en Concord, Massachusetts, en 1817. Se graduó en Harvard en 1837. La semana que se graduó, escuchó un discurso de Ralph Waldo Emerson y se convirtió en discípulo del famoso ensayista y poeta. Thoreau intentó dedicarse a la docencia, pero presentó su dimisión tras negarse a aplicar a sus alumnos el castigo corporal, parte integral del método de disciplina imperante en esa época. En 1839, Thoreau, de vacaciones, realizó con su hermano una travesía por el río Concord. El viaje engendró su primer libro, *Una semana en los ríos Concord y Merrimack*. Él junto con su hermano también fundaron una escuela privada, donde puso en práctica su idea de realizar excursiones al campo con sus alumnos para estudiar la naturaleza.

El filósofo y escritor Ralph Waldo Emerson alentó a Thoreau a que llevara un diario y escribiera poesía y ensayos. El 4 de julio de 1845, Thoreau empezó su famoso "experimento en vivir" en la laguna Walden y se fue a vivir a una cabaña en el bosque.

Escribió, "Me fui al bosque porque quería vivir de forma deliberada. . . " Las anotaciones que hizo en su diario el tiempo que vivió en la laguna Walden se publicaron después y se convirtieron en un clásico de la literatura estadounidense de no ficción, *Walden.*

Conocido como individualista y no conformista, alguien que no siempre estaba de acuerdo con el resto de la sociedad, Thoreau escribió asimismo el ensayo "Sobre el deber de la desobediencia civil". [Véanse las páginas 243 y 244]. El ensayo fue escrito a consecuencia de su encarcelamiento de un día por rehusarse a pagar un impuesto de capitación para financiar la guerra contra México. También se opuso a la esclavitud y se esforzó sobremanera en 1859 por presentar al público al abolicionista John Brown como mártir. Thoreau murió de tuberculosis en Concord en 1862.

Sus obras—en particular, "Sobre el deber de la desobediencia civil"—fueron posteriormente leídas por Mahatma Gandhi de la India y Martin Luther King, Jr. Sus ideas sobre la desobediencia civil y la resistencia pasiva fueron puestas en práctica por Gandhi y King en sus protestas contra el gobierno. En la actualidad, Thoreau está considerado como uno de los grandes pensadores y escritores de toda la historia de Estados Unidos.

1. Es significativo el hecho de que Thoreau se trasladara a la laguna Walden el 4 de julio de 1845, porque
    (1) eran sus primeras vacaciones como profesor.
    (2) quería atraer la atención mundial a su causa.
    (3) la laguna era más bella en el mes de julio.
    (4) se estaba ocultando de la ley.
    (5) en esa fecha se celebraba la independencia de la nación.

2. En *Walden*, Thoreau escribe: "Me fui al bosque porque quería vivir de forma deliberada, para afrontar solamente los hechos esenciales de la vida, y ver si no podía aprender lo que ella tenía para enseñarme, y no, que a la hora de morir, descubriera que no he vivido". Si siguiéramos el consejo de Thoreau,

(1) viviríamos y trabajaríamos en la ciudad de New York.

(2) participaríamos en el quehacer político nacional.

(3) viviríamos alejados de la civilización.

(4) dedicaríamos un tiempo para pensar acerca del significado y la belleza de la vida.

(5) nos convertiríamos en corredores de bolsa y trataríamos de amasar la mayor cantidad de dinero posible.

3. Según este bosquejo biográfico, la obra de Thoreau que ha tenido más influencia

(1) es el ensayo "Sobre el deber de la desobediencia civil".

(2) es el libro *Una semana en los ríos Concord y Merrimack*.

(3) es el libro *Walden*.

(4) son sus diarios.

(5) es su poesía.

4. Si quisiéramos explicar el significado de desobediencia civil, diríamos que consiste sobre todo en

(1) no hacer caso de todas las leyes aprobadas por el gobierno.

(2) una resistencia no violenta a las leyes injustas.

(3) violar las leyes que no sean de nuestro agrado.

(4) vivir la vida con un espíritu libre.

(5) intentar derrocar el gobierno de forma violenta.

Historia oral: El lenguaje hablado

No todas las obras biográficas documentan la vida de un individuo famoso o distinguido. El libro *Tiempos difíciles* de Studs Terkel relata sucesos e impresiones sobre la vida de diversas "personas comunes y corrientes" que se vieron afectadas por la Gran Depresión de los años 30. En muchos casos, los autores de no ficción entrevistan a la fuente para luego resumir la entrevista con sus propias palabras. En el extracto de abajo, Terkel presenta las preguntas que hiciera a César Chávez, el jefe anterior de los *United Farm Workers of America* (*Trabajadores Agrícolas Unidos de América*) así como las respuestas de Chávez.

EJERCICIO 2: HISTORIA ORAL

Instrucciones: Lea el pasaje y conteste las preguntas que siguen.

¿QUÉ RECUERDA CHÁVEZ DE LA DEPRESIÓN?

[*Chávez*] Habíamos sido pobres, pero sabíamos que *allí* teníamos una cama y que *aquí* teníamos nuestro cuarto. Había una cocina. Era una vida bastante estable; y teníamos pollos y puercos, huevos y todas esas cosas. Pero, de repente, todo cambió. Cuando uno es pequeño, uno no puede entender estas cosas. Sabes que hay algo que no está bien y no te gusta, pero no lo cuestionas y no dejas que eso te influya negativamente. Sigues yendo por inercia.

Pero esto afectó mucho a mi padre. Él estaba acostumbrado a ser propietario de su tierra y súbitamente ya no tenía tierra. Lo que oí. . . lo que pude entender de las conversaciones entre mi madre y mi padre—cosas como, "trabajaremos esta temporada y reuniremos suficiente dinero y compraremos un terreno en Arizona"—cosas como ésas—, se convirtieron en una especie de hábito. Nunca perdió la esperanza de que algún día se recuperaría y compraría un terreno.

Entiendo pero muy, muy bien esta sensación. Estas conversaciones eran como melancólicas. Supongo que mis hermanos y mis hermanas también podían ver esa expresión de tristeza que tenía mi padre.

[*Terkel*] ¿Ese terreno que quería. . .?

[*Chávez*] No, nunca. Eso no pasó nunca. Dejó de hablar de eso hace años. El anhelo de una tierra, es una fuerza muy poderosa.

Cuando nos mudamos a California, trabajábamos después de la escuela. A veces no asistíamos a clase. "Siguiendo las cosechas", perdimos muchos días de clase. Tratábamos de ganar lo suficiente para poder sobrevivir el invierno siguiente. Toda la familia recolectaba albaricoques, nueces, ciruelas. Éramos novatos en esto, nunca habíamos sido trabajadores migratorios.

Escriba *V* si la afirmación es verdadera o *F* si es falsa.

_____ **1.** Chávez recuerda su experiencia con amargura.

_____ **2.** Según Chávez, los niños siguen adelante incluso cuando no entienden lo que pasa.

_____ **3.** Ser un trabajador migratorio afectó la posibilidad de que Chávez recibiera una buena instrucción escolar.

_____ **4.** La Gran Depresión no afectó en gran manera a la familia Chávez.

Autobiografía: Sobre uno mismo

Sólo usted puede escribir su *autobiografía,* es decir, la historia de su vida. La autobiografía es la biografía de su vida escrita por usted mismo. Un gran número de escritores autobiográficos no son escritores profesionales propiamente, sino individuos notables que deciden hacernos una relación de sus vidas. Entre las autobiografías más notables se destacan *El Diario de Anne Frank,* joven judía que se ocultó de los nazis durante la Segunda Guerra Mundial; *Fuera de África,* autobiografía de Isak Dinesen, en la que se basó la película del mismo título; y la *Autobiografía de Malcolm X* que inspiró la película de Spike Lee sobre esta figura política. Las autobiografías también reciben el nombre de *memorias.*

Al igual que la literatura de ficción, la literatura de no ficción presenta ciertos rasgos de estilo característicos. Las autobiografías, en particular, tienden a ser escritas en un estilo más informal, dado que los escritores revelan detalles más íntimos de sus vidas. En el pasaje siguiente, Dick Gregory, escritor, cómico y activista social, hace uso de gran cantidad de fragmentos de frases: imágenes rápidas para establecer el ambiente. Observe su estilo y los efectos que logra con él.

EJERCICIO 3: AUTOBIOGRAFÍA

Instrucciones: Lea el pasaje y conteste las preguntas que siguen.

¿QUÉ PIENSA DICK GREGORY DE LA ESCUELA?

La maestra creía que yo era tonto. No sabía escribir, no sabía leer, no sabía aritmética. Simplemente tonto. Los maestros nunca se interesaron en averiguar que no me podía concentrar porque tenía mucha hambre, porque no había desayunado. En lo único en que podía pensar era en el mediodía, ¿cuándo llegaría? En una de ésas, podría entrar a hurtadillas en el guardarropa y comerme un bocado del almuerzo de otro niño del bolsillo de su abrigo. Un bocado de algo. Pasta. No se puede hacer una comida de verdad con pasta, o ponerla en pan para hacer un sándwich; pero a veces podía comerme unas cucharadas del frasco de pasta en la parte de atrás de la clase. Las mujeres embarazadas tienen caprichos extraños. Yo estaba embarazado de pobreza. Embarazado de suciedad y de olores que hacían que la gente no se me acercara, embarazado de frío y de zapatos que nunca me compraron nuevos, embarazado con otras cinco personas en mi cama y sin un papá en el cuarto de al lado, y embarazado de hambre. La pasta no sabe tan mal cuando se tiene hambre.

La maestra creía que era un alborotador. Todo lo que veía desde el frente de la clase era un niñito negro que se retorcía en su asiento de idiota y hacía ruidos y golpeaba a los niños a su alrededor. Supongo que no podía ver a un niño que hacía ruidos porque él quería que alguien se percatara de que estaba allí.

—DICK GREGORY: "No pobre, sino arruinado".
Negro: Una autobiografía. (Fragmento)

1. Según el punto de vista del autor, la maestra era todo lo siguiente excepto que
   (1) no sabía que pasaba hambre.
   (2) era indiferente a las necesidades que estaba pasando.
   (3) sabía de su comportamiento perturbador.
   (4) no estaba interesada en él.
   (5) entendía sus problemas.

2. César Chávez y Dick Gregory se parecían en que ambos
   (1) vivieron en hogares sin padre.
   (2) sufrieron interrupciones en sus primeros años de instrucción escolar.
   (3) no tenían hermanos ni hermanas.
   (4) se hicieron famosos a pesar de la pobreza sufrida en la niñez.
   (5) perdieron la fe en todos los adultos.

3. El título del capítulo del que ha sido extraído este fragmento es, "No pobre, sino arruinado". Este título sugiere que Gregory
   (1) no era pobre, sino que simplemente se había gastado el dinero del almuerzo.
   (2) estaba acostumbrado a la pobreza, por lo que no le molestaba.

(3) supone que ser pobre es lo mismo que estar arruinado.

(4) cree que estar arruinado es mejor que ser pobre.

(5) piensa que aquéllos a quienes la gente llama pobres no se consideran necesariamente pobres ellos mismos.

Diarios y cartas

Los *diarios* son una relación "día a día" que hace un individuo de sus actividades, acontecimientos o reflexiones. Al escribir su autobiografía, el autor suele consultar sus diarios como fuente de información. Ralph Waldo Emerson llamaba a sus diarios los "bancos de ahorro" en que depositaba sus pensamientos. A continuación se transcribe una anotación hecha en uno de sus diarios.

EJERCICIO 4: ANOTACIONES DE UN DIARIO

Instrucciones: Lea el pasaje y conteste las preguntas que siguen.

¿CUÁL ES LA ACTITUD DE EMERSON HACIA LA VIDA?

11 de noviembre de 1842 [*edad treinta y nueve años*]

No sea demasiado tímido y miedoso con lo que hace. La vida toda es un experimento. Cuantos más experimentos haga, mejor. ¿Qué pasa si son un poco accidentados, y se le mancha o se le desgarra el abrigo? ¿Qué pasa si fracasa, y queda cubierto de barro una o dos veces? Levántese otra vez; no debe tener nunca miedo de una caída.

1. Según la cita anterior, ¿con cuál de estas afirmaciones sobre la vida estaría de acuerdo Emerson?
   (1) La vida es muy fácil y agradable.
   (2) La vida es un don precioso que no debe malgastarse.
   (3) La vida es una carrera de obstáculos.
   (4) La vida no es justa.
   (5) La vida es riesgo; arriesgarse es estar vivo.

2. ¿Cuál de estas ocupaciones expresa mejor las ideas de Emerson?
   (1) filósofo
   (2) escritor
   (3) astronauta
   (4) médico
   (5) historiador

Artículo: Nada más que los hechos

Los *artículos* son narraciones breves de no ficción, que aparecen en periódicos o revistas, en que el escritor presenta datos factuales, normalmente de manera objetiva. Los artículos principales suelen tratar temas de gran interés para el lector: un artículo puede mostrar a los lectores cómo hacer algo práctico o puede simplemente proporcionar esparcimiento y diversión. La lectura de un periódico importante le permite practicar de forma regular sus destrezas de lectura y comprensión así como disfrutar de una dosis diaria de interesante literatura de no ficción. El índice del periódico le servirá de guía para localizar los artículos y captar las diferencias que existen entre informes objetivos y subjetivos.

Ensayo: Opinión del autor

Un *ensayo* es una obra de no ficción en la que el autor presenta un punto de vista personal acerca de un tema determinado. El ensayo ha sido tradicionalmente un género de escritura de tipo formalista: una obra que "expone" y analiza un tema.

Más abajo ofrecemos un extracto de un conocido ensayo de tipo formalista, "Sobre el deber de la desobediencia civil", de Henry David Thoreau. Recuerde que el ensayo fue escrito después de que encarcelaran a Thoreau por no pagar un impuesto de capitación que consideraba contribuía a la guerra contra México. El ensayo es personal en cuanto que Thoreau lo utiliza para explicar sus puntos de vista; además, tiene un tono serio y un vocabulario algo más elevado que la prosa actual. Las ideas expuestas en este fragmento del extenso ensayo fueron compartidas por muchos líderes del movimiento en pro de los derechos civiles en los años 60 y 70, los opositores de los nazis en los años 30 y 40, y otros.

EJERCICIO 5: ENSAYO DE TIPO FORMALISTA

Instrucciones: Lea el pasaje y conteste las preguntas que siguen.

¿CUÁL ES EL PROPÓSITO DEL GOBIERNO?

Acepto a cabalidad el dicho de que "El mejor gobierno es el gobierno que gobierna menos"; y me gustaría verlo en acción de forma rápida y sistemática. Llevado a la práctica, finalmente representa esto—que también creo—de que "El mejor gobierno es el que no gobierna en absoluto"; y cuando los seres humanos estén preparados para ello, ése será el tipo de gobierno que tendremos. El gobierno es a lo sumo conveniente; pero, por lo general, la mayoría de los gobiernos son inconvenientes y todos los gobiernos lo son en ocasiones. Las objeciones que se han opuesto en contra de un ejército permanente, que son muy numerosas e importantes, y que merecen prevalecer, también pueden oponerse a la idea de un gobierno permanente. El ejército permanente es nada más que un arma del gobierno permanente. El gobierno mismo, que es sólo la modalidad que ha escogido la gente para ejecutar su voluntad, está igualmente expuesto a ser abusado y pervertido antes de que la gente pueda actuar por su intermedio. Testigo de ello es el caso de la presente guerra contra México, fruto de la labor de relativamente pocos individuos que utilizan el gobierno permanente como su instrumento; ya que, en el principio, la gente no habría consentido a esto.

Este gobierno de Estados Unidos, ¿qué es, sino una tradición, aunque reciente, dedicada a transmitirse incólume a la posteridad, pero perdiendo a cada instante parte de su integridad? No posee la vitalidad ni la fuerza de un solo ser humano con vida; ya que un solo ser humano puede doblegarla a su voluntad. Es una especie de fusil de madera para las personas mismas, que, si alguna vez se deciden a usarlo contra otro de verdad, de seguro se habrá de partir. . . .

1. El título del ensayo da a entender que el ciudadano
   (1) que desobedece las leyes es desleal.
   (2) debe servir en el ejército.
   (3) debe valorar la ciudadanía estadounidense.
   (4) está obligado a violar una ley injusta.
   (5) debe votar en todas las elecciones.

2. Donde dice "El gobierno mismo, que es la única modalidad que ha escogido la gente para ejecutar su voluntad. . .", la palabra *ejecutar* quiere decir:
   (1) dar la pena capital a los criminales.
   (2) matar durante una guerra.
   (3) llevar a cabo; realizar.
   (4) hacer caso omiso de los deseos de alguien.
   (5) crear; originar.

3. Conforme a la interpretación de Thoreau, el gobierno
   (1) es la gente misma.
   (2) está formado por líderes expertos.
   (3) es un instrumento del ejército permanente.
   (4) debe dar menos libertades a sus ciudadanos.
   (5) estimula la libertad individual.

EJERCICIO 6: COMPARACIÓN Y CONTRASTE DE ESTILOS

El *estilo,* uso particular y exclusivo que hace el autor del lenguaje al expresar una idea, es el rasgo que distingue un ensayo de tipo formalista de otro más informal. A continuación se transcriben dos ensayos sobre computadoras: uno de ellos presenta un enfoque más leve—una conversación entre un cliente y un trabajador de una línea aérea—; el otro trata sobre el peligro de las computadoras en el lugar de trabajo. Observe las diferencias de estilo y método.

Instrucciones: Lea los pasajes y conteste las preguntas que siguen.

Pasaje 1

¿QUÉ SIENTE EL ESCRITOR HACIA LAS COMPUTADORAS?

Una de las expresiones de la lengua que más horrorizan es "La computadora no funciona"; y cada vez se la oye con más frecuencia cuando intentamos desempeñar nuestras funciones en el trabajo.

El otro día estaba en el aeropuerto tratando de comprar un boleto para Washington y el agente me dijo: —Lo siento, no le puedo vender el boleto. Nuestra computadora no funciona.

—¿Cómo que no funciona? ¿Está apagada?

—No, no está apagada. Es que no funciona.

—Si la computadora no funciona, relléneme entonces a mano un boleto.

—No le puedo rellenar el boleto. La computadora es la única que está autorizada a emitir los boletos.

Miré a lo largo del mostrador, y todos los agentes estaban tomando café y mirando a una pantalla en blanco.

—¿Qué es lo que hacen ustedes?

—Nosotros entramos en la computadora la información sobre el viaje, y después la computadora nos dice si usted puede volar con nosotros o no.

—Por eso cuando no funciona, ustedes tampoco funcionan.

—Buena observación, señor. Nunca antes me lo habían dicho de esa manera.

—¿Por cuánto tiempo va a estar así la computadora? —quería saberlo.

—No tengo la menor idea. A veces el sistema se va por 10 minutos, a veces por dos horas. No hay manera de saberlo, a menos que se lo preguntemos a la computadora; pero, como no funciona, no nos responderá.

—ART BUCHWALD: "La computadora no funciona". (Fragmento)

1. En este pasaje se encuentran todos los elementos de estilo siguientes excepto
   (1) exageración.
   (2) narración en primera persona.
   (3) largos párrafos explicativos.
   (4) diálogo.
   (5) sarcasmo.

2. "No hay manera de saberlo, a menos que se lo preguntemos a la computadora; pero, como no funciona, no nos responderá". Esta frase revela lo siguiente del agente de la línea aérea:
   (1) irritación con el cliente
   (2) creatividad
   (3) capacidad para afrontar una crisis
   (4) dependencia total en la computadora
   (5) experiencia en el trabajo

Pasaje 2

¿QUÉ OPINA ESTE ESCRITOR DE LAS COMPUTADORAS?

Cada vez se hace más probable que los millones de personas de los niveles inferiores de las jerarquías electrónicas [*redes de computadoras que conectan gerentes con trabajadores*] pasen sus días aislados en tierra de nadie, esclavos de los sistemas de información inteligentes que informan de su progreso a supervisores invisibles en lugares alejados. Como las computadoras miden la cantidad mejor que la calidad, dichos sistemas tienden a recompensar a los empleados que trabajan más rápido en vez de a los que trabajan mejor. Existe un aumento pronunciado de soledad y desconexión a medida que los individuos desempeñan sus funciones con ímpetu ciego. Las personas que atienden a los clientes por teléfono o en la caja registradora cortan bruscamente cualquier intento de conversación ociosa, debido a que su rendimiento es supervisado electrónicamente. Antes se les juzgaba por su capacidad de comunicarse con los clientes o de resolver situaciones inesperadas. Ahora son evaluados por el número de transacciones que completan en un turno o por el número de pulsaciones de teclado que les toma para redactar un documento. En estas "fábricas de explotación electrónicas", las computadoras mandan sobre las personas, y no al revés.

—MARY S. GLUCKSMAN: "La cara siniestra de la bonanza".
(Fragmento)

3. El tono de este pasaje, comparado con el del Pasaje 1, es más
   (1) jocoso.
   (2) satírico.
   (3) conversacional.
   (4) serio.
   (5) informal.

4. La idea principal del extracto es que las oficinas electrónicas
   (1) son el futuro del ámbito laboral.
   (2) representan un avance si las comparamos con las oficinas del pasado.
   (3) crean problemas sicológicos en los trabajadores.
   (4) aumentan la productividad de Estados Unidos.
   (5) ayudan a los empleados a desarrollar su capacidad de resolución de problemas.

5. ¿Con cuál de estas afirmaciones estarían de acuerdo ambos autores?
   (1) El mundo sería mejor si no hubiera computadoras.
   (2) La industria de las líneas aéreas sería más segura sin computadoras.
   (3) Las computadoras forman parte indispensable de la vida humana.
   (4) El ser humano debe controlar las computadoras y no dejar que éstas lo controlen a él.
   (5) El gobierno debe controlar todas las computadoras.

Discurso: Decir las cosas como son

El ensayo puede presentar una serie de tonos, estilos, lenguaje y temas. El *discurso,* comunicación *pronunciada en público* sobre un tema, se asemeja al ensayo en cuanto a su organización. El orador debe realizar una presentación que mantenga la atención y el interés del oyente, debe respaldar la idea principal con argumentos y llegar a una conclusión clara. Dado que los discursos no son normalmente obras de ficción, se los puede analizar examinando su tono, estilo, mensaje y propósito.

Entre los discursos más notables, se puede mencionar la "Alocución de Gettysburg" de Abraham Lincoln, el "Discurso inaugural" de John F. Kennedy y "Tengo un sueño" de Martin Luther King Jr. El discurso de King ha sido publicado, grabado y ampliamente reconocido como piedra angular del movimiento de derechos civiles.

EJERCICIO 7: PRÁCTICA DE LECTURA DE DISCURSOS

Instrucciones: Lea el fragmento del "Discurso inaugural" de John F. Kennedy y conteste las preguntas que siguen.

¿QUÉ PIDE EL PRESIDENTE DE SUS CONCIUDADANOS?

En sus manos, compatriotas, más que en las mías, radica el éxito o el fracaso final de nuestra empresa. Desde que se fundó este país, cada generación de americanos ha sido llamada a dar testimonio de su lealtad nacional. Las tumbas de los jóvenes americanos que respondieron a la llamada al servicio se encuentran por todo el planeta. Ahora el clarín nos llama otra vez: no para tomar las armas, aunque necesitamos armas; no al combate, aunque estamos siendo combatidos; sino a asumir la responsabilidad de una larga y sombría lucha, sin interrupción, "regocijándonos en la esperanza, pacientes en la congoja", una lucha contra los enemigos comunes de la humanidad: tiranía, pobreza, enfermedad y la guerra misma.

¿Podemos derrotar a estos enemigos formando una gran alianza mundial, norte y sur, este y oeste, que puede asegurarnos una vida más fructífera para toda la humanidad? ¿Se unirán ustedes conmigo en este esfuerzo histórico?

En la larga historia del mundo, solamente se ha otorgado a unas pocas generaciones el papel de defender la libertad en su hora de máximo peligro. No me evado de esta responsabilidad; le doy la bienvenida. No creo que ninguno de nosotros cambiaríamos nuestros sitios por el de otras personas u otra generación. La energía, la fe, la devoción que aportamos a esta empresa iluminará a nuestro país y a todos los que le sirven, y el resplandor de esa llama puede realmente iluminar el mundo.

Así pues, compatriotas, no pregunten lo que puede hacer su país por ustedes; pregunten lo que ustedes pueden hacer por su país.

Ciudadanos del mundo, no pregunten lo que puede hacer Estados Unidos por ustedes, sino lo que podemos nosotros hacer juntos por la libertad del mundo.

1. El tono del discurso es más bien de
   (1) sarcasmo.
   (2) despreocupación.
   (3) enojo.
   (4) exhortación.
   (5) tristeza.

2. Una de las finalidades del discurso es motivar a los oyentes a
   (1) preservar el derecho a portar armas.
   (2) alistarse en las fuerzas armadas.
   (3) servir al país.
   (4) jurar su lealtad a la patria.
   (5) prepararse para el combate.

3. El discurso se vale de todos estos recursos estilísticos excepto
   (1) un patrón rítmico predecible y el uso de rima.
   (2) el uso de la primera persona plural que establece una relación con los oyentes.
   (3) expresiones pegadizas en las que los sujetos y los objetos están invertidos.
   (4) repetición de palabras clave.
   (5) preguntas que invitan a los lectores a responder "sí" en silencio.

El estilo y el lenguaje del comentario

El *comentario* es un subgénero de la literatura de no ficción en que el escritor "comenta", es decir, emite su juicio o opinión acerca de una obra de literatura o de arte: cine, televisión, danza, música, bellas artes y teatro. El *crítico,* persona que escribe comentarios, evalúa la obra de arte: sus aspectos positivos como negativos. Puesto que el crítico describe al igual que analiza la obra de arte, el estilo y el lenguaje del comentario suele ser muy descriptivo. El lector del comentario debe poder analizar el estilo así como el tono de la crítica para interpretar la opinión que tiene el crítico de una determinada obra de arte.

Lectura en dos niveles

Para entender las críticas literarias, se debe ser capaz de leer en dos niveles: en primer lugar, se han de comprender los datos factuales referentes a la obra de arte y su autor; luego se han de comprender las opiniones del crítico.

Hágase estas preguntas:

1. ¿Qué dice el crítico sobre el autor o el talento del autor?
2. ¿Qué aspectos de la obra agradan al crítico? ¿Qué le desagrada? ¿Qué frases expresan lo que piensa el crítico de la obra?
3. ¿Qué afirmaciones se basan en datos factuales referentes a la obra? ¿Qué afirmaciones se basan en la opinión o reacción personal del crítico a la obra?
4. ¿Recomienda el crítico la obra? ¿Reconoce el crítico el valor literario de la misma?

EJERCICIO 8: LEER LA CRÍTICA DE UN LIBRO

Instrucciones: Lea esta crítica de una novela y conteste las preguntas que siguen.

Crítica de *Buscando a Bobby*
de Gloria Norris, Knopf, $15.95

La narradora de esta en muchas ocasiones graciosa novela, Marianne, es una mujer de Mississippi que acaba de caer en la cuenta de que, a pesar de tener un esposo rico y apuesto y casi perfecto, su matrimonio ha sido un error. Se marcha a la ciudad de New York, esperando encontrar a su primo hermano Bobby. Una vez cuando eran niños y ella se perdió en una cacería de zorros, Bobby la encontró y le dijo: "Incluso si estás a mil millas de distancia, seguiré estando cerca de ti y sabré lo que estás pensando. No importa lo que pase, cuando seamos mayores, estaré siempre a tu lado. Todo lo que tienes que hacer es pensar en mí y estaré cerca de ti". El relato del noviado y de la boda de Marianne, su conversadora suegra, y las escenas de New Orleans son todas maravillosas. Pero los problemas empiezan a acumularse, incluso para un lector compasivo, cuando Marianne, en New York, se entera de que Bobby ha pasado de vender acciones a dirigir una obra en Broadway. El almuerzo con un productor en Sardi es absurdo, y Bobby y su tan ponderado carisma se hacen igualmente difíciles de creer. Nada de lo que hace comunica al lector esa imagen de magnetismo que parece impresionar a todos en el libro. Después, gracias a Bobby, Marianne entra al mundo del espectáculo y se convierte en una próspera representante. También se topa con él en México y se entera de su secreto. Lo que llega a saber de su pasado no es para nada sorprendente (con un buen terapeuta se le puede arreglar el problema en un par de semanas.). Norris, que ha publicado numerosos cuentos cortos, posee el don de crear personajes excéntricos, exagerados, pero que son mucho más entretenidos si estuvieran en el verdadero Sur que cuando los encaja en el estereotipadamente descrito mundo del espectáculo de New York o Hollywood.

Instrucciones: Escriba un signo (+) en el espacio en blanco si la afirmación expresa una opinión positiva, un signo (–) si expresa una opinión negativa, y una *F* si la afirmación se refiere a un dato del argumento de la novela.

_____ **1.** "La narradora de esta en muchas ocasiones graciosa novela, Marianne. . ."

_____ **2.** "Pero los problemas empiezan a acumularse, incluso para un lector compasivo, cuando Marianne, en New York, se entera de que Bobby ha pasado de vender acciones a dirigir una obra en Broadway".

_____ **3.** "También se topa con él en México y se entera de su secreto".

EJERCICIO 9: LEER LA CRÍTICA DE UNA NOVELA

Instrucciones: Escoja la mejor respuesta para cada una de las siguientes preguntas.

1. El crítico dice, "Norris, que ha publicado numerosos cuentos cortos, posee el don de crear personajes excéntricos, exagerados. . . " En esta cita, la palabra *exagerados* quiere decir:
   (1) grandes; obesos
   (2) demasiados personajes para la duración del libro
   (3) inapropiados; fuera de lugar
   (4) dominantes; altaneros; hoscos
   (5) memorables; únicos

2. ¿Con cuál de las siguientes afirmaciones estaría de acuerdo el crítico?
  (1) Norris debería más bien escribir cuentos cortos y no novelas.
  (2) Un defecto importante de la novela es la forma en que están escritas las escenas de New York.
  (3) Las escenas más interesantes de la novela se ambientan en México.
  (4) *Buscando a Bobby* es una novela excepcionalmente bien escrita.
  (5) El personaje de Marianne debe estar mejor desarrollado.

Lectura de otras clases de comentarios

Las tres críticas que siguen son comentarios sobre música, arte y televisión respectivamente. A medida que vaya leyendo las críticas, preste atención a qué aspectos de la obra evalúan los distintos críticos. Pregúntese: ¿Qué datos sobre la obra misma incluye el crítico? ¿Le gusta o no esta obra al crítico? ¿Por qué? ¿Qué dice el crítico sobre los antecedentes del artista? ¿Cuál es el estilo del crítico? ¿Cómo presenta el mensaje?

EJERCICIO 10: LEER UNA CRÍTICA DE MÚSICA
Instrucciones: Lea la crítica de música y conteste las preguntas que siguen.

¿QUIÉN ES WYNTON MARSALIS Y QUÉ PIENSA ESTE CRÍTICO DE ÉL?
Crítica de *Flores de invernadero* de Wynton Marsalis
(Nota de cuatro estrellas) ★★★★

La historia y evolución del jazz está marcada por la llegada de trompetistas precoces de gran talento que fueron revolucionando la forma en que se percibía el jazz, tanto por parte del público como por parte de los músicos que lo interpretaban.

King Oliver, Louis Armstrong, Roy Eldridge, Dizzy Gillespie, Clifford Brown, Miles Davis, Lee Morgan y Lester Bowie, entre otros, entraron en escena y lo cambiaron todo de manera radical, avanzando en nuevas direcciones o simplemente poniendo en evidencia algo que se había pasado por alto. Aunque sólo ha escrito tres álbumes como director, Wynton Marsalis ya forma parte de esta élite, al menos en reputación.

En parte, lo que distingue a Marsalis es que parece haber asimilado la historia del jazz a la temprana edad de veintitrés años. A estas alturas solamente su bello tono e impresionante técnica son suyos propios, ya que ha optado por trabajar, en su mayor parte, dentro de estilos más conocidos. Quizá aquí radique la clave de su genio. Marsalis ha logrado evadir la trampa en que caen tantos músicos jóvenes que tratan de ser diferentes sólo por ser diferentes. Es evidente que Marsalis disfruta haciendo comparaciones con Miles Davis (de la década del 50) en "Melancolía". Su especialidad es reconocer primeramente dicha deuda y después tocar la pieza de un modo tal como para convertirla en una expresión total de sí mismo. El que Wynton Marsalis sea también un músico consumado puede explicar en parte su entendimiento de cómo se puede fomentar una tradición en vez de simplemente copiarla.

1. Esta crítica revela
   (1) el desagrado del crítico por los músicos jóvenes.
   (2) la admiración y el aprecio del crítico por Marsalis.
   (3) la parcialidad contra los estilos de jazz más viejos o conocidos.
   (4) la falta de conocimientos del crítico acerca de los músicos de jazz clásicos.
   (5) la creencia de que la música clásica es mejor que el jazz.

2. El crítico dice: "se puede fomentar una tradición en vez de simplemente copiarla". Esta afirmación apoya la opinión del crítico de que un músico debe
   (1) hacer caso omiso de otros músicos en su camino a la fama.
   (2) mejorar, no simplemente repetir, el arte.
   (3) rechazar a todos los músicos del pasado.
   (4) experimentar con todo tipo de música.
   (5) grabar la música de artistas previos.

EJERCICIO 11: LEER UNA CRÍTICA DE ARTE

Instrucciones: Lea esta crítica de pintura y conteste las preguntas que siguen.

¿QUÉ VE EL CRÍTICO EN LA OBRA DE WYETH?
Crítica del artista Andrew Wyeth y su obra
de Frieda Davenport

Podemos tomar fotografías para "capturar momentos" de nuestro pasado. No nos consideramos artistas, ya que usamos la cámara para fijar el recuerdo para nosotros mismos. Cuando vemos una pintura que capta un momento y le da significado, la llamamos arte.

Andrew Wyeth, uno de los artistas estadounidenses más populares de nuestra época, tiene esa capacidad de captar momentos en lienzo. Sus pinturas al temple y acuarelas presentan colores naturales: térreos tonos de marrones, grises y apagados matices de rosa. Wyeth usa el blanco mejor que nadie.

Sus temas y paisajes son rurales: sus composiciones reflejan una sencillez meditativa, como si hubiera creado fotografías "impresionistas". No sólo capta un paisaje sino un objeto contra un horizonte como fondo, granjas antiguas, baldes abollados, cortinas de encaje rasgadas y marcos de ventanas.

Estudiar a Wyeth es ver una de sus pinturas: *El mundo de Christina* (1948), su obra más famosa. Christina, una amiga del pintor, se encuentra a gatas con la espalda hacia el observador. Se inclina hacia una granja en el horizonte, quizás anhelándola. En el centro de la pintura y en el horizonte hay una choza, un granero, que está a la izquierda de la casa.

Los tres focos—la joven, el granero y la granja—están "equilibrados" en un campo de hierba estéril. La "sencillez" es característica de Wyeth. Cada vez que vemos el cuadro, nos sentimos atraídos por Christina, el "centro" del lienzo y su mundo.

A Wyeth se le encasilla a menudo en la categoría del realismo estadounidense, pero el clasificar artistas es limitar nuestras opiniones de sus logros. La sencillez de la obra de Wyeth se opone a la complejidad de pensamiento, y se nos deja solos para disfrutar por completo del momento que nos crea.

1. La crítica trata de todo menos de lo siguiente:
   (1) la popularidad del artista
   (2) los tipos de pinturas y las técnicas utilizados
   (3) la preferencia del artista por los colores
   (4) una pintura específica
   (5) el precio de una de las pinturas de Wyeth

2. La cualidad de Wyeth que más le gusta al crítico en *El mundo de Christina*
   (1) es la precisión.
   (2) son los colores.
   (3) es la sencillez.
   (4) es la complejidad.
   (5) es la descripción de los años 40.

Leer una crítica de televisión

En muchas de las críticas, el crítico reacciona ante un libro, una película o una obra de arte. Sin embargo, las críticas pueden tratar de las tendencias o características de un determinado género de arte. La crítica de televisión que se ofrece más abajo presenta opiniones acerca de la naturaleza de la programación televisiva. A medida que vaya leyendo, preste atención a la distinción entre afirmaciones basadas en datos factuales y afirmaciones basadas en opiniones. Recuerde que la mayor parte de las críticas no son sino ensayos de persuasión. La finalidad del crítico se ilustra con detalles y ejemplos. Observe el estilo, tono y uso del lenguaje del crítico.

EJERCICIO 12: LEER UNA CRÍTICA DE TELEVISIÓN
Instrucciones: Lea esta crítica de televisión y conteste las preguntas que siguen.

¿CÓMO CALIFICA EL CRÍTICO LAS MEJORES COMEDIAS DE TV DE "TODOS LOS TIEMPOS"?
"M★A★S★H"

Mientras que "Lucy" creó una nueva forma de comedia para televisión y "Todo en familia" utilizó temas sociales como blanco de su humor, "M★A★S★H" hizo lo que sólo pueden hacer las comedias geniales, las clásicas: mezclar la hilaridad con la tragedia, a menudo en partes iguales. "M★A★S★H" nos hizo reír hasta que llorábamos. Y, aunque su mensaje antibelicista ocasionalmente era torpe, nunca fue a costa de la risa o el personaje. Al igual que las otras grandes comedias, tuvo éxito principalmente explorando, de hecho celebrando, las relaciones entre los personajes. El último episodio de "M★A★S★H" fue el programa más visto en la historia de la televisión y con mucha razón. Sí, el episodio final de "Cheers" puede que lo supere, pero "M★A★S★H" tiene una urgencia subyacente en su comedia—trata de la vida, la muerte, la guerra y la gracia redentora del humor— que la convierte, en nuestra opinión, en la mejor comedia de televisión de toda la historia.

1. Si tuviera que cambiar el título de la crítica, ¿cuál de estos títulos escogería?
   (1) Dejando todo en familia
   (2) Cómo "Lucy" cambió nuestra forma de ver televisión
   (3) La última de las mejores
   (4) ¿Está mejorando o empeorando la televisión?
   (5) Riendo y llorando con un clásico

2. El crítico está de acuerdo en que una comedia que espera ser la mejor de la historia de la televisión debe
   (1) contener mensajes antibelicistas muy claros.
   (2) establecer estrechas relaciones entre los personajes.
   (3) seguir muy de cerca el formato cómico del programa "Lucy".
   (4) usar "Todo en familia" como modelo de guión.
   (5) emplear humor para ocultar la tragedia del relato.

3. ¿Cuál es el tono de la crítica?
   (1) apreciativo
   (2) cuestionador
   (3) despectivo
   (4) irresoluto
   (5) sarcástico

PRUEBA 5: MATEMÁTICAS

La Prueba de Matemáticas del GED presenta una serie de preguntas de
opción múltiple. Casi todas las preguntas consisten en problemas de
enunciado verbal o se basan en determinados gráficos o ilustraciones. Con
estos ejercicios matemáticos se pretende poner a prueba no sólo sus
conocimientos de aritmética, álgebra y geometría, sino también su capacidad
para resolver problemas. Para poder tener un buen rendimiento, será
necesario estimar la respuesta, seguir los pasos necesarios para la resolución
de un problema y seleccionar únicamente aquellos datos relevantes al
problema. En algunos casos, se habrá de determinar si la información
proporcionada es o no suficiente para la obtención de una respuesta.

¿Cuántas preguntas hay en la prueba?

Se presentan alrededor de 56 problemas y se dispone de 90 minutos para
hacer la prueba. Aproximadamente un tercio de los ejercicios se han de basar
en diagramas, tablas o gráficos. Algunas preguntas aparecerán en grupos de
información, es decir, en forma de un conjunto de uno o más párrafos o de un
dibujo seguido por dos o más problemas. En algunos casos, se presentarán
problemas en que no sea necesaria la realización de ningún tipo de cálculo.
En casos como éstos, se habrá de buscar cómo plantear el problema para
hallar la solución correspondiente.

¿De qué consta la prueba?

La Prueba de Matemáticas del GED se puede dividir según las áreas de
contenido que aborda y las destrezas que pone a prueba. El contenido de
estas pruebas es el siguiente: Aritmética (Medidas; Relaciones Numéricas;
Análisis de Datos)—50%; Álgebra—30%; y Geometría—20%.

Cómo prepararse para la prueba

A continuación ofrecemos una serie de recomendaciones que le serán de
utilidad:

1. Estudiar con detenimiento los ejercicios que se dan de ejemplo a fin de
   interiorizar los nuevos conceptos. Procurar resolver estos ejercicios por
   su propia cuenta.
2. Aprenderse las reglas resumidas en los cuadros que figuran en cada
   sección. Intentar luego repetir esas reglas en voz alta y explicar cómo se
   usan.
3. Verificar los ejercicios con la Clave de Respuestas que se adjunta a
   partir de la página 466. Es necesario darse cuenta de inmediato si se
   comprende o no el concepto estudiado.
4. Hacer uso de todas las estrategias de resolución de problemas
   proporcionadas en esta sección. En particular, se dará usted cuenta de
   que trazando un diagrama con los datos provistos y estimando el
   resultado podría llegar a entender un problema que a primera vista
   parecía confuso.
5. Hacer los ejercicios de práctica a lápiz, escribiendo con cuidado toda la
   información necesaria para la resolución del problema.

Cómo hacer para no ponerse nervioso

Son muchos los que creen que "no son buenos para las matemáticas". Si usted se cuenta entre éstos, le presentamos a seguir algunas ideas que le podrán ser de utilidad:

1. Tenga presente que, aunque a usted las matemáticas lo ponen algo nervioso, esto también sucede con la mayoría de la gente.
2. Las matemáticas requieren de lógica; no obstante, la intuición también suele ser esencial. No tema emplear las ideas que le surjan en la mente al razonar los problemas.
3. Sea creativo cuando la ocasión lo permita. La resolución de un problema de una forma distinta a la indicada en el libro también es aceptable.
4. Estimar las respuestas es útil en un gran número de problemas.
5. Utilice todos los instrumentos que tenga a mano: dedos, papel, lápiz, ilustraciones, en fin, cualquier cosa que le sirva.
6. Tenga confianza en sí mismo y en su capacidad de absorber los conceptos matemáticos y de probar nuevos métodos.

Repaso de números enteros y resolución de problemas

La mayor parte de los problemas que aparecen en la Prueba de Matemáticas son problemas de enunciado verbal. A fin de resolver estos problemas, se hace menester la posesión de sólidos fundamentos en lo que a operaciones matemáticas respecta. La capacidad que posea para manejar decimales, fracciones y otros conceptos matemáticos determinará la velocidad y la precisión con que podrá usted efectuar estos cálculos.

1
DECIMALES

La temperatura normal de Maxine es de 98.6°. Cuando tuvo gripe, le subió a 102.4°.

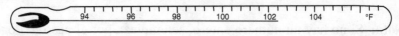

Elena trabaja de recepcionista. Le pagan $6.55 la hora y gana $245.63 por semana.

Los números como 98.6, 102.4 y 245.63 son números decimales. Usted, de seguro, está ya familiarizado con estos números y los maneja en su vida cotidiana. Para comprender cómo se usan los decimales, es importante conocer primero lo que son los valores de posición.

Empleo de los decimales

Nuestro *sistema numérico* (sistema de numeración) consta de diez *dígitos*— 0, 1, 2, 3, 4, 5, 6, 7, 8, 9—con los cuales se pueden representar todos los números. La posición que ocupa un dígito en un número determinado indica el valor que tiene ese dígito; es decir, cada dígito posee un *valor de posición.* Podemos usar la tabla siguiente para leer el valor de posición de los números. Los números enteros se ubican a la izquierda del *punto decimal.* Los decimales, los cuales son partes de un número entero, se ubican a la derecha del punto decimal. Los decimales también reciben el nombre de *fracciones decimales.* Los lugares situados a la derecha del punto decimal se denominan *posiciones decimales.* Obsérvese que los nombres de las posiciones decimales terminan en "-ésimo/-écimo" (o "-ésima/-écima").

Billones	Centenas de millón	Decenas de millón	Millones	Centenas de millar	Decenas de millar	Millares	Centenas	Decenas	Unidades (con)	Décimos	Centésimos	Milésimos	Diezmilésimos	Cienmilésimos	Millonésimos
							3	2	6 •	7	5				

▶ **Nota:** Se usa el punto decimal para separar las posiciones de los números enteros de las posiciones decimales. El punto se lee "con" (o "y").

En el número 326.75, el 3 está ubicado en la posición de las centenas, el 2 en la de las decenas, el 6 en la de las unidades, el 7 en la de los décimos y el 5 en la de los centésimos. El número 326.75 posee dos posiciones decimales. El número se lee "326 con 75 centésimos" (o "326 y 75 centésimas"). La parte .75 se lee "75 centésimos", ya que damos a todo el decimal el nombre de la última posición decimal que ocupa. Ésta es también la razón por la que $326.75 se lee "326 dólares con 75 centavos".

> ## LECTURA DE DECIMALES
>
> 1. Leer primero la parte entera.
> 2. El punto decimal se lee "con" (o "y").
> 3. Leer la parte decimal.
> 4. Nombrar el valor de posición del último dígito.

▶ **Nota:** Si no hay un número entero, se empieza por el paso 3. Por ejemplo: .008 se lee "ocho milésimos".

Los ceros en los decimales

El *cero* desempeña un papel muy importante en la escritura y en la lectura de números decimales. A fin de poder comprender la importancia de los ceros, conviene leer los decimales mixtos indicados a continuación. Los ***decimales mixtos*** son números que combinan números enteros con fracciones decimales.

$$12.5 \qquad 12.05 \qquad 12.005$$

Los números de arriba se leen: "12 con 5 décimos", "12 con 5 centésimos" y "12 con 5 milésimos" respectivamente. Los únicos dígitos usados para escribir estos números son 0, 1, 2 y 5. El valor real del número depende del valor de posición de cada dígito. Los ceros en los otros dos números "retienen" al número 5 en una posición decimal determinada, es decir, en la posición de los centésimos en el número 12.05 y en la posición de los milésimos en el número 12.005.

LAS RESPUESTAS DE LOS EJERCICIOS DE ESTE CAPÍTULO EMPIEZAN EN LA PÁGINA 466.

EJERCICIO 1: LECTURA DE DECIMALES
Instrucciones: Encierre en círculo el número que corresponda al valor escrito. Recuerde que la palabra "con" representa el punto decimal.

1. cinco centésimos   500   .05   .5
2. cien con dos milésimos   102.00   100.2   100.002
3. Escriba con cifras los siguientes números:
   (a) siete décimos
   (b) dos mil con ocho centésimos
   (c) trescientos cinco con cincuenta y seis milésimos
   (d) sesenta y cinco diezmilésimos

Comparación y orden de los decimales

A veces, es necesario comparar decimales para determinar cuál es el mayor. Es en casos como éstos en que resulta útil agregar ceros después del último dígito decimal, puesto que es más fácil comparar números que poseen el mismo número de posiciones decimales. Al añadir ceros a la derecha del último dígito decimal, no se cambia el valor de un número. Por ejemplo,

12.5, 12.50 y 12.500 tienen todos el mismo valor. Para comparar .14 con .126, agregue primero un cero después de .14 para convertirlo en .140. De esta forma, tanto .126 como .140 se expresan en milésimos y tienen el mismo número de posiciones decimales:

$$.14 = .140 \qquad .126 = .126$$

Ahora se puede apreciar mejor que 126 milésimos es menor que 140 milésimos, ya que 126 es menor que 140.

> *Ejemplo:* Ordene de *menor a mayor* los siguientes números: 4.8, 4.12, 4.2 y 4.1003.

> PASO 1. Añada ceros, de modo que cada número tenga la misma cantidad de posiciones decimales. Después numere los decimales mixtos en orden de *menor a mayor.*

4.8	= 4.8000	4º
4.12	= 4.1200	2º
4.2	= 4.2000	3º
4.1003	= 4.1003	1º

> PASO 2. En base a la numeración dada, ordene los números iniciales de *menor a mayor.*

1º	4.1003
2º	4.12
3º	4.2
4º	4.8

EJERCICIO 2: COMPARACIÓN DE DECIMALES
Instrucciones: Resuelva cada uno de los problemas.

1. Elija el número mayor de cada par.

    (a) .005; .05   **(b)** 4.10; 4.01   **(c)** .7; .68   **(d)** .5; .51   **(e)** 1.033; 1.03

2. Sarah tiene que apilar estas cajas según su peso, comenzando desde abajo por la caja más pesada y terminando con la caja más liviana arriba de todas. ¿Cuál es el orden correcto en que se deben apilar las cajas? (Indique los pesos de abajo hacia arriba.)

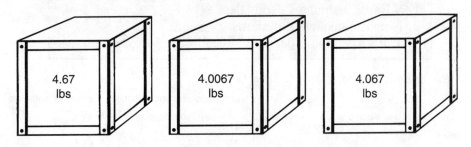

4.67
lbs

4.0067
lbs

4.067
lbs

Redondeo de decimales

Se puede a veces dar el caso de que al resolver un problema que trate de dinero lleguemos, por ejemplo, a una respuesta igual a $25.128. Dado que el dinero se expresa en centavos, debemos redondear la respuesta a dólares y centavos. A continuación, indicamos los pasos que deben seguirse para redondear la respuesta.

Ejemplo: Redondee $25.128 al centavo más cercano.

PASO 1. Subraye el valor de posición al que $25.1<u>2</u>8
esté redondeando.

PASO 2. Identifique el dígito a la derecha de la $25.1<u>2</u>8 ← número a
posición a la que esté redondeando.   la derecha
                                                            igual o
PASO 3. (a) Si este dígito es igual o mayor que $25.1<u>2</u>8 ← mayor
5, aumente en 1 el dígito de la posición   +   1   que 5
a la que esté redondeando y elimine los $25.13
dígitos de la derecha.

(b) Si este dígito es menor que 5, conserve el mismo dígito en
la posición a la que esté redondeando y elimine los dígitos de
la derecha.

EJERCICIO 3: REDONDEO DE DECIMALES
Instrucciones: Resuelva cada uno de los problemas.

1. Una broca de taladro de $\frac{3}{8}$ pulgadas tiene un diámetro de .375 pulgadas.
   ¿Cual es el diámetro de la broca, redondeado al centésimo de pulgada
   más cercano?
2. El ancho de un barco es de 8.275 pies. ¿Cuál es el ancho, redondeado al
   décimo de pie más cercano?
3. La temperatura de Juanita era de 101.68 grados. ¿Cuál era su
   temperatura, redondeada al grado más cercano?

Suma y resta de decimales
Hay tres reglas básicas a saber:

SUMA Y RESTA DE DECIMALES
1. Alinear los puntos decimales.
2. Sumar o restar los números.
3. Colocar el punto decimal alineado con los otros puntos.

Ejemplo 1: Sume: 2.1, .48, 38 y .005.

Los ceros añadidos permiten alinear las columnas.
↓↓
Lea este espacio como si fuera un cero. ⌐ 2.100 ── Alinee los puntos decimales.

```
    2.100
     .480
   38.000
 +   .005
 ────────
   40.585
```

Al restar decimales, se hace a veces necesario agregar ceros para llenar
las posiciones decimales.

Ejemplo 2: Reste .0856 de 12.1.

```
                     0 9 9 1
   12.1           12.1̶0̶0̶0̶  ←── Hay que agregar ceros.
 − .0856         − .0856
 ────────        ────────
                   12.0144
```

EJERCICIO 4: SUMA Y RESTA DE DECIMALES

Instrucciones: Resuelva cada uno de los problemas.

1. Sume 5.9, 2.46, 6, 3.07 y .48.
2. Reste 5.2 de 43.
3. Halle la distancia alrededor del terreno de la ilustración. Todas las dimensiones están dadas en metros.

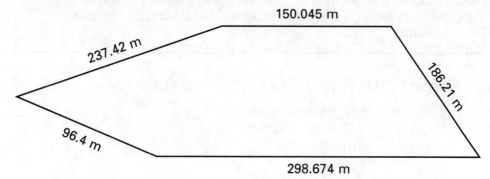

4. ¿Sabe cómo reconciliar una chequera? Al principio de la semana, el saldo era de $472.24. Durante la semana se escribieron cheques por valor de $42.87, $5.93, $10, $17.48 y $38.40. ¿Cuál es el saldo actual?

A continuación se ofrece una factura por servicios de mantenimiento. Utilice la información dada para contestar la *Pregunta 5.*

Cdad.	Pieza	Precio		Trabajo	Precio por mano de obra	
1	Lubricación			1. Prep. invierno	70	00
	engranajes	17	50	2. Soldar talón quilla	90	00
1	Grasa	4	95	3. Reparar escala	—	
1	Aceite	6	00			
1	Gasolina	13	44			
3	Anticongelante	60	75			
				Total mano de obra	160	00
				Total piezas		
				Impuestos	2	63
	Total			Total factura		

LAKE MARINE SERVICE Fecha: 8/12   Nombre: Kim Yang

5. ¿Cuál es el total de la factura para el barco del Sr. Yang?

Multiplicación y división de decimales

Los decimales se multiplican de la misma manera que los números enteros. Terminado este primer paso, se coloca en la respuesta el punto decimal. Existen tres reglas para multiplicar decimales.

Ejemplo 1: Multiplique 3.2 por 4.05.

$$4.05 \quad \text{dos posiciones decimales}$$
$$\times \quad 3.2 \quad \text{una posición decimal}$$
$$\overline{810}$$
$$\underline{12\ 15}$$
$$12.960 = 12.96 \quad \text{tres posiciones decimales en total}$$
$$\text{(Se puede eliminar el último cero.)}$$

Ejemplo 2: $28 \times .06$

$$28 \quad \text{no tiene posiciones decimales}$$
$$\underline{\times .06} \quad \text{dos posiciones decimales}$$
$$1.68 \quad \text{dos posiciones decimales en total}$$

En el ejemplo 3 se enseña cómo agregar ceros al comienzo del resultado para llenar posiciones decimales.

Ejemplo 3: $.043 \times .0056$

$$.0056 \quad \text{cuatro posiciones decimales}$$
$$\underline{\times .043} \quad \text{tres posiciones decimales}$$
$$168$$
$$\underline{224}$$
$$2408 \quad \text{Se necesitan 7 posiciones decimales en total.}$$

En este caso, ponga tres ceros al comienzo del número: **.0002408**

▶ **Nota:** Se facilita la multiplicación si se coloca el número más largo en el multiplicando (número de arriba).

División de decimales

¿Cuántas hamburguesas de $.59 se pueden comprar con $8.00? Para contestar esta pregunta, hay que realizar una división de decimales. Existen dos tipos básicos de división de decimales: (1) división de decimales entre números enteros y (2) división de decimales entre decimales. A continuación se presentan ejemplos de cada uno de estos tipos de división.

El *Ejemplo 1* ilustra cómo se divide un decimal por un número entero.

Ejemplo 1: 36.48 ÷ 4

$$
\begin{array}{r}
9.12 \\
4\overline{)36.48} \\
-36 \\
\hline
04 \\
-4 \\
\hline
08 \\
-8 \\
\hline
0
\end{array}
$$

Se coloca el punto decimal en el cociente alineado con el punto del dividendo.

Según se indica en el *Ejemplo 2,* se dan a veces problemas con números enteros en que es necesario agregar el punto decimal y ceros.

Ejemplo 2: 12 ÷ 25

$$
\begin{array}{r}
.48 \\
25\overline{)12.00} \\
-10\,0 \\
\hline
2\,00 \\
-2\,00 \\
\hline
0
\end{array}
$$

Se coloca el punto decimal en el cociente alineado con el punto del dividendo y los ceros debajo.

El *Ejemplo 3* ilustra un problema que suele a menudo presentar dificultad. Si el primer número entero del divisor no cabe en el primer número que sigue al punto decimal, se debe *necesariamente* agregar un cero antes de proseguir con la división.

Ejemplo 3: .35 ÷ 7

$$
\begin{array}{r}
.05 \\
7\overline{)\,.35}
\end{array}
$$

Se coloca el cero seguido al punto decimal.

División de decimal entre decimal

Para dividir decimales entre sí, hay que convertir el divisor a número entero. En consecuencia, se habrá también de correr el punto decimal del dividendo el mismo número de lugares.

Ejemplo 1: 4.864 ÷ .32

Se corre el punto decimal dos lugares a la derecha. →

$$
\begin{array}{r}
15.2 \\
.32\overline{)4.86\,4} \\
-3\,2 \\
\hline
1\,66 \\
-1\,60 \\
\hline
6\,4 \\
-6\,4 \\
\hline
0
\end{array}
$$

Se coloca el punto decimal en el cociente alineado con el punto decimal del dividendo.

Se corre el punto decimal dos lugares a la derecha.

En algunos casos se habrán de añadir ceros para mover el punto decimal.

Ejemplo 2: 25 ÷ .125

$$
\begin{array}{r}
200. \\
.125\overline{)25.000} \\
-25\ 0 \\
\hline
00 \\
-0 \\
\hline
0 \\
-0 \\
\hline
0
\end{array}
$$

Se corre el punto decimal → (izquierda) tres lugares a la derecha.

← Se agregan tres ceros y se corre el punto decimal tres lugares a la

---

DIVISIÓN DE DECIMAL ENTRE DECIMAL

1. Corra el punto decimal del divisor al extremo derecho.
2. Corra el punto decimal del dividendo el mismo número de lugares a la derecha.
3. Colocar el punto decimal del cociente alineado con el punto del dividendo.
4. Efectuar la división como si ambos números fueran enteros.

▶ **Nota:** El método más fácil de multiplicar o dividir por múltiplos de 10 (10, 100, 1000, etc.) consiste simplemente en mover el punto decimal. Al multiplicar, se corre el punto decimal hacia la derecha. Al dividir, se corre hacia la izquierda. En ambos casos, se corre el punto decimal tantos lugares como ceros haya en el múltiplo de 10. (Como se puede apreciar en los ejemplos, se agregan ceros cuando sea necesario).

Ejemplos: $.13 \times 1000 = 130$ $9.5 \div 100 = .095$

3 ceros 3 posiciones   2 ceros 2 posiciones

EJERCICIO 5: MULTIPLICACIÓN Y DIVISIÓN DE DECIMALES
Instrucciones: Resuelva cada uno de los problemas.

1. Multiplique $.342 \times 1.5$
2. Multiplique $\$6.50 \times 3.5$
3. Divida 6.005 por .05
4. $.012 \div 3$
5. $472 \times 10,000$
6. $456.12 \div 100$
7. En la tienda, Mike compró un pollo de 3.5 libras a $1.19 la libra y 2 galones de leche a $2.30 el galón. ¿Qué expresión representa lo que pagó Mike?
   (1) $(3.5 + 1.19) + (2 + 2.30)$
   (2) $(3.5 + 2) + (1.19 + 2.30)$
   (3) $(3.5 \times 1.19) + (2 \times 2.30)$
   (4) $2.5 (1.19 + 2.30)$
   (5) $2 (1.19 + 2.30)$

2
FRACCIONES

Tipos de fracciones

Las *fracciones* representan partes de una unidad, es decir, de un todo. Al número que está arriba de la raya de fracción se le llama **numerador** y al número de abajo se le llama **denominador**.

$\dfrac{5}{8}$

numerador
indica el número de partes que se toman de la unidad

denominador
indica el número de partes en que está dividida la unidad

Este círculo está dividido en 8 partes. $\frac{5}{8}$ de este círculo están sombreados. $\frac{3}{8}$ no lo están.

Existen diversos tipos de fracciones:

Fracciones propias:	fracciones cuyo numerador es menor que el denominador.	$\frac{1}{2},\frac{2}{5},\frac{1}{7},\frac{3}{9}$
Fracciones impropias:	fracciones cuyo numerador es igual o mayor que el denominador.	$\frac{5}{4},\frac{3}{2},\frac{7}{3},\frac{5}{5}$
Fracciones semejantes:	fracciones que tienen el mismo denominador.	$\frac{1}{8},\frac{3}{8},\frac{6}{8},\frac{5}{8}$
Fracciones desemejantes:	fracciones que tienen denominadores diferentes.	$\frac{1}{4},\frac{7}{8},\frac{3}{5},\frac{9}{2}$
Números mixtos:	fracciones que combinan un número entero con una fracción propia.	$2\frac{1}{3},3\frac{1}{4},6\frac{1}{5}$

LAS RESPUESTAS DE LOS EJERCICIOS DE ESTE CAPÍTULO EMPIEZAN EN LA PÁGINA 467.

EJERCICIO 1: TIPOS DE FRACCIONES

Instrucciones: Basándose en la información de arriba, clasifique los siguientes grupos de fracciones. (Hay grupos que encajan en dos categorías.)

1. $\frac{2}{3},\frac{5}{3},\frac{1}{3},\frac{7}{3}$ _____

2. $1\frac{3}{4},7\frac{1}{5},2\frac{1}{8}$ _____

3. $\frac{1}{2},\frac{1}{4},\frac{2}{5},\frac{3}{7}$ _____

Ampliación y reducción de fracciones

A fin de facilitar el manejo de las fracciones, se puede *ampliar* las mismas a términos mayores o *reducirlas* a términos menores. En ambos casos, se convierte tanto el numerador como el denominador de la fracción. Al ampliar o reducir una fracción, se está hallando una *fracción equivalente,* es decir, una fracción que posee el mismo valor que la fracción inicial. Por ejemplo, una moneda de medio dólar tiene el mismo valor que dos *quarters.* Puesto que son equivalentes las fracciones, se pueden escribir como $\frac{1}{2} = \frac{2}{4}$. Esta relación también se puede representar por medio de una gráfica.

$$\frac{1}{2} = \frac{2}{4}$$

CÓMO AMPLIAR UNA FRACCIÓN A TÉRMINOS MAYORES

Multiplicar el numerador y el denominador por el mismo número, obteniéndose así una fracción equivalente.

Ejemplo 1: $\dfrac{5\,(\times 2) = 10}{8\,(\times 2) = 16}$

CÓMO REDUCIR UNA FRACCIÓN A TÉRMINOS MENORES

Dividir el numerador y el denominador por el mismo número, obteniéndose así una fracción equivalente. (Indicación: Elíjase un número que divida de forma exacta tanto el numerador como el denominador).

Ejemplo 2: $\dfrac{12\,(\div 4) = 3}{16\,(\div 4) = 4}$

Una fracción se halla reducida a su *mínima expresión* si no hay un número entero que no sea 1 que divida de forma exacta el numerador y el denominador. El proceso de reducir una expresión a su mínima expresión recibe el nombre de *simplificación.* Por ejemplo, 3/8 ya está simplificado o reducido a su mínima expresión, ya que no hay otro número entero que no sea 1 por el que puedan dividirse de forma exacta 3 y 8. Se deberá siempre simplificar las fracciones de los resultados. De hecho, todas las fracciones que aparecen en las respuestas de la Prueba de Matemáticas se dan de forma simplificada.

EJERCICIO 2: AMPLIACIÓN Y REDUCCIÓN DE FRACCIONES
Instrucciones: Resuelva cada uno de los problemas.

1. Amplíe cada fracción a términos mayores según se indica.

    (a) $\dfrac{3\,(\times 3)}{8\,(\times 3)} = \dfrac{}{24}$ (b) $\dfrac{6}{7} = \dfrac{}{28}$

2. Reduzca cada fracción a términos menores según se indica.

(a) $\dfrac{12\,(\div 4)}{16\,(\div 4)} = \dfrac{}{4}$

(b) $\dfrac{30}{42} = \dfrac{}{7}$

3. Reduzca cada una de las fracciones a su mínima expresión.

(a) $\dfrac{6}{8}$

(b) $\dfrac{25}{30}$

Relación entre fracciones y decimales

En muchos problemas aritméticos, se habrá de trabajar tanto con fracciones como con decimales. Toda fracción se puede expresar en forma de decimal y viceversa. Los decimales pueden considerarse como fracciones cuyos denominadores son múltiplos de 10 (10, 100, 1000, etc.)

Por ejemplo: una posición decimal $= \dfrac{}{10}$

dos posiciones decimales $= \dfrac{}{100}$

tres posiciones decimales $= \dfrac{}{1000}$

En consecuencia: $.1 = \frac{1}{10}$ y $.03 = \frac{3}{100}$. Repasemos ahora los métodos utilizados para convertir decimales a fracciones y fracciones a decimales.

Ejemplo 1: Convierta .75 a fracción.

PASO 1. En el numerador: escriba el número 75 sin el punto decimal. $\underline{75}$

PASO 2. En el denominador: escriba 100, valor de la última posición decimal.   Esta fracción se puede reducir a $\frac{3}{4}$ $\dfrac{75}{100}$

Ejemplo 2: Convierta .039 a fracción.

$$.039 = \dfrac{39}{1000} \begin{array}{l} \leftarrow \text{número sin punto decimal} \\ \leftarrow \text{tres posiciones decimales son milésimos} \end{array}$$

CONVERSIÓN DE DECIMAL A FRACCIÓN

1. En el numerador: escribir el número sin el punto decimal.
2. En el denominador: escribir el número que corresponde al valor de la última posición decimal.

Para convertir de fracción a decimal, divida el numerador por el denominador. Si dividimos es porque la raya de fracción también indica división. En otras palabras, se puede leer $\frac{5}{8}$ como $5 \div 8$ ó $8\overline{)5}$.

Ejemplo 1:

$$\frac{5}{8} = 8\overline{)5.000} \quad \begin{array}{r} .625 \\ \hline \end{array}$$

$$
\begin{array}{r}
.625 \\
8\overline{)5.000} \\
\underline{-\;4\,8} \\
20 \\
\underline{-\;16} \\
40 \\
\underline{-\;40} \\
0
\end{array}
$$

Ejemplo 2:

$$\frac{2}{3} = 3\overline{)2.00} \quad .66\frac{2}{3}$$

$$\underline{-18}$$
$$20$$
$$\underline{-18}$$
$$2$$

▶ **Nota:** El *Ejemplo 2* es un decimal periódico. Cuando se obtiene un cociente de más de dos posiciones decimales, se pueden expresar las demás posiciones en forma de fracción con el resto como numerador y el divisor como denominador. De ser necesario, se pueden redondear los decimales; por ejemplo: $.66\frac{2}{3} = .67$.

CONVERSIÓN DE FRACCIÓN A DECIMAL

Dividir el numerador por el denominador. Caso haya más de dos posiciones decimales en el cociente, expresar el resto en forma de fracción.

EJERCICIO 3: CONVERSIÓN DE FRACCIÓN A DECIMAL

Instrucciones: Resuelva cada uno de los problemas.

1. Convierta estos decimales a fracciones. Redúzcalos a su mínima expresión de ser necesario.

   (a) $.07 = \dfrac{}{100}$ **(b)** $.32$ **(c)** 3.1

2. Convierta estas fracciones a decimales. Exprese el resto en forma de fracción si obtiene un cociente de más de dos posiciones decimales.

   (a) $\frac{3}{8}$ **(b)** $\frac{4}{3}$ **(c)** $\frac{5}{6}$

Relación entre números mixtos y fracciones impropias

Al trabajar con fracciones, se habrán de convertir los números mixtos a fracciones impropias y viceversa.

Ejemplo 1: Convierta $3\frac{7}{8}$ a fracción impropia.

    PASO 1. Multiplique el número entero por el denominador. $(3 \times 8) = 24$

    PASO 2. Sume el producto al numerador de la fracción. $24 + 7 = 31$

    PASO 3. Escriba el total de la suma sobre el denominador inicial. $3\frac{7}{8} = \frac{31}{8}$

CONVERSIÓN DE NÚMERO MIXTO A FRACCIÓN IMPROPIA

1. Multiplicar el número entero por el denominador. Sumar el producto al numerador de la fracción.
2. Escribir el total de la suma sobre el denominador original.

Ejemplo 2: Convierta $\frac{11}{5}$ a número mixto.

PASO 1. Divida el numerador por el denominador.

$$\frac{11}{5} = 5\overline{)11} \atop \atop -10 \atop \overline{1}$$

PASO 2. Ponga el resto sobre el denominador.

$$\frac{11}{5} = 2\frac{1}{5} = 5\overline{)11} \atop -10 \atop \overline{1}$$

CONVERSIÓN DE FRACCIÓN IMPROPIA A NÚMERO MIXTO

1. Dividir el numerador por el denominador.
2. Usar el cociente como parte entera del número mixto.
3. Colocar el resto sobre el denominador para obtener la parte fraccionaria del número mixto.

EJERCICIO 4: CONVERSIÓN DE FRACCIÓN IMPROPIA A NÚMERO MIXTO Y VICEVERSA

Instrucciones: Resuelva cada uno de los problemas.

1. Convierta a fracción impropia.
   (a) $12\frac{1}{4}$ **(b)** $6\frac{2}{3}$

2. Convierta a número entero o mixto.
   (a) $\frac{9}{9}$ **(b)** $\frac{17}{5}$

Comparación de números
La recta numérica

La *recta numérica* es semejante a una regla, con la excepción de que no tiene ni principio ni fin. Esta característica de infinidad se indica con flechas que se colocan en ambos extremos de la recta. Se puede decir que en esta recta están representados todos los números, aunque sería imposible escribirlos todos. Observe que los números aumentan al desplazarnos hacia la derecha de la recta.

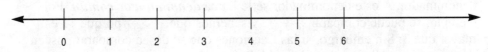

Se puede representar en la recta numérica tanto los números enteros como los números mixtos.

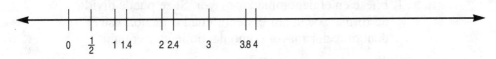

Como se puede observar en la ilustración, un mismo punto puede indicar fracciones y decimales iguales. Por ejemplo, $1\frac{1}{2}$ tiene el mismo valor que 1.5.

Se puede utilizar la recta numérica para comparar números e indicar su orden. Dados dos números cualesquiera, una de estas tres expresiones habrá de ser verdadera:

1. Los dos números son iguales.
2. El primer número es mayor que el segundo.
3. El primer número es menor que el segundo.

Existen símbolos que representan estas relaciones:

Símbolo	Significado	Ejemplo
=	es igual a	4 = 4
>	es mayor que	7 > 3
<	es menor que	2 < 9

▶ **Nota:** La "flecha" siempre apunta hacia el número menor.

Comparación de decimales

Al comparar decimales, conviene cerciorarse de que haya en cada número la misma cantidad de posiciones decimales. Agregue tantos ceros como sean necesarios a la derecha de la última cifra del decimal. Recuerde que, al añadir ceros a la derecha de un número decimal, *no* se altera su valor.

Ejemplo: Compare .064 y .06.

.064 tiene 3 posiciones decimales   .064 ⌉ Ambos tienen ahora 3 posiciones decimales.

.06 tiene 2 posiciones decimales   .060 ⌋

Ahora ambos números están expresados en milésimos. Como 64 > 60, entonces .064 > .060. Por lo tanto: .064 > .06.

Comparación de fracciones

Al comparar fracciones, debemos asegurarnos de que tengan el mismo denominador. A este denominador se le llama ***denominador común.*** Por ejemplo, se puede comparar $\frac{3}{16}$ y $\frac{11}{16}$, y sabemos que $\frac{11}{16} > \frac{3}{16}$ porque 11 es mayor que 3. Sin embargo, si las fracciones que se desea comparar poseen denominadores distintos, se deberá hallar un denominador común.

Ejemplo 1: ¿Cuál es mayor: $\frac{5}{8}$ ó $\frac{1}{2}$?

PASO 1. Fíjese en el denominador mayor. Si se puede dividir $\frac{5}{8}$ $\frac{1}{2}$
de forma exacta por el denominador menor, use el denominador mayor como denominador común.

PASO 2. Escriba ambas fracciones con el mismo denominador. $\frac{5}{8} = \frac{5}{8}$
Convierta la fracción de denominador menor a
términos mayores.

$$\frac{1\,(\times 4)}{2\,(\times 4)} = \frac{4}{8}$$

PASO 3. Compare y determine qué fracción es mayor.

$\frac{5}{8} > \frac{4}{8}$

por lo que

$\frac{5}{8} > \frac{1}{2}$

En algunos casos, el denominador mayor no se puede dividir de forma exacta por el denominador menor. En estos casos, se pueden multiplicar los dos denominadores entre sí si es que son lo suficientemente pequeños como para dar un denominador manejable.

Ejemplo 2: ¿Cuál es mayor: $\frac{2}{3}$ ó $\frac{3}{4}$?

PASO 1. Multiplique los denominadores para obtener un denominador común.

$3 \times 4 = 12$

PASO 2. Déles el mismo denominador a los dos. En este caso será 12.

$$\frac{2\,(\times 4) = 8}{3\,(\times 4) = 12}$$

Multiplique $\frac{2}{3}$ por 4 y $\frac{3}{4}$ por 3.

$$\frac{3\,(\times 3) = 9}{4\,(\times 3) = 12}$$

PASO 3. Compare las fracciones.

$\frac{9}{12} > \frac{8}{12}$, por lo que

$\frac{3}{4}$ es mayor que $\frac{2}{3}$

En otros casos, el denominador común que se obtiene al multiplicar los denominadores puede ser demasiado grande como para permitir un fácil manejo. En este caso, hay que buscar múltiplos de cada uno de los denominadores y utilizar como denominador común el múltiplo más pequeño que éstos tengan en común.

Ejemplo 3: ¿Cuál es mayor: $\frac{5}{12}$ ó $\frac{3}{10}$?

PASO 1. Busque los múltiplos de cada uno de los denominadores. El menor múltiplo común a ambos será el denominador común.

12: 12, 24, 36, 48, 60
10: 10, 20, 30, 40, 50, 60

PASO 2. Amplíe ambas fracciones a términos mayores. Divida 60 por los denominadores para calcular por qué números debe multiplicar las fracciones:

$$\frac{5\,(\times 5) = 25}{12\,(\times 5) = 60}$$

$60 \div 12 = 5$ y $60 \div 10 = 6$

$$\frac{3\,(\times 6) = 18}{10\,(\times 6) = 60}$$

PASO 3. Compare las fracciones.

$$\frac{25}{60} > \frac{18}{60},\text{ por lo que}$$

$$\frac{5}{12}\text{ es mayor que }\frac{3}{10}$$

CÓMO HALLAR UN DENOMINADOR COMÚN

Observar el denominador mayor:

1. Si es divisible por el otro denominador, el denominador mayor será el denominador común.
2. Si no es divisible, tratar de multiplicar los denominadores entre sí.
3. Si el producto de la multiplicación es muy grande, buscar múltiplos de ambos denominadores hasta hallar el mínimo común múltiplo.

Comparación de fracciones y decimales

Es posible comparar fracciones y decimales, pero primero se deberá convertir el decimal a fracción o la fracción a decimal.

Ejemplo: Compare: $\frac{7}{8}$ y .75.

PASO 1. Convierta $\frac{7}{8}$ a decimal.

$$\frac{7}{8} = 8\overline{)7.000}\ \ .875$$

PASO 2. Escriba .75 con 3 posiciones decimales, ya que .875 tiene 3 posiciones decimales.

$.75 = .750$

PASO 3. Compare.

$.875 > .750$, por lo que $\frac{7}{8}$ es mayor que .75.

EJERCICIO 5: COMPARACIÓN DE NÚMEROS

Instrucciones: Resuelva cada uno de los problemas.

1. ¿Cuál de los dos números siguientes es mayor?

   (a) $\frac{7}{8}$ ó $\frac{3}{5}$ (b) $\frac{2}{3}$ ó $\frac{4}{9}$

2. Compare los números utilizando los símbolos >, <, ó =. Por ejemplo, 6 $\boxed{<}$ 9.

   (a) 3 $\boxed{}$ 8   (d) $\frac{9}{9}$ $\boxed{}$ $\frac{2}{2}$

   (b) $\frac{3}{4}$ $\boxed{}$ $\frac{2}{3}$ (e) .07 $\boxed{}$ .0873

   (c) $2\frac{3}{8}$ $\boxed{}$ $\frac{5}{2}$

Operaciones con fracciones

Suma y resta de fracciones

Cuando haya que sumar o restar fracciones o números mixtos, conviene cerciorarse de que las fracciones tengan denominadores comunes. De no ser así, se deberán convertir las fracciones a otras equivalentes que tengan denominadores comunes antes de proceder a sumar o restar.

Ejemplo 1: Sume: $\frac{3}{8}$ y $\frac{1}{8}$.

PASO 1. Como los denominadores son iguales, sume los numeradores.

$$\begin{array}{r} \frac{3}{8} \\ +\frac{1}{8} \\ \hline \end{array}$$

PASO 2. Reduzca la respuesta.

$$\frac{4}{8} \begin{array}{c} (\div 4) \\ (\div 4) \end{array} = \frac{1}{2}$$

Ejemplo 2: Sume: $\frac{1}{10}$ y $\frac{3}{5}$.

PASO 1. Halle el denominador común y las fracciones equivalentes.

PASO 2. Sume los numeradores.

$$
\begin{array}{r}
\frac{1}{10} = \frac{1}{10} \\
+ \frac{3\,(\times 2)}{5\,(\times 2)} = \frac{6}{10} \\
\hline
\frac{7}{10}
\end{array}
$$

Ejemplo 3: $\frac{2}{3} + \frac{1}{6} + \frac{3}{4}$

PASO 1. Halle el denominador común a todos los números.

PASO 2. Sume los numeradores y coloque el total sobre el denominador común.

PASO 3. Convierta la fracción impropia a número mixto.

$$
\begin{array}{r}
\frac{2}{3} = \frac{8}{12} \\
\frac{1}{6} = \frac{2}{12} \\
+\frac{3}{4} = \frac{9}{12} \\
\hline
\frac{19}{12} = 1\frac{7}{12}
\end{array}
$$

CÓMO SUMAR FRACCIONES

1. Cerciorarse de que todas las fracciones tengan un denominador común.
2. Sumar los numeradores.
3. Colocar el total sobre el denominador común y simplificar.

Se aplica el mismo método al sumar números mixtos. Primero se suman las fracciones en caso de que sea necesario combinar su total fraccionario con los números enteros.

Ejemplo 4: Jorge compró $1\frac{3}{4}$ libras de pollo y $6\frac{2}{3}$ libras de carne molida para el picnic. ¿Cuántas libras compró en total?

PASO 1. Halle el denominador común: 12.

PASO 2. Sume las fracciones. Convierta la fracción impropia $\frac{17}{12}$ al número mixto $1\frac{5}{12}$.

PASO 3. Sume $1\frac{5}{12}$ a 7 para obtener $8\frac{5}{12}$.

$$
\begin{array}{r}
1\frac{3}{4} = 1\frac{9}{12} \\
+6\frac{2}{3} = 6\frac{8}{12} \\
\hline
7\frac{17}{12} = 7 + 1\frac{5}{12} = 8\frac{5}{12}
\end{array}
$$

CÓMO SUMAR NÚMEROS MIXTOS

1. Cerciorarse de que las partes fraccionarias tengan un denominador común.
2. Sumar las partes fraccionarias y simplificar.
3. Sumar los números enteros.
4. Simplificar el resultado.

El proceso de resta de fracciones es similar al de la suma.

Ejemplo 5: $\frac{7}{16} - \frac{3}{16}$

$$
\begin{array}{r}
\frac{7}{16} \\
-\frac{3}{16} \\
\hline
\frac{4}{16} = \frac{1}{4}
\end{array}
$$

Ejemplo 6: Reste $\frac{3}{8}$ de $\frac{11}{12}$.

$$
\begin{array}{r}
\frac{11}{12} = \frac{22}{24} \\
-\frac{3}{8} = \frac{9}{24} \\
\hline
\frac{13}{24}
\end{array}
$$

Una de las diferencias entre la suma y la resta de números mixtos es que en la resta es a veces necesario reagrupar las fracciones.

Ejemplo 7: Miriam necesita adelgazar $9\frac{1}{4}$ libras. Ya ha perdido $5\frac{3}{4}$ libras. ¿Cuántas libras le quedan por bajar?

PASO 1. Al plantear el problema, se ve que no se puede restar $\frac{3}{4}$ de $\frac{1}{4}$. Hay que reagrupar. Reste 1 de 9. Como 1 se puede expresar como $\frac{4}{4}$, reemplace el 9 con $8\frac{4}{4}$.

$$9\frac{1}{4} = 8\frac{4}{4} + \frac{1}{4} = 8\frac{5}{4}$$
$$-5\frac{3}{4} \qquad -5\frac{3}{4}$$
$$\overline{\phantom{-5\frac{3}{4}}}$$
$$3\frac{2}{4} = 3\frac{1}{2} \text{ libras}$$

PASO 2. Sume los numeradores y obtendrá $\frac{5}{4}$.

PASO 3. Reste las fracciones y los números enteros. Simplifique el resultado.

▶ **Nota:** Para saber cómo convertir un 1 de un número entero que necesite reagrupar, fíjese en el denominador de la fracción que se vaya a restar. Por ejemplo, si va a restar $\frac{3}{8}$, escriba el 1 en forma de $\frac{8}{8}$, o si va a restar $\frac{5}{6}$, exprese 1 como $\frac{6}{6}$.

EJERCICIO 6: SUMA Y RESTA DE FRACCIONES

Instrucciones: Resuelva cada uno de los problemas.

1. $\frac{2}{3}$
   $+\frac{1}{4}$

2. $3\frac{7}{8}$
   $2\frac{5}{6}$
   $+3\frac{1}{3}$

3. $\frac{9}{10}$
   $-\frac{3}{10}$

4. $\frac{4}{5}$
   $-\frac{1}{2}$

5. $25\frac{1}{6}$
   $-11\frac{1}{2}$

6. 10
   $-3\frac{2}{17}$

Multiplicación de fracciones

No hay necesidad de hallar un denominador común para multiplicar o dividir. En algunos casos, la multiplicación se hace directamente, multiplicando los numeradores entre sí y los denominadores entre sí.

Ejemplo 1: $\frac{3}{4} \times \frac{1}{2} = \frac{3}{8}$

En otros casos, los problemas se pueden resolver con más facilidad por **supresión** (o **eliminación**), es decir, reduciendo un numerador y un denominador divisible por el mismo factor.

Ejemplo 2: $\frac{6}{15} \times \frac{5}{12}$

PASO 1. El 15 y el 5 son divisibles por 5. $\frac{6}{\cancel{15}_3} \times \frac{\cancel{5}^1}{12}$

PASO 2. El 6 y el 12 son divisibles por 6. $\frac{\cancel{6}^1}{3} \times \frac{1}{\cancel{12}_2}$

PASO 3. Multiplique numeradores y luego denominadores entre sí. Simplifique si es necesario. $\frac{1}{3} \times \frac{1}{2} = \frac{1}{6}$

CÓMO MULTIPLICAR FRACCIONES

1. Reducir los numeradores y los denominadores por supresión o eliminación.
2. Multiplicar numeradores y luego denominadores entre sí.
3. Simplificar el resultado.

También se puede emplear el proceso de supresión con más de dos fracciones. En estos casos, tendrá a veces que "saltarse" un número intermedio.

Ejemplo 3: $\frac{3}{8} \times \frac{4}{7} \times \frac{5}{9}$

PASO 1. Divida el 3 y el 9 entre 3. $\frac{\cancel{3}^1}{8} \times \frac{4}{7} \times \frac{5}{\cancel{9}_3}$

PASO 2. Divida el 4 y el 8 por 4. $\frac{\cancel{3}^1}{\cancel{8}_2} \times \frac{\cancel{4}^1}{7} \times \frac{5}{\cancel{9}_3} = \frac{5}{42}$

PASO 3. Multiplique numeradores y luego denominadores entre sí.

El *Ejemplo 4* ilustra un caso de multiplicación de números mixtos.

Ejemplo 4: Sarah suele correr $2\frac{1}{3}$ millas al día. Esta semana ha corrido esta distancia 3 días seguidos y $\frac{1}{2}$ de la distancia al día siguiente. ¿Cuántas millas en total ha corrido Sarah?

PASO 1. Convierta los números mixtos a fracciones impropias. $2\frac{1}{3} \times 3\frac{1}{2} = \frac{7}{3} \times \frac{7}{2}$

PASO 2. Multiplique y vuelva a convertir la fracción impropia a número mixto. $\frac{7}{3} \times \frac{7}{2} = \frac{49}{6} = 8\frac{1}{6}$

CÓMO MULTIPLICAR NÚMEROS MIXTOS

1. Convertir los números mixtos en fracciones impropias.
2. Simplificar los números divisibles por un mismo número por supresión.
3. Multiplicar numeradores y luego denominadores entre sí.
4. Simplificar el resultado.

EJERCICIO 7: MULTIPLICACIÓN DE FRACCIONES

Instrucciones: Resuelva cada uno de los problemas.

1. $\frac{3}{8} \times \frac{2}{15} \times \frac{6}{7}$

2. $8\frac{1}{6} \times 4$

3. $2\frac{1}{2} \times 2\frac{1}{3}$

4. $2\frac{3}{4} \times \frac{6}{7}$

División de fracciones

La división es la operación inversa a la multiplicación. Por ejemplo, cuando dividimos un número por 2, en realidad estamos multiplicando por $\frac{1}{2}$.

$$12 \div 2 = \frac{\cancel{12}^{6}}{1} \times \frac{1}{\cancel{2}_{1}} = \frac{6}{1} = 6$$

La fracción $\frac{1}{2}$ se dice que es el **recíproco** de 2. Dos números son recíprocos cuando su producto es 1. Como $5 \times \frac{1}{5} = 1$, los números 5 y $\frac{1}{5}$ son recíprocos. Para hallar el recíproco de un número, simplemente inviértalo, es decir, use el numerador como denominador y el denominador como numerador. Para dividir una fracción, utilice el siguiente método:

Ejemplo 1: Divida $\frac{7}{8}$ por $\frac{3}{4}$.

PASO 1. Multiplique la primera fracción por el recíproco de la segunda.

$\frac{7}{8} \div \frac{3}{4} = \frac{7}{8} \times \frac{4}{3}$

PASO 2. Multiplique numeradores y luego denominadores entre sí y convierta la fracción impropia a número mixto.

$\frac{7}{\cancel{8}_{2}} \times \frac{\cancel{4}^{1}}{3} = \frac{7}{6} = 1\frac{1}{6}$

Para dividir un número mixto, conviértalo a fracción impropia.

Ejemplo 2: ¿Cuánto es $4\frac{2}{3} \div 1\frac{1}{2}$?

PASO 1. Convierta ambos números mixtos a fracciones impropias.

$\frac{14}{3} \div \frac{3}{2}$

PASO 2. Multiplique la primera fracción por el recíproco de la segunda y vuelva a convertir la fracción impropia resultante a número mixto.

$\frac{14}{3} \times \frac{2}{3} = \frac{28}{9} = 3\frac{1}{9}$

CÓMO DIVIDIR FRACCIONES O NÚMEROS MIXTOS

1. Convertir los números mixtos a fracciones impropias.
2. Multiplicar la primera fracción por el recíproco de la segunda.
3. Volver a convertir las fracciones impropias a números mixtos.

EJERCICIO 8: DIVISIÓN DE FRACCIONES

Instrucciones: Resuelva cada uno de los problemas.

1. $\frac{2}{5} \div 4$

2. $\frac{3}{7} \div \frac{6}{35}$

3. $9 \div 2\frac{1}{2}$

Simplificación de problemas de fracciones

La mejor forma de simplificar problemas de enunciado verbal con fracciones es plantear el problema con números enteros.

▶ **Nota:** Conviene siempre identificar las palabras clave o conceptos básicos que indiquen qué operación debe usarse. Una palabra clave usada con frecuencia en problemas con fracciones es "de". El problema le puede pedir calcular $\frac{1}{2}$ *de* algo ó $\frac{2}{3}$ *de* algo. Siempre que se calcula una fracción de algo, se efectúa una multiplicación.

Ejemplo: El empleado de una compañía de limpieza de tapicerías asigna $1\frac{1}{2}$ horas por cada sillón que limpia. Si trabaja $7\frac{1}{2}$ horas, ¿cuántos sillones limpiará?

Replanteado el problema reemplazando las fracciones por números enteros, tendríamos: "El empleado asigna 2 horas por cada sillón. Si trabaja 8 horas, ¿cuántos sillones limpiará?"

Solución: Después de replantear el problema, se hace más evidente que se trata de un problema de división. El empleado de la compañía de limpieza está dividiendo el día en partes más pequeñas. En razón de ello, decidimos hacer uso de la división en el problema original.

$$7\frac{1}{2} \div 1\frac{1}{2} = \frac{15}{2} \div \frac{3}{2} = \frac{\overset{5}{\cancel{15}}}{\underset{1}{\cancel{2}}} \times \frac{\overset{1}{\cancel{2}}}{\underset{1}{\cancel{3}}} = 5$$

El empleado limpiará 5 sillones.

▶ **Nota:** Cerciórese de colocar la cantidad a ser dividida a la izquierda de la división. En el ejemplo de arriba, el período de $7\frac{1}{2}$ horas se divide en partes iguales de $1\frac{1}{2}$ horas.

Grupos de información

Los grupos de información se refieren a un conjunto de datos proporcionados en uno o dos párrafos o en una ilustración, seguidos de una serie de preguntas (por lo general de 3 a 5) basadas en esos datos.

▶ **Nota:** La clave para resolver un problema basado en un grupo de información es identificar y utilizar únicamente la información necesaria para contestar dicha pregunta.

EJERCICIO 9: GRUPOS DE INFORMACIÓN

Instrucciones: Escriba la información necesaria para la resolución de cada problema y resuelva el problema. Las *Preguntas 1–3* están basadas en el diagrama adjunto.

El dueño de un campamento piensa agregar dos nuevas calles, Birch Trail y Pine Way. El campamento mide $\frac{7}{8}$ de milla de ancho y $\frac{19}{20}$ de milla de largo.

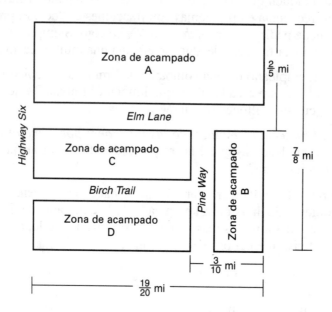

1. ¿Cuál es la longitud de Pine Way?
    Información necesaria: _____
    (1) $\frac{1}{8}$ de milla **(2)** $\frac{7}{20}$ de milla **(3)** $\frac{19}{40}$ de milla **(4)** $1\frac{11}{40}$ millas **(5)** $1\frac{2}{3}$ millas

2. ¿Cuál es la longitud total de las dos nuevas calles?
    Información necesaria: _____
    (1) $\frac{19}{40}$ de milla **(2)** $\frac{13}{20}$ de milla **(3)** $\frac{21}{23}$ de milla **(4)** $1\frac{1}{8}$ millas **(5)** $1\frac{1}{4}$ millas

3. ¿Cuánto mide de ancho Elm Lane?
    Información necesaria: _____
    (1) $\frac{1}{5}$ de milla **(2)** $\frac{2}{5}$ de milla **(3)** $\frac{19}{40}$ de milla **(4)** $\frac{19}{20}$ de milla
    (5) no se da suficiente información

3
RAZÓN Y PROPORCIÓN

Razón

En matemáticas, se denomina *razón* al resultado de comparar dos cantidades; por ejemplo: "Seis de cada ocho estudiantes asistieron al concierto". Si la razón compara dos cantidades de distinta unidad, se le llama *tasa.* Por ejemplo, 55 *millas por hora* es una tasa. Sea cual fuere el nombre que le demos a la comparación, razón o tasa, la misma se puede expresar ya sea en forma de fracción, ya en forma de comparación utilizando la palabra *a,* o bien como comparación utilizando los dos puntos. Con todo, se puede establecer una razón siempre que se comparen dos números.

Ejemplo 1: Seis de cada ocho estudiantes asistieron al concierto.

La razón es: 6 a 8 ó 6:8 ó $\frac{6}{8}$
Simplificando $\frac{6}{8}$ obtenemos $\frac{3}{4}$

Ejemplo 2: "Iba por la carretera a 55 millas por hora".

La tasa es: 55 millas a 1 hora ó 55:1 ó $\frac{55}{1}$

La palabra *por* suele indicar que se ha de establecer una razón. Esta razón es una tasa puesto que compara dos unidades distintas: *millas* a *horas.*

▶ **Nota:** En las razones, a diferencia de las fracciones, se mantiene el número 1 en el denominador.

LAS RESPUESTAS DE LOS EJERCICIOS DE ESTE CAPÍTULO EMPIEZAN EN LA PÁGINA 468.

EJERCICIO 1: RAZÓN

Instrucciones: Utilice la forma de fracción para expresar estas comparaciones como razones o tasas. Cerciórese de simplificar al mínimo cada una de las fracciones.

1. 30 minutos a 1 hora
2. 3 libras de carne para 4 personas
3. 88 pies en 8 segundos
4. $80 por 12 tablas

EJERCICIO 2: APLICACIÓN DE RAZONES

Instrucciones: Resuelva cada uno de los problemas.

Las *Preguntas 1–2* se basan en los datos de la tabla adjunta. Escriba las razones en forma de fracción para comparar los gastos.

GASTOS SEMANALES DE LOS PINTORES				TOTAL
Herramientas	Materiales	Transporte	Teléfono	
$25	$120	$40	$15	$200

1. Compare el costo de los materiales con el total de gastos.
2. ¿Cuántas veces mayor que los gastos de transporte es el total de gastos?
3. Si usted posee 300 acciones de Consolidated Merchants y recibe un dividendo de $729, ¿cuánto es el dividendo por acción?

Proporción

Una *proporción* es una expresión de igualdad entre dos razones (fracciones) equivalentes. La expresión aritmética $\frac{7}{8} = \frac{14}{16}$ es un ejemplo de proporción y se lee: "7 es a 8 como 14 es a 16". Una proporción es verdadera si los *productos cruzados* son iguales. Por producto cruzado entendemos el resultado de multiplicar entre sí los extremos y luego los medios de las fracciones equivalentes.

Ejemplo 1: $\frac{7}{8} \leftarrows = \rightarrows \frac{14}{16}$

$$7 \times 16 = 8 \times 14 \qquad \text{7 × 16 y 8 × 14 son productos cruzados.}$$

$$112 \qquad 112$$

Existen proporciones de las que se desconoce uno de los términos de una de las razones. El número que falta se representa con una letra. Para hallar el valor de esa letra, aplicamos la llamada *Regla de tres,* como se ilustra a continuación en el *Ejemplo 2.*

Ejemplo 2: Si 3 manzanas cuestan 50 centavos, halle el costo de 15 manzanas a la misma tasa. Esta situación se puede plantear en forma de proporción.

PASO 1. Escriba una proporción donde c represente el costo de las manzanas.

$$\frac{3 \text{ manzanas}}{\$.50} = \frac{15 \text{ manzanas}}{c}$$
$$\frac{3}{.50} = \frac{15}{c}$$

PASO 2. Multiplique los dos números que se pueden multiplicar en diagonal.

$$15 \times .50 = \$7.50$$

PASO 3. Divida el resultado por el número restante.

$$\$7.50 \div 3 = \$2.50$$
$$c = \$2.50$$

Por lo tanto: si 3 manzanas cuestan 50 centavos, 15 manzanas costarán $2.50.

$$\frac{3}{\$.50} = \frac{15}{\$2.50}$$

Sabemos que esto es verdadero ya que los productos cruzados son iguales.

$$3 \times \$2.5 = 15 \times \$.50$$
$$\$7.50 = \$7.50$$

REGLA DE TRES
1. Multiplicar los dos números de la proporción que se puedan multiplicar en diagonal.
2. Dividir el producto por el tercer número de la proporción.

Al despejar la incógnita, se puede también representar las operaciones de la forma siguiente.

1. Escriba la proporción. $\qquad\qquad\qquad\qquad\qquad$ $\frac{b}{8} = \frac{5}{20}$

2. Escriba la multiplicación encima de la raya de fracción. $\qquad$ 8×5
(Recuerde que la raya de fracción también significa
"dividido por".)

3. Escriba el número restante debajo de la barra de la fracción. $\quad$ $\frac{8 \times 5}{20}$

4. Despeje la incógnita hallando el producto del numerador y $\quad$ $\frac{40}{20} = 2$
dividiéndolo por el denominador.

EJERCICIO 3: REGLA DE TRES

Instrucciones: Halle el valor de la incógnita de las siguientes proporciones.

1. $\frac{2}{5} = \frac{m}{10}$

2. $\frac{x}{7} = \frac{3}{21}$

3. $\frac{5}{y} = \frac{15}{20}$

Aplicación de la regla de tres

Son numerosas las aplicaciones que se pueden dar a la Regla de tres. Si se le presenta un problema en el que se comparan dos tipos de cantidades y se pide calcular el valor del término que falta, es conveniente emplear la regla de tres en la resolución del problema.

Ejemplo: Si un jugador de béisbol pega 10 jonrones en los primeros 45 juegos de la temporada, ¿cuántos jonrones más espera marcar durante toda la temporada de 162 juegos si sigue a ese mismo ritmo?

PASO 1. Plantee el problema con la $\qquad$ 10 jonrones en 45 juegos.
información dada e identifique $\qquad$ j jonrones en 162 juegos.
la incógnita.

PASO 2. Escriba una proporción, colocando $\qquad$ $\frac{10 \text{ jonrones}}{45 \text{ juegos}} = \frac{j}{162 \text{ juegos}}$
la misma unidad en los numeradores
y la misma unidad en los denominadores.

PASO 3. Despeje la incógnita. $\qquad\qquad$ $\frac{162 \times 10}{45} = \frac{1620}{45} = 36$

Si sigue a ese ritmo, el jugador habrá de pegar 36 jonrones en los 162 juegos.

EJERCICIO 4: APLICACIÓN DE PROPORCIONES

Instrucciones: Resuelva cada uno de los problemas.

1. Se desea ampliar el dibujo de la derecha. Si se ampliara el dibujo a 8 pulgadas de ancho, ¿cuánto mediría de largo?

 7 pulgadas

5 pulgadas

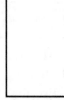 8 pulgadas

2. En los almacenes Foster, la razón entre gerentes y vendedores es de 2:9. Si Foster tiene ahora 180 vendedores, ¿cuántos gerentes hay?

3. Dos panqueques contienen 120 calorías. Si Ellen ha comido 7 panqueques, ¿cuántas calorías ha consumido?

4
PORCENTAJES

¿Qué son los porcentajes?

Los porcentajes, al igual que los decimales y las fracciones, constituyen otra manera de expresar una parte determinada de una unidad. El *porcentaje* es la parte de un todo que se ha dividido en 100 porciones iguales. De ahí la palabra "porcentaje" o tanto "por ciento".

El porcentaje se expresa con un número seguido del signo %. Por ejemplo: 50% representa lo mismo que $\frac{50}{100}$ ó 0.50. Al trabajar con porcentajes, se hace a veces necesario convertirlos a decimales o fracciones equivalentes. La tabla adjunta indica la relación que existe entre porcentajes, fracciones y decimales.

Porcentaje	Fracción	Decimal
1%	$\frac{1}{100}$	.01
5%	$\frac{5}{100} = \frac{1}{20}$	.05
10%	$\frac{10}{100} = \frac{1}{10}$	.10
25%	$\frac{25}{100} = \frac{1}{4}$	.25
$33\frac{1}{3}\%$	$\frac{33\frac{1}{3}}{100} = \frac{1}{3}$	$.33\frac{1}{3}$
50%	$\frac{50}{100} = \frac{1}{2}$	.50
$66\frac{2}{3}\%$	$\frac{66\frac{2}{3}}{100} = \frac{2}{3}$	$.66\frac{2}{3}$
75%	$\frac{75}{100} = \frac{3}{4}$	.75
100%	$\frac{100}{100} = 1$	1.00

▶ **Nota:** Dado que el 100% representa la unidad—el todo—cualquier número menor que 100% es menor que la unidad. Por ejemplo, el 75% de una cantidad es sólo una parte de esa cantidad.

Conversión a fracciones y decimales

Muchos problemas requieren conversiones entre fracciones, decimales y porcentajes. Para convertir un porcentaje a fracción o a decimal, hay que tener presente lo que significa el símbolo %: "por ciento".

% significa "$\times \frac{1}{100}$" y % significa "$\times .01$"

Ejemplo 1: Exprese 13% en forma de fracción equivalente y de decimal equivalente.

En forma de fracción: $13 \times \frac{1}{100} = \frac{13}{1} \times \frac{1}{100} = \frac{13}{100}$

En forma de decimal: $13 \times .01 = .13$

▶ **Nota:** Obsérvese que al multiplicar por .01 se corre el punto decimal 2 lugares a la izquierda. $13\% = .13. = .13$

Ejemplo 2: Exprese los siguientes porcentajes en forma de fracción equivalente y de decimal equivalente. Simplifique las fracciones al mínimo.

80%   *En forma de fracción:* $80 \times \frac{1}{100} = \frac{\cancel{80}^{4}}{1} \times \frac{1}{\cancel{100}_{5}} = \frac{4}{5}$

En forma de decimal: $80 \times .01 = .80$ or $.8$

$33\frac{1}{3}$%   *En forma de fracción:* $33\frac{1}{3} \times \frac{1}{100} = \frac{\cancel{100}}{3} \times \frac{1}{\cancel{100}_{1}} = \frac{1}{3}$

En forma de decimal: $33\frac{1}{3} \times .01 = .33\frac{1}{3}$

150%   *En forma de número mixto:* $150 \times \frac{1}{100} = \frac{\cancel{150}^{3}}{1} \times \frac{1}{\cancel{100}_{2}} = \frac{3}{2} = 1\frac{1}{2}$

En forma de decimal: $150 \times .01 = 1.50$ ó 1.5

Algunos porcentajes se pueden escribir de esta forma: .6%. Este porcentaje representa "seis décimos de uno por ciento" y es menor que 1%.

Ejemplo 3: Exprese .6% en forma de fracción y en forma de decimal.

En forma de fracción:
Escriba primero la parte decimal en forma de fracción. Luego multiplique esta fracción por $\frac{1}{100}$.

$.6 = \frac{6}{10} = \frac{3}{5}$

$\frac{3}{5} \times \frac{1}{100} = \frac{3}{500}$

En forma de decimal:
Escriba la parte decimal y multiplíquela por .01.

$.6 \times .01 = .006$

▶ **Nota:** Lea siempre con atención los porcentajes para determinar qué representan. Todo número mayor que 100% es *mayor que la unidad.* Por ejemplo: 200% es lo mismo que 2 veces la unidad. Así pues, el 200% de 6 es 12.

Toda fracción propia o decimal seguida de % representa una cifra *menor que* el 1%. Por ejemplo, $\frac{3}{4}$% significa "tres cuartos de uno por ciento", y .75% significa "setenta y cinco centésimos de uno por ciento" y *no* 75%.

| LAS RESPUESTAS DE LOS EJERCICIOS DE ESTE CAPÍTULO EMPIEZAN EN LA PÁGINA 469. |

EJERCICIO 1: CONVERSIÓN A FRACCIÓN Y A DECIMAL

Instrucciones: Exprese los porcentajes en forma de fracción equivalente y de decimal equivalente.

1. 87%   **2.** $66\frac{2}{3}$%   **3.** 12.5%   **4.** 18%   **5.** $\frac{1}{2}$%

CONVERSIÓN A PORCENTAJE

- Para convertir de fracción a porcentaje, multiplicar por 100 y agregar el signo %.
- Para convertir de decimal a porcentaje, multiplicar por 100 y agregar el signo %.

Ejemplo 1: Exprese $\frac{7}{8}$ en forma de porcentaje.

$$\frac{7}{8} \times 100 = \frac{7}{8} \times \frac{100}{1} = \frac{700}{8} = 87\frac{1}{2} = 87\frac{1}{2}\%$$

Ejemplo 2: Exprese .3 en forma de porcentaje.

$$.3 \times 100 = 30 = 30\%$$

Ejemplo 3: Exprese el número mixto 2.04 con un porcentaje equivalente.

$$\frac{2.04}{1} \times \frac{100}{1} = \frac{204}{1} = 204 = 204\%$$

EJERCICIO 2: CONVERSIÓN A PORCENTAJE

Instrucciones: Exprese los siguientes números con porcentajes equivalentes.

1. $\frac{3}{8}$ **2.** 4.5   **3.** 625   **4.** $2\frac{1}{4}$

Cómo usar las proporciones

Los problemas de enunciado verbal sobre porcentajes pueden resolverse por medio de una proporción. Este método se conoce con el nombre de método de "la *parte* sobre el *todo*" o de "la *parte* sobre la *unidad*". La proporción siguiente nos da la pauta de cómo plantear este tipo de problemas.

$$\frac{\text{PARTE}}{\text{UNIDAD}} = \frac{\% \text{ (PARTE)}}{100\% \text{ (UNIDAD)}}$$

También podemos expresar esta relación de la siguiente forma:

PARTE	%
UNIDAD	100

En el caso de un 25%, la proporción sería:

parte $\searrow$ $\frac{25}{100} = \frac{25\%}{100\%}$ $\swarrow$ porcentaje (parte)

unidad $\nearrow$ $\nwarrow$ siempre 100%

Esta proporción indica que la relación que existe entre la parte y la unidad es la misma que existe entre un porcentaje y el 100%. Para resolver un problema de enunciado verbal sobre porcentajes, se aconseja leer el problema con detenimiento y determinar en primer lugar si lo que se pide es el *porcentaje,* la *parte* o la *unidad.* Represente con *n* el número que se desea hallar y recuerde que el 100 que figura en el denominador de la derecha *nunca* cambia.

Ejemplo 1: Halle el 40% de 120.

Solución: Se pide aquí hallar la PARTE desconocida.

parte desconocida $\searrow$ $\frac{n}{120} = \frac{40}{100}$ $\swarrow$ parte del porcentaje

unidad $\nearrow$ $\nwarrow$ siempre 100

Multiplique en diagonal: $120 \times 40 = 4800$

Divida: $4800 \div 100 = 48$

La parte desconocida es 48. Es decir que: el 40% de 120 es 48.

▶ **Nota:** Al calcular un porcentaje, resulta a veces más fácil convertir primero el porcentaje a decimal o a fracción y luego multiplicar. Por ejemplo, para hallar el 40% de 120: $120 \times .40 = 48$ ó $120 \times \frac{2}{5} = 48$.

Ejemplo 2: ¿Qué porcentaje de 72 es 18?

> *Solución:* Se pide aquí hallar el PORCENTAJE.

$$\underset{\text{unidad}}{\overset{\text{parte}}{\searrow\nearrow}} \quad \frac{18}{72} = \frac{n}{100} \quad \underset{\text{siempre 100}}{\overset{\text{porcentaje desconocido}}{\swarrow\nwarrow}}$$

> *Multiplique en diagonal:* $18 \times 100 = 1800$

> *Divida:* $1800 \div 72 = 25$

El porcentaje desconocido es 25. Es decir que:18 es el 25% de 72.

Ejemplo 3: ¿De qué número es 60 el 120%?

> *Solución:* Se pide aquí hallar la UNIDAD.

$$\underset{\text{unidad desconocida}}{\overset{\text{parte}}{\searrow\nearrow}} \quad \frac{60}{n} = \frac{120}{100} \quad \underset{\text{siempre 100}}{\overset{\text{porcentaje}}{\swarrow\nwarrow}}$$

> *Multiplique en diagonal:* $60 \times 100 = 6000$

> *Divida:* $6000 \div 120 = 50$

La unidad desconocida es 50. Es decir que: el 120% de 50 es 60.

Observe que en el *Ejemplo 3,* la parte (60) es mayor que la unidad (50). Esto se debe a que el porcentaje en cuestión es del 120%, el cual es mayor que el 100%.

RESOLUCIÓN DE PROBLEMAS SOBRE PORCENTAJES

1. Determinar si lo que se pide es la parte, la unidad o el porcentaje. Representar con *n* el número desconocido.
2. Establecer la proporción ubicando los números conocidos así como la incógnita *n* en su lugar correspondiente.

$$\frac{\text{Parte}}{\text{Unidad}} = \frac{\text{Porcentaje (\%)}}{100}$$

3. Multiplicar los dos números que se pueden multiplicar en diagonal.
4. Dividir por el número restante.

EJERCICIO 3: PROBLEMAS SOBRE PORCENTAJES
Instrucciones: Escriba primero lo que pide el problema (parte, unidad o porcentaje) y luego resuélvalo.

1. Halle el 4% de 30.
2. ¿De qué número es 10 el 2.5%?
3. ¿Qué porcentaje de $340 es $30.60?
4. ¿Cuánto es $\frac{1}{2}$% de 62?

Problemas sobre porcentajes

Existen tipos especiales de problemas sobre porcentajes que consisten en hallar el interés, descuentos y pagos de préstamos. Por lo general, los problemas sobre porcentajes son problemas de pasos múltiples. Hemos visto que, una vez establecida una proporción, se debe siempre efectuar una multiplicación y una división. Sin embargo, con este tipo de problemas es posible que también tenga que efectuar algunas sumas o restas para llegar al resultado final.

Ejemplo 1: Para aprobar la prueba de ciencias, Amy debe acertar el 75% de los problemas. De 80 preguntas, ¿cuántos problemas debe contestar correctamente?

Datos conocidos: 75%—porcentaje de la prueba

80—toda la prueba

Incógnita: n—número de problemas que acertar (parte)

En este problema, la proporción sería:

$$\text{parte} \searrow \quad \frac{n}{80} = \frac{75}{100} \quad \swarrow \text{porcentaje}$$
$$\text{unidad} \nearrow \qquad\qquad \nwarrow \text{siempre 100}$$

Ejemplo 2: Érica paga un 21% de cargos de financiación sobre el saldo sin pagar de sus tarjetas de crédito. Si su banco le dice que debe $42 de cargos de financiación, ¿cuál es su saldo sin pagar?

En este problema, la proporción sería:

$$\text{cargo de financiación} \searrow \quad \frac{42}{n} = \frac{21}{100} \quad \swarrow \text{porcentaje}$$
$$\text{saldo} \nearrow \qquad\qquad \nwarrow \text{siempre 100}$$

EJERCICIO 4: PROBLEMAS SOBRE PORCENTAJES

Instrucciones: Resuelva cada uno de los problemas.

1. Jesse gana $2100 al mes. Él ahorra el 12% de su sueldo y gasta $420 al mes en alquiler. ¿Cuánto ahorra Jesse cada mes?

2. La Sra. Rogers entregó un 15% inicial para la compra de un nuevo automóvil. Si el pago inicial fue de $1800, ¿cuánto costó el carro?

3. Durante una campaña política se realizó una encuesta para determinar los votos que el candidato podía esperar recibir. Los resultados fueron los que se dan más abajo. Según éstos, ¿qué porcentaje de votantes estaba indeciso?

Allen	Gault	Indecisos
200	120	180

4. Los empleados de Todds's Musicmart reciben un descuento del 20% en todas sus compras. Si Hosea compra tres casetes a $7.49 cada uno, ¿cuánto le toca pagar después de aplicarle el descuento que le corresponde como empleado?

Problemas de interés

Si pide un préstamo o si invierte dinero, se le aplicará una *tasa de interés* expresada en forma de porcentaje. Las tasas de interés se calculan en base a un período de un año. Si la duración del préstamo es mayor o menor que un año, la cantidad de interés anual se habrá de multiplicar por dicho período de duración.

La duración del préstamo debe ser expresada siempre en años o partes de un año. Si el período de tiempo fuere dado en meses, se escriben los meses en forma de fracción, comparando el número indicado de meses con el total de 12 meses que tiene un año.

$$\text{Por ejemplo: } 9 \text{ meses} = \frac{9 \text{ meses}}{12 \text{ meses}} = \frac{3}{4} \text{ de año}$$

Si el tiempo fuere dado en días, exprésclo como fracción de un año comparando el número indicado de días con 360 (el número aproximado de días que tiene un año).

$$\text{Por ejemplo: } 120 \text{ días} = \frac{120 \text{ días}}{360 \text{ días}} = \frac{1}{3} \text{ de año}$$

Ejemplo 1: Con el objeto de ampliar una de sus tiendas, un fabricante de toallas realiza un préstamo de $35,000 por $2\frac{1}{2}$ años a una tasa de interés anual del 7%. ¿Qué interés pagará el fabricante por el préstamo?

PASO 1. Halle el interés acumulado en un 1 año. $\qquad \frac{n}{35,000} = \frac{7}{100}$

PASO 2. Multiplique en diagonal y divida. $\qquad \frac{35,000 \times 7}{100} = 2450$

PASO 3. Halle el interés acumulado en $2\frac{1}{2}$ años. $\quad 2450 \times 2\frac{1}{2} = \$6125$

Ejemplo 2: La Sra. Barnes pidió prestado $4000 por 3 años. Halle la cantidad que tuvo que devolver siendo la tasa anual de interés del 9%.

PASO 1. Halle el interés acumulado en un 1 año. $\qquad \frac{n}{4000} = \frac{9}{100}$

$$\frac{9 \times 4000}{100} = \frac{36,000}{100} = 360$$

PASO 2. Halle el interés acumulado en 3 años. $\quad 360 \times 3 = 1080$

PASO 3. Halle la cantidad que devolvió. $\quad 4000 + 1080 = \$5080$

▶ **Nota:** Algunos problemas de interés piden que se calcule solamente el interés y otros que se halle la cantidad total del préstamo o de la inversión. El total es el monto al que asciende el préstamo más el interés. Conviene por ello leer los problemas detenidamente para cerciorarse de que lo que se le pide es el *interés* o la *cantidad a devolver,* como sucede en el ejemplo 2.

RESOLUCIÓN DE PROBLEMAS DE INTERÉS

1. Establecer una proporción y despejar el interés. $\quad \frac{\text{Interés}}{\text{Monto inicial}} = \frac{\text{Porcentaje}}{100}$
2. Para hallar el interés total, multiplicar el interés por la duración del préstamo.
3. Para hallar la cantidad total del préstamo o de la inversión, sumar la cantidad inicial al interés total.

> **Nota:** Un método muy utilizado para hallar el interés consiste en usar la fórmula $I = ct\%$, siendo c = capital (monto inicial), t = tiempo (que dura el préstamo) y $\%$ = tasa (de interés).

EJERCICIO 5: PROBLEMAS DE INTERÉS

Instrucciones: Resuelva cada uno de los problemas.

1. A fin de aprovechar unas rebajas, el propietario de un motel toma prestados $31,000 para la compra de 124 televisores en color. El préstamo es de 90 días a una tasa de interés anual del 12.5%. Halle la cantidad total que debe pagar.

   (1) $968.75   **(2)** $3,875   **(3)** $31,968.75   **(4)** $34,875
   (5) no se indica suficiente información

2. ¿Qué expresión representa cómo hallar el interés acumulado en un año por un capital de $1500 al 8 1/2% anual?

   (1) $\dfrac{1500 \times 8\frac{1}{2}}{100}$ **(2)** $\dfrac{1500 \times 100}{8\frac{1}{2}}$ **(3)** $\dfrac{1500}{100 \div 8\frac{1}{2}}$ **(4)** $\dfrac{100}{1500 \times 8\frac{1}{2}}$ **(5)** $\dfrac{100}{1500 \div 8\frac{1}{2}}$

3. Alex pidió prestado dinero por un año a una tasa del 8% anual. Si pagó $360 en intereses ese año, ¿cuánto recibió en préstamo?

   (1) $28.80   **(2)** $288   **(3)** $2,880   **(4)** $4,500   **(5)** $36,000

5
MEDIAS

Unidades de medida estándar

Las unidades de medida que se citan a continuación son las utilizadas con más frecuencia en los Estados Unidos. Se les suele llamar también unidades de medida estándar o estadounidenses.

Unidades de medida estándar

Unidades de longitud		*Unidades de peso*	
12 pulgadas	= 1 pie	2000 libras (lb)	= 1 tonelada (T)
3 pies	= 1 yarda (yd)	16 onzas	= 1 libra
36 pulgadas	= 1 yarda		
5280 pies	= 1 milla (mi)		

Unidades de volumen		*Unidades de tiempo*	
4 cuartos (qt)	= 1 galón (gal)	12 meses	= 1 año
2 pintas (pt)	= 1 cuarto	52 semanas	= 1 año
2 tazas	= 1 pinta	365 días	= 1 año
8 onzas (oz)	= 1 taza	7 días	= 1 semana
		24 horas (hr)	= 1 día
		60 minutos (min)	= 1 hora
		60 segundos (seg)	= 1 minuto

Conversión de unidades

Al resolver problemas con medidas, conviene a menudo cambiar las unidades de medida. Este cambio recibe el nombre de *conversión*. Existen dos tipos de conversiones: de una unidad mayor a una menor o de una unidad menor a una mayor. La siguiente tabla le será de utilidad en la conversión de unidades.

CONVERSIÓN DE UNIDADES		
Para convertir una unidad mayor a otra menor	se multiplica $\times$	En este caso, se busca una mayor cantidad de unidades menores.
Para convertir una unidad menor a otra mayor	se divide $\div$	En este caso, se busca una menor cantidad de unidades mayores.

Ejemplo 1: Convierta 7 pies a pulgadas.

Al pasar de pies (unidad mayor) a pulgadas (unidad menor), se multiplica. (Recordar que: 12 pulgadas = 1 pie.)

$$\begin{array}{r} 12 \text{ pulgadas} \\ \times\ 7 \\ \hline 84 \text{ pulgadas} \end{array}$$

Ejemplo 2: Convierta 6 toneladas a libras.

Al pasar de una unidad mayor a una unidad menor, se multiplica. (Recordar que: 2000 libras = 1 tonelada.)

$$\begin{array}{r} 2000 \text{ libras} \\ \times \quad 6 \\ \hline 12{,}000 \text{ libras} \end{array}$$

Ejemplo 3: Convierta 48 onzas a pintas.

Al pasar de una unidad menor (onzas) a una mayor (pintas), se divide. (Recordar que: 8 onzas = 1 taza; 2 tazas = 1 pinta.)

Antes de efectuar la división para hallar el número de pintas, se debe primero encontrar el número de onzas que hay en una pinta.

Primero, se multiplican 8 onzas por 2 tazas y se obtiene que una pinta tiene 16 onzas. $8 \times 2 = 16$

Después, se divide 48 onzas por 16. $48 \div 16 = 3$

Hay 3 pintas en 48 onzas.

LAS RESPUESTAS DE LOS EJERCICIOS DE ESTE CAPÍTULO EMPIEZAN EN LA PÁGINA 470.

EJERCICIO 1: CONVERSIONES

Instrucciones: Efectúe las conversiones en los problemas siguientes.

1. 96 horas = _____ días

2. 20 cuartos = _____ galones

3. 2 días = _____ minutos

4. Si Pike's Peak mide 14,110 pies de alto, ¿cuál es su elevación en millas (redondeada al décimo más cercano)?

Operaciones básicas con medidas

En la vida cotidiana solemos encontrarnos con la necesidad de sumar, restar, multiplicar o dividir medidas. Repasemos pues estos fundamentos.

Ejemplo 1: Sume 3 libras 8 onzas y 15 onzas.

$$\begin{array}{r} 3 \text{ lb} \quad 8 \text{ oz} \\ + \quad 15 \text{ oz} \\ \hline 3 \text{ lb } 23 \text{ oz} \end{array}$$ Asegúrese de sumar onzas con onzas.

Como 23 onzas es más que 16 onzas (1 libra), simplifique la cifra dividiendo por 16.

$$\begin{array}{r} 1 \text{ r } 7 = 1 \text{ lb } 7 \text{ oz} \\ 16\overline{)23} \\ - \ 16 \\ \hline 7 \end{array}$$

3 libras 23 onzas = 3 libras + 1 libra 7 onzas = 4 libras 7 onzas

Ejemplo 2: Reste 5 libras 7 onzas de 8 libras 12 onzas.

$$\begin{array}{r} 8 \text{ lb } 12 \text{ oz} \\ - 5 \text{ lb } 7 \text{ oz} \\ \hline 3 \text{ lb } 5 \text{ oz} \end{array}$$

Reste las onzas de las onzas.
Después, reste las libras de las libras.

Ejemplo 3: Multiplique 4 pies 8 pulgadas por 3.

$$\begin{array}{r} 4 \text{ pies } 8 \text{ pulg} \\ \times \phantom{4 \text{ pies }}3 \\ \hline 12 \text{ pies } 24 \text{ pulg} \end{array}$$

← Multiplique 3 por 8 pulgadas, después multiplique 3 por 4 pies.

← Como 12 pulgadas = 1 pie, simplifique la respuesta.

12 pies 24 pulg = 12 pies + 2 pies = 14 pies

Ejemplo 4: Divida 2 cuartos 5 onzas por 3.

$$\begin{array}{r} 0 \text{ qt } 23 \text{ oz} \\ 3\overline{)2 \text{ qt } 5 \text{ oz}} \\ -0 \phantom{ \text{ qt } 5 \text{ oz}} \\ \hline \end{array}$$

2 qt = 64 oz   ← 2 no es divisible por 3. Convierta 2 cuartos a 64 onzas.
+ 5 oz   ← Sume 5 onzas a 64 onzas. Después divida por tres.

69 oz ÷ 3 = 23 oz = 1 qt 7 oz

OPERACIONES BÁSICAS CON MEDIDAS	
SUMA	1. Sumar unidades semejantes. 2. Expresar el resultado en su forma más sencilla.
RESTA	1. Restar unidades semejantes. 2. Reagrupar las unidades cuando fuere necesario. 3. Expresar el resultado en su forma más sencilla.
MULTIPLICACIÓN	1. Multiplicar las unidades semejantes cuando participen distintas unidades. 2. Expresar el resultado en su forma más sencilla.
DIVISIÓN	1. Dividir primero la unidad mayor. 2. Convertir el resto a la unidad menor y sumar dicha cantidad a la cantidad de unidad semejante. 3. Dividir luego la unidad menor. 4. Expresar el resultado en su forma más sencilla.

EJERCICIO 2: OPERACIONES BÁSICAS CON MEDIDAS

Instrucciones: En los ejercicios siguientes, sume, reste, multiplique o divida según se indique. Asegúrese de expresar el resultado en su forma más sencilla. Por ejemplo, si el resultado es 15 pulgadas, se deberá convertir a 1 pie 3 pulgadas.

1. 22 pies 6 pulgadas ÷ 3
2. 5 horas 20 minutos ÷ 8
3. ¿Qué diferencia de peso hay entre dos cajas de cereal: una de 1 libra 4 onzas y otra de 13 onzas?

4. A un precio de $415 por onza, ¿cuál de las siguientes expresiones representa el valor de 1 libra 3 onzas de oro?

   (1) 3($415)   **(2)** 16($415)   **(3)** 3 + 16 + $415   **(4)** 19($415)
   (5) $\frac{\$415}{19}$

5. Shane trabaja tiempo parcial en una ferretería. Gana $5 la hora. La semana pasada trabajó los siguientes días: lunes, 2 horas 30 minutos; miércoles, 3 horas; viernes, 4 horas 45 minutos; sábado, 7 horas 15 minutos; y domingo, 4 horas. ¿Cuánto ganó esa semana en la ferretería?

   (1) $28   **(2)** $66   **(3)** $72   **(4)** $86   **(5)** $107.50

El sistema métrico

El *sistema métrico* es un sistema de medidas internacional utilizado para simplificar y facilitar las actividades comerciales entre las naciones. La unidad básica de medida de longitud es el *metro.* Un metro es algo más largo que una yarda. La unidad básica de peso es el *gramo.* Un clip pesa aproximadamente un gramo. El kilogramo (1000 gramos) equivale aproximadamente a unas 2 libras del sistema estadounidense. La medida básica para expresar volumen es el *litro.* Un litro es algo mayor que un cuarto.

Todas las demás unidades del sistema métrico derivan de las unidades básicas: metro (longitud), gramo (peso) y litro (volumen). Los nombres de las demás unidades se forman anteponiendo prefijos a los nombres de las unidades básicas. Estos prefijos indican qué cantidad de la unidad básica contiene dicha unidad. Por ejemplo, el prefijo *centi-* quiere decir *centésimo;* por lo tanto, un centímetro es un centésimo de un metro, un centigramo es un centésimo de un gramo y un centilitro es un centésimo de un litro.

PREFIJO	VALOR
kilo	1000
hecto	100
deca	10
UNIDAD BÁSICA	
deci	$\frac{1}{10}$ (.1)
centi	$\frac{1}{100}$ (.01)
mili	$\frac{1}{1000}$ (.001)

El diagrama siguiente relaciona los prefijos métricos con el sistema decimal ya visto.

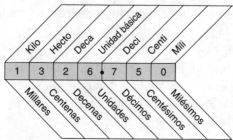

El cuadro adjunto presenta las unidades métricas más comunes.

LONGITUD

1 kilómetro (km) = 1000 m   1 centímetro (cm) = .01 m
1 metro (m) = 1 m   1 milímetro (mm) = .001 m

<table>
<tr><td colspan="1">PESO</td><td>VOLUMEN</td></tr>
</table>

PESO	VOLUMEN
1 kilogramo (kg) = 1000 g	1 kilolitro (kl) = 1000 l
1 gramo (g) = 1 g	1 litro (l) = 1 l
1 miligramo (mg) = $\frac{1}{1000}$ g (.001 g)	1 mililitro (ml) = $\frac{1}{1000}$ l (.001 l)

Conversiones en el sistema métrico

Para convertir de una unidad métrica a otra unidad métrica equivalente, se corre el punto decimal ya sea a la derecha o a la izquierda.

El diagrama siguiente ilustra los prefijos en orden de mayor a menor.

kilo	hecto	deca	unidad	deci	centi	mili

Ejemplo 1: Convierta 420 metros a kilómetros.

PASO 1. Tenga en cuenta que al convertir metros a kilómetros hay que pasar de una unidad menor a otra mayor. (1000 metros = 1 kilómetro) Trace una flecha para indicar esto.

kilómetros ⟵ metros
izquierda (÷)

PASO 2. Como kilo significa "mil", corra el punto 3 lugares.

km hm Dm m dm cm mm
420 = .420

Ejemplo 2: Convierta 4.2 kilogramos a gramos.

kg hg Dg g dg cg mg
3 lugares a la derecha

4.2 kg = 4.200 g = 4200 g
3 lugares a la derecha

Ejemplo 3: Convierta 4 metros 48 centímetros a centímetros.

Primero, convierta 4 metros a centímetros.

km hm Dm m dm cm mm
2 lugares a la derecha

4 M = 4.00 cm = 400 cm
2 lugares a la derecha

Después, sume.

400 cm + 48 cm = 448 cm

CÓMO CONVERTIR ENTRE UNIDADES MÉTRICAS

1. Escribir las unidades en orden de mayor a menor.
2. Marcar la unidad inicial.
3. Ir unidad por unidad hasta la unidad deseada y contar cuántos lugares hacia la derecha o hacia la izquierda se ha corrido.
4. Correr el punto decimal ese mismo número de lugares en el mismo sentido.

EJERCICIO 3: MEDIDAS MÉTRICAS

Instrucciones: Convierta a las unidades indicadas.

1. Halle la longitud total en metros de este eje.

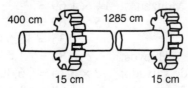

2. La dosis diaria recomendada de vitamina C es de 857 *miligramos*. ¿Cuántos *gramos* de vitamina C tomará Max en una semana si toma la dosis diaria recomendada?

3. Si la velocidad máxima en Canadá es de 80 kilómetros por hora y en ciertas partes de EE.UU. es de 55 millas por hora, ¿en qué país se permite conducir a mayor velocidad? (1 kilómetro = .621 millas)

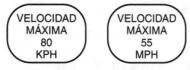

4. Terry compitió en una carrera de patinaje de 1000 metros. ¿Cuántos kilómetros patinó?

5. ¿Qué expresión se puede utilizar para hallar el costo de .75 kilogramos de queso a un precio de $6.40 por kilogramo?

  (1) $\frac{\$6.40}{.75}$

  (2) $.75 \times \$6.40$

  (3) $\frac{\$6.40}{2}$

  (4) $.75 + \$6.40$

  (5) $\$6.40 - .75$

Temas especiales sobre medidas
Problemas con dinero

En este apartado dirigiremos nuestra atención hacia problemas que requieren de cálculos de sumas de dinero. Utilizaremos la fórmula $c = nr$. Las *fórmulas* se valen de letras para representar reglas que se aplican en el cálculo de distintas cantidades o medidas. Al trabajar con fórmulas, se pueden sustituir las letras por números. Para hallar el costo total *(c)*, se multiplica el número de unidades *(n)* por el costo unitario *(r)*. Esta regla se escribe: $c = nr$. (En las fórmulas, dos letras juntas una de otra indican que las dos cantidades se multiplican.)

Ejemplo: Margaret hizo la siguiente compra el 15 de mayo: $1\frac{1}{2}$ docenas de manzanas a $1.69 la docena, 2 docenas de huevos a 84¢ la docena, 2 cajas de hojuelas de salvado a $3.15 cada una, 1 libra de margarina a $1.58 la libra y 3 latas de sopa a 79¢ la lata. Si Margaret pagó con un billete de 20 dólares, ¿cuánto recibió de cambio?

PASO 1. Use la fórmula $c = nr$ para calcular el costo total de cada artículo que compró. Después, halle el costo total de la compra.

Manzanas: $1\frac{1}{2} \times 1.69 =$
$1.5 \times 1.69 =$
$2.535 = \$2.54$
Huevos: $2 \times .84 = 1.68$
Hojuelas de salvado: $2 \times 3.15 = 6.30$
Margarina: $1 \times 1.58 = 1.58$
Sopa: $3 \times .79 = \underline{+2.37}$
Total: $\$14.47$

PASO 2. Reste para hallar el cambio de $20.

$\$20.00$
$\underline{-14.47}$
$\$5.53$

▶ **Nota:** Redondee siempre el dinero a la posición de los centésimos. Por lo general, se redondea a un número mayor y no a un número menor.

EJERCICIO 4: PROBLEMAS CON DINERO

Instrucciones: Resuelva cada uno de los problemas.

1. En la tienda del Sr. Barnes tienen en existencia 2 toneladas de arena en sacos de 50 libras. La arena cuesta $138 por tonelada. Si el Sr. Barnes vende todos los sacos de arena a $5.95 el saco, ¿cuál será su ganancia?

   (1) $3.19   **(2)** $69   **(3)** $200   **(4)** $276   **(5)** $470.40

2. Se necesitan 48 pies de moldura para terminar de decorar la sala. ¿Cuál es el costo total de la moldura si cada tramo de 1 yarda cuesta 98 centavos?

   (1) $3.92   **(2)** $15.68   **(3)** $47.04   **(4)** $392.00   **(5)** $470.00

3. Una medicina de marca contra los resfriados cuesta $6.48 por 36 cápsulas. El equivalente genérico cuesta $4.32 por 36 cápsulas. ¿Cuánto dinero se ahorra por dosis usando la marca genérica si cada dosis es de 2 cápsulas?

   (1) $.06   **(2)** $.12   **(3)** $.18   **(4)** $1.08   **(5)** $2.16

Problemas de tiempo

En muchos trabajos hay que marcar tarjeta al entrar y al salir del trabajo. La tarjeta registra el tiempo de entrada y el tiempo de salida.

RELOJ

A.M. quiere decir "horas comprendidas entre medianoche y mediodía".

P.M. quiere decir "horas comprendidas entre mediodía y medianoche".

A la izquierda de los dos puntos se ubican las horas. **3:30** A la derecha de los dos puntos se ubican los minutos.

Ejemplo 1: Tina trabajó sobretiempo el jueves. Empezó a las 7:30 A.M. y terminó a las 6:45 P.M. ¿Cuánto tiempo trabajó?

PASO 1. Halle las horas trabajadas por la mañana.

$$\begin{array}{r}
{\scriptstyle 11\ 6\ 0} \\
\cancel{12}{:}\cancel{00} \\
-\ 7{:}30 \\
\hline
4{:}30
\end{array}$$ ó 4 horas 30 minutos

Preste 60 minutos de las horas

PASO 2. Halle las horas trabajadas por la tarde.

Del mediodía a las 6:45 son 6 horas 45 minutos.

PASO 3. Halle el total de horas.

$$\begin{array}{r}
4{:}30 \\
+6{:}45 \\
\hline
10{:}75
\end{array} = 11{:}15$$

Como 75 minutos es más que 60 minutos (una hora), se puede simplificar a 1 hora y 15 minutos y luego sumarle este tiempo a las 10 horas.

11:15 se puede expresar como *11 hr 15 min* u $11\frac{15}{60} = 11\frac{1}{4}$ hr.

CÓMO CALCULAR EL TIEMPO

1. Hallar el total de horas correspondientes a la mañana.
2. Hallar el total de horas correspondientes a la tarde.
3. Sumar las horas de la mañana y las de la tarde
4. Expresar el resultado en su forma más sencilla.

EJERCICIO 5: PROBLEMAS SOBRE TIEMPO

Instrucciones: Resuelva cada uno de los problemas.

1. Roger trabaja durante el turno del almuerzo de 10:00 A.M. a 2:30 P.M., de lunes a viernes todas las semanas a $8.00 la hora. ¿Qué expresión representa lo que gana él cada cuatro semanas?

   (1) $4\frac{1}{2}+8+5+4$ **(4)** $4\frac{1}{2}(8+5+4)$

   (2) $(4\frac{1}{2}\times8)+(5\times4)$ **(5)** $4\frac{1}{2}\times8$

   (3) $4\frac{1}{2}\times8\times5\times4$

Las *Preguntas 2–4* se refieren a la siguiente ficha de trabajo:

MARSHALL MANUFACTURING					
NOMBRE: Tom Wolper SS# 000-45-0000					
Fecha	5/20	5/21	5/22	5/23	5/24
De	8:00 A.M.	8:00 A.M.	8:00 A.M.	8:00 A.M.	8:00 A.M.
A	4:00 P.M.	5:30 P.M.	6:45 P.M.	4:00 P.M.	4:30 P.M.
Total de horas regulares _____ a $7.85					
Total de horas de sobretiempo _____ a $12.00 (por encima de 40 horas)					

2. Según esta ficha, Tom Wolper trabajó la semana del 5/20 al 5/24. ¿Cuántas horas de sobretiempo (horas que sobrepasan las ocho horas de un turno regular) trabajó esa semana?

(1) $3\frac{3}{4}$ (2) 4   (3) $4\frac{1}{4}$ (4) $4\frac{1}{2}$ (5) $4\frac{3}{4}$

3. ¿Cuánto recibe Tom antes de aplicársele las deducciones? (Incluya las horas regulares y las horas de sobretiempo.)

(1) $57   (2) $314   (3) $351   (4) $371   (5) $537

4. Si la retención de impuestos estatales es del 1%, la de los impuestos federales es del 25% y la de los impuestos de seguridad social (FICA) es del 7%, ¿cuál es el ingreso neto de Tom después de aplicadas estas deducciones?

(1) $122.43   (2) $155.82   (3) $215.18   (4) $248.57   (5) $493.43

5. Un avión vuela a 960 millas por hora. ¿Qué expresión indica la distancia que recorre en veinte minutos?

(1) 960×20 (2) $960 \times \frac{1}{3}$ (3) $\frac{960}{20}$ (4) $\frac{3}{960}$ (5) $\frac{(\frac{1}{3})}{960}$

Lectura e interpretación de escalas y medidores

LECTURA DE ESCALAS Y MEDIDORES
Al momento de resolver problemas con escalas y medidores, hacemos las siguientes recomendaciones.
1. Leer detenidamente las unidades del medidor.
2. Si se proporcionan instrucciones, referirse al medidor al leerlas.
3. Anotar la lectura del medidor.
4. Hacer caso omiso de toda información superflua para la resolución del problema.

Dibujos a escala

Los **mapas** son representaciones gráficas de un área en una superficie plana. Cuando se dibuja un mapa a escala (en proporción al área que representa), se adjunta una **clave** para calcular las distancias representadas en el mapa. La clave proporciona información sobre la razón aritmética aplicable a ese mapa. La escala puede ser empleada para establecer una proporción a fin de hallar distancias reales. Dirijamos ahora nuestra atención al mapa abajo. Consulte el mapa y conteste las preguntas que siguen. Observe la escala en millas que aparece en la parte superior del mapa.

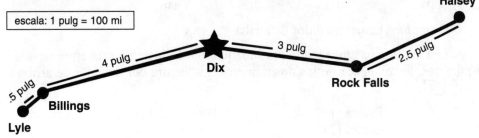

Ejemplo: Si en el mapa la distancia de Halsey a Rock Falls es de 2.5 pulgadas, ¿cuál es la distancia real entre esos dos sitios?

La razón es: 1 pulgada por cada 100 millas. Si en el mapa la distancia entre Halsey y Rock Falls es de 2.5 pulgadas, podemos establecer la siguiente proporción para resolver el problema. Obsérvese que nos estamos valiendo de una proporción para comparar dos cosas (pulgadas con millas).

$$\frac{1 \text{ pulg}}{100 \text{ mi}} = \frac{2.5 \text{ pulg}}{n \text{ mi}}$$

Multiplique en diagonal: $100 \times 2.5 = 250$

Divida: $250 \div 1 = 250$

Lectura de medidores

Los **medidores** son dispositivos utilizados para medir el tiempo, la velocidad, la distancia y la energía utilizada. De seguro está ya usted familiarizado con algunos tipos de medidores como, por ejemplo, el velocímetro, el barómetro o el termómetro. Los medidores nos dan información útil para la resolución de problemas. Pasemos entonces a un ejemplo.

El contador eléctrico

Los aparatos como los refrigeradores, ventiladores, radios, televisores y lavaplatos requieren de electricidad para su funcionamiento. El **contador eléctrico** es un instrumento que mide en **kilovatios-hora (kwh)** la cantidad de electricidad utilizada. Los números ubicados encima de la esfera indican cuánto representa un giro completo de la aguja alrededor de la esfera. Observe que en algunas esferas las agujas se mueven en sentido horario mientras que en otras giran en sentido antihorario.

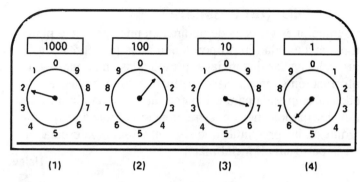

La esfera (1) mide la cantidad de 1000 kwh.

La esfera (2) mide la cantidad de 100 kwh.

La esfera (3) mide la cantidad de 10 kwh.

La esfera (4) mide la cantidad de 1 kwh.

(1)   (2)   (3)   (4)

Ejemplo: Lea el medidor de arriba.

Lea las esferas empezando por la izquierda. Si la aguja está entre dos números, lea el *menor* de los dos números. La lectura del medidor de arriba es 2176 .

Esfera (1) 2	2×1000	$= 2000$
Esfera (2) 1	1×100	$= 100$
Esfera (3) 7	7×10	$= 70$
Esfera (4) 6	6×1	$= 6$
Total de kwh usados:		2176

EJERCICIO 6: ESCALAS Y MEDIDORES

Instrucciones: Resuelva cada uno de los problemas.

1. ¿Cuál es la escala de un mapa en que se representan 2000 millas como 10 pulgadas?
   (1) 1 pulg = 2 mi
   (2) 1 pulg = 20 mi
   (3) 1 pulg = 200 mi
   (4) 1 pulg = 1/2 mi
   (5) 1 pulg = 100 mi

2. La última lectura de Emma de su contador eléctrico fue de 3843 kwh. Su nueva lectura viene indicada en el contador que se ilustra abajo. Si el precio por kwh es de 12.5 centavos, ¿cuál será el total de la factura de electricidad de Emma?

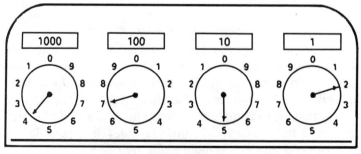

KILOVATIOS-HORA

(1) $113.63   **(2)** $909   **(3)** $2,020   **(4)** $2,562.50   **(5)** $11,362.50

6
GRÁFICOS, ESTADÍSTICA
Y PROBABILIDAD

Los gráficos, cuadros y tablas estadísticas nos permiten organizar la información. Cuando se nos presenta cualquier material que ha sido previamente organizado conforme a determinados criterios, se debe prestar atención a detalles tales como el título, el subtítulo, los encabezados de las columnas y de las filas, la clave (si se adjunta una) y el tipo de información dada. Este proceso recibe el nombre de interpretación de *datos.* La *estadística* es la ciencia que estudia los *datos.* Con la estadística, se organizan los datos y se sacan conclusiones en base a los mismos.

Media y mediana

El calcular la media y la mediana de un conjunto de datos son tipos comunes de problemas de estadística. La *media* es el promedio de las cantidades. Para calcular el promedio, se suman los datos y se divide el total por el número de datos.

Por ejemplo, la noche pasada Brenda fue a jugar boliche y anotó 132, 147 y 108. Para calcular su puntuación media (promedio), se suman los puntajes: $132 + 147 + 108 = 387$ y después se divide el total por 3 (número de puntajes): $387 \div 3 = 129$. Por lo tanto, la media, o promedio, de su puntuación es de 129.

La *mediana* de un conjunto de datos se calcula ordenando los números de menor a mayor e identificando luego el número del medio del conjunto. Este número del medio es la mediana. Los tres puntajes de Brenda son, en orden de menor a mayor: 108, 132, 147. El puntaje del medio es 132; por lo que la mediana es 132.

CÓMO CALCULAR LA MEDIA O PROMEDIO
1. Sumar las cantidades.
2. Dividir por el número de cantidades.

CÓMO CALCULAR LA MEDIANA
1. Poner los números en orden de menor a mayor.
2. Identificar el número del medio. (Si hay dos números en el medio, se halla el promedio de los dos números.)

Ejemplo: Con el objeto de realizar un estudio acerca del número de comensales que van a cenar al Shamrock Inn, Shannon reunió la siguiente información durante los 17 primeros días de marzo. ¿Cuál es la mediana del número de comensales?

35, 37, 43, 28, 32, 38, 45, 21, 26, 27, 44, 46, 29, 39, 42, 86, 117

La mediana es 38, mientras que la media (promedio) es 43.24.

En este caso, la mediana de 38 es más representativa de la cantidad normal de comensales. El promedio sufre un desajuste debido al gran número de comensales que asistieron el 17º día, fiesta de San Patricio. En casos como éstos, se suele usar la mediana dado que la media no ofrece una representación aproximada de la realidad a causa de la presencia de cifras anormalmente altas o bajas.

LAS RESPUESTAS DE LOS EJERCICIOS DE ESTE CAPÍTULO EMPIEZAN EN LA PÁGINA 472.

EJERCICIO 1: MEDIA Y MEDIANA

Instrucciones: Resuelva cada uno de los problemas. Las *Preguntas 1–2* se basan en los siguientes datos. Redondee las respuestas al número entero más cercano.

El encargado de llevar un registro de los resultados de los partidos del equipo de básquetbol Union Town anotó el marcador final de los últimos seis juegos.

Fecha	Adversario	Union Town vs. Adversario
12/4	Hinkley	48 a 37
12/6	Barton	45 a 63
12/10	Angel Park	53 a 42
12/12	Eagle Rock	72 a 24
12/18	Bennett	68 a 44
12/20	Alton	74 a 51

1. ¿Cuál es el promedio de puntos anotados por los adversarios?

2. ¿Cuál es la mediana de la puntuación obtenida por el Union Town?

3. El precio de una misma chaqueta de invierno en cinco tiendas distintas es de $48.95, $39.95, $44.80, $52.25 y $42.88 respectivamente. ¿Cuál es la mediana del precio de esa chaqueta?

Gráficos

Los *gráficos,* cuadros y tablas son útiles recursos que nos permiten organizar datos y representarlos en forma visual. De este modo, se simplifica el manejo de la información. A menudo se puede captar toda una situación con sólo echar una rápida mirada a un gráfico. Al organizar los datos visualmente, los gráficos, cuadros y tablas nos ayudan a interpretar, comparar y analizar números.

Gráficos circulares

En los *gráficos circulares,* el círculo representa la unidad o cantidad total.

El círculo de la derecha representa el total de gastos comerciales de Hampton Products, una pequeña empresa familiar. Si sumamos todos los sectores del círculo, se obtiene un total del 100%.

GASTOS COMERCIALES DE HAMPTON PRODUCTS

- Varios 3%
- Materiales y equipos 7%
- Seguro 10%
- Alquiler y servicios 25%
- Salarios 55%

Ejemplo: Si el año pasado el total de gastos comerciales de Hampton Products ascendió a $125,000, ¿cuánto fueron los gastos de alquiler y servicios? Según indica el gráfico, el alquiler y los servicios representan un 25% del total. Necesitamos, por lo tanto, hallar el 25% de $125,000.

$$\frac{n}{125,000} = \frac{25}{100}$$

$$125,000 \times \frac{25}{100} = \$31,250$$

EJERCICIO 2: GRÁFICOS CIRCULARES

Instrucciones: Resuelva cada uno de los problemas.

Las *Preguntas 1–3* se basan en el gráfico de la derecha.

1. ¿Cuál es el gasto *mensual* promedio de alquiler?

2. ¿Cuánto se gasta en ropa durante el año?

   (1) $320   **(2)** $480
   (3) $800   **(4)** $3200
   (5) no se da suficiente información

3. ¿Cuál es la razón de ahorros a ingresos totales?

   (1) 1 a 10   **(2)** 10 a 1   **(3)** 10 a 32   **(4)** 32 a 10
   (5) no se da suficiente información

DISTRIBUCIÓN DE $32,000 DE INGRESOS ANUALES

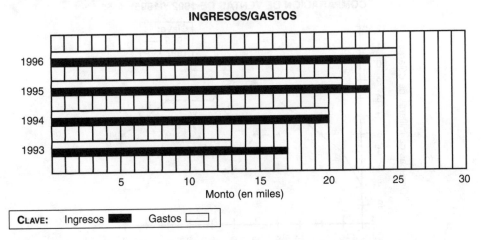

(Gráfico circular: Varios 5%, Gastos médicos 4%, Servicios 8%, Diversión 10%, Ahorros 10%, Alquiler 25%, Automóvil 15%, Comida 23%)

Gráficos de barras

Los *gráficos de barras* son valiosas herramientas que nos ayudan a realizar comparaciones entre cantidades. En el gráfico de barras abajo, compare los ingresos con los gastos incurridos en un determinado año.

EJERCICIO 3: GRÁFICOS DE BARRAS

Instrucciones: Use el gráfico siguiente para contestar las preguntas.

INGRESOS/GASTOS

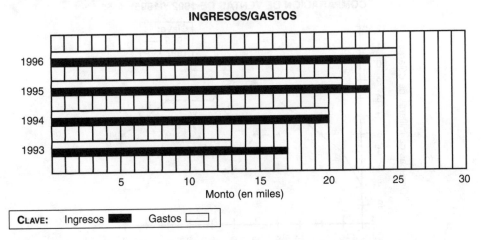

(Gráfico de barras con años 1996, 1995, 1994, 1993; eje Monto (en miles) de 5 a 30. CLAVE: Ingresos ■ Gastos □)

1. ¿Cuál fue el promedio de gastos para los años 1993–1996?

2. En 1995, ¿cuál fue la diferencia entre ingresos y gastos?

   (1) $200   **(2)** $2,000   **(3)** $20,000   **(4)** $21,000   **(5)** $23,000

Gráficos lineales

Los **gráficos lineales** se utilizan para representar tendencias y patrones. En un gráfico lineal, cada punto encierra en sí dos valores: su valor en el eje vertical ($\updownarrow$) y su valor en el eje horizontal ($\leftrightarrow$).

Al estudiar el gráfico lineal de la derecha, obsérvese lo siguiente:

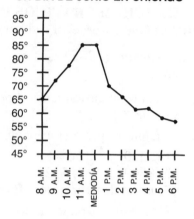

TEMPERATURAS EXTERIORES EN UN DÍA DE JUNIO EN CHICAGO

1. El título indica de qué trata el gráfico.

2. Los valores de la escala vertical se ubican a la izquierda del gráfico. Cada línea representa un incremento de 5°. Los valores de la escala horizontal se ubican debajo del gráfico. Cada línea representa un incremento de 1 hora.

3. La línea muestra la tendencia siguiente: la temperatura subió hasta las 11:00 A.M., y luego permaneció estable hasta el mediodía. Después la temperatura bajó.

Los gráficos lineales también se pueden usar para comparar dos tendencias distintas. Más abajo, se ofrece un ejemplo de este tipo: una de las tendencias está representada con una línea continua, mientras que la otra está representada con una línea intermitente. Cuando un gráfico utiliza dos o más líneas, se puede comparar la información dada por las líneas.

EJERCICIO 4: GRÁFICOS LINEALES

Instrucciones: Use este gráfico para contestar las *Preguntas 1–4* en la página siguiente.

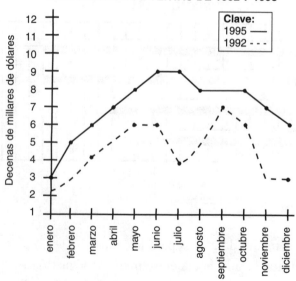

COMPARACIÓN DE VENTAS DE 1992 Y 1995

Clave:
1995 ——
1992 - - -

1. El título nos indica que el gráfico compara _____ del año _____ y del año _____.

2. Los valores de la escala vertical son _____.

3. En junio de 1992, las ventas fueron de aproximadamente

   _____.

4. El gráfico muestra que tanto en 1992 como en 1995 se produjeron máximos y mínimos de temporada. En términos generales, 1995 generó una cantidad considerablemente _____ de ventas en todo el año.

EJERCICIO 5: PRÁCTICA MIXTA DE GRÁFICOS
Instrucciones: Resuelva cada uno de los problemas.

Las *Preguntas 1–3* se basan en el gráfico circular de la derecha.

DISTRIBUCIÓN DE GANANCIAS

1. Si usted gana $25,000 al año, ¿cuál es su contribución anual a la seguridad social?

2. Si quisiera recibir un salario neto de $20,000, ¿cuáles tendrían que ser sus ganancias totales?

3. Un año, Mike ganó $24,000. Las deducciones que se le aplicaron fueron de impuestos federales, FICA e impuestos estatales. ¿Cuál fue su salario neto ese año?

Las *Preguntas 4–6* se refieren al gráfico de barras de la derecha.

4. ¿Cuál es la diferencia de altura entre el Empire State Building y el Sears Tower?

5. ¿Cuántas veces más alto es el World Trade Center que el Monumento a Washington?

6. ¿Cuál es la mediana de las alturas de las seis estructuras?

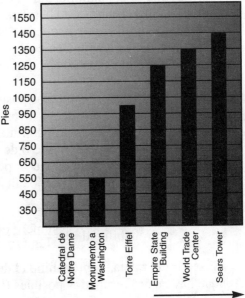

EDIFICIOS ALTOS

Las *Preguntas 7–8* se basan en el siguiente gráfico lineal.

ASISTENCIA A CONCIERTOS - VERANO 1996

7. ¿En qué meses fue la asistencia de jóvenes mayor que la de adultos?

8. Si los boletos para adultos costaban $8.50 y los boletos para jóvenes $5.75, ¿cuáles fueron los ingresos percibidos por los conciertos realizados en agosto?

Probabilidad

Se puede decir que la *probabilidad* es el lenguaje de la incertidumbre. El meteorólogo dice que la probabibilidad de que llueva hoy es del 40%; pero seguimos sin saber si va a llover o no. La probabilidad nos ayuda a predecir o pronosticar el futuro basándose en un análisis del pasado. La probabilidad se puede expresar en forma de fracción, razón o porcentaje. Una probabilidad de 0 significa que no va a ocurrir un suceso. Una probabilidad de 1 significa que es seguro que ocurra un suceso. Los números comprendidos entre 0 y 1 (fracciones) indican si el suceso se aproxima más a 0 (más probable que no ocurra) o a 1 (más probable que ocurra).

Usemos una ruleta para ilustrar el concepto de probabilidad. Supongamos que la ruleta está perfectamente equilibrada y que existe la misma posibilidad de que se detenga en cualquier color. Cada giro de la ruleta es un *suceso*. El color en el que se detiene es el *resultado* del suceso.

Al girar la ruleta, los resultados posibles son cuatro: rojo, azul, verde y anaranjado. Se produce un suceso favorable cuando al girar la ruleta se obtiene el color deseado. La probabilidad de que se produzca un resultado favorable es la razón entre el número de resultados favorables y el número de resultados posibles. La probabldad se puede expresar en forma de fracción o razón como se puede apreciar abajo. También conviene recordar que se puede expresar en forma de porcentaje.

$$\text{Probabilidad} = \frac{\text{Número de resultados favorables}}{\text{Número de resultados posibles}}$$

Si se gira la ruleta, la probabilidad de que se detenga en el rojo es de $\frac{1}{4}$. Aunque hay cuatro resultados posibles (rojo, azul, verde o anaranjado), sólo hay un resultado favorable (rojo). La probabilidad de $\frac{1}{4}$ también se puede expresar como 25%; en razón de lo cual se puede decir que existe una probabilidad de un 25% de que la ruleta se detenga en el rojo.

Ahora, halle la probabilidad de que la ruleta se detenga en el rojo *o* en el verde. En este caso hay dos resultados posibles que pueden ser favorables. La probabilidad es:

$\frac{2}{4}$ número de resultados favorables
número de resultados posibles

$\frac{2}{4}$ se pueden reducir a $\frac{1}{2}$. Así, la probabilidad de que se detenga en el rojo o en el verde es de $\frac{1}{2}$, ó 50%.

Probabilidad de 0 ó 1

Una probabilidad de 0 ó del 0% indica que el suceso en cuestión no se dará. Volviendo nuevamente a nuestra ruleta, la probabilidad de que se detenga en el violeta es 0, porque el número de resultados favorables de color violeta en esta ruleta es 0. Por lo tanto, tenemos que $\frac{0}{4} = 0$. La probabilidad de que se detenga en el violeta es del 0%.

Una probabilidad de 1 ó del 100% indica que el suceso en cuestión se dará con certeza. Hallemos la probabilidad de que la ruleta se detenga en el rojo, el verde, el azul o el anaranjado. El número de resultados favorables es 4, y el número de resultados posibles es 4. Ahora tenemos $\frac{4}{4} = 1$.

EJERCICIO 6: PROBABILIDAD
Instrucciones: Resuelva cada uno de los problemas.

1. Si se escoge al azar una carta de una baraja de 52 cartas, ¿cuál es la probabilidad de que salga el as de picas?

2. En la misma baraja de 52 cartas, ¿cuál es la probabilidad de que salga corazón? Indique la respuesta en forma de porcentaje. (*Pista:* Hay 13 cartas en cada palo.)

Las *Preguntas 3–5* se refieren al dado que se ilustra abajo. Considere que se lanza un dado con los siguientes números en sus caras.

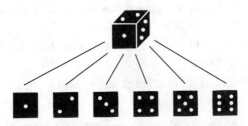

3. ¿Cuál es la probabilidad de que salga un 5?
   (1) $\frac{1}{6}$ **(2)** $\frac{1}{5}$ **(3)** $\frac{1}{3}$ **(4)** $\frac{1}{2}$ **(5)** $\frac{5}{6}$

4. ¿Cuál es la probabilidad de que salga un número par?
   (1) $16\frac{2}{3}\%$ **(2)** 20%   **(3)** 30%   **(4)** $33\frac{1}{3}\%$ **(5)** 50%

5. ¿Cuál es la probabilidad de que salga un número mayor que 6?
   (1) 0   **(2)** $\frac{1}{6}$ **(3)** $\frac{1}{3}$ **(4)** $\frac{1}{2}$ **(5)** 1

6. Si se lanza una moneda al aire nueve veces y en todos los lanzamientos sale cara, ¿cuál es la probabilidad de que salga cara la décima vez que se lance la moneda?

(1) $\frac{1}{9}$ **(2)** $\frac{1}{10}$ **(3)** $\frac{1}{2}$ **(4)** $\frac{9}{10}$ **(5)** no se da suficiente información

Probabilidad dependiente

Supongamos que una caja contiene dos bolas verdes y tres bolas rojas. Si se saca una bola de la caja, la probabilidad de sacar una bola verde es $\frac{2}{5}$ y la probabilidad de sacar una bola roja es $\frac{3}{5}$. Si no se vuelve a introducir la bola sacada, quedan solamente cuatro bolas en la caja. La probabilidad de sacar la bola siguiente depende ahora de qué bola se sacó la primera vez.

Posibilidad 1: Se sacó una bola verde

Si se sacó una bola *verde* la primera vez, la caja contiene ahora una bola verde y tres bolas rojas. En este caso, la probabilidad de sacar una bola verde la siguiente vez es de $\frac{1}{4}$ y la probabilidad de sacar una bola roja es de $\frac{3}{4}$.

Posibilidad 2: Se sacó una bola roja

Si se sacó una bola *roja* la primera vez, la caja contiene ahora dos bolas verdes y dos bolas rojas. La probabilidad de sacar una bola verde la siguiente vez es de $\frac{2}{4}$ ó $\frac{1}{2}$, y la probabilidad de sacar una bola roja es de $\frac{2}{4}$ ó $\frac{1}{2}$.

Vemos que la segunda vez *depende* de la primera. De ahí el nombre de *probabilidad dependiente.*

EJERCICIO 7: PROBABILIDAD DEPENDIENTE
Instrucciones: Resuelva cada uno de los problemas.

Las *Preguntas 1–2* se basan en el caso siguiente. Exprese las respuestas en forma de fracción. De ser necesario, trace un diagrama que le ayude a plantear el problema y hallar la solución.

De una baraja de 52 cartas se extraen dos cartas de forma consecutiva sin volver a introducir la primera carta en la baraja.

1. Si en la primera carta sale un as, ¿cuál es la probabilidad de que en la segunda carta salga otro as?

2. ¿Cuál es la probabilidad de que salga un as en la segunda carta si en la primera carta no hubiese salido un as?

Las *Preguntas 3–4* se basan en el caso siguiente. Exprese el resultado en forma de fracción.

Un monedero contiene 3 *nickels*, 4 *dimes* y 2 *quarters.*

3. ¿Cuál es la probabilidad de que la primera moneda sacada del monedero sea un *quarter?*

4. Si la primera moneda sacada del monedero fue un *nickel*, ¿cuál es la probabilidad de que la moneda siguiente sea un *quarter*?

7
NUMERACIÓN

La *numeración* es el estudio de las relaciones numéricas. En este capítulo, repasaremos las potencias, las raíces y el orden de las operaciones. Estudiaremos el uso de las fórmulas y la sustitución por valores. También estudiaremos las series numéricas, las propiedades de los números, el orden de los números y la notación científica.

Potenciación y radicación
Potenciación

Cuando se multiplica un número por sí mismo, decimos que **se *eleva al cuadrado.*** Esto se indica poniendo un pequeño 2 en la parte superior derecha del número. Por ejemplo, $7^2 = 7 \times 7 = 49$. Esto significa que siete al cuadrado es igual a 7×7, ó sea 49.

En la expresión 7^2, el dos es la *potencia* o *exponente,* y el siete es la *base.* Se puede decir que el exponente es como una instrucción. El exponente indica lo que se debe hacer con la base. Cuando el exponente es 2, se eleva la base al cuadrado, es decir, se multiplica por sí misma.

Ejemplos: $3^2 = 3 \times 3 = 9$ $\qquad\qquad (\frac{1}{3})^2 = \frac{1}{3} \times \frac{1}{3} = \frac{1}{9}$

El exponente también puede ser un número distinto de 2. El exponente indica el número de veces que hay que multiplicar la base por sí misma. Por ejemplo:

$$3^4 = 3 \times 3 \times 3 \times 3 = 81 \qquad (\frac{1}{2})^3 = \frac{1}{2} \times \frac{1}{2} \times \frac{1}{2} = \frac{1}{8}$$

REGLAS ESPECIALES DE POTENCIACIÓN

1. El número 1 elevado a cualquier potencia es siempre 1.
   $1^5 = 1 \times 1 \times 1 \times 1 \times 1 = 1$
2. Todo número elevado a la potencia 1 es igual a la base. $\quad 6^1 = 6$
3. Todo número elevado a la potencia 0 es igual a 1. $\quad 14^0 = 1$

LAS RESPUESTAS DE LOS EJERCICIOS DEL CAPÍTULO EMPIEZAN EN LA PÁGINA 472.

EJERCICIO 1: POTENCIACIÓN

Instrucciones: Multiplique por sí misma la base de cada número el número de veces que indique su exponente.

1. 5^2 **4.** 1^{10} **6.** $(.2)^3$

2. 9^3 **5.** 4^0 **7.** 0^2

3. $(\frac{3}{4})^3$

Radicación

La operación inversa a la potenciación es la radicación. La operación inversa a elevar un número al cuadrado es extraer la *raíz cuadrada*. Por ejemplo, $5^2 = 25$, por lo que $\sqrt{25} = 5$. El signo $\sqrt{}$ es el signo de la radicación. Se denomina *radical* e indica que hay que calcular la raíz cuadrada del número que está dentro del radical. $\sqrt{36}$ se lee "raíz cuadrada de 36". Si se saben los cuadrados perfectos, es relativamente fácil calcular las raíces cuadradas. Por ejemplo, $\sqrt{100} = 10$ porque $10^2 = 100$. $\sqrt{49} = 7$ y $\sqrt{4} = 2$.

Si se desea extraer la raíz cuadrada de un número que no es un cuadrado perfecto, se puede optar por simplificar la raíz cuadrada. Por ejemplo, $\sqrt{75}$ puede expresarse como $\sqrt{25 \times 3} = \sqrt{25} \times \sqrt{3} = 5\sqrt{3}$. Se descompone el número en 25 y 3 porque 25 es un cuadrado perfecto del cual se puede extraer una raíz cuadrada exacta.

EJERCICIO 2: SIMPLIFICACIÓN DE RAÍCES CUADRADAS

Instrucciones: Simplifique las siguientes raíces cuadradas.

1. $\sqrt{48}$ **2.** $\sqrt{8}$ **3.** $\sqrt{27}$

Aproximación de raíces cuadradas

Las raíces cuadradas de números que no sean cuadrados perfectos conocidos se pueden calcular con la ayuda de calculadoras y tablas. Si no se dispone de una tabla o de una calculadora, resulta útil hacer *aproximaciones.* Por ejemplo, hallemos la raíz cuadrada de 75. Para calcular $\sqrt{75}$, nos fijamos en los cuadrados perfectos más próximos a 75. Éstos son 64 y 81.

$\sqrt{64} = 8$

$\sqrt{75}$ Observe que $\sqrt{75}$ está comprendida entre $\sqrt{64}$ y $\sqrt{81}$.

$\sqrt{81} = 9$

Por lo tanto, $\sqrt{75}$ está comprendida entre 8 y 9. Como 75 se aproxima más a 81 que a 64, $\sqrt{75}$ se aproximará más a 9. Aproxime el resultado a 8.7.

EJERCICIO 3: RAÍCES CUADRADAS

Instrucciones: Halle la raíz cuadrada de los siguientes números. Si el número es un cuadrado perfecto, escriba el resultado exacto. Si el número no es un cuadrado perfecto, escriba un resultado aproximado o simplificado.

1. $\sqrt{81}$ **3.** $\sqrt{28}$ **5.** $\sqrt{10}$ **7.** $\sqrt{225}$

2. $\sqrt{1}$ **4.** $\sqrt{52}$ **6.** $\sqrt{16}$

Orden de operaciones

A continuación se menciona una serie de pasos conocida como *orden de operaciones*.

ORDEN DE OPERACIONES

1°: Calcular todas las potencias y raíces en orden de izquierda a derecha.

2°: Efectuar todas las multiplicaciones y divisiones en orden de izquierda a derecha.

3°: Efectuar todas las sumas y restas en orden de izquierda a derecha.

Ejemplo: $16 - 4 \times 2 + 2^4 \div 8$

PASO 1. Eleve el número con exponente a la potencia indicada.

PASO 2. Multiplique y divida. $16 - \underbrace{4 \times 2} + \underbrace{16 \div 8}$

PASO 3. Sume y reste. $16 - \quad (8 \quad + \quad 2)$

$16 - 10 = 6$

▶ **Nota:** Si no se sigue el orden prescrito de operaciones, *no* se obtendrá un resultado correcto. Por ejemplo, al calcular $8 + 2 \times 2$, se deberá obtener $8 + 4$, es decir, 12. Si simplemente calcula de izquierda a derecha, obtendría *incorrectamente* $8 + 2 = 10$; $10 \times 2 = 20$, lo cual sería incorrecto.

EJERCICIO 4: ORDEN DE OPERACIONES

Instrucciones: Simplifique las expresiones siguientes.

1. $7 - 5 + 3 - 5$ **2.** $8 + 3 \times 5$ **3.** $6 + 21 \div 3 - 5$ **4.** $4 + 3^3 + 3 \times 2 - 2^2$

Paréntesis

Al calcular una expresión aritmética, se debe seguir siempre el orden de operaciones arriba citado. Sin embargo, si en la expresión se han usado paréntesis ( ), realice primero los cálculos dentro del paréntesis.

Así tenemos que el orden de las operaciones es:

1°: Realizar todos los cálculos dentro de los paréntesis y en el numerador y denominador de las fracciones.

2°: Hallar las potencias y raíces cuadradas.

3°: Multiplicar y dividir.

4°: Sumar y restar.

Ejemplo 1: $4 \times (3 + 5)$

$4 \times (\underbrace{3 + 5})$ ⟵——— Primero haga los cálculos dentro del paréntesis

$4 \times \quad 8 \ = 32$

Ejemplo 2: $(8^2 + 3) \times (5 + 4)$

Calcule primero → $(\underbrace{8^2} + 3) \times (5 + 4)$

Calcule a seguir → $(\underbrace{64 + 3}) \times (\underbrace{5 + 4})$

Ahora multiplique ⟶ $67 \quad \times \quad 9 \ = 603$

Ejemplo 3:

Haga todos los cálculos en el numerador y denominador de la fracción $\dfrac{10-4}{4-2}$

La raya de fracción indica una división $\dfrac{6}{2} = 3$

Fórmulas

Las letras del alfabeto se suelen usar para representar números cuyo valor se desconoce y se desea calcular. Por ejemplo, como recordará, la fórmula de la distancia es $d = vt$. Las letras d, v, t se usan para representar los valores de distancia (d), velocidad (v) y tiempo (t). Las letras usadas de esta forma reciben el nombre de *incógnitas* o *variables*. Gracias al empleo de estas letras podemos expresar relaciones generales entre los números.

Las *fórmulas* son conjuntos de símbolos que sirven para expresar estas relaciones generales. Como ejemplo de fórmulas comunes y útiles tenemos el área del círculo ($A = \pi r^2$), el perímetro del rectángulo ($P = 2l + 2a$) y el teorema de Pitágoras ($a^2 = b^2 + c^2$). La Prueba de Matemáticas del GED adjunta una página de fórmulas que le será de utilidad en la resolución de algunos de los problemas de la prueba. Al leer los problemas, tendrá que decidir qué fórmula utilizar para resolverlo. Por esta razón, se recomienda estudiar detenidamente las fórmulas de la página 28.

Evaluación de fórmulas

Cuando reemplazamos las letras de una fórmula por números, estamos *sustituyendo* las letras con valores determinados. Si realizamos operaciones matemáticas con estos valores, estamos *evaluando* la fórmula.

Al evaluar fórmulas, es muy importante seguir el orden de operaciones citado a continuación:

1. Resuelva las expresiones dentro de los paréntesis y las del numerador y denominador de las fracciones.
2. Halle las potencias y las raíces.
3. Multiplique y divida.
4. Sume y reste.

Ejemplo: Halle el volumen de una caja rectangular que tenga 7 pulgadas de largo, 5 pulgadas de ancho y 3 pulgadas de alto.

PASO 1. Elija la fórmula apropiada de la página de fórmulas. $V = lah$

PASO 2. Sustituya las letras por los valores dados. $V = (7)(5)(3)$

PASO 3. Multiplique. (Los paréntesis indican multiplicación.) $V = 105 \text{ m}^3$ (metros cúbicos)

EJERCICIO 5: EVALUACIÓN DE FÓRMULAS

Instrucciones: Seleccione la fórmula apropiada de la página de fórmulas. Sustituya con valores numéricos las letras de la fórmula y evalúela. Las unidades que corresponden a la respuesta se indican en paréntesis.

1. Halle el volumen de un cubo siendo uno de los lados (*l*) de 5 pulgadas. *(pulgadas cúbicas)*

2. Halle el interés simple para un capital (*c*) de $800 a un rédito o tasa de interés (%) del 12% anual durante 3 años (*t*). *(dólares)*

3. Halle el área de un círculo siendo $\pi \cong 3.14$ y el radio (*r*) 3 pulgadas. *(pulgadas cuadradas)*

4. Halle el perímetro de un rectángulo de longitud (*l*) de 14 pies y de 2 yardas de ancho (*a*). *(pies)*

Notación científica

Nuestro sistema numérico se basa en múltiplos de diez. La *notación científica* hace uso de esta idea de una base 10 para abreviar y así facilitar la escritura de números muy extensos. Esta notación es ampliamente utilizada por las ciencias, pero también la solemos ver cada vez con más frecuencia en nuestra vida cotidiana a medida que se va extendiendo el uso de las calculadoras y computadoras.

Las potencias fraccionarias de diez también se pueden expresar por medio de exponentes negativos. El signo menos se utiliza para indicar el recíproco. (El recíproco de 10 es $\frac{1}{10}$). Por ejemplo, $10^{-1} = \frac{1}{10} = .1$.

Observemos algunas potencias de diez de exponentes positivos y negativos:

$$10^0 = 1 \qquad\qquad 10^{-1} = \tfrac{1}{10} = .1$$
$$10^1 = 10 \qquad\qquad 10^{-2} = \tfrac{1}{10^2} = \tfrac{1}{100} \text{ ó } .01$$
$$10^2 = 100 \qquad\qquad 10^{-3} = \tfrac{1}{10^3} = \tfrac{1}{1000} \text{ ó } .001$$
$$10^3 = 1000 \qquad\qquad 10^{-4} = \tfrac{1}{10^4} = \tfrac{1}{10,000} \text{ ó } .0001$$
$$10^4 = 10,000$$

CÓMO EXPRESAR UN NÚMERO EN NOTACIÓN CIENTÍFICA

La notación científica consiste en expresar una cantidad mediante un producto de dos números:

1. El primero es un número o decimal mixto entre 1 y 10 cuya parte entera es de un solo dígito.
2. El segundo factor es una potencia de 10.

Gracias a la notación científica se pueden escribir ciertos números en forma abreviada. Para determinar qué potencia de 10 usar, se cuenta el número de lugares que se debe correr el punto decimal. Ese número será el exponente. La potencia de 10 es positiva si el número es entero y negativa si el número es una fracción o decimal.

Ejemplo 1: Exprese 86,200,000 en notación científica. (Se entiende que en el caso de números enteros, el punto decimal está al final del número).

PASO 1. Escriba el primer factor en forma de decimal mixto entre 1 y 10. Inserte el punto decimal entre 8 y 62 para obtener 8.62.

$$86.200,200 = 8.62 \times 10^7$$

PASO 2. Cuente el número de lugares que se ha corrido el punto decimal para pasar de 86,200,000 a 8.62. Como el punto se ha tenido que correr 7 lugares a la izquierda, el exponente de 10 es 7.

$$86.200,200 = 8.62 \times 10^7$$

7 lugares a la izquierda

Ejemplo 2: Exprese .00098 en notación científica.

PASO 1. Escriba el primer factor en forma de decimal mixto entre 1 y 10.

Inserte el punto decimal entre 9 y 8 para obtener 9.8.

$$.00098 = 9.8 \times 10^{-4}$$

4 lugares a la derecha

PASO 2. Cuente el número de lugares que se ha corrido el punto decimal para pasar de .00098 a 9.8. Como el punto se ha tenido que correr 4 lugares a la derecha, la potencia de 10 es −4.

EJERCICIO 6: NOTACIÓN CIENTÍFICA

Instrucciones: Exprese estos números en notación científica.

1. .0082
2. 38,200

Cada uno de los números siguientes está escrito en notación científica. Halle su valor real.

3. 1.624×10^3
4. 3.12×10^{-1}

8
GEOMETRÍA

La *geometría* centra su estudio en las figuras y las relaciones que existen entre las mismas. Los conocimientos de geometría que se necesitarán manejar en la Prueba de Matemáticas son de tipo fundamental y práctico. No se le pedirá que "demuestre" teoremas, como en una clase normal de geometría, sino que se habrán de trabajar los conceptos básicos de esta disciplina y aplicarlos a situaciones cotidianas.

Ángulos

El *ángulo* está formado por la intersección de dos rectas. El punto de intersección es el *vértice* del ángulo. En este ángulo, el punto S es el vértice. *ST* y *SR* son los dos lados.

Los ángulos se representan por medio de un pequeño símbolo ∠ y tres puntos, dos de ellos situados en los extremos del ángulo y el tercero ubicado en el vértice: ∠ *RST*. A veces, el ángulo se indica simplemente por su vértice, como por ejemplo ∠ *S*.

Los ángulos se miden en *grados.* El símbolo de los grados es conocido por ser el que se usa en las mediciones de temperatura, como por ejemplo 72°.

Una revolución completa alrededor de un punto equivale a 360°. Un cuarto de revolución son 90°. Los ángulos de 90° o *ángulos rectos* son de gran utilidad para el campo de la construcción. A veces se suele representar el ángulo recto con un pequeño cuadrado colocado en el vértice. Si, al inter-sectarse, dos rectas forman un ángulo recto, se dice que estas rectas son *perpendiculares* entre sí. El símbolo que se usa para representar rectas perpendiculares es ⊥.

Pares especiales de ángulos

En la Prueba de Matemáticas se le proporcionarán datos sobre ángulos y después se le pedirá que utilice los conocimientos que posee acerca de las relaciones que existen entre los ángulos. Repasemos a seguir algunas reglas que se aplican a ciertos pares de ángulos.

Los *ángulos complementarios* son dos ángulos cuya suma es igual a 90°; es decir que, juntos, estos dos ángulos forman un ángulo recto. Un ángulo de 60° y un ángulo de 30° son complementarios entre sí porque la suma de ambos es igual a 90°.

Ejemplo 1: ¿Cuál es el complemento de un ángulo de 53°?

Solución: 90° − 53° = 37°

Los *ángulos suplementarios* son dos ángulos cuya suma es igual a 180°. Cuando los dos ángulos se ubican de manera contigua, sus lados forman una línea recta, o ángulo de 180° *(ángulo llano)*. Un ángulo de 110° es el suplemento de un ángulo de 70° porque la suma de ambos es igual a 180°.

Ejemplo 2: ¿Cuál es el suplemento de un ángulo de 30°?

   Solución: 180° − 30° = 150°

Los *ángulos opuestos por el vértice* se forman de la intersección de dos rectas. Los dos ángulos opuestos entre sí son iguales. En el dibujo de la derecha, ∠ *ABC* y ∠ *DBE* son ángulos opuestos por el vértice. Por lo tanto, ∠ *ABC* es igual a ∠ *DBE,* que expresamos como: ∠ *ABC* = ∠ *DBE.* ∠ *ABD* y ∠ *CBE* también son ángulos opuestos por el vértice; por lo que, ∠ *ABD* = ∠ *CBE.* En algunos problemas, como en el *Ejemplo 3,* se puede proporcionar como dato un par de rectas que se intersectan y la medida de un ángulo. A partir de ese ángulo, se podrán medir los demás ángulos.

Ejemplo 3: Halle cuánto mide el ángulo ∠ *EFG.*

   Solución: ∠ *EFG* y ∠ *HFJ* son ángulos opuestos por el vértice y, por lo tanto, son iguales. ∠ *EFG* = 130°

Ejemplo 4: Halle cuánto mide el ángulo ∠ *GFJ.*

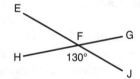

   PASO 1. Observe que ∠ *GFJ* es el suplemento de ∠ *EFG.* Juntos, forman una línea recta que es igual a un ángulo de 180°.

   PASO 2. Reste de 180° el ángulo conocido.
   180° − 130° = 50°
   ∠ *GFJ* = 50°

Dado que, en muchos casos, los ángulos son datos esenciales para la resolución de un problema, es de gran utilidad conocer estas relaciones angulares (complementariedad, suplementariedad y oposición por el vértice). Si usted busca un par de ángulos formados por líneas que se intersectan, se dará cuenta de la utilidad de estas relaciones entre ángulos.

Ejemplo 5: Halle cuánto mide el ángulo indicado.

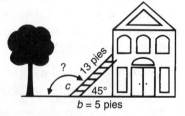

   La escalera forma un ángulo suplementario con el terreno.

   Para calcular el ángulo que falta, reste 45° de 180°.

   Solución: 180° − 45° = 135°

LAS RESPUESTAS DE LOS EJERCICIOS DE ESTE CAPÍTULO EMPIEZAN EN LA PÁGINA 473.

EJERCICIO 1: PARES DE ÁNGULOS

Instrucciones: Resuelva cada uno de los problemas.

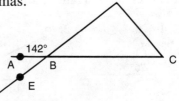

Use el dibujo para contestar las *Preguntas 1–3.*

1. Halle cuánto mide ∠ *DBC.*
2. Halle cuánto mide ∠ *ABE.*
3. Halle cuánto mide ∠ *EBC.*
4. Dos piezas de un rompecabezas encajan formando un ángulo recto. Si una pieza tiene un ángulo de 52°, ¿cuál es el ángulo de la pieza complementaria?

Triángulos

Los triángulos son la base de la medición de terrenos conocida como agrimensura. Se utilizan también en ciencias, navegación y construcción de edificios. Los astrónomos se valen de triángulos para calcular la distancia de la Tierra a las estrellas. Es, además, importante el uso que se da a los triángulos en mapas, dibujos a escala y planos de arquitectura.

¿Qué es un triángulo?

El *triángulo* es una figura cerrada que tiene tres lados. El punto en que se intersectan o cortan los lados se denomina *vértice.* En cada vértice hay un ángulo. La figura de la derecha es el triángulo *ABC,* que expresamos como △ *ABC.* Este triángulo posee tres ángulos: ∠ *A,* ∠ *B,* ∠ *C.* Tiene, además, tres lados: *a, b, c.* Los lados se pueden representarse con una sola letra o con las dos letras que representan los ángulos situados en los extremos del lado. Por ejemplo, también se le puede llamar *BC* al lado *a; AC* al lado *b;* y *AB* al lado *c.*

La suma de los tres ángulos de un triángulo es igual a 180°. Por lo tanto, podemos escribir: ∠ *A* + ∠ *B* + ∠ *C* = 180°. Con esta fórmula se puede hallar la medida del tercer ángulo de un triángulo cuando sólo se conoce la medida de dos de sus ángulos, como sucede en el ejemplo siguiente.

Ejemplo: Halle cuánto mide ∠ *C* del triángulo de la derecha.

PASO 1. Primero, sume las medidas de los dos ángulos conocidos.

$$40° + 100° = 140°$$

PASO 2. Después, reste la suma de 180°.

$$180° - 140° = 40°$$

EJERCICIO 2: ÁNGULOS DE TRIÁNGULOS

Instrucciones: Halle la medida del ángulo que falta en estos triángulos.

1.   **2.** 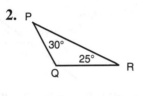 **3.** 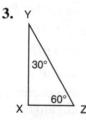 **4.**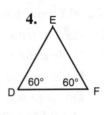

Tipos de triángulos

Los triángulos se pueden clasificar según la longitud de sus lados. Conforme a este criterio, los triángulos pueden ser *escalenos, isósceles* o *equiláteros.*

- El **triángulo escaleno** tiene tres lados distintos y tres ángulos distintos. En la figura de la derecha, $\triangle ABC$ es escaleno. El lado *AB* no es igual al lado *BC* o al lado *AC*.

- El **triángulo isósceles** tiene dos lados iguales y dos ángulos iguales. En la figura de la derecha, ($\triangle DEF$), *DF* es la **base** del triángulo, *DE* y *EF* son los lados del triángulo, $\angle D$ y $\angle F$ son los **ángulos de la base**, y $\angle E$ es el **ángulo del vértice.** Como *DE = EF*, el triángulo es isósceles. Los dos ángulos de la base son iguales: $\angle D = \angle F$.

- El **triángulo equilátero** tiene tres lados iguales y tres ángulos iguales. Como los tres ángulos del triángulo deben sumar 180°, cada uno de los ángulos debe medir 60°. $\triangle PQR$ es equilátero porque *PQ = QR = PR*. También es cierto que $\angle P = \angle Q = \angle R$. (A los triángulos equiláteros se les suele también llamar **triángulos equiangulares.)**

- El **triángulo rectángulo** (o **triángulo recto**) es una clase especial de triángulo que se utiliza con frecuencia en los problemas de geometría. El triángulo rectángulo tiene un ángulo recto (de 90°). Se utiliza a veces un pequeño cuadrado colocado en la esquina del ángulo recto para indicar que el triángulo es rectángulo. En $\triangle XYZ$ de la derecha, $\angle X$ es el ángulo recto. El lado opuesto al ángulo recto (*YZ*) se llama **hipotenusa.**

EJERCICIO 3: TIPOS DE TRIÁNGULOS

Instrucciones: Resuelva cada uno de los problemas.

1. Indique si cada uno de los triángulos es escaleno, isósceles, equilátero o rectángulo.

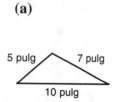

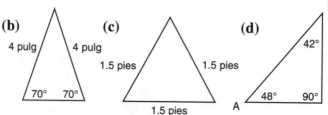

2. En el triángulo isósceles *ABC,* los ángulos de la base miden 52° cada uno. Calcule cuánto mide el tercer ángulo.

3. Si un triángulo rectángulo contiene un ángulo de 60°, ¿cuánto mide el tercer ángulo?

Triángulos semejantes

Los *triángulos semejantes* son figuras geométricas que presentan la misma forma. Las figuras semejantes se suelen usar para calcular longitudes difíciles de medir, como por ejemplo, la distancia que hay de una orilla a otra de un lago o la altura de un edificio. Los triángulos semejantes son triángulos cuyos *ángulos correspondientes* son iguales y cuyos *lados correspondientes* son proporcionales.

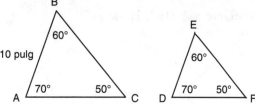

Obsérvense Δ *ABC* y Δ *DEF.* Estos triángulos son semejantes porque tienen la misma forma. Podemos ver que los ángulos correspondientes son iguales: ∠ *A* = ∠ *D*; ∠ *B* = ∠ *E* y ∠ *C* = ∠ *F.* Por lo tanto, los dos triángulos no son del mismo tamaño, pero son proporcionales en cuanto a sus lados. Expresamos esta relación como:

$$\frac{AB}{DE} = \frac{BC}{EF} = \frac{AC}{DF}$$

Ejemplo 1: En un día soleado, el inspector municipal se valió de triángulos semejantes para calcular la altura de un mástil sin necesidad de subirse al mismo. Observó que su ayudante, que mide 6 pies de alto, proyectaba una sombra de 10 pies al mismo tiempo que el mástil proyectaba una sombra de 40 pies. ¿Cuánto medía el mástil?

PASO 1. Observe que la ayudante y el mástil forman ángulos rectos con el terreno. Construya una proporción.

$$\frac{\text{mástil}}{\text{ayudante}} = \frac{\text{sombra del mástil}}{\text{sombra de la ayudante}}$$

PASO 2. Sustituya los términos de la proporción por sus valores correspondientes. Llamemos *m* al mástil.

$$\frac{m}{6} = \frac{40}{10}$$

PASO 3. Multiplique en diagonal y divida.

$$m = \frac{6 \times 40}{10} = \frac{240}{10} = 24 \text{ pies}$$

▶ **Nota:** Busque siempre triángulos semejantes al comparar dos triángulos.

EJERCICIO 4: TRIÁNGULOS SEMEJANTES

Instrucciones: Resuelva cada uno de los problemas.

1. $\triangle ABC$ es semejante a $\triangle DEF$. Halle DF.

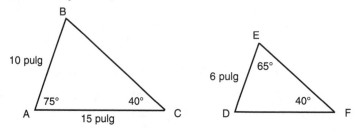

2. Un roble que hay en un parque proyecta una sombra de 18 pies a la vez que un semáforo de 8 pies proyecta una sombra de 12 pies. Calcule la altura del árbol.

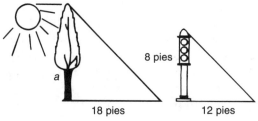

3. Suponga que necesitamos calcular la distancia d que hay de una orilla a otra de un estanque, pero no podemos nadar hasta el otro lado y medir la distancia directamente. Aun así, es posible calcular la distancia. Identifique una señal en una orilla del estanque. En la orilla opuesta, clave una estaca en el terreno directamente enfrente de la señal. Mida una distancia dada c perpendicular a la recta determinada por la señal y la estaca. Después forme dos triángulos como en el esquema de abajo.

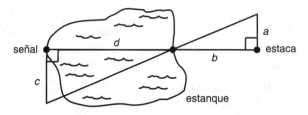

(a) Con estas medidas, ¿qué haría primero para determinar la distancia d?

(b) Calcule la distancia que hay de una orilla a otra del estanque siendo $a = 2$ pies, $b = 6$ pies y $c = 50$ pies.

El teorema de Pitágoras

El *teorema de Pitágoras* fue postulado por el matemático griego Pitágoras alrededor del año 500 a.C. No obstante su antigüedad, su empleo continúa vigente en la actualidad. Como el teorema se aplica solamente a triángulos rectángulos, el problema debe incluir un ángulo de 90° para que el teorema de Pitágoras se pueda aplicar. En los triángulos rectángulos, el lado opuesto al ángulo recto recibe el nombre de *hipotenusa,* y los otros dos lados se dan en llamar *catetos* del triángulo.

Según el teorema de Pitágoras, el cuadrado de la hipotenusa de un triángulo rectángulo es igual a la suma de los cuadrados de los catetos. Conforme al diagrama, el teorema de Pitágoras se escribiría: $a^2 = b^2 + c^2$ (siendo a hipotenusa del triángulo rectángulo y b y c los catetos).

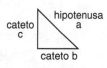

Ejemplo: Calcule la longitud de la hipotenusa de un triángulo rectángulo con catetos de 6 y 8 pulgadas respectivamente.

Primero, dibuje un triángulo rectángulo e indique los lados. A continuación, reemplace las letras del teorema de Pitágoras con valores numéricos y resuelva la ecuación.

PASO 1. Escriba el teorema de Pitágoras. $a^2 = b^2 + c^2$

PASO 2. Sustituya b y c (catetos del triángulo) con números. $a^2 = 6^2 + 8^2$

PASO 3. Eleve los números al cuadrado. $a^2 = 36 + 64$

PASO 4. Sume los números. $a^2 = 100$

PASO 5. Extraiga la raíz cuadrada. $c = \sqrt{100} = 10$ pulg

---

CÓMO RESOLVER PROBLEMAS SOBRE EL TEOREMA DE PITÁGORAS

1. Diagramar el triángulo con los nombres de cada parte y los datos dados.
2. Identificar el ángulo recto y luego la hipotenusa.
3. Sustituir con valores numéricos los términos de la fórmula $a^2 = b^2 + c^2$.
4. Elevar los valores al cuadrado.
5. Sumar si se está buscando la hipotenusa, o restar si se está buscando un cateto.
6. Extraer la raíz cuadrada.

EJERCICIO 5: EL TEOREMA DE PITÁGORAS

Instrucciones: Resuelva cada uno de los problemas.

1. Siendo b y c catetos de un triángulo rectángulo y a la hipotenusa, hallar la longitud del lado que falta si $b = 9$ y $c = 12$.

2. La pantalla del televisor de Alberto tiene las medidas indicadas en el dibujo de la derecha. Calcule cuánto mide la diagonal del televisor de Alberto.

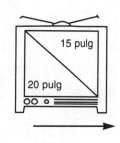

3. En el campamento de verano, el trayecto de natación recorre el largo *(L)* de un pequeño lago. Para determinar la longitud del recorrido, los empleados del campamento miden los dos catetos "secos" de un triángulo rectángulo. ¿Cuál sería la longitud en metros del trayecto de natación según la figura de abajo?

   (1) 75
   (2) 90
   (3) 100
   (4) 120
   (5) 144

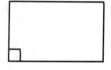

4. Se apoya una escalera de 13 pies contra una casa. La base de la escalera está a 5 pies de la base de la casa. ¿A cuántos pies del suelo hace contacto la escalera con la casa?

   (1) 10
   (2) 12
   (3) 15
   (4) 16
   (5) 20

Figuras planas

Los rectángulos y los cuadrados se emplean con gran frecuencia en la construcción de edificios. Las baldosas, las tapas de las mesas, los vidrios de las ventanas, las puertas, los libros y los marcos de cuadros son algunos de los objetos que suelen presentar forma rectangular o cuadrada. En la Prueba de Matemáticas del GED se le pedirá que reconozca estas figuras y resuelva problemas en base a las mismas.

Tipos de figuras

El *rectángulo* es una figura cerrada que tiene cuatro lados. Los puntos donde se intersectan los cuatro lados se denominan *vértices.* En cada vértice hay un ángulo recto (90°).

1. La suma de los cuatro ángulos es igual a 360°.
2. Los lados opuestos son iguales.
3. Los lados opuestos son paralelos.
4. Los cuatro ángulos son iguales (90°).

El *paralelogramo* es una figura cerrada que tiene cuatro lados. Tiene cuatro ángulos (no necesariamente de 90°).

1. La suma de los cuatro ángulos es igual a 360°.
2. Los lados opuestos son iguales.
3. Los lados opuestos son paralelos.
4. Los ángulos opuestos son iguales.

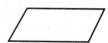

El *cuadrado* es una figura cerrada que tiene cuatro lados y cuatro ángulos rectos.

1. Los cuatro lados son iguales.
2. Los cuatro ángulos son iguales: de 90° cada uno.
3. Los lados opuestos son paralelos.

Círculos

En geometría, se define el *círculo* como un conjunto de puntos situados a igual distancia del centro. La distancia que hay de un punto cualquiera del círculo al centro del mismo se denomina *radio*. El *diámetro* es el segmento de recta que pasa por el centro del círculo y cuyos extremos son los puntos en que la recta intersecta al círculo. La longitud del diámetro es dos veces la del radio.

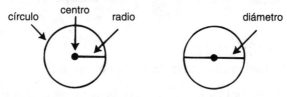

Medición de figuras

Perímetro

El *perímetro* es la medida del contorno de una figura. La medición que se realiza para instalar una cerca que rodee un patio o un zócalo en el contorno de una sala son algunas de las prácticas aplicaciones que se le puede dar al perímetro. En la página de fórmulas de la Prueba de Matemáticas del GED se adjuntan las fórmulas de perímetro para las distintas figuras.

▶ **Nota:** Como el perímetro de una figura es el total de las dimensiones del contorno de una figura, se pueden también sumar todos los lados de la figura para hallarlo.

El *perímetro de un cuadrado* es $P = 4l$, siendo P el perímetro y l uno de los lados. Como los cuatro lados del cuadrado son iguales, se multiplica por 4 uno de los lados para calcular el contorno total del cuadrado.

Ejemplo 1: Halle el perímetro de este cuadrado.

7 yardas

$P = 4l$
$P = 4 \times 7 = 28$ yardas

El *perímetro de un rectángulo* es $P = 2l + 2a$, siendo P el perímetro, l el largo y a el ancho. Como los lados opuestos de un rectángulo son iguales, se multiplica por dos el largo y el ancho, y después se suman para calcular el contorno del rectángulo.

Ejemplo 2: Halle el perímetro de este rectángulo.

7 pies
3 pies

$P = 2l + 2a$
$P = (2 \times 7) + (2 \times 3) = 20$ pies

El **perímetro de un triángulo** es $P = a + b + c$, siendo P el perímetro y a, b y c las longitudes de los tres lados. Para calcular el perímetro, sume las longitudes de los tres lados.

Ejemplo 3: Halle el perímetro de este triángulo.

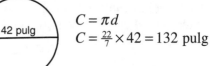

$$P = a + b + c$$
$$P = 4 + 7 + 9 = 20 \text{ pies}$$

La **circunferencia de un círculo** es el perímetro (o contorno) del círculo. La fórmula es $C = \pi d$, siendo C la circunferencia, pi o $\pi \cong 3.14$, y d el diámetro. La circunferencia es aproximadamente igual a 3.14 veces el diámetro. También se puede usar $\frac{22}{7}$ como valor de π cuando el diámetro o el radio esté expresado en forma de fracción o cuando sea más fácil resolver el problema con $\frac{22}{7}$.

Ejemplo 4. Halle la circunferencia de este círculo.

42 pulg

$$C = \pi d$$
$$C = \tfrac{22}{7} \times 42 = 132 \text{ pulg}$$

EJERCICIO 6: PERÍMETRO

Instrucciones: Resuelva cada uno de los problemas.

1. Un campo de béisbol es un cuadrado cuyos lados tienen las dimensiones indicadas en el diagrama. Si un jugador consigue un jonrón, ¿qué distancia recorrerá?

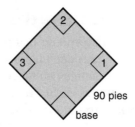

2. ¿Qué cantidad de ribete se necesita para cubrir el contorno de la vela triangular del barquito del dibujo?

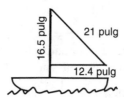

3. Un granjero desea cercar un campo rectangular de 400 yardas por 224 yardas. El costo de la cerca es de $5.75 por tramo de ocho pies. ¿Cuánto le costará la cerca?

4. Halle el perímetro de la figura diagramada a la derecha.

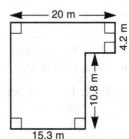

5. ¿Cuántos pies de cerca se necesitan para el jardín de esta casa?

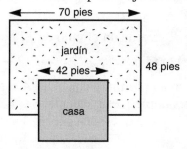

Área

El *área* es la cantidad de superficie que ocupa un objeto. El área se mide en *unidades cuadradas* como las pulgadas cuadradas o los pies cuadrados. Imagine un cuadrado de una pulgada de lado. Esto sería una pulgada cuadrada.

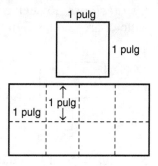

Cuando se nos pide calcular el área en pulgadas cuadradas, estamos en realidad calculando el número de cuadrados de una pulgada por una pulgada que caben en la superficie que estamos midiendo. Por ejemplo, el rectángulo de la derecha contiene 8 pulgadas cuadradas de área.

▶ **Nota:** Las respuestas de los problemas sobre áreas están dadas en unidades cuadradas (pulgadas cuadradas, metros cuadrados, etc.).

El *área de un cuadrado* es $A = l^2$, siendo A el área y l uno de los lados. El área es igual al lado multiplicado por el lado. Dado un cuadrado con un lado de 7 pulgadas, el área sería igual a 7 pulgadas × 7 pulgadas = 49 pulgadas cuadradas (ó 49 pulg^2).

El *área de un rectángulo* es $A = la$, siendo A el área, l el largo y a el ancho. El área es igual al largo por el ancho.

Ejemplo 1: ¿Cuál es el área de la tabla de una mesa de 3 pies por 5 pies?

Solución: El área A es la = 3 pies × 5 pies = 15 pies cuadrados, ó 15 pies^2

El *área de un triángulo* es $A = \frac{1}{2}bh$, siendo A el área, b la base y h la altura. Para calcular el área de un triángulo, multiplique la base por la altura y halle $\frac{1}{2}$ de esa cantidad.

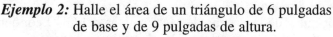

Ejemplo 2: Halle el área de un triángulo de 6 pulgadas de base y de 9 pulgadas de altura.

PASO 1. Multiplique la base por la altura.

PASO 2. Divida el producto por 2 para hallar $\frac{1}{2}$.

$A = \frac{1}{2}bh$
$A = \frac{1}{2}(6 \times 9) = \frac{1}{2}(54)$
$A = \frac{1}{2}(54) = 27$ pulgadas cuadradas, ó 27 pulg^2.

El **área de un círculo** es $A = \pi r^2$, siendo A el área, π aproximadamente 3.14 ó $\frac{22}{7}$, y r el radio.

Ejemplo 3: Halle el área de un círculo de 12 pulgadas de diámetro.

PASO 1. Halle el radio. $\qquad\qquad 12 \div 2 = 6$

PASO 2. Sustituya la fórmula con $\qquad A = \pi r^2$
valores numéricos y calcule. $\quad A = 3.14(6)^2$
$$A = 3.14(36)$$
$$A = 113.04 \text{ pulgadas cuadradas,}$$
$$\text{ó } 113.04 \text{ pulg}^2$$

EJERCICIO 7: ÁREA

Instrucciones: Resuelva cada uno de los problemas. En las *Preguntas 1–2,* halle el área de las figuras.

1.

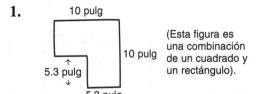

10 pulg

10 pulg

5.3 pulg

5.3 pulg

(Esta figura es una combinación de un cuadrado y un rectángulo).

2.

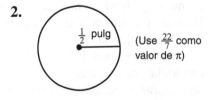

$\frac{1}{2}$ pulg

(Use $\frac{22}{7}$ como valor de π)

3. ¿Cuántas yardas cuadradas de alfombra se necesitan para una sala de 30 pies por 15 pies? $(1 \text{ yarda}^2 = 9 \text{ pies}^2)$

4. ¿Cuántos pies cuadrados mediría la alfombra circular de mayor tamaño que se pudiera colocar en el suelo de una sala de 10 pies por 12 pies?

Volumen

El **volumen** es la cantidad de espacio que ocupa un cuerpo tridimensional. Como ejemplos de cuerpos geométricos se puede citar el paralelepípedo (caja rectangular), el cubo y el cilindro.

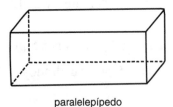
paralelepípedo

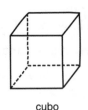
cubo

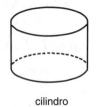
cilindro

El volumen se mide en **unidades cúbicas**, como los pies cúbicos, las pulgadas cúbicas o las yardas cúbicas. Por ejemplo, una pulgada cúbica es un cubo con aristas de 1 pulgada.

La página de fórmulas de la Prueba de Matemáticas del GED contiene fórmulas para el cáculo del volumen del cubo, el paralelepípedo y el cilindro. Repasemos estas fórmulas.

El **volumen de un cubo** es $V = l^3$, siendo V el volumen y l la arista del cubo. Los dados y las cajas cuadradas son ejemplos de cubos. Todas las aristas del cubo tienen la misma longitud. De esta forma, el volumen del cubo es igual a la arista elevada al cubo; es decir, arista por arista por arista.

Ejemplo 1: Halle el volumen del cubo de la derecha.

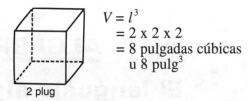

$V = l^3$
$= 2 \times 2 \times 2$
$= 8$ pulgadas cúbicas
u 8 pulg^3

El **volumen de un paralelepípedo** (recipiente rectangular) es $V = lah$, siendo V el volumen, l el largo, a el ancho y h el alto. El volumen es igual al largo por el ancho por el alto.

Ejemplo 2: ¿Cuál es el volumen del recipiente rectangular?

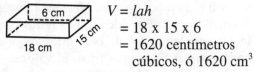

6 cm
18 cm
15 cm

$V = lah$
$= 18 \times 15 \times 6$
$= 1620$ centímetros cúbicos, ó 1620 cm^3

El **volumen de un cilindro** es $V = \pi r^2 h$, siendo V el volumen, r el radio de la base circular y h la altura del cilindro. π es aproximadamente igual a 3.14 ó $\frac{22}{7}$.

Ejemplo 3: Halle el volumen del recipiente cilíndrico.

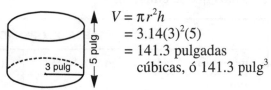

3 pulg
5 pulg

$V = \pi r^2 h$
$= 3.14(3)^2(5)$
$= 141.3$ pulgadas cúbicas, ó 141.3 pulg^3

EJERCICIO 8: VOLUMEN

Instrucciones: Resuelva cada uno de los problemas.

1. ¿Cuántos galones de agua se requieren para llenar un acuario de 18 pulgadas por 12 pulgadas por 48 pulgadas? (Un galón tiene 231 pulgadas cúbicas.) Redondee su respuesta al galón más cercano.

2. ¿Cuánta tierra se necesita para cubrir un jardín de 25 pies por 40 pies con una capa de 6 pulgadas de altura?

3. El silo del agricultor tiene las dimensiones indicadas abajo. ¿Cuál es el volumen del silo? (Use $\frac{22}{7}$ como valor de π.)

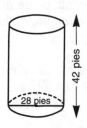

42 pies
28 pies

9
ÁLGEBRA

El lenguaje algebraico

El *álgebra,* una extensión de la aritmética, es un sistema organizado de reglas de gran utilidad en la resolución de problemas. El álgebra se vale de letras del alfabeto para representar números o cantidades desconocidas. Estas letras reciben el nombre de *variables,* así llamadas debido a que sus valores "varían" según el problema. Las letras pueden ser mayúsculas, minúsculas o incluso ser letras del alfabeto griego; por ejemplo: *x, t, B, R* y *P.* Las *constantes* son números fijos. El valor de una constante es conocido y no cambia de un problema a otro; por ejemplo: 8, 75, 0, π y $\sqrt{3}$.

Aun en álgebra se siguen utilizando las cuatro operaciones de suma, resta, multiplicación y división. En la tabla siguiente se pueden apreciar los símbolos que se emplean.

TABLA DE OPERACIONES			
Operación	Símbolo	Ejemplo	Significado
Suma	+	$5 + x$	5 más x
Resta	−	$8 - x$ $y - 8$	8 menos x y menos 8
Multiplicación	• (punto) ( ) paréntesis sin símbolo	$5 \cdot 3$ $10(2)$ xy	5 por 3 10 por 2 x por y
División	÷ — (raya de fracción)	$x \div y$ $\frac{x}{12}$ $\frac{3}{x}$	x dividido por y x dividido por 12 3 dividido por x

Cuando la variable va precedida de un número que la multiplica, este número recibe el nombre de *coeficiente* de la variable. En la expresión $7x$, el coeficiente de x es 7; es decir que, el 7 multiplica la variable x.

▶ **Nota:** Si la variable no presenta un número que la precede, se entiende que el coeficiente es 1. Así pues, y significa $1y$, donde el coeficiente es 1.

Expresiones algebraicas

Las *expresiones algebraicas* relacionan variables con variables o variables con constantes valiéndose de los signos de las operaciones. Por ejemplo: $a + 4$; $5 - 3y$, al igual que $\frac{m+n}{4}$ son expresiones algebraicas. En la expresión $x + 5$, x es la variable que representa la incógnita y 5 es el valor constante. La operación en cuestión es de suma.

$$x \qquad\qquad + \qquad\qquad 5$$
$$\uparrow \qquad\qquad \uparrow \qquad\qquad \uparrow$$
$$\text{variable} \qquad \text{operación} \qquad \text{constante}$$

Las expresiones algebraicas constan de ***términos.*** Un término puede ser un número, una variable o la multiplicación o división de números y variables. Por ejemplo, son términos los siguientes:

5 (número) $7y$ (producto de número y variable)
y (variable) $\frac{y}{3}$ (cociente de variable y número)

En las expresiones algebraicas, los términos están separados por los signos $+$ y $-$. El signo que precede un término pertenece a ese término.

Ejemplos: $\frac{x}{5}$ -2
                    ↑   ↑
            Primer término   Segundo término

es una expresión que consta de dos términos: $\frac{x}{5}$ y -2.

            $8x^2$ $-4x$ $+7$
            ↑   ↑   ↑
    Primer término   Segundo término   Tercer término

es una expresión que consta de tres términos: $8x^2$, $-4x$ y $+7$.

▶ **Nota:** Mantenga el signo $+$ o el signo $-$ junto al término, como se había visto arriba en el caso de -2.

LAS RESPUESTAS DE LOS EJERCICIOS DE ESTE CAPÍTULO EMPIEZAN EN LA PÁGINA 475.

EJERCICIO 1: TÉRMINOS

Instrucciones: Identifique los términos de las siguientes expresiones.

1. $8x + 7y - 5$ **2.** $2x^2 - \frac{3}{x}$ **3.** $8ab + 12$

Ecuaciones

Las ***ecuaciones algebraicas*** expresan una igualdad entre dos expresiones o entre una expresión y un valor.

    $x + 7$ $=$ 10 $x + 3$ $=$ $2x - 9$
    ↑   ↑   ↑   ↑   ↑   ↑
expresión   igual a   valor   expresión   igual a   expresión

TODA ECUACIÓN ALGEBRAICA CONSTA SIEMPRE DE TRES PARTES:

1. primer miembro (o expresión de la izquierda)
2. signo igual (=)
3. segundo miembro (o expresión de la derecha)

La ecuación $x + 7 = 10$ indica que un número que se desconoce (x) sumado a 7 es igual a 10. Sabemos que 3 más 7 es igual a 10, por lo que 3 es la solución de la ecuación. La ***solución*** es el valor que satisface la ecuación, es decir, el valor que hace que la expresión sea verdadera. Se ***resuelve*** la ecuación cuando se halla la solución de la variable, o sea, cuando se ***despeja*** la incógnita. En la Prueba de Matemáticas, se le presentarán casos en que deberá "traducir" o expresar el enunciado verbal de un problema en forma de ecuación algebraica. También tendrá que escribir ecuaciones e interpretarlas.

Ejemplo: $2x + 5 = 17$. Esta expresión indica que un número multiplicado por 2 y sumado a 5 es igual a 17. El número es 6, ya que $2(6) + 5 = 17$.

EJERCICIO 2: ECUACIONES
Instrucciones: Exprese con palabras lo que representan las expresiones. Refiérase a cada letra como "un número", como se había indicado en el ejemplo anterior.

1. $5 + 7y = 19$ **2.** $a - 5 = 23$ **3.** $\frac{10}{y} - 5 = 0$

Resolución de ecuaciones de un paso

Entre las aplicaciones más importantes del álgebra se encuentran la resolución de ecuaciones y el uso de ecuaciones en la resolución de problemas de enunciado verbal.

Cálculo "a ojo" de la solución

Resolver una ecuación significa hallar el valor de la variable que satisfaga la ecuación. Algunas ecuaciones son bastante fáciles de resolver porque únicamente requieren de cálculos sencillos que se pueden hacer de forma mental. Si con sólo ver la ecuación se puede saber la respuesta, se está calculando "a ojo" la ecuación. Por ejemplo, en la ecuación algebraica $x + 3 = 10$, ¿qué valor de x satisface la ecuación? Diríamos que $x = 7$ porque sabemos que $7 + 3 = 10$.

Soluciones algebraicas

Pasemos revista a los métodos algebraicos de resolución de ecuaciones de un paso. Antes de embarcarse a resolver ecuaciones, se debe demostrar cabal comprensión de los conceptos matemáticos. En primer lugar, toda ecuación representa un equilibrio perfecto entre lo que hay a la izquierda del signo igual y lo que hay a la derecha del signo.

Si se realiza un cambio en el miembro de la izquierda, se debe necesariamente realizar el mismo cambio en el miembro de la derecha. Por ejemplo, si sumamos 7 al miembro de la izquierda, debemos también sumar 7 al miembro de la derecha para que ambos miembros sigan siendo iguales. De esta forma nos aseguramos de que el resultado sea verdadero.

En segundo lugar, al resolver una ecuación, el objetivo es aislar la variable en uno de los miembros de la ecuación. Es decir, el objetivo es despejar esa variable o incógnita. Por ello, conviene centrarse en la variable. En la ecuación $x + 3 = 10$, fijémonos en la x. Vemos que a x se le está sumando 3. Esto le indicará cómo resolver la ecuación.

Para resolver la ecuación, efectúe la operación opuesta, es decir, ***inversa.***

La suma y la resta, por ejemplo, son operaciones inversas. En la ecuación $x + 3 = 10$, vemos que a x se le está sumando 3. Lo opuesto a "sumar 3" es "restar 3". Si resta 3 de ambos lados, aislará la x. La incógnita queda así despejada.

Ejemplo 1: $x + 3 = 10$

PASO 1. Fíjese en la x. Se le está sumando 3. $x + 3 = 10$

PASO 2. Reste 3 de ambos miembros. $x + \underbrace{3 - 3}_{0} = 10 \underbrace{- 3}_{7}$

PASO 3. Resuelva la ecuación. $x = 7$

AL RESOLVER UNA ECUACIÓN, HAY QUE RECORDAR:

1. Mantener la ecuación en equilibrio.
2. Centrarse en la variable.
3. Efectuar la operación opuesta.

Ejemplo 2: $7x = 21$

PASO 1. Fíjese en la x. El 7 la multiplica. $7x = 21$

PASO 2. Divida por 7 en ambos miembros. Los 7 del miembro izquierdo "se suprimen". $\frac{\cancel{7}x}{\cancel{7}} = \frac{21}{7}$

PASO 3. Resuelva la ecuación. $x = 3$

Compruebe las respuestas de los problemas reemplazando la incógnita de la ecuación con la solución. Por ejemplo, cuando resolvimos $7x = 21$, obtuvimos $x = 3$. Podemos comprobar dicha respuesta sustituyendo x por 3.

$7x \quad = 21$
$7(3) = 21$ Sustituya x por 3.
$21 \quad = 21$ Este enunciado es verdadero; por lo que $x = 3$ es la solución de la ecuación.

EJERCICIO 3: ECUACIONES DE UN PASO

Instrucciones: Despeje x. Compruebe las respuestas.

1. $3 + x = 7$ **2.** $\frac{x}{3} = 12$ **3.** $x - 8 = 0$ **4.** $5x = 75$

Resolución de problemas algebraicos de enunciado verbal

Si queremos valernos del álgebra para resolver problemas de matemáticas, hay que "traducir" o expresar el problema en lenguaje algebraico. Utilicemos una letra del alfabeto, una variable, que represente la cantidad desconocida. Las letras x, y, z son las letras que más se suelen usar como variables.

1. Primero asigne una variable a la cantidad desconocida.
2. Al escribir la expresión, emplee dicha variable cada vez que se mencione la cantidad desconocida.
3. Identifique las frases que indican la operación matemática a efectuar.
4. Escriba la operación en la expresión.

Traduzca: "El cuadrado de un número disminuido por ese número".

1. Sea x el número.

2. El cuadrado de un número es x^2.

3. "Disminuido por" significa "restado por".

4. Escriba $x^2 - x$.

TABLA DE TRADUCCIÓN		
Frase en español	**Operación**	**Expresión algebraica**
la *suma* de dos números	+ (sumar)	$x + y$
cinco *más que* un número		$x + 5$
un número *aumentado en* 4		$x + 4$
un número *sumado a* otro número		$x + y$
nueve *más* un número		$9 + x$
la *diferencia* entre dos números	– (restar)	$x - y$
siete *disminuido por* un número	(El número restado debe seguir al signo de resta.)	$7 - x$
un número *reducido en* 4		$x - 4$
tres *menos que* un número		$x - 3$
seis *restado* de un número		$x - 6$
seis *menos* un número		$6 - x$
el *producto* de dos números	multiplicar	xy
seis *por* un número	( )	$(6)(x)$
dos veces un número	o: •	$2 \cdot x$
dos tercios *de* un número	o: sin signo	$(\frac{2}{3})x$ ó $\frac{2x}{3}$
el *doble* de un número		$2x$
un número *multiplicado* por otro número		xy

el *cociente* de dos números	dividir	$\frac{x}{y}$ $x \div y$
un número *dividido* por tres	(El número que divide debe estar en el denominador de la fracción o a continuación del signo de división.)	$\frac{x}{3}$
siete *dividido por* un número		$\frac{7}{x}$
la *mitad* de un número		$\frac{x}{2}$ ó $\frac{1}{2}x$
un número *al cuadrado*	elevar a la segunda potencia	x^2
un número *al cubo*	elevar a la tercera potencia	y^3
la *raíz cuadrada* de un número	extraer la raíz cuadrada	$\sqrt{x}$

Guiándose por la tabla, exprese las siguientes frases en forma de expresión algebraica.

Ejemplos: cuatro más que un número

$$4 \quad + \quad x \qquad\qquad = 4 + x$$

seis disminuido por la mitad de un número

$$6 \quad - \quad \tfrac{1}{2}x \qquad = 6 - \tfrac{1}{2}x \text{ ó } 6 - \tfrac{x}{2}$$

doce dividido por un número al cuadrado

$$12 \quad \div \quad x^2 \qquad = \frac{12}{x^2}$$

dos veces la suma de un número y 4

$$2 \quad (x + 4) \qquad = 2(x + 4)$$

la suma de dos veces un número y 4

$$+ \quad 2x \quad 4 \qquad = 2x + 4$$

EJERCICIO 4: TRADUCCIÓN DE ESPAÑOL A ÁLGEBRA

Instrucciones: Exprese las siguientes frases en forma de expresión algebraica representando las incógnitas con x e y.

1. la diferencia entre dos números, dividida por 3
2. la suma de un número al cuadrado y otro número al cuadrado
3. cuatro veces la suma de diez y un número
4. siete menos que dos veces un número
5. un número al cubo dividido por 4
6. cinco veces un número dividido por dos veces el mismo número

Traducción de frases a ecuaciones

Ahora pasaremos a practicar la traducción de un enunciado verbal a ecuación algebraica. Recuerde que toda ecuación consta de tres partes: primer miembro (o expresión de la izquierda), signo igual y segundo miembro (o expresión de la derecha).

Existen varias palabras o frases clave que quieren decir "igual", como se puede apreciar en la lista adjunta:

igual a	es/fue/era...	se obtiene
equivale a	son/fueron/eran...	tenemos
es igual a	el cociente es	la respuesta es
igual que	el producto es	da/dio/daba...
lo mismo que	el resultado es	queda
la suma es	la diferencia es	deja

TRADUCCIÓN DE FRASES A ECUACIONES

1. Asigne una variable a la cantidad desconocida.
2. Escriba dos expresiones: una en cada miembro.
3. Ubique el signo igual entre los miembros.

Ejemplo 1:

Tres por un número es uno más que el doble del número.

$$3x \quad = \quad 1 \quad + \quad 2x \qquad \text{o sea: } 3x = 1 + 2x$$

Ejemplo 2: Cuatro más que un número es igual a 15.

$$x + 4 \qquad = \qquad 15 \quad \text{o sea: } 4 + x = 15$$

▶ **Nota:** Para identificar la variable en el enunciado verbal de un problema, aísle el término o el elemento que desconozca. Asigne después una letra a ese término.

EJERCICIO 5: TRADUCCIÓN DE FRASES A ECUACIONES

Instrucciones: Exprese cada frase con una ecuación algebraica equivalente.

1. Un cuarto de un número es igual a 18.

2. Nueve aumentado por la mitad de un número da un resultado de 13.

3. La diferencia entre dos números es 8.

4. El doble de un número, reducido en 3, es igual a 5 veces el mismo número aumentado en 9.

En las *Preguntas 5–7,* elija la ecuación adecuada para hallar la incógnita del problema.

5. Doug tenía x pelotas de golf. Después de jugar dieciocho hoyos, había perdido 5 pelotas y le quedaban 19. ¿Cuántas pelotas tenía antes de empezar los dieciocho hoyos?

    (1) $x - 5 = 19$ **(2)** $\frac{x}{5} = 19$ **(3)** $x - 18 = 19$ **(4)** $x + 5 = 19$

6. En una competición de lucha libre, Mike obtuvo 5 puntos, que representaron un séptimo de la puntuación final de su equipo. ¿Cuál fue la puntuación final x?

(1) $x + \frac{1}{7} = 5$ (2) $x - 5 = \frac{1}{2}$ (3) $x - 5 = 7$ (4) $\frac{x}{7} = 5$

7. Sue no quiere decir qué edad tiene (x). Sin embargo, dentro de seis años, tendrá $\frac{7}{6}$ más edad de la que tiene ahora. ¿Cómo se puede expresar su edad?

(1) $x + 6 = \frac{7}{6}x$ (2) $x - \frac{7}{6}x = 1$ (3) $\frac{x}{6} = \frac{7}{6}x$ (4) $\frac{7}{6}x = 6$

Resolución de problemas de un paso

Este próximo ejercicio combina práctica de traducción, planteo y resolución de problemas de álgebra de un paso. Veamos, mientras tanto, un ejemplo antes de comenzar con el ejercicio.

Ejemplo: Sue tiene x dólares y Tom tiene $\frac{2}{3}$ de la cantidad que tiene Sue. Si Tom tiene $48, ¿cuánto tiene Sue?

PASO 1. Traduzca y plantee el problema.

Tom tiene $48.

$\frac{2}{3}$ del dinero de Sue equivalen a $48 $\frac{2}{3}x = 48$

PASO 2. Resuelva la ecuación. Divida ambos miembros por $\frac{2}{3}$.

$$\frac{2}{3}x = 48$$
$$\frac{2}{3}x \div \frac{2}{3} = 48 \div \frac{2}{3}$$
$$x = 48 \times \frac{3}{2}$$
$$x = \$72$$

EJERCICIO 6: RESOLUCIÓN DE PROBLEMAS DE UN PASO

Instrucciones: Resuelva cada uno de los problemas.

1. Jack ahorró un octavo de la mensualidad que le dan sus padres. Si su ahorro fue de $2.50, ¿cuánto le dan sus padres?

2. Amanda vendió su equipo de sonido por $120 menos de lo que le costó. Si el equipo se vendió por $72, ¿cuánto le había costado originalmente a Amanda?

3. Después de cortar $5\frac{1}{2}$ pies de una viga de madera, quedaron $6\frac{1}{2}$ pies. ¿Cuál era la longitud original de la viga?

4. Al adquirir una flotilla de automóviles para sus vendedores, Tower Manufacturing obtiene un descuento de $927 por cada vehículo comprado. Esto representa un 16% del precio normal. Halle el precio normal.

Resolución de problemas de pasos múltiples

Son muchas las expresiones algebraicas que constan de dos o más términos. Por ejemplo, $2x - 7$ tiene dos términos, mientras que $3x - 9y + 7z$ tiene tres términos. Conviene siempre escribir las expresiones algebraicas de la forma más sencilla posible.

Simplificación de expresiones algebraicas

Para simplificar una expresión algebraica, combine los términos semejantes y elimine los *signos de agrupación* como las llaves, paréntesis y corchetes.

Simplificación por combinación de términos semejantes

Los *términos semejantes* son términos que contienen la misma variable elevada a la misma potencia.

Ejemplos de términos semejantes: $4x$ $7x$ $12x$ $\quad 2xy$ xy $17xy$ $\quad 9x^2$ $4x^2$ x^2

Ejemplos de términos desemejantes: $3x$ $4y$ $\quad 2$ $2xy$ $\quad 3x$ $4y$ $3x^2$ $\quad 2x$ -5

Los términos semejantes se pueden combinar a fin de simplificar una expresión.

> *Ejemplo 1:* $3x + 5x = 8x$ $\quad$ (Simplemente sume los coeficientes, es decir, los números.)

> *Ejemplo 2:* $7y^2 - 5y^2 = 2y^2$ (Los coeficientes también se pueden restar.)

> *Ejemplo 3:* $2x - 3y - 5y + 2 + 4x - 6 = 6x - 8y - 4$

Combine los términos x:	Combine los términos y:	Combine los números:
$2x + 4x = 6x$	$-3y - 5y = -8y$	$-6 + 2 = -4$

▶ **Nota:** Observe que en el *Ejemplo 3,* dos de los términos dieron resultados con signo menos. Se trata de *números negativos,* de los que se hablará más adelante en las páginas 361–364. Si los signos de los números son iguales (+ o –), sume los números y agregue simplemente el signo (+6 y +3 = +9; –6 y –3 = –9). Si los signos son diferentes, halle la diferencia entre los números y escriba el resultado con el signo del número mayor (–6 + 2 = –4).

EJERCICIO 7: COMBINACIÓN DE TÉRMINOS SEMEJANTES

Instrucciones: Simplifique las expresiones combinando los términos semejantes.

1. $2x + 3y + 6y + 7x$ $\qquad$ **4.** $9a^2 + 4a + a + 3a^2$

2. $7x^2 + 3x + 4x - 2x$ $\qquad$ **5.** $5xy + 7x - 3y - x + 4xy$

3. $x + 2y - y$

Eliminación de los signos de agrupación

A veces es necesario agrupar las expresiones algebraicas. Entre los signos de agrupación tenemos a los paréntesis, los corchetes y las llaves. A estos signos debemos dirigir nuestra atención cuanto tengamos que simplificar una expresión.

> *Ejemplo 1:* $3(2x - 4)$

> $\qquad$ Multiplique: 3 por $2x$ y 3 por (-4).

> $\qquad$ $3(2x - 4) = 3(2x) - 3(4) = 6x - 12$

Si hay un signo más o no hay signo delante del paréntesis, los términos no varían al eliminar el paréntesis.

Ejemplo 2: $6x + (2x - 7) = 6x + 2x - 7 = 8x - 7$

Si hay un signo menos delante de un paréntesis, los signos de los términos del paréntesis se invierten. Si, además del signo menos, hay un número, se cambian los signos, se multiplican los números y se combinan los términos semejantes.

signo cambiado

Ejemplo 3: $3x - 2(6x - 4) = 3x - 12x + 8 = -9x + 8$

CÓMO ELIMINAR LOS SIGNOS DE AGRUPACIÓN

1. Elimine los paréntesis primero y luego los corchetes.
2. Distribuya la multiplicación a cada término del paréntesis.

EJERCICIO 8: ELIMINACIÓN DE LOS SIGNOS DE AGRUPACIÓN

Instrucciones: Simplifique las expresiones eliminando los signos de agrupación.

1. $5(3x + 2)$
2. $6x + 2(12x - 7)$
3. $3(2x + 4 - 3y)$
4. $-6(5x - 12)$
5. $2(x - y)$

Resolución de ecuaciones de pasos múltiples

1°. Simplificar las expresiones de ambos miembros de la ecuación.
2°. Pasar todas las variables al miembro de la izquierda de la ecuación efectuando una suma o resta a partir del miembro de la derecha.
3°. Centrarse en la variable y *suprimir sumas o restas* mediante la operación inversa.
4°. Centrarse en la variable y *suprimir multiplicaciones y divisiones* mediante la operación inversa.

Ejemplo: $3(x - 2) + 18 = 6 + 2(x + 6)$

PASO 1. $3x - 6 + 18 = 6 + 2x + 12$

$\qquad 3x + 12 = 2x + 18$

PASO 2. $3x - 2x + 12 = 2x - 2x + 18$

$\qquad\quad x \qquad\qquad\quad 0$

$\qquad x + 12 = 18$

PASO 3. $x + 12 - 12 = 18 - 12$

$\qquad\qquad 0$

$\qquad x = 6$

EJERCICIO 9: RESOLUCIÓN DE ECUACIONES DE PASOS MÚLTIPLES

Instrucciones: Resuelva las ecuaciones siguientes.

1. $2x - 26 = 2$

2. $\frac{x}{3} + 4 = 9$

3. $\frac{4x}{3} - 14 = 14$

4. $2(5x - 11) + 12x = 0$

Traducción en problemas de pasos múltiples

A fin de poder plantear un problema de pasos múltiples, se deberá traducir el enunciado verbal a una expresión algebraica. Conviene siempre comprobar el resultado para ver si satisface la ecuación.

Ejemplo: Tony trabajó 35 horas la semana pasada y sólo unas pocas horas esta semana. Si su sueldo es de $9 la hora y le pagaron $477 (sin descontar impuestos) por las dos semanas, ¿cuántas horas trabajó esta semana?

PASO 1. Sea x el número de horas que Tony trabajó esta semana.

PASO 2. $x + 35$ es el total de horas trabajadas durante las dos semanas. $9(x + 35)$ es la cantidad de dinero que recibió por trabajar $x + 35$ horas a $9 por hora.

PASO 3. $9(x + 35) = 477$ (La cantidad de dinero que recibió es igual a $477.)

PASO 4. $9x + 315 = 477$

$9x + \underbrace{315 - 315}_{0} = 477 - 315$

$9x = 162$

$\frac{9x}{9} = \frac{162}{9}$

$x = 18$ horas esta semana

EJERCICIO 10: PLANTEO Y RESOLUCIÓN DE ECUACIONES DE PASOS MÚLTIPLES

Instrucciones: Resuelva cada uno de los problemas.

1. Oscar fue a esquiar a las montañas y estuvo 3 días y 3 noches. El albergue le costó $32 por noche y compró un boleto de telesilla cada día. Su factura total fue de $123. Halle el costo x del boleto diario del telesilla. ¿Cuál es la ecuación que representa mejor el problema?

(1) $x + 96 = 123$ (2) $3x + 32 = 123$ (3) $x + 32 = 123$

(4) $3(x + 32) = 123$ (5) no se da suficiente información

2. El perímetro de un triángulo es de 56 pulgadas. Si un lado mide 24 pulgadas y los otros dos lados son iguales, halle la longitud x de uno de estos dos lados. ¿Cuál es la ecuación que mejor describe el problema?

(1) $x + 24 = 56$ (2) $2x + 56 = 24$ (3) $2x - 24 = 56$

(4) $2x + 24 = 56$ (5) $x - 24 = 56$

3. La edad de Nick es seis años menos que dos veces la edad de Tom (x). La suma de sus dos edades es 42. Halle la edad de Tom. ¿Cuál es la ecuación que mejor describe el problema?

(1) $2x - 6 = 42$ **(2)** $x - 6 = 42$ **(3)** $x + 2x = 42$

(4) $(2x - 6) + x = 42$ **(5)** no se da suficiente información

4. Eric compró un automóvil nuevo por $10,200. Hizo un pago inicial de $4,800 y acordó pagar el resto en 36 cuotas mensuales iguales. ¿Cuánto pagará cada mes? ¿Qué ecuación representa mejor el problema? Sea x la cantidad del pago mensual.

(1) $36x = 10,200$ **(2)** $36x = 4,800$ **(3)** $36x - 4,800 = 10,200$

(4) $4,800 - 36x = 10,200$ **(5)** $4,800 + 36x = 10,200$

5. Se vendió el doble de boletos de adultos que de niños para un partido de fútbol y se dieron gratis algunos boletos a los ganadores de un concurso. Si la asistencia al partido fue de 8,324 personas, ¿cuántos boletos de cada clase se vendieron? ¿Qué ecuación representa mejor el problema? Sea x el número de boletos para niños vendidos.

(1) $x + 2\text{x} = 8,324$ **(2)** $x\,(2x) = 8,324$ **(3)** $2(x + 2) = 8,324$

(4) $2(x - 2) = 8,324$ **(5)** no se da suficiente información

Números con signo

Recta numérica

La *recta numérica,* que se ilustra abajo, representa todos los números reales que utilizamos. En álgebra, se usan el cero y los números mayores que cero, llamados *números positivos;* pero también se usan los números menores que cero, llamados *números negativos.* Los *números con signo* comprenden todos los números positivos, el cero y todos los números negativos.

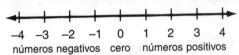

Los números positivos están indicados por un signo más antepuesto, como por ejemplo, +7, o bien pueden escribirse sin signo, como por ejemplo, 8. A los números negativos se les antepone un signo menos, como por ejemplo, –2 (se lee "menos dos"). Los números con signo se representan como puntos en la recta numérica. Abajo, se puede apreciar cómo se representan los números –3.5, –1 y 3.

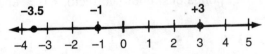

Con la recta numérica se puede ilustrar la relación que existe entre los números con signo. Todo número ubicado en la recta numérica a la derecha de otro número es mayor que (>) el número de la izquierda. Todo número ubicado a la izquierda de otro número es menor que (<) el número de la derecha.

▶ **Nota:** Los símbolos < y > siempre apuntan al número más pequeño.

Ejemplo 1: $1 > -3$

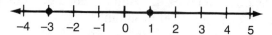

1 es mayor que –3 porque está situado a la derecha de –3 en la recta numérica.

Ejemplo 2: $-3\frac{1}{2} < -\frac{1}{2}$

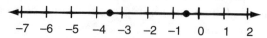

$-3\frac{1}{2}$ es menor que $-\frac{1}{2}$ porque está a la izquierda de $-\frac{1}{2}$.

EJERCICIO 11: RECTA NUMÉRICA

Instrucciones: Identifique las relaciones existentes entre los números representados abajo.

1. **2.**

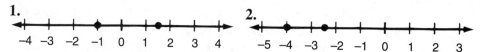

Valores absolutos

El *valor absoluto* es la distancia que hay en la recta numérica entre el cero y el número. Como la distancia es siempre un valor positivo, el valor absoluto de un número también es siempre positivo o cero. El símbolo para el valor absoluto es | |.

| 7 | = 7 El valor absoluto de 7 es 7.
| –2 | = 2 El valor absoluto de –2 es 2.

▶ **Nota:** El valor absoluto de un número positivo es igual a ese número. El valor absoluto de un número negativo es el mismo número pero con signo positivo. El valor absoluto de cero es cero.

EJERCICIO 12: NÚMEROS CON SIGNO

Instrucciones: Resuelva cada uno de los problemas. Para las *Preguntas 1–2,* represente las cantidades con números positivos o negativos.

1. una pérdida de tres yardas en el segundo "down" de un partido de fútbol americano

2. un aumento del valor de las acciones de $4\frac{1}{2}$ puntos en una semana

Para las *Preguntas 3–5,* ponga el símbolo correcto, < o >, entre los pares numéricos.

3. –9 –4   **4.** –3 1   **5.** $-\frac{1}{4}$ $-\frac{1}{2}$

Para las *Preguntas 6–7,* halle los valores.

6. $| 2\frac{1}{3} |$ **7.** $| -3 |$

Operaciones con números con signo

Los números con signo se pueden sumar, restar, multiplicar y dividir.

Combinación de números con signo

Si los números que se combinan son *todos positivos* o *todos negativos*, sume los números y conserve el mismo signo.

Ambos positivos
$+ 8 + 7 = +15$

Ambos negativos
$-8 - 7 = -15$

Si se combinan dos números *de signo contrario*, reste los números y escriba el resultado con el signo del número con el mayor valor absoluto.

Signos contrarios
$-8 + 7 = -1$
↑   ↑
signo del número mayor

Signos contrarios
$-7 + 8 = +1$ ó 1
↑   ↑
signo del número mayor

El problema siguiente contiene varios números. Algunos son positivos y otros son negativos. Para resolver el problema, nos valdremos de ambas reglas.

Ejemplo: $-6 + 1 + 14 - 2 - 8 + 6 - 9$

Primero, combine los números positivos: $1 + 14 + 6 = 21$

Después, combine los números negativos: $-6 - 2 - 8 - 9 = -25$

La diferencia entre 21 y -25 es 4.

El valor absoluto de -25 (número negativo) es mayor, por lo que la respuesta es -4.

EJERCICIO 13: COMBINACIÓN DE NÚMEROS CON SIGNO

Instrucciones: Resuelva cada uno de los problemas.

1. $-9 - 8$ **3.** $-127 + 94$ **5.** $-5 - 7 - 1 - 6$

2. $6 - 8$ **4.** $-12 + 6 + 3$ **6.** $-4.5 - 3.2$

Eliminación de signos dobles

En algunos caso nos encontraremos con números que llevan dos signos seguidos delante. Estos signos dobles deben ser siempre eliminados. Existen dos reglas para la eliminación de los mismos:

1. Si los signos dobles son iguales, reemplácelos con +.

   Ejemplos:
   $$+ (+3) = +3$$
   $$- (-8) = +8$$
   $$-4 - (-12) = -4 \underbrace{- (-12)}_{\text{iguales}} = -4 + 12 = +8$$

   (*Observación:* Si un número negativo va precedido de un signo −, el número negativo cambia su signo a + como en los dos últimos ejemplos de arriba.)

2. Si los signos dobles son contrarios, reemplácelos con −.

   Ejemplos:
   $$+ (-4) = -4$$
   $$-(+2) = -2$$
   $$5 + (-7) = 5 \underbrace{+ (-7)}_{\text{contrarios}} = 5 - 7 = -2$$

EJERCICIO 14: ELIMINACIÓN DE SIGNOS DOBLES

Instrucciones: Resuelva cada uno de los problemas.

1. $-6 + (-2) - (-9)$

2. Un jugador de fútbol americano ha corrido en seis jugadas el siguiente número de yardas: +23, −4, +8, +3, −6, −2. ¿Cuántas yardas ha ganado o perdido en total?

3. ¿De cuánto es el descenso de temperatura si el termómetro pasa de 12°F a −7°F?

4. En el Hipódromo de Arlington Park, Larry tenía $140 al empezar el día. En la primera carrera, ganó $56; en la segunda carrera, perdió $14; en la tercera carrera, perdió $32; en la cuarta carrera, perdió $18; y en la quinta carrera, ganó $26. ¿Cuánto dinero tenía al final de las 5 carreras?

Multiplicación y división de números con signo

1. Si los dos números que se multiplican o se dividen *son del mismo signo:*
   a. Multiplique o divida.
   b. Haga la respuesta positiva.

Ambos positivos	*Ambos negativos*
$8(7) = 56$	$-8(-7) = 56$
$26 \div 2 = 13$	$-32 \div -16 = 2$

2. Si los dos números que se multiplican o se dividen *son de signo contrario:*
   a. Multiplique o divida.
   b. Haga la respuesta negativa.

Signos contrarios	*Signos contrarios*
$-7(8) = -56$	$8(-7) = -56$
$\frac{-48}{12} = -4$	$\frac{-56}{7} = -8$

MULTIPLICACIÓN Y DIVISIÓN DE NÚMEROS CON SIGNO
1. Al multiplicar o dividir dos números *del mismo signo,* el resultado es *positivo.*
2. Al multiplicar o dividir dos números *de signo contrario,* el resultado es *negativo.*

Al multiplicar una serie de números con signo, se puede contar el número de signos negativos para determinar si el resultado es positivo o negativo.

a. Número par de signos negativos: el resultado es positivo.

b. Número impar de signos negativos: el resultado es negativo.

Ejemplo 1: $(-3)(-2)(-1)(-5) = 30$ (4 signos negativos, PAR: resultado +)

$$(+6) \quad (+5)$$

$$(+30)$$

EJERCICIO 15: MULTIPLICACIÓN Y DIVISIÓN DE NÚMEROS CON SIGNO

Instrucciones: Resuelva cada uno de los problemas.

1. $(8)(5)$

2. $12(-12)$

3. $(-6)(-7)(-2)$

4. $-\frac{25}{5}$

5. $\frac{-48}{-16}$

6. $\frac{56}{-14}$

7. A-One Sales compró 9 teléfonos para automóvil a \$2,476 cada uno. ¿Cuánto dinero debe la compañía por los teléfonos? (Exprese la respuesta en forma de número negativo.)

Desigualdades e inecuaciones

La relación que existe entre dos cosas no es siempre de igualdad, por lo que no podemos siempre valernos de una ecuación para resolver un problema. Si la relación dada es de **desigualdad,** podemos valernos de inecuaciones del tipo < (es menor que) o > (es mayor que) para resolver el problema. Las **inecuaciones** son desigualdades en las que hay una o más incógnitas. Por ejemplo, $x + 3 > 10$ es una inecuación algebraica. ¿Qué valor de x satisfaría la expresión? Hay varios valores de x que satisfacen esta expresión: x puede representar 8 porque $8 + 3 > 10$. También podría tener un valor 25 porque $25 + 3 > 10$. De hecho, x puede ser cualquier número mayor que 7. Llegamos entonces a la solución: $x > 7$.

Es muy frecuente que, al resolver una inecuación, el número de soluciones posibles sea infinito. Se debe conocer cuál es el límite de la solución. En este caso, el límite es 7; es decir que x no puede ser 7, pero sí puede ser cualquier número mayor que 7.

Resolución de inecuaciones

Los métodos algebraicos que se emplean en la resolución de inecuaciones son similares a los utilizados en las ecuaciones algebraicas.

RESOLUCIÓN DE INECUACIONES

1. Mantener la inecuación equilibrada. Sea cual fuere la operación que efectúe en uno de los miembros de la inecuación, efectúe la misma en el otro miembro.
2. Centrarse en la variable. El objetivo es aislar la variable en uno de los miembros de la inecuación.
3. Realizar la operación inversa, efectuando primero la suma o la resta y luego la multiplicación o la división.

Ejemplo: $x + 3 > 10$

Fíjese en la x. Se le está sumando un 3.
Reste 3 de ambos lados. La inecuación está resuelta (x ha sido aislada en el primer miembro de la inecuación).

$$x + 3 > 10$$
$$x + 3 - 3 > 10 - 3$$
$$\underbrace{\qquad}$$
$$0$$
$$x > 7$$

Comprobación: Elija cualquier número mayor que 7. Por ejemplo: 9.

$$x + 3 > 10$$
$$9 + 3 > 10$$
$$12 > 10$$

Existe una regla principal que se debe tener en cuenta al resolver una inecuación.

Al multiplicar o dividir ambos miembros de una inecuación por un número negativo, el sentido del signo de la inecuación cambia.

Por ejemplo, sabemos que $8 < 12$.
Si multiplicamos ambos miembros por –2, obtenemos 8(–2), igual a –16, y 12(–2), igual a –24. Como habíamos visto anteriormente, –16 es mayor que –24. Por lo que la respuesta es

$$8 < 12$$
$$8(-2) > 12(-2)$$

Observe que la flecha ha cambiado de dirección de menor que a mayor que.

$$-16 > -24$$

En ocasiones, se podrá encontrar con los signos ≤ y ≥, que quieren decir respectivamente "menor o igual que" y "mayor o igual que". Así pues, si se obtiene un resultado igual a $x \geq 3$, esto significa que la respuesta es 3 ó un número mayor que 3.

EJERCICIO 16: INECUACIONES DE UN PASO
Instrucciones: Despeje x. Compruebe los resultados.

1. $x - 3 > -5$
2. $-3 + x < -10$
3. $\frac{x}{-3} < 12$
4. $x - 5 \geq -1$
5. $-4x > -16$

Factorización

Algunos problemas requieren la factorización de las expresiones algebraicas. *Factorizar* (o *factorear*) significa descomponer en factores, es decir, identificar y separar las cantidades que multiplicadas dan un producto que es igual a la cantidad inicial. Con este ejemplo prestado de la aritmética se podrá captar a mayor cabalidad el concepto de factorización. Existen dos formas en que se puede descomponer el número 15: 3 x 5 = 15 y 15 x 1 = 15. Podemos decir entonces que 3 y 5 son factores de 15 y que 1 y 15 también son factores de 15. Los *factores* son los números que se multiplican.

La *factorización* (o *factoreo*) es el proceso que consiste en hallar los factores del producto de una multiplicación. Este proceso se puede usar para resolver algunos tipos de ecuaciones y simplificar ciertas expresiones. Al igual que con la aritmética, toda expresión algebraica es igual al producto de una multiplicación. Partiendo de esta premisa, debemos determinar qué expresiones se multiplicaron para llegar a ese producto.

Multiplicación de expresiones algebraicas

Las expresiones algebraicas se pueden multiplicar entre sí. Una expresión algebraica puede constar de un número (coeficiente), una letra (variable) y un exponente (potencia). Como recordará, el exponente es el número de tamaño reducido ubicado en la parte superior derecha de la variable.

Cuando se multiplican variables con exponentes, la base de estas variables debe ser la misma. Por ejemplo: x^2, x^3 y x^5 tienen la misma base x. Sin embargo, x^2 e y^2 tienen bases diferentes: x e y.

CÓMO MULTIPLICAR VARIABLES CON EXPONENTES

1. Conservar la misma base.
2. Sumar los exponentes

Ejemplos: $x^2 \cdot x^3 = x^{2+3} = x^5$ $\quad\quad$ $x^2 y^3 \cdot x^4 y^5 = x^{2+4} \cdot y^{3+5} = x^6 y^8$

$\quad\quad\quad\quad\quad$ $y^4 \cdot y^7 = y^{4+7} = y^{11}$ $\quad\quad$ $x \cdot x^3 = x^1 \cdot x^3 = x^{1+3} = x^4$

▶ **Nota:** Según se observa en el último ejemplo, aunque la letra x no presenta exponente, se entiende que su exponente es igual a 1. Del mismo modo, aunque las variables de arriba no presentan coeficiente, se entiende que su coeficiente es igual a 1. Los ejemplos que se ofrecen a continuación ilustran lo que debe hacerse con los coeficientes de las variables.

TÉRMINO MULTIPLICADO POR OTRO TÉRMINO

1. Multiplique los coeficientes.
2. Multiplique las variables, conservando la misma base y sumando los exponentes.

Ejemplos: $4x \cdot 7x^2 = 4 \cdot 7 \cdot x^1 \cdot x^2 = 28x^{1+2} = 28x^3$

$\quad\quad\quad\quad\quad$ $-3y^2 \cdot 5xy = -3 \cdot 5 \cdot x^1 \cdot y^2 \cdot y^1 = -15x \cdot y^{2+1} = -15xy^3$

Ejemplos: $5x(2x + 3) = 5x \cdot 2x + 5x \cdot 3$

$$= 10x^2 + 15x$$

$$-x(2x^2 + 3x - 7) = -x \cdot 2x^2 - x \cdot 3x - x(-7)$$

$$= -2x^3 - 3x^2 + 7x$$

EJERCICIO 17: MULTIPLICACIÓN DE EXPRESIONES ALGEBRAICAS

Instrucciones: Resuelva cada uno de los problemas.

1. $8x \cdot 3x^2$

2. $7xy(-4x)$

3. $(-6ab^2)(3a^2)$

4. $3y(2y^2 - 4y - 7)$

Cálculo del máximo común factor

La expresión $2x + 10$ consta de dos términos: $2x$ y 10. Para factorizar $2x + 10$, se ha de hallar el número mayor que sea un factor común a $2x$ y a 10: $2x = 2 \cdot x$ y $10 = 5 \cdot 2$. Por lo tanto, 2 es un factor común a $2x$ y 10. Factorizando, tenemos: $2x + 10 = 2(x + 5)$.

Ejemplo 1: Factorice: $65y^3 - 35y^2 + 15y$

El máximo común factor de los términos de esta expresión es $5y$.

$$65y^3 - 35y^2 + 15y =$$

$$\boxed{5y} \cdot 13y^2 + \boxed{5y} \cdot -7y + \boxed{5y} \cdot 3 =$$

$$5y(13y^2 - 7y + 3)$$

Ejemplo 2: Factorice: $3x^2 + x$

El máximo común factor de los términos de esta expresión es x.

$$3x^2 + x =$$

$$3x(x) + 1(x) =$$

$$x(3x + 1)$$

Observe que 1 es factor de x, ya que x equivale a "1 por x". Por lo tanto, si no se puede factorizar una variable de ninguna otra forma, exprésela como 1 multiplicado por la variable.

EJERCICIO 18: MÁXIMO COMÚN FACTOR

Instrucciones: Factorice cada una de las expresiones.

1. $21x^3 - 14x^2$

2. $121p^5 - 33p^4$

3. $9x^3y^2 + 36x^2y^3$

4. $5x^4 + 25x^3 - 20x^2$

Factorización por agrupación

En expresiones de cuatro o más términos, podemos usar el método de *factorización por agrupación* para descomponer la expresión en factores. Se suele agrupar los cuatro términos de la expresión en dos pares de términos. Después se extrae el factor común a cada par. De ser posible, se factoriza el factor común de los resultados.

Ejemplo: $x^2 + 5x + 2x + 10$

PASO 1. Agrupe en pares los términos. $\boxed{x^2 + 5x} + \boxed{2x + 10}$

PASO 2. Factorice cada par. $x(x + 5) + 2(x + 5)$

PASO 3. Ponga el factor común $(x + 5)$ delante. $(x + 5)(x + 2)$

CÓMO FACTORIZAR POR AGRUPACIÓN

1. Agrupar en pares los cuatro términos que tengan factores comunes.
2. Extraer el factor común de cada par de términos.
3. Colocar el factor común delante de los demás factores.

EJERCICIO 19: FACTORIZACIÓN POR AGRUPACIÓN

Instrucciones: Factorice por agrupación las expresiones siguientes.

1. $x^2 + 4x + 3x + 12$ **2.** $8y^2 + 6yz + 12yz + 9z^2$

Representación gráfica

Los gráficos también se pueden usar para representar ecuaciones.

Coordenadas rectangulares

Para comprender el gráfico de una ecuación, debemos primero conocer cómo se grafican los puntos en una cuadrícula. La cuadrícula se denomina *plano rectangular de coordenadas.* Este plano de coordenadas está formado por una recta numérica horizontal llamada *eje x* y una recta numérica vertical llamada *eje y* que se cortan en un punto llamado *origen.*

Cada uno de los puntos graficados se identifica por medio de un *par ordenado* de números (x,y). Al primer número del par ordenado se le llama *coordenada x,* y al segundo número *coordenada y.* El orden de las coordenadas es muy importante. La coordenada x se da siempre primero en el par ordenado seguida de la coordenada y.

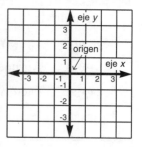

Ejemplo 1: Grafique el punto (3,4).

Empiece por el origen.

x es 3 → corra el punto 3 unidades a la derecha.

y es 4 → corra el punto 4 unidades hacia arriba.

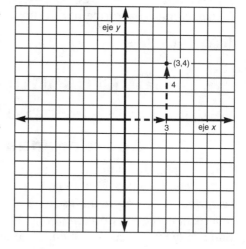

Ejemplo 2: Grafique el punto (−3, 5).

Empiece por el origen.

x es −3 → corra 3 unidades a la izquierda.

y es 5 → corra 5 unidades hacia arriba.

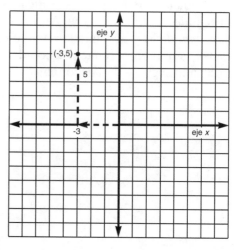

EJERCICIO 20: PARES ORDENADOS

Instrucciones: Complete los pares ordenados en base a los datos de la cuadrícula.

1. A (,   )   **4.** G (,   )

2. C (,   )   **5.** H (,   )

3. F (,   )

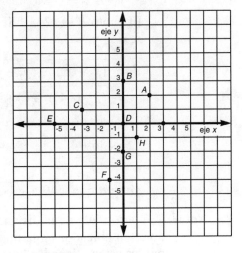

Distancia entre dos puntos

Existen dos métodos para hallar la distancia existente entre dos puntos de un gráfico. Si los dos puntos se encuentran en la misma línea horizontal o en la misma línea vertical, basta con contar las unidades que separan a los dos puntos.

Distancia por conteo

Para hallar la distancia entre los puntos C y A de la cuadrícula, cuente las unidades que hay de C a A. La distancia es de 10 unidades.

Para hallar la distancia entre los puntos A y B de la cuadrícula, cuente las unidades que hay de A a B. La distancia es de 7 unidades.

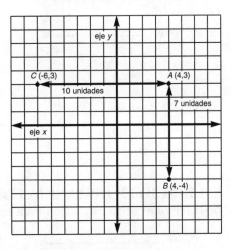

Distancia mediante una fórmula

El segundo método para hallar la distancia entre dos puntos se vale de la fórmula $d = \sqrt{(x_2 - x_1)^2 + (y_2 - y_1)^2}$ para dos puntos. No le será necesario a usted memorizarla, ya que está dada en la página de fórmulas de la Prueba de Matemáticas. Mediante esta fórmula se puede calcular la distancia que hay entre dos puntos cualesquiera, estén o no en la misma línea horizontal o vertical.

En la fórmula, x_1 es la coordenada x de uno de los puntos graficados y x_2 es la coordenada x del otro. Asimismo, y_1 es la coordenada y del primer punto representado e y_2 es la coordenada y del otro.

Ejemplo: Halle la distancia de *A* a *B*.

El punto *A* es (–4, 5). Si lo llamamos (x_1, y_1), entonces: $x_1 = -4; y_1 = 5$.

El punto *B* es (2, 3). Si lo llamamos (x_2, y_2), entonces: $x_2 = 2; y_2 = 3$.

$$d = \sqrt{(x_2 - x_1)^2 + (y_2 - y_1)^2}$$
$$= \sqrt{(2-(-4))^2 + (3-5)^2}$$
$$= \sqrt{6^2 + (-2)^2}$$
$$= \sqrt{36+4}$$
$$d = \sqrt{40}$$

Simplifique $\sqrt{40}$ a $\sqrt{4 \cdot 10} = 2\sqrt{10}$

▶ **Nota:** Use la fórmula de la distancia solamente en caso de que los puntos no estén ubicados en la misma línea horizontal o vertical. Si los puntos están alineados horizontal o verticalmente, basta con contar las unidades que hay entre ellos.

EJERCICIO 21: DISTANCIA POR CONTEO
Instrucciones: Halle la distancia entre los puntos siguientes.

1. *A* a *B* _____

2. *C* a *D* _____

3. *D* a *E* _____

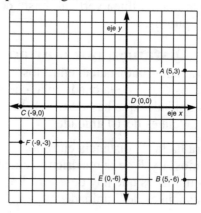

EJERCICIO 22: DISTANCIA ENTRE DOS PUNTOS
Instrucciones: Use el gráfico para hallar las distancias indicadas.

1. *I* a *J* _____

2. *E* a *F* _____

3. *G* a *H* _____

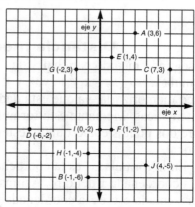

Pendiente de una recta

Una ecuación cuyo gráfico es una línea recta tiene un número especial asociado a esa recta. Este número se conoce como la *pendiente* de la recta. La pendiente es, en realidad, la razón entre la variación de los valores y y la variación de los valores x al pasar de un punto a otro de la recta.

Observe el gráfico de la recta $2x - 3y = 6$.

Al pasar de $(-3, -4)$ a $(0, -2)$, hay una variación de 2 unidades en los valores de y al mismo tiempo que hay una variación de 3 unidades en los valores de x.

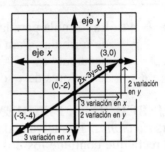

La pendiente es entonces:

$$\frac{\text{variación en } y}{\text{variación en } x} = \frac{2}{3}$$

Ejemplo 1: Halle la pendiente de la recta que contiene los puntos $(-6, -3)$ y $(-2, -1)$.

Variación en y: $-3 - (-1) = -3 + 1 = -2$

Variación en x: $-6 - (-2) = -6 + 2 = -4$

Pendiente $= \frac{\text{variación en } y}{\text{variación en } x} = \frac{-2}{-4} = \frac{1}{2}$

La pendiente es $\frac{1}{2}$. La recta tiene una pendiente positiva y se inclina hacia arriba.

Ejemplo 2: Halle la pendiente de la recta graficada a la derecha.

Variación en y: $6 - 0 = 6$

Variación en x: $0 - 2 = -2$

Pendiente $= \frac{6}{-2} = -3$

La pendiente es -3. La recta tiene una pendiente negativa y se inclina hacia abajo.

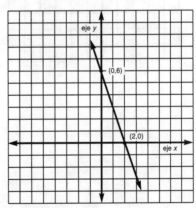

La pendiente de las rectas que se inclinan hacia arriba de izquierda a derecha es un número positivo. Las rectas que se inclinan hacia abajo tienen pendiente negativa. Las rectas paralelas al eje x tienen pendiente cero, mientras que las rectas paralelas al eje y carecen de pendiente.

1. Elegir dos puntos de una recta.
2. Restar los valores y para hallar la variación en y.
3. Restar los valores x para hallar la variación en x.
4. Escribir la pendiente en forma de razón: $\frac{\text{variación en } y}{\text{variación en } x}$

▶ **Nota:** La fórmula para la pendiente de una recta viene dada en la página de fórmulas. Para dos puntos cualesquiera (x_1, y_1) y (x_2, y_2), la pendiente es $\frac{y_2 - y_1}{x_2 - x_1}$. Esto indica que la pendiente es la variación de los valores de y sobre la variación de los valores de x.

EJERCICIO 23: PENDIENTE DE UNA RECTA

Instrucciones: Resuelva cada uno de los problemas. Halle la pendiente de la recta que contiene los dos puntos dados en las *Preguntas 1–2.*

1. $(0, 0)$ y $(3, 4)$ **2.** $(-5, -1)$ y $(6, 0)$

Para las *Preguntas 3–4,* halle la pendiente de las rectas representadas en el gráfico.

3.
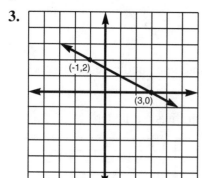

4.
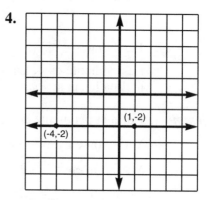

PRUEBAS POSTERIORES

INSTRUCCIONES GENERALES:
Dado que la práctica es la base de la perfección, las Pruebas Posteriores serán los indicadores finales de su aptitud para el Examen del GED; y las Tablas de Evaluación que se adjuntan en el libro le servirán para estimar su rendimiento. En lo que respecta a las Pruebas Posteriores, hacemos las siguientes recomendaciones:

1. Hacer sólo una Prueba Posterior cada vez. Trate de acabar la prueba en el tiempo asignado para poder determinar la velocidad con que ha de responder a las preguntas el día del examen. Si no termina en el período de tiempo fijado, señale la parte hasta la que pudo llegar y termine la prueba. Conviene que termine la Prueba Posterior para que pueda hacer uso de las Tablas de Evaluación.

2. Después de haber acabado cada Prueba Posterior, comprobar las respuestas en la Clave de Respuestas y llenar la Tabla de Evaluación para dicha prueba. Las Claves de Respuestas y las Tablas de Evaluación se encuentran en las páginas 479–494. En caso de haber contestado mal alguna pregunta, lea la explicación que se da de las respuestas correctas.

3. Si la información recogida en las Tablas de Evaluación indica la necesidad de enfocarse en un área determinada, consultar las páginas de repaso que se mencionan en las tablas.

4. Después de haber concluido las pruebas, comprobado las respuestas y rellenado las Tablas de Evaluación, transferir las puntuaciones de las Tablas de Evaluación a la Hoja de Comprobación de Aptitud para el GED que se adjunta en la página 425. La Hoja de Comprobación le ayudará a determinar si está listo para el día del examen.

5. Aunque sean éstas meramente pruebas de práctica, poner en ella todo su empeño. Cuando un ejercicio le resulte difícil, señálelo y vuelva al mismo más adelante. Conteste siempre todas las preguntas, incluso si tiene que tratar de adivinar la respuesta. A veces, puede que usted sepa más de lo que cree. El día del examen del GED, cada pregunta no contestada equivaldrá a una pregunta mal contestada. Por ello, conviene siempre contestar todas las preguntas.

¡Buena suerte con las Pruebas Posteriores y con el GED!

Tiempo asignado a cada Prueba Posterior

Expresión Escrita	Parte 1	38 minutos
	Parte 2	45 minutos
Estudios Sociales		43 minutos
Ciencias		48 minutos
Arte y Literatura		33 minutos
Matemáticas		45 minutos

PRUEBA POSTERIOR 1: EXPRESIÓN ESCRITA

Parte 1: Convenciones del español

Instrucciones: La Parte 1 de la Prueba Posterior de Expresión Escrita consta de 27 preguntas de opción múltiple. Las preguntas se basan en párrafos cuyas oraciones han sido numeradas. La mayor parte de estas oraciones presenta errores, pero hay unas cuantas que están bien escritas. Lea los párrafos y luego conteste las preguntas en base a ellos. *Para cada pregunta, escoja ya sea la respuesta que contenga la corrección que la oración necesita, o bien la mejor de las nuevas versiones propuestas para la oración u oraciones, o la combinación de oraciones más eficaz.* La respuesta elegida deberá guardar coherencia con el sentido y el estilo del resto del párrafo. Donde sea relevante, si a su parecer la versión original es la mejor, escoja la opción (1).

Le llevará aproximadamente 38 minutos contestar las preguntas de la prueba. Si, al cabo de los 38 minutos no ha terminado, deténgase y señale hasta dónde ha llegado; luego, termine la prueba y rellene la Tabla de Evaluación para analizar su rendimiento.

PRUEBA POSTERIOR 1: TABLA DE RESPUESTAS DE EXPRESIÓN ESCRITA

1 ① ② ③ ④ ⑤	8 ① ② ③ ④ ⑤	15 ① ② ③ ④ ⑤	22 ① ② ③ ④ ⑤
2 ① ② ③ ④ ⑤	9 ① ② ③ ④ ⑤	16 ① ② ③ ④ ⑤	23 ① ② ③ ④ ⑤
3 ① ② ③ ④ ⑤	10 ① ② ③ ④ ⑤	17 ① ② ③ ④ ⑤	24 ① ② ③ ④ ⑤
4 ① ② ③ ④ ⑤	11 ① ② ③ ④ ⑤	18 ① ② ③ ④ ⑤	25 ① ② ③ ④ ⑤
5 ① ② ③ ④ ⑤	12 ① ② ③ ④ ⑤	19 ① ② ③ ④ ⑤	26 ① ② ③ ④ ⑤
6 ① ② ③ ④ ⑤	13 ① ② ③ ④ ⑤	20 ① ② ③ ④ ⑤	27 ① ② ③ ④ ⑤
7 ① ② ③ ④ ⑤	14 ① ② ③ ④ ⑤	21 ① ② ③ ④ ⑤	

Las *Preguntas 1–6* se refieren al siguiente pasaje.

(1) La meditación es uno de los métodos más utilizados para combatir el estrés. (2) Muchos dedican a diario unos diez minutos de su tiempo para meditar en silencio. (3) La meditación les permite regresar a sus quehaceres con fuerzas y energías renovadas. (4) Los ejercicios de meditación son bastante sencillos: primero, siéntese cómodamente en una silla manteniendo la espalda erguida pero no rígida. (5) Relájese: ponga las manos sobre el regazo y apóyese los pies en el piso, de manera que toda la superficie de la planta del pie esté en contacto con el suelo. (6) Cierre los ojos y sienta como se expande su abdomen al inhalar y se contrae al exhalar. (7) Si las preocupaciones diarias le siguen asaltando, no lo rechace: mejor olvídese de ellas. (8) Una vez que haya avanzando en su técnica de meditación y ha podido pasar a un nivel más elevado, con una sesión de tan sólo diez minutos de meditación verá que queda descansado como si hubiera dormido durante toda una noche.

1. Oración 1: **La meditación es uno de los métodos** más utilizados para combatir el estrés.
   (1) La meditación es uno de los métodos
   (2) La meditación es una de los métodos
   (3) La meditación es uno de los metodos
   (4) La meditasión es uno de los métodos
   (5) La meditasion es uno de los métodos

2. Oraciones 2–3: **Muchos dedican a diario unos diez minutos de su tiempo para meditar en silencio. La meditación les permite regresar a sus quehaceres con fuerzas y energías renovadas.**

   ¿Cuál es la mejor manera de combinar estas dos oraciones?
   (1) silencio; así que la meditación les permite regresar a sus quehaceres con fuerzas y energías renovadas.
   (2) silencio, permitiendo la meditación regresar a sus quehaceres con fuerzas y energías renovadas.
   (3) silencio; pero la meditación les permite regresar a sus quehaceres con fuerzas y energías renovadas.
   (4) silencio, permitiendo regresar a sus quehaceres con fuerzas y energías renovadas.
   (5) silencio, y luego regresan a sus quehaceres con fuerzas y energías renovadas.

3. Oración 5: **Relájese: ponga las manos sobre el regazo y apóyese los pies en el piso, de manera que toda la superficie de la planta del pie esté en contacto con el suelo.**
   (1) regazo y apóyese los pies en el piso,
   (2) regazo y apóyase los pies en el piso,
   (3) regaso y apóyese los pies en el piso,
   (4) regazo y apoye los pies en el piso,
   (5) regazo; apoye los pies en el piso,

4. Oración 6: **Cierre los ojos y sienta como se expande su abdomen al inhalar y se contrae al exhalar.**
   (1) reemplace *expande* por *espande*

(2) sustituya *como* por *cómo*

(3) sustituya *abdomen* por *abdómen*

(4) reemplace *al inhalar* por *inhalando*

(5) ponga una coma entre ojos e y entre *inhalar* e *y*

5. Oración 7: **Si las preocupaciones diarias le siguen asaltando, no lo rechace: mejor olvídese de ellas.**

(1) reemplace *Si* por *Como*

(2) elimine la coma después de *asaltando*

(3) sustituya *olvídese* por *olbídese*

(4) cambie *no* por *ni*

(5) cambie *lo* por *las*

6. Oración 8: **Una vez que haya avanzado en su técnica de meditación y ha podido pasar a un nivel más elevado, con una sesión de tan sólo diez minutos de meditación verá que queda descansado como si hubiera dormido durante toda una noche.**

(1) reemplace *haya avanzado* por *aya avanzado*

(2) sustituya *ha podido* por *haya podido*

(3) reemplace *verá* por *verrá*

(4) cambie *hubiera dormido* por *hubiere dormido*

(5) cambie *hubiera dormido* por *habría dormido*

Las *Preguntas 7–14* se refieren al siguiente pasaje.

(1) Según estadísticas de años anteriores, se desecharon un promedio anual de aproximadamente 1,500 libras de basura por persona. (2) Ahora, sin embargo, en tiempos tan arduos, es imprescindible tener que ahorrar más, hoy más que nunca resulta extremadamente difícil que una familia pueda vivir de acuerdo con sus ingresos. (3) La mayoría de la gente trata de buscar cómo vivir de una forma más sencilla de la que acostumbraban. (4) Incluso las personas de ingresos elevados ahora optan en cambiar sus BMW por automóviles más pequeños y de más bajo consumo. (5) Una de las mejores formas de ahorrar es evitar comprar a crédito. (6) El interés es excesivamente alto. (7) Otra forma sería eliminando de la dieta la carne un día a la semana y preparar en su lugar una comida sin carne. (8) Las pastas, el arroz y comer otros granos y cereales son mucho más económicos que la carne. (9) Cuando fuera a la tienda o al supermercado, trate de no comprar nada de forma impulsiva: se sorprenderá de todo lo que podrá ahorrar.

7. Oración 1: **Según estadísticas de años anteriores, se desecharon un promedio anual de aproximadamente 1,500 libras de basura por persona.**

(1) cambie *desecharon* por *desechó*

(2) sustituya *aproximadamente* por *apróximadamente*

(3) reemplace *basura* por *vasura*

(4) cambie *años anteriores* por *anteriores años*

(5) no es necesario hacer correcciones

8. Oración 2: **Ahora, sin embargo, en tiempos tan arduos, es imprescindible tener que <u>ahorrar más, hoy más</u> que nunca resulta extremadamente difícil que una familia pueda vivir de acuerdo con sus ingresos.**

(1) ahorrar más, hoy más

(2) ahorrar más—hoy más

(3) ahorrar más: hoy más

(4) aorrar más, hoy más

(5) aorrar mas, hoy mas

9. Oración 3: **La mayoría de la gente trata de buscar cómo vivir de una forma más sencilla de la que acostumbraban.**
   (1) reemplace *trata* por *tratan*
   (2) cambie *vivir* por *bibir*
   (3) sustituya *acostumbraban* por *acostumbraba*
   (4) cambie *de lo que* por *de que*
   (5) reemplace *más* por *mas*

10. Oración 4: **Incluso las personas de ingresos elevados ahora optan en cambiar sus BMW por automóviles más pequeños y de más bajo consumo.**
    (1) sustituya *automóviles* por *automóbiles*
    (2) cambie *Incluso* por *Incluyendo*
    (3) ponga una coma después de *elevados*
    (4) cambie *optan en* por *optan por*
    (5) cambie *optan en* por *optan a*

11. Oraciones 5–6: **Una de las mejores formas de ahorrar es evitar comprar a <u>crédito. El interés</u> es excesivamente alto.**

    ¿Cuál es la mejor manera de combinar estas dos oraciones?
    (1) crédito, incluso si el interés
    (2) crédito, porque el interés
    (3) crédito, aunque el interés
    (4) crédito; sin embargo, el interés
    (5) crédito, y el interés

12. Oración 7: **Otra forma sería eliminando de la dieta la carne un día a la semana y preparar en su lugar una comida sin carne.**
    (1) reeemplace *eliminando* por *eliminar*
    (2) cambie *día* por *dia*
    (3) ponga una coma después de *semana*

(4) sustituya *en su lugar* por *en su sitio*
(5) no es necesario hacer correciones

13. Oración 8: **Las pastas, el arroz y comer otros granos y cereales son mucho más económicos que la carne.**
    (1) ponga una coma después de *arroz*
    (2) elimine *comer*
    (3) cambie *mucho* por *muchos*
    (4) sustituya *económicos* por *economicos*
    (5) no es necesario hacer correcciones

14. Oración 9: **Cuando fuera a la tienda o al supermercado, trate de no comprar nada de forma impulsiva: se sorprenderá de todo lo que podrá ahorrar.**
    (1) reemplace *ahorrar* por *aorrar*
    (2) sustituya los dos puntos por coma
    (3) cambie *trate de* por *intente de*
    (4) sustituya *fuera* por *fuese*
    (5) reemplace *fuera* por *vaya*

Las *Preguntas 15–20* se refieren al siguiente pasaje.

(1) Según un estudio médico, la gente se resfría un promedio de cuatro veces al año y faltan al trabajo unos siete días. (2) La mejor forma de mantenerse sano es no exponerse a los gérmenes que causan los resfríos (también llamados resfriados). (3) Los resfríos son causados por gérmenes y se contagian normalmente a través del contacto con las manos; por ejemplo, al dar la mano a una persona enferma que acabó de tocarse los ojos o incluso al

utilizar el teléfono de una persona que haya estado estornudando. (4) Mientras que el virus del resfrío no puede penetrar la piel, puede penetrar las membranas mucosas de la boca, la nariz y los ojos. (5) Si acaso tuviera la mala fortuna de resfriarse, recuerde que la mejor cura es descansar, la buena alimentación y evitar el estrés. (6) Sigue estas recomendaciones y deje que la enfermedad siga su curso.

15. Oración 1: **Según un estudio médico, la gente se resfría un promedio de cuatro veces al año y faltan al trabajo unos siete días.**
  (1) cambie *resfría* por *resfrían*
  (2) cambie *resfría* por *resfria*
  (3) cambie *faltan* por *falta*
  (4) cambie *veces* por *veses*
  (5) no es necesario hacer correcciones

16. Oración 2: **La mejor forma de mantenerse sano es no exponerse a los gérmenes que causan los resfríos (también llamados resfriados).**
  (1) cambie *resfríos* por *resfrios*
  (2) cambie *exponerse* por *esponerse*
  (3) ponga una coma después de *es*
  (4) ponga una coma después de *gérmenes*
  (5) no es necesario hacer correcciones

17. Oración 3: **Los resfríos son causados por gérmenes y se contagian normalmente a través del contacto con las manos; por ejemplo, al dar la mano a una persona enferma que acabó de tocarse los ojos o incluso al utilizar el teléfono**

de una persona que haya estado estornudando.
  (1) no es necesario hacer correcciones
  (2) persona enferma, que acabó de tocarse los ojos
  (3) persona enferma que acaba de tocarse los ojos
  (4) persona enferma acabando de tocarse los ojos
  (5) persona enferma que acabó tocándose los ojos

18. Oración 4: **Mientras que el virus del resfrío no puede penetrar la piel puede penetrar las membranas mucosas de la boca, la nariz y los ojos.**
  (1) Ya que
  (2) Por lo tanto
  (3) Como
  (4) Aunque
  (5) Dado que

19. Oración 5: **Si acaso tuviera la mala fortuna de resfriarse, recuerde que la mejor cura es descansar, la buena alimentación y evitar el estrés.**
  (1) sustituya *tuviera* por *tenga*
  (2) reemplace *recuerde* por *recuerda*
  (3) elimine la coma después de *resfriarse*
  (4) cambie *descansar* por *el descanso*
  (5) reemplace *la buena alimentación* por *alimentarse bien*

20. Oración 7: **Sigue estas reco-mendaciones y deje que la enfermedad siga su curso.**
  (1) reemplace *recomendaciones* por *recomendaciónes*
  (2) sustituya *y* por punto y coma
  (3) cambie *Sigue* por *Siga*
  (4) ponga una coma después de *recomendaciones*
  (5) no es necesario hacer correcciones

Las *Preguntas 21–27* se refieren al siguiente pasaje.

(1) ¿Sabía usted que ay personas que se especializan en basurología? (2) Según estudios realizados por estos expertos, la mayor parte de los desechos depositados en los basurales no se descomponen ni se transforma en suelo útil. (3) Han encontrado salchichas—aunque usted no lo crea—de hace 40 años y periódicos viejos que todavía se pueden leer. (4) Para que usted se haga una idea, una suscripción anual del *New York Times* ocupa el mismo espacio como 19,000 latas de aluminio aplastadas. (5) De entre los alimentos no procesados, las cáscaras de papa ocupan la mayor cantidad de espacio. (6) También se ha descubierto que la mayoría de las personas consumen tanto alimentos saludables como comida "basura". (7) Por esta razón, siempre que se encuentran restos de lechuga y pan de salvado se sabe que los envoltorios de dulces no pueden estar muy lejos. (8) El contenido de los basurales varían dependiendo de la zona geográfica y del nivel económico de la población.

21. Oración 1: **¿Sabía usted que ay personas que se especializan en basurología?**
    (1) reemplace *Sabía* por *Savía*
    (2) cambie *Sabía* por *Sabia*
    (3) reemplace *ay* por *áy*
    (4) sustituya *ay* por *hay*
    (5) cambie *especializan* por *espesializan*

22. Oración 2: **Según estudios realizados por estos expertos, la mayor parte de los desechos depositados en los basurales no se descomponen ni se transforma en suelo útil.**

(1) elimine la coma después de *expertos*
(2) reemplace *desechos* por *deshechos*
(3) sustituya *depositados en* por *depositados a*
(4) cambie *descomponen* por *descompone*
(5) reemplace *transforma* por *transforman*

23. Oración 3: **Han encontrado salchichas—aunque usted no lo crea—de hace 40 años y periódicos viejos que todavía se pueden leer.**
    (1) cambie *Han* por *Se han*
    (2) elimine la raya larga después de *crea*
    (3) ponga una coma después de la segunda raya larga
    (4) reemplace *de hace* por *hace*
    (5) no es necesario hacer correcciones

24. Oración 4: **Para que usted se haga una idea, una suscripción anual del *New York Times* ocupa el mismo espacio como 19,000 latas de aluminio aplastadas.**
    (1) elimine la coma después de *idea*
    (2) ponga una coma después del *New York Times*
    (3) reemplace *como* por *que*
    (4) sustituya *como* por *cómo*
    (5) no es necesario hacer correcciones

25. Oración 6: **También se ha descubierto que la mayoría de las personas consumen tanto alimentos saludables como comida "basura".**
    (1) reemplace *También* por *Tan bien*
    (2) sustituya *ha* por *han*
    (3) ponga una coma después de *personas*
    (4) sustituya *tanto* por *tantos*
    (5) no es necesario hacer correcciones

26. Oración 7: **Por esta razón, siempre que se encuentran restos de lechuga y pan de salvado se sabe que los envoltorios de dulces no pueden estar muy lejos.**

   (1) elimine la coma después de *razón*

   (2) ponga una coma después de *lechuga*

   (3) ponga una coma después de *salvado*

   (4) reemplace *envoltorios* por *emboltorios*

   (5) sustituya *dulces* por *dulses*

27. Oración 8: **El contenido de los basurales varían dependiendo de la zona geográfica y del nivel económico de la población.**

   (1) cambie *El contenido* por *Los contenidos*

   (2) reemplace *varían* por *varía*

   (3) sustituya *la zona* por *la área*

   (4) ponga una coma después de *geográfica*

   (5) sustituya *población* por *poblasión*

Las respuestas empiezan en la página 479.

Parte 2: La redacción

Instrucciones: El objetivo de esta sección es evaluar cómo usted escribe. La prueba consta de una pregunta que se le pide presente una opinión acerca de un tema o explique algún tópico. Al preparar la respuesta a esta pregunta, se recomienda seguir los siguientes pasos:

1. Lea toda la información que acompaña a la pregunta.

2. Piense detenidamente la respuesta antes de empezar a escribir.

3. Use papel borrador para hacer apuntes.

4. Escriba la respuesta en una hoja de papel aparte.

5. Lea detenidamente lo que ha escrito y efectúe los cambios que contribuyan a mejorar su redacción.

6. Verifique los párrafos, la estructura de las oraciones, la ortografía, la puntuación y el uso, y realice las correcciones necesarias.

Usted dispone de 45 minutos para pensar y escribir sobre el tema que se cita a continuación. Escriba con pluma de forma legible.

Tema

El número creciente de películas disponibles en videocasete es uno de los motivos por los que el público prefiere no ir al cine sino alquilar o comprar la película para verla en la comodidad del hogar. Este factor sigue ejerciendo una gran influencia en toda la industria cinematográfica.

Escriba una redacción de unas 200 palabras de extensión que describa cómo afecta a su vida esta disponibilidad de películas en videocasete. Puede escribir sobre los aspectos positivos y negativos de la revolución del videocasete, así como de sus gustos y razones en lo que respecta al modo en que prefiere ver las películas. Sea concreto y argumente con razones válidas su punto de vista.

En las páginas 481 y 482 encontrará información acerca de cómo evaluar su redacción.

PRUEBA POSTERIOR 2: ESTUDIOS SOCIALES

Instrucciones: La Prueba Posterior de Estudios Sociales consta de 32 preguntas de opción múltiple. Algunas de las preguntas están basadas en un mapa, una tabla, una gráfica, una caricatura o un pasaje de lectura. Lea el pasaje o estudie la ilustración cuidadosamente antes de elegir una respuesta.

Le llevará aproximadamente 43 minutos contestar las preguntas de la prueba. Si, al cabo de los 38 minutos no ha terminado, deténgase y señale hasta dónde ha llegado; luego, termine la prueba y rellene la Tabla de Evaluación para analizar su rendimiento.

PRUEBA POSTERIOR 2: TABLA DE RESPUESTAS DE ESTUDIOS SOCIALES

1 ① ② ③ ④ ⑤	**9** ① ② ③ ④ ⑤	**17** ① ② ③ ④ ⑤	**25** ① ② ③ ④ ⑤
2 ① ② ③ ④ ⑤	**10** ① ② ③ ④ ⑤	**18** ① ② ③ ④ ⑤	**26** ① ② ③ ④ ⑤
3 ① ② ③ ④ ⑤	**11** ① ② ③ ④ ⑤	**19** ① ② ③ ④ ⑤	**27** ① ② ③ ④ ⑤
4 ① ② ③ ④ ⑤	**12** ① ② ③ ④ ⑤	**20** ① ② ③ ④ ⑤	**28** ① ② ③ ④ ⑤
5 ① ② ③ ④ ⑤	**13** ① ② ③ ④ ⑤	**21** ① ② ③ ④ ⑤	**29** ① ② ③ ④ ⑤
6 ① ② ③ ④ ⑤	**14** ① ② ③ ④ ⑤	**22** ① ② ③ ④ ⑤	**30** ① ② ③ ④ ⑤
7 ① ② ③ ④ ⑤	**15** ① ② ③ ④ ⑤	**23** ① ② ③ ④ ⑤	**31** ① ② ③ ④ ⑤
8 ① ② ③ ④ ⑤	**16** ① ② ③ ④ ⑤	**24** ① ② ③ ④ ⑤	**32** ① ② ③ ④ ⑤

Las *Preguntas 1–2* se basan en los diagramas circulares siguientes.

PRINCIPALES CATEGORÍAS DE
GASTOS E INGRESOS FEDERALES
AÑO FISCAL 1991

CUÁLES HAN SIDO LOS GASTOS:

Desarrollo físico, humano y comunal 14%

Cumplimiento de la ley y gobierno general 2%

Programas sociales 14%

Seguridad Social, Medicare y otros impuestos de jubilación 32%

Interés neto sobre deuda 14%

Defensa, veteranos y relaciones exteriores 24%

DE DÓNDE PROVIENEN LOS INGRESOS:

Impuesto al valor añadido, a la propiedad, a la herencia, aduaneros y otros 7%

Impuestos a la renta de corporaciones 7%

Impuestos a la renta de individuos 35%

Préstamos para cubrir déficit 21%

Seguridad Social, Medicare, desempleo y otros impuestos de jubilación 30%

1. Según los diagramas, ¿cuál es la fuente de la mayor parte de los ingresos del gobierno federal?
   (1) una serie de impuestos gravados a los individuos
   (2) los impuestos gravados a las sociedades comerciales
   (3) el impuesto a la renta exclusivamente
   (4) el impuesto gravado a los productos
   (5) el comercio con otros países

2. De acuerdo con los diagramas circulares, ¿qué afirmación es verdadera respecto a los gastos del gobierno federal en 1991?
   (1) Se gastó más en programas sociales que en el desarrollo físico, humano y comnal.
   (2) Se gastó más en Seguridad Social, Medicare y otros impuestos de jubilación que lo que se ingresó a través de los impuestos.
   (3) Se gastó más en los intereses del déficit que en lo que se ingresó a través de los préstamos.
   (4) El siete por ciento del dinero prestado se empleó para pagar el déficit propiamente.
   (5) Los gastos de defensa representaron el mayor desembolso.

La *Pregunta 3* se basa en el siguiente pasaje.

Los seres humanos tienen en común con otros animales dos métodos de aprendizaje: el llamado aprendizaje situacional individual y el aprendizaje situacional social. El aprendizaje situacional individual es aquél en el cual el individuo aprende de sus propias experiencias; por ejemplo: tanto la persona como el animal son capaces de aprender que, si se quedan al descubierto cuando llueve, se mojan. Por otra parte, el aprendizaje situacional social es aquél en el cual el comportamiento se aprende de otros miembros de un grupo social a través de la observación. Los gatitos, por ejemplo, aprenden a cazar ratones imitando a la madre, así como los niños aprenden los juegos observando a otros niños. Existe asimismo un tercer método de aprendizaje que es particular al ser humano. El aprendizaje cultural se vale de conceptos y valores para guiar el comportamiento; por ejemplo, las madres que enseñan a sus hijos a que compartan los juguetes o bien la gente que aprende que ciertos comportamientos están bien o mal vistos. No se ha observado a ningún otro animal realizar su aprendizaje de esta manera.

3. ¿Cuál de los siguientes puntos es conclusión del autor?
   (1) El aprendizaje cultural es una característica exclusiva del ser humano.
   (2) El aprendizaje cultural se basa en conceptos y valores.
   (3) Las madres enseñan a sus hijos a compartir.
   (4) La gente aprende que ciertos comportamientos están bien o mal vistos.
   (5) No existe otro animal que aprenda conceptos y valores.

Las *Preguntas 4–5* se basan en el siguiente pasaje.

El *Bill of Rights* (o Declaración de Derechos), que los más de los ciudadanos de este país no valoran en toda su amplitud, no fue unánimemente aceptado por las trece primeras colonias. Los delegados Federalistas que asistieron a la Convención Constitucional de 1787 opinaban que no había necesidad de una declaración de derechos y afirmaban que la mayoría de los estados daba a sus ciudadanos la protección que les era necesaria. Los Antifederalistas, por su parte, creían que una declaración nacional de derechos era de suma importancia para proteger a los ciudadanos de un gobierno central excesivamente poderoso. La ratificación final del *Bill of Rights* (o diez primeras enmiendas a la Constitución de Estados Unidos) se dio en 1791.

4. ¿En cuál de estos supuestos se basaba el argumento de los Federalistas?
   (1) Un gobierno central podría tener precedencia sobre los derechos de los estados.
   (2) Los estados eran lo suficientemente poderosos como para proteger los derechos de sus ciudadanos.
   (3) Los derechos de los ciudadanos carecían de importancia.
   (4) Los derechos de los ciudadanos eran muy importantes como para ser ignorados.
   (5) Llevaría mucho tiempo ratificar una declaración de derechos.

5. ¿A cuál de las siguientes conclusiones da apoyo el pasaje?
   (1) No hacía falta, en realidad, un *Bill of Rights*.
   (2) El *Bill of Rights* no fue ratificado por los trece primeros estados.
   (3) Los fundadores de la nación diferían en su opinión acerca del papel que debía desempeñar el gobierno central.
   (4) Los miembros de la Convención Constitucional concordaron en todos los asuntos políticos.
   (5) El gobierno federal es excesivamente poderoso.

6. La tala de bosques con miras a obtener madera y tierras de pasto ha sido identificada como una de las principales causas de la erosión del suelo. El pastoreo de ganado vacuno en tierras recientemente desbrozadas

tiende a dejar el suelo despro-
visto de vegetación. Como los
pequeños sistemas de raíces de
los arbustos y las hierbas no son
capaces de retener el suelo, la
capa superficial del terreno se
pierde debido a la acción del
viento y de la lluvia.

¿Cuál de estas medidas ayudaría
a evitar la erosión del suelo?
(1) poner a pastar ovejas en
lugar de ganado vacuno
(2) dejar que la naturaleza siga
su curso
(3) regar la tierra intensamente
(4) replantar árboles y hierbas
de inmediato
(5) talar más bosques

La *Pregunta 7* se basa en los
siguientes datos.

Los sociólogos definen *multitud*
como un grupo de personas que se
congregan temporalmente con una
finalidad común. Se identifican cinco
tipos generales de multitud:

multitud casual: la que comparte
brevemente un interés de forma
no planeada

multitud convencional: la que
resulta de una planificación
deliberada y formal

multitud expresiva: la que comparte
de modo informal una
experiencia emocional o de
diversión

multitud activa: la que comete actos
violentos y destructivos

multitud de protesta: la que
promueve intencionalmente un
objetivo político

7. Un grupo de personas reunidas
para presenciar un partido de
hóckey sobre hielo se disgustó
con una de las decisiones del
árbitro. La gente empezó a
arrojar objetos a la pista de hielo
y luego empezó a saltar las
barricadas y a atacar a los
jugadores. Esto es un ejemplo de
(1) multitud casual.
(2) multitud convencional.
(3) multitud expresiva.
(4) multitud activa.
(5) multitud de protesta.

8. Los psicólogos opinan que los
juegos sociales desempeñan un
papel preponderante en el
desarrollo infantil. Según los
resultados de un estudio, los
juegos de adivinanzas fomentan
las capacidades lingüísticas y
lógicas del niño. Éste no sólo se
conforma con repetir las tradicionales adivinanzas, sino que
suele ir más allá y experimentar
con la invención de nuevas
adivinanzas en base a estructuras ya aprendidas. Según este
párrafo, se puede concluir que
(1) en el caso de los niños, los
juegos verbales son más que
una simple forma de
diversión.
(2) el niño que no inventa
adivinanzas no se
desarrollará adecuadamente.
(3) el niño que sólo repite
adivinanzas tradicionales no
entiende la estructura de las
mismas.
(4) los psicólogos no tienen
razón en dar tanto
importancia a los juegos
infantiles.
(5) las capacidades lingüísticas
y lógicas no se pueden
aprender por medio de
juegos infantiles.

Las *Preguntas 9–10* se basan en los
siguientes datos.

Los miembros del gabinete del
Presidente de los Estados Unidos son
los que con frecuencia aconsejan al

presidente en los asuntos que atañen a la nación. Estos consejeros son en la mayoría de los casos jefes o secretarios de uno de los departamentos del gobierno ejecutivo, los cuales tienen la función de regular y servir a diversos aspectos del quehacer nacional. Los servicios generales que competen a cinco de estos departamentos son los siguientes:

Departamento de Agricultura:
mejorar las granjas y los ingresos de éstas, y reducir la pobreza, el hambre y la desnutrición

Departamento de Comercio:
fomentar el comercio internacional y el crecimiento económico y evitar las prácticas comerciales injustas

Departamento del Interior:
conservar los terrenos públicos y los recursos naturales, incluyendo la fauna y flora silvestre y los lugares históricos

Departamento de Estado: formular y llevar a cabo la política exterior y proteger los intereses del país en el extranjero

Departamento de Transporte:
planear y brindar seguridad en autopistas, transportes públicos, ferrocarriles, aviación y vías fluviales

9. Existe un organismo que ayuda a establecer y desarrollar empresas de las minorías. ¿Qué miembro del gabinete está al frente del departamento que regula a este organismo?
   (1) secretario de comercio
   (2) secretario de agricultura
   (3) secretario del interior
   (4) secretario de estado
   (5) secretario de transporte

10. Existe un organismo que protege y se encarga del mantenimieno del sistema de parques y áreas de recreo nacionales. ¿Qué miembro del gabinete está al frente del departamento que regula a este organismo?
    (1) secretario de comercio
    (2) secretario de agricultura
    (3) secretario del interior
    (4) secretario de estado
    (5) secretario de transporte

11. Uno de los factores que participan en la ley de la oferta y la demanda es la proporción entre vendedores y compradores. Cuanto más vendedores haya de un producto, más opciones tendrán los compradores. Este principio de la oferta y la demanda produce un efecto especial en el mercado inmobiliario. Si por largo tiempo permanecen en el mercado más casas a la venta que compradores, ¿qué es más probable que ocurra?
    (1) El comprador ofrecerá más que lo que pide el vendedor.
    (2) El vendedor se negará a considerar una oferta menor que el precio de venta pedido.
    (3) El vendedor aceptará una oferta menor que el precio que pide.
    (4) Habrá más personas que pongan a la venta sus casas.
    (5) Los compradores potenciales esperarán a que bajen los precios de las casas.

12. La *aculturación* es el proceso mediante el cual los miembros de una cultura adoptan las costumbres y gustos de la cultura a la que se han incorporado. Sin embargo, el contacto directo entre dos culturas puede también influenciar a la cultura dominante. Los estadounidenses de origen chino han adoptado muchas costumbres de los Estados Unidos.

¿Cuál de éstos ilustra mejor cómo se han adaptado a su vez los estadounidenses a la cultura china?

(1) el comercio con Hong Kong
(2) el viaje diplomático de Nixon a China
(3) el uso de las linternas chinas en las fiestas al aire libre
(4) el uso de bicicletas como medio de transporte en el centro de la ciudad
(5) la aceptación de la cocina china como comida popular del país

Las *Preguntas 13–14* se basan en el gráfico adjunto.

13. Según el gráfico, ¿cuál de estas afirmaciones sobre la población mundial es verdadera?

(1) La población de las regiones desarrolladas y de las en vías de desarrollo ha alcanzado ya su punto más alto.
(2) La población de las regiones desarrolladas disminuirá mientras que la de las regiones en vías de desarrollo seguirá en aumento.
(3) Un aumento brusco de la población mundial no empezará antes del año 2000.
(4) La población de las regiones desarrolladas y de las en vías de desarrollo aumentará y disminuirá a un ritmo similar.
(5) La población de las regiones desarrolladas seguirá creciendo, mientras que la de las regiones en vías de desarrollo bajará.

14. ¿Cuál es la causa más probable del cambio que se produjo en la población de las regiones en vías de desarrollo entre 1950 y 1990?

(1) Las regiones en vías de desarrollo comenzaron a usar medios eficaces de control de natalidad.
(2) Un gran número de habitantes de las regiones en vías de desarrollo emigraron a las regiones desarrolladas.
(3) Las regiones en vías de desarrollo mejoraron las condiciones sanitarias y adoptaron prácticas agrícolas más productivas.
(4) La tasa de embarazos en las regiones desarrolladas comenzó a bajar.
(5) Las mujeres de las regiones desarrolladas se dieron cuenta del valor económico que suponía el tener una familia numerosa.

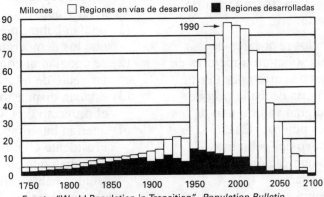

POBLACIÓN MUNDIAL: CRECIMIENTO ANUAL MEDIO EN CADA DÉCADA, 1750–2100 (PROYECTADO)

Millones ☐ Regiones en vías de desarrollo ■ Regiones desarrolladas

Fuente: "World Population in Transition", *Population Bulletin,* de Thomas W. Merrick y el staff de PRB

Las *Preguntas 15–16* se basan en el siguiente pasaje.

El primer envío de correo para el Oeste de los Estados Unidos que hizo la oficina postal salió en barco de vapor con destino a Panamá, luego cruzó por ferrocarril el istmo hasta el Pacífico y de ahí siguió otra vez en barco hasta San Francisco. Este proceso tardó un mes, por lo menos, y las cartas llegaron amontonadas en grandes pilas sin clasificar.

Los envíos oficiales por tierra comenzaron a realizarse en 1858 con la compañía de diligencias de John Butterfield, la cual transportaba el correo a través de un trayecto de 2,800 millas en tan sólo veinticuatro días. El Pony Express, de corta existencia, redujo aun más este tiempo: a un mínimo de diez días. Sin embargo, esta empresa no estaba exenta de peligros. El anuncio que solicitaba mensajeros decía: "Se necesitan: hombres jóvenes, delgados y enjutos menores de 18 años de edad. Deben ser jinetes expertos y estar dispuestos a arriesgar la vida a diario. Se prefieren huérfanos".

La terminación del ferrocarril transcontinental en 1869 cambió para siempre los envíos de correo al Oeste. Las cartas y los paquetes comenzaron a llegar a las ciudades así como a los pueblos de una forma rápida y preclasificada.

15. En 1856, los residentes de California solicitaron mejoras en los envíos de correo por tierra. Tomaron esta decisión porque daban un gran valor a uno de los siguientes puntos. ¿Cuál?
(1) el apoyo del gobierno
(2) la comunicación con amigos y familiares
(3) dar empleo a los huérfanos
(4) las dificultades de la vida en los confines del Oeste
(5) los viajes por ferrocarril

16. El cambio importante que se produjo en el servicio de correos al Oeste es comparable
(1) al asentamiento gradual de los estados de la región central de Estados Unidos.
(2) al aumento de las tarifas postales.
(3) al desarrollo de pequeñas compañías telefónicas a causa de la desmonopolización de la AT&T.
(4) al aumento de la competencia entre compañías que fabrican computadoras personales.
(5) a la mejora de las comunicaciones telefónicas internacionales tras la instalación del cable transatlántico.

17. En abril de 1993, los republicanos obstruyeron la aprobación de un paquete presentado por el Presidente Clinton para estimular el empleo a corto plazo. La norma de debate ilimitado permite a los senadores utilizar la técnica del *filibustering*, es decir, el hacer uso de la palabra durante el tiempo suficiente para forzar la retirada del proyecto de ley que se somete a discusión. Con su táctica de obstruccionismo, los republicanos dieron a entender que
(1) podían hablar más tiempo que los demócratas.
(2) se oponían al contenido del proyecto de ley.
(3) estaban dispuestos a aprobar el proyecto de ley.
(4) querían humillar al Presidente Clinton.
(5) opinaban que en Estados Unidos había suficientes plazas de trabajo.

La *Pregunta 18* se basa en la siguiente caricatura.

Letonia está estable por el momento; Georgia está agitada. Una columna de camiones se dirige hacia Croacia, como el acuerdo en la región se está por romper una vez más...

Salón de actualización de mapas de Rand McNally--Edición 1999

18. ¿Cuál de estas afirmaciones expresa *mejor* la opinión que tiene el artista sobre los cartógrafos?

(1) Hacer mapas exactos hoy en día es tan complicado como ir a la guerra.

(2) Los cartógrafos dependen excesivamente de informes de segunda mano.

(3) Los cartógrafos no se esfuerzan por estar al día con los cambios que se registran en el mundo.

(4) Los cartógrafos deberían interesarse más sobre las cuestiones de geografía política.

(5) Los cartógrafos toman demasiado en serio su trabajo.

Las *Preguntas 19–20* se basan en los siguientes datos.

La función principal de los *grupos de presión* es influir en la política interna y externa del país. Se pueden mencionar cinco tipos generales:

grupos de presión económicos: representantes de empresas e industrias estadounidenses que tratan de influenciar la política nacional e internacional del país en beneficio propio

grupos de presión étnicos: representantes de asociaciones formadas en base a raíces nacionales o culturales comunes

grupos de presión de gobiernos extranjeros: representantes de países extranjeros que tratan de influenciar la legislación en beneficio de las empresas e intereses de su nación

grupos de presión de interés público: representantes que trabajan por la protección del bienestar de la mayor parte o de la totalidad de la población estadounidense

grupos de presión unitemáticos: representantes que tratan de fomentar legislación que afecta a un único asunto, por lo general no relacionado a la economía

19. Un grupo que se dedica a promover leyes que protejan el medio ambiente es un
(1) grupo de presión económico.
(2) grupo de presión étnico.
(3) grupo de presión de un gobierno extranjero.
(4) grupo de presión de interés público.
(5) grupo de presión unitemático.

20. Un grupo que se dedica a promover leyes que declaren la ilegalidad del aborto es un
(1) grupo de presión económico.
(2) grupo de presión étnico.
(3) grupo de presión de un gobierno extranjero.
(4) grupo de presión de interés público.
(5) grupo de presión unitemático.

21. El término *crisol de culturas* fue acuñado en 1907 por Israel Zangwell para expresar la noción de que los inmigrantes de los diversos países del mundo venían a América para formar una nación. La visión que abrigaba Zangwell era la de un pueblo unido, resultado de la cohesión de gentes diversas al compartir su cultura y tradiciones. Cincuenta años después, Jesse Jackson diría de Estados Unidos que era más bien como una "sopa de verduras". Con esta expresión, Jackson quiso decir que
(1) en Estados Unidos convivía una diversidad de gentes pero sin renunciar a su identidad propia.
(2) todos los habitantes del país tenían el mismo aspecto y actuaban de la misma forma.
(3) los habitantes del país jamás serían capaces de convivir en paz.

(4) los habitantes del país mostraban más interés por la comida que por las ideas culturales.
(5) no se consideraba a gentes de otras culturas como estadounidenses auténticos.

La *Pregunta 22* está basada en el siguiente gráfico.

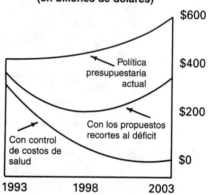

DÉFICIT FEDERAL PROYECTADO
(en billones de dólares)

22. Según el gráfico, el control de costos de salud pública producirá
(1) un aumento sostenido del déficit federal.
(2) un déficit federal mayor que el que habría si se mantuviera la política presupuestaria actual.
(3) la misma reducción del déficit federal que se daría con los recortes al déficit que se proponen ahora.
(4) una reducción importante del déficit federal.
(5) cambios mínimos o nulos en el déficit federal.

23. La lluvia ácida es un subproducto tóxico de las industrias que queman hulla y combustibles derivados del petróleo, de las centrales eléctricas y de los gases que emite el escape de los automóviles. Debido al ciclo natural del agua, la lluvia ácida puede desplazarse hasta 2500 millas de su fuente de origen. ¿Qué conclusión se podría sacar en base a esta información?

(1) No se puede considerar la lluvia ácida como un problema de contaminación localizado.

(2) La lluvia ácida es un fenómeno natural.

(3) Los efectos de la lluvia ácida se pueden contener fácilmente dentro de las áreas industriales.

(4) La lluvia ácida se limita a las ciudades.

(5) Las áreas rurales están exentas de los efectos de la lluvia ácida.

Las *Preguntas 24–25* se basan en los siguientes datos.

Toda nueva empresa debe arrostrar una serie de problemas y obstáculos. Son cinco las principales barreras con que se tienen que enfrentar las nuevas empresas que entran a competir en el mercado:

patente previa de un producto: La patente garantiza a su propietario el derecho a la producción exclusiva del producto por un término de diecisiete años. Si el producto está patentado, aun cuando no haya salido al mercado, el inventor de un producto similar no puede fabricar su producto hasta que la patente previa haya expirado o le haya sido comprada al titular de la patente.

licencias del gobierno: El gobierno federal, estatal y local puede restringir el número de empresas similares dentro de un área determinada mediante la expedición de un número limitado de licencias.

control de la materia prima: El acceso a los materiales necesarios para la fabricación de un producto puede estar controlado por otros.

tamaño limitado del mercado: El mercado debe ser lo suficientemente grande como para dar cabida a un número suficiente de consumi-dores que adquieran un producto o servicio.

gran inversión de capital: Se necesita una suma considerable de dinero para abrir y mantener una empresa, incluyendo equipos, materia prima y salarios.

24. Un restaurante que acababa de abrir en la ciudad quería empezar a servir bebidas alcohólicas con la cena para poder atraer a una clientela más amplia; pero los propietarios descubrieron que la ciudad sólo expedía un número limitado de licencias para servir licores y no habría licencias disponibles hasta que un negocio existente renunciara a la suya. ¿A qué barrera competitiva se refiere este caso?

(1) patente previa de un producto

(2) licencias del gobierno

(3) control de la materia prima

(4) tamaño limitado del mercado

(5) gran inversión de capital

25. Una pareja que administraba una tienda de alquiler de películas de video se muda a un nuevo vecindario y piensa abrir una tienda parecida en la zona. Pronto se enteran de que ya hay dos tiendas de video que operan en ese lugar. ¿Con qué barrera competitiva se enfrenta la pareja?

(1) patente previa de un producto

(2) licencias del gobierno

(3) control de la materia prima

(4) tamaño limitado del mercado

(5) gran inversión de capital

26. La primera persona que propuso Bill Clinton para la Procuraduría General de la nación, Zoe Baird, fue rechazada por el Senado por haber contratado en el pasado a extranjeros indocumentados para trabajar en su casa y no haber pagado impuestos sobre los salarios. El Congreso aprobó más tarde el nombramiento de Janet Reno, la primera mujer en ocupar este importante cargo. En base a lo acontecido, ¿qué conclusión se puede sacar respecto a los miembros del Senado?

(1) No querían que el Procurador General fuera una mujer.

(2) Querían que la futura Procuradora General obedeciera las leyes.

(3) No confiaban en la elección del presidente.

(4) Creían que no se debería discriminar contra los trabajadores indocumentados.

(5) Preferían a Baird más que a Reno.

27. El trastorno de estrés postraumático es una recreación aleatoria de un evento aterrador en la mente de la persona que lo experimentó. Las víctimas que padecen de este trastorno sufren también de episodios de depresión, pesadillas, pérdida de la memoria o sentimientos retardados de aislamiento, culpabilidad y furia. ¿Cuál de éstas podría ser causa de este trastorno?

(1) haber visto una película violenta

(2) verse envuelto en un accidente masivo de tráfico

(3) presenciar un incendio

(4) oír que un amigo ha sido asesinado

(5) leer en el periódico un caso de violación

Las *Preguntas 28–29* se basan en el siguiente pasaje.

Aristóteles dijo que era la recompensa de una vida activa vivida con dulce razón. Sigmund Freud dijo que era, en gran parte, una cuestión de trabajo y amor. Charles Shultz, el conocido caricaturista y filósofo, dijo que era en realidad un cachorrito cariñoso. De modo que, ¿qué es eso que llamamos felicidad? Por siglos y siglos, la gente ha estado muy ocupada buscándola como para dedicarse a analizarla. Ahora, finalmente, un grupo de investigadores, pioneros en su ramo, ha decidido agarrar al toro por las astas—o al menos tomarle las medidas. . . Y la respuesta que dan a este misterio de tiempos inmemoriales es que todo depende.

La felicidad depende de aquello que hace que nos sintamos felices, razón por la cual los psicólogos la suelen llamar "bienestar subjetivo". A pesar de esto, gracias a los estudios realizados con varios grupos de población y edad en Estados Unidos y el extranjero, se ha llegado a algunas conclusiones objetivas acerca de los ingredientes que entran en la felicidad. En casi todos los resultados, no figuran en los primeros lugares de las tablas el éxito, la juventud, la belleza física o la posesión de una de esas envidiables fortunas, como muchos podrían suponer. Como ganador indiscutible aparecen las relaciones personales—aquéllas de lazos íntimos y estrechos—; y, en segundo lugar, figuran los matrimonios dichosos. Luego viene la fe religiosa, de casi cualquier tipo. "Los lazos íntimos de apoyo con otras personas parecen tener suma importancia", afirma el psicólogo David Myers, cuyo libro *La búsqueda de la felicidad* es una de las numerosas publicaciones que se han editado recientemente sobre el tema.

28. Según este pasaje, ¿cuál es la causa primordial de la felicidad?
    (1) el éxito
    (2) la juventud
    (3) el atractivo personal
    (4) las relaciones estrechas
    (5) la fe religiosa

29. En base al pasaje, ¿qué conclusión se puede sacar respecto a la felicidad?
    (1) Los antiguos filósofos fueron los que mejor definieron lo que es la felicidad.
    (2) La felicidad es fácil de definir.
    (3) No existe una definición clara de la felicidad.
    (4) Existe una sola definición de felicidad.
    (5) Los psicólogos han logrado finalmente definir la felicidad.

30. Las 1,950 millas de frontera que hay entre Estados Unidos y México se conocen con el nombre de *La Línea*, la cual atrae a miles de inmigrantes sin trabajo provenientes del interior de México. Para ellos, *La Línea* representa mucho más que una frontera nacional. ¿A qué se asemeja el cruce de las aguas turbias del Río Tijuana y el Río Grande por estas familias?
    (1) al cruce del Atlántico por Colón
    (2) al cruce del Atlántico por los esclavos de origen africano
    (3) al cruce del mar por los antepasados de los estadounidenses de origen irlandés, polaco y chino
    (4) al cruce del Río Delaware por las tropas de Washington
    (5) al cruce del Canal de la Mancha por los soldados estadounidenses

Las *Preguntas 31–32* se basan en el siguiente mapa.

LOS ALIADOS RESPONDEN A SADDAM, 1991

Tras la violación de los acuerdos internacionales por parte de Saddam Hussein con el envío de sus tropas a Kuwait y misiles a otros países vecinos, los aliados respondieron con una acción militar.

Fuente: U.S. News & World Report

31. ¿Qué parte de las acciones aliadas se detallan en el mapa?
  (1) la campaña terrestre en el desierto
  (2) la campaña aérea en el área de Bagdad
  (3) la batalla en la frontera entre Kuwait e Irak
  (4) las bases aliadas en Arabia Saudita
  (5) el movimiento de las tropas aliadas en Irak

32. ¿En cuál de los siguientes supuestos se basó la estrategia de este ataque?

  (1) El ataque destruiría totalmente la economía de Irak.
  (2) Saddam Hussein sería asesinado durante el ataque.
  (3) Saddam Hussein se vería forzado a renovar su ofensiva.
  (4) Los residentes de Bagdad unirían fuerzas con los aliados.
  (5) La destrucción de los centros militares más importantes ayudaría a poner rápido fin al conflicto.

Las respuestas comienzan en la página 483.

PRUEBA POSTERIOR 3: CIENCIAS

Instrucciones: La Prueba Posterior de Ciencias consta de 33 preguntas de opción múltiple. Algunas de las preguntas están basadas en un pasaje de lectura o requieren que Ud. interprete una tabla o un diagrama. Lea el pasaje o estudie la tabla cuidadosamente antes de elegir una respuesta.

Le llevará aproximadamente 48 minutos en contestar las preguntas de la prueba. Si, al cabo de los 48 minutos no ha terminado, deténgase y señale hasta dónde ha llegado; luego, termine la prueba y rellene la Tabla de Evaluación para analizar su rendimiento.

PRUEBA POSTERIOR 3: TABLA DE RESPUESTAS DE CIENCIAS

1 ① ② ③ ④ ⑤	10 ① ② ③ ④ ⑤	19 ① ② ③ ④ ⑤	28 ① ② ③ ④ ⑤
2 ① ② ③ ④ ⑤	11 ① ② ③ ④ ⑤	20 ① ② ③ ④ ⑤	29 ① ② ③ ④ ⑤
3 ① ② ③ ④ ⑤	12 ① ② ③ ④ ⑤	21 ① ② ③ ④ ⑤	30 ① ② ③ ④ ⑤
4 ① ② ③ ④ ⑤	13 ① ② ③ ④ ⑤	22 ① ② ③ ④ ⑤	31 ① ② ③ ④ ⑤
5 ① ② ③ ④ ⑤	14 ① ② ③ ④ ⑤	23 ① ② ③ ④ ⑤	32 ① ② ③ ④ ⑤
6 ① ② ③ ④ ⑤	15 ① ② ③ ④ ⑤	24 ① ② ③ ④ ⑤	33 ① ② ③ ④ ⑤
7 ① ② ③ ④ ⑤	16 ① ② ③ ④ ⑤	25 ① ② ③ ④ ⑤	
8 ① ② ③ ④ ⑤	17 ① ② ③ ④ ⑤	26 ① ② ③ ④ ⑤	
9 ① ② ③ ④ ⑤	18 ① ② ③ ④ ⑤	27 ① ② ③ ④ ⑤	

1. ¿Cuál de los siguientes hechos es la mejor evidencia de que el helio es más ligero que el aire?
   (1) El helio no arde al entrar en contacto con una llama en presencia del oxígeno.
   (2) En cuanto al volumen, el helio constituye el 0.0005 por ciento del aire.
   (3) Los átomos de helio no se combinan con otros átomos del aire.
   (4) Los globos de helio se elevan en el aire.
   (5) El helio tiene el punto de ebullición más bajo de todos los elementos conocidos.

2. Con el objeto de combatir los efectos de la lluvia ácida, los científicos de muchos países vierten grandes cantidades de carbonato de calcio en los lagos contaminados. En base a esta medida tomada por los científicos, podemos deducir que el carbonato de calcio
   (1) es un ácido.
   (2) es una base.
   (3) es una sustancia neutra.
   (4) es una sustancia en polvo.
   (5) no es dañino para los peces.

La *Pregunta 3* se basa en el siguiente pasaje.

Cuando la célula de una planta verde se expone a la luz solar, se produce una reacción química denominada fotosíntesis. Durante la fotosíntesis, el gas dióxido de carbono (CO_2) reacciona con el agua (H_2O) formando tres compuestos: un tipo de azúcar llamado glucosa ($C_6H_{12}O_6$), oxígeno (O_2) y agua. La ecuación química de la fotosíntesis se escribe:

$$6CO_2 + 12H_2O$$
$$\downarrow$$
$$C_6H_{12}O_6 + 6O_2 + 6H_2O$$

3. ¿Cuál de estos productos tiene que estar presente para que se pueda realizar la fotosíntesis?
   (1) glucosa
   (2) oxígeno libre
   (3) nitrógeno
   (4) agua
   (5) tierra

4. La precipitación es el proceso mediante el cual el vapor de agua atmosférico regresa a la superficie de la Tierra de una forma determinada. Los siguientes ejemplos son tipos de precipitación, *excepto:*
   (1) la lluvia
   (2) la escarcha
   (3) el polvo
   (4) la nieve
   (5) el granizo

Las *Preguntas 5–6* se basan en el siguiente pasaje.

Los organismos varían enormemente en complejidad. Los organismos unicelulares, como las bacterias, por ejemplo, son mucho menos complejos que los organismos multicelulares como las flores. Seguidamente veremos cinco de los niveles más comunes de organización estructural.

orgánulo: estructura organizada que se encuentra en el citoplasma de la célula. Cada orgánulo participa en algún tipo de función celular. Ejemplo: las células vegetales contienen cloroplastos que absorben la energía de la luz solar para elaborar el alimento que necesita la célula.

célula: unidad estructural y funcional básica de la vida. Las células usan energía, se mueven, crecen, responden a cambios en su medio ambiente y se reproducen. En los organismos multicelulares, la célula desempeña una función específica. Ejemplo: la célula nerviosa humana.

tejido: grupo de células de estructura semejante que se asocian y organizan para realizar la misma actividad. Ejemplo: en la célula vegetal, el tejido vascular transporta agua y alimentos nutritivos a toda la célula.

órgano: unidad estructural compuesta por varios tejidos que trabajan en conjunto para realizar una función específica. Ejemplo: el corazón.

sistema de órganos: asociación de varios órganos que trabajan en conjunto para realizar una o más funciones. Ejemplo: el sistema muscular.

5. En la planta, la epidermis es una capa especial de células que recubre y protege a las raíces, los tallos, las hojas, las flores y las semillas. Se puede decir que esta capa de células especializadas es
   (1) un orgánulo.
   (2) una célula.
   (3) un tejido.
   (4) un órgano.
   (5) un sistema de órganos.

6. Cuando Derek cumplió cuarenta y tres años, su páncreas dejó de producir la cantidad necesaria de insulina, hormona que controla el nivel de azúcar presente en la sangre. Le diagnosticaron diabetes, una afección que en muchos casos se puede controlar si se sigue una dieta adecuada. Puesto que está formado por varios tipos de tejidos especializados, se puede decir que el páncreas es
   (1) un orgánulo.
   (2) una célula.
   (3) un tejido.
   (4) un órgano.
   (5) un sistema de órganos.

7. ¿Cuál de los siguientes casos demuestra que la luz solar se puede transformar en energía calorífica?
   A. Una lupa al enfocar un rayo luminoso.
   B. El hecho de que se tiene más calor bajo el sol que en la sombra.
   C. La superficie de un auto que se calienta cuando está bajo la luz directa del sol.
   D. La luz solar que se refleja en un espejo sin calentarlo de forma apreciable.

   (1) A y B
   (2) A y C
   (3) A y D
   (4) B y C
   (5) B y D

Las *Preguntas 8–9* se basan en el siguiente pasaje.

Desde tiempos remotos, en los países asiáticos, se ha usado el apio en el tratamiento de la hipertensión o alta presión arterial. Recientemente, un grupo de investigadores de la Universidad de Chicago ha encontrado una posible explicación a este beneficio médico del apio. Se descubrió que el apio contiene un compuesto químico llamado ftaluro de 3-n butilo; y se cree que este compuesto ftaluro ocasiona que los músculos que recubren a las paredes de los vasos sanguíneos se relajen, permitiendo así que los vasos se ensanchen, lo cual reduce la presión arterial.

En un experimento realizado con ratas, estos investigadores descubrieron que una dosis de este compuesto ftaluro equivalente a cuatro ramas de apio para los seres humanos bajaba la presión arterial un 13 por ciento. Se espera que futuros estudios

permitan desarrollar un tratamiento más efectivo y seguro de
la hipertensión.

Las afirmaciones de las *Preguntas
8–9* se pueden clasificar en una de
estas cinco categorías.

experimento: procedimiento usado
para investigar un problema

hallazgo: resultado experimental o
conclusión obtenidos en una
investigación

hipótesis: explicación razonable,
aunque no probada, de un
fenómeno observado

predicción: opinión acerca de algo
que puede ocurrir en el futuro

dato no esencial: dato que no contribuye a la comprensión del
problema que se está investigando

8. Los investigadores creen que
   comer apio ayuda a reducir la
   presión arterial haciendo que los
   músculos que recubren a las
   paredes de los vasos sanguíneos
   se relajen. Se puede decir que
   esta afirmación es
   (1) un experimento.
   (2) un hallazgo.
   (3) una hipótesis.
   (4) una predicción.
   (5) un dato no esencial.

9. Los investigadores descubrieron
   que el ftaluro de 3-n-butilo es
   capaz de reducir la presión
   arterial de las ratas. Se puede
   decir que esta afirmación es
   (1) un experimento.
   (2) un hallazgo.
   (3) una hipótesis.
   (4) una predicción.
   (5) un dato no esencial.

Las *Preguntas 10–12* se basan en el
siguiente pasaje.

En los últimos años, los científicos han descubierto que la
temperatura de la Tierra está
aumentando paulatinamente. De
hecho, los científicos creen que la
temperatura promedio actual es
varios grados más alta que la
temperatura promedio de principios de la revolución industrial
a finales del siglo XVIII. Se cree
que este calentamiento es
causado por el fenómeno conocido como *efecto invernadero.*

En un invernadero, la luz solar
pasa por el techo de vidrio y
suministra la energía necesaria
para el crecimiento de las plantas
que están en el interior. El vidrio
impide que escape el calor del
invernadero. De manera semejante, la luz solar pasa por
nuestra atmósfera y calienta la
superficie terrestre. Gran parte
del calor de la superficie no
escapa porque es absorbida por
los gases de invernadero que hay
en la atmósfera. Siempre que no
aumente el nivel promedio de
gases de invernadero, la temperatura de la Tierra permanecerá
constante.

Dos de los gases de invernadero más importantes son el
dióxido de carbono y el monóxido de carbono. Desde la
revolución industrial, los seres
humanos han causado un
aumento en la cantidad de
dióxido de carbono presente en
la atmósfera al quemar combustibles fósiles (madera, carbón
y petróleo), tanto para la generación de electricidad como la
generación de calor (calefacción).
Con el uso de vehículos, los seres
humanos han ocasionado un
aumento en la cantidad de
monóxido de carbono presente
en la atmósfera, el cual emiten
los caños de escape.

Los científicos advierten que,
si la temperatura promedio de la
Tierra sigue subiendo, podría dar
como resultado el derretimiento
de los casquetes polares y el

cambio de los patrones meteorológicos en todo el mundo.

10. ¿Cuál de éstos ilustra mejor el efecto invernadero?
    (1) una parrilla para barbacoa redonda con tapa
    (2) un acuario climatizado
    (3) un auto con las ventanas cerradas estacionado bajo el sol
    (4) una calculadora solar
    (5) un horno de microondas

11. ¿Qué es lo más probable que ocurra como consecuencia del aumento gradual de la temperatura promedio de la Tierra?
    (1) un aumento gradual en la duración de los días
    (2) un aumento gradual en la duración de los años
    (3) una baja en el nivel del mar
    (4) un aumento gradual en el número de volcanes activos
    (5) un aumento gradual del nivel del mar

12. Los científicos pronostican que si no se toman medidas para detener el aumento de los gases de invernadero presentes en la atmósfera, la temperatura promedio de la Tierra podría aumentar unos 6° F a 10° F en los próximos cincuenta años. ¿Cuál de las siguientes medidas sería más efectiva para combatir el efecto invernadero?
    (1) reducir la dependencia que tiene la población de todos los tipos de combustibles fósiles
    (2) aumentar los impuestos sobre combustibles de vehículos
    (3) restringir el uso de las chimeneas sólo al invierno
    (4) desarrollar automóviles eléctricos eficientes que sustituyan a los autos de gasolina

    (5) registrar los cambios que se produzcan en la temperatura promedio de la Tierra durante los próximos cincuenta años

La *Pregunta 13* se basa en la siguiente tabla.

COMPOSICIÓN DEL AIRE SECO PURO

Gas	Símbolo o fórmula	Porcentaje en volumen
Nitrógeno	N_2	78.1%
Oxígeno	O_2	20.9%
Argón	Ar	0.9%
Dióxido de carbono	CO_2	0.03%
Neón	Ne	
Helio	He	
Criptón	Kr	
Xenón	Xe	cantidades mínimas
Hidrógeno	H_2	
Óxido nitroso	N_2O	
Metano	CH_4	

13. ¿Qué se puede determinar a partir de los datos de la tabla?
    A. la diferencia entre el porcentaje de helio y de oxígeno presente en el aire seco puro
    B. el volumen de oxígeno presente en una muestra de un pie cúbico de aire seco puro
    C. la diferencia entre el porcentaje de argón y de dióxido de carbono presente en el aire seco puro
    D. el volumen de vapor de agua presente en un 100 por ciento de aire húmedo

    (1) A y B
    (2) A y C
    (3) B y C
    (4) B y D
    (5) C y D

La *Pregunta 14* se basa en el siguiente pasaje.

La temperatura y la presión afectan la cantidad de gas que se puede disolver en un líquido. Al aumentar la temperatura, disminuye la cantidad de gas disuelto; mientras que, al aumentar la presión, aumenta la cantidad de gas disuelto.

14. Las bebidas gaseosas burbujean porque contienen dióxido de carbono disuelto. Si se deja abierta la botella de una bebida gaseosa, ¿qué ocurriría?
 (1) La cantidad de dióxido de carbono disuelto permanecería igual.
 (2) Aumentaría la cantidad de dióxido de carbono disuelto.
 (3) Disminuiría la cantidad de dióxido de carbono disuelto.
 (4) Disminuiría la temperatura de la bebida gaseosa.
 (5) Aumentaría la presión que ejerce la bebida gaseosa sobre la botella.

La *Pregunta 15* se basa en el siguiente pasaje.

¿En qué se asemeja un barco a remo de aluminio a un globo lleno de helio? Tanto el barco como el globo exhiben flotabilidad, es decir, la tendencia que tiene un objeto a flotar en un líquido o a elevarse en un gas.

El barco y el globo están sometidos a dos fuerzas: una fuerza gravitacional que impulsa hacia abajo (igual al peso del objeto) y una fuerza de flotabilidad que impulsa hacia arriba. La fuerza de flotabilidad es igual al peso del líquido o el gas que el objeto desplaza.

• El barco a remo flota en el agua porque la fuerza de flotabilidad que lo impulsa hacia arriba se equilibra de forma exacta con la fuerza gravitacional que lo impulsa hacia abajo. Un barco a remo de 500 libras se hunde en el momento en que desplace un poco menos de 500 libras de agua.

• Las piedras se hunden en el agua porque la fuerza gravitacional es mayor que la fuerza de flotabilidad.

• Los globos inflados con helio se elevan en el aire porque desplazan un volumen de aire que pesa más que el peso del globo de helio. En otras palabras, la fuerza de flotabilidad es mayor que la fuerza gravitacional.

15. Aproximadamente el 11 por ciento del volumen de los icebergs no se sumerge en el agua, sino que sobresale por encima de su superficie. De acuerdo con el pasaje anterior, se puede decir que el peso del agua desplazada por el iceberg es
 (1) un 11 por ciento mayor que el peso del iceberg
 (2) un 11 por ciento menor que el peso del iceberg
 (3) igual al peso de la parte del iceberg que sobresale por encima de la superficie.
 (4) igual al peso de la parte del iceberg que está sumergida.
 (5) igual al peso total del iceberg.

La *Pregunta 16* se basa en la siguiente ilustración.

CONDICIONES NORMALES DIURNAS

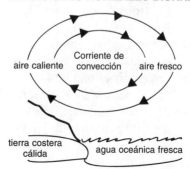

16. Se denomina corriente de convección al movimiento del
  (1) aire causado por diferencias de elevación.
  (2) aire causado por diferencias en la distancia de la masa de aire al océano.
  (3) aire causado por diferencias de temperatura.
  (4) agua causado por la presencia de la tierra.
  (5) agua causado por diferencias de elevación.

La *Pregunta 17* se basa en el siguiente pasaje.

El proceso de respiración se realiza en las células del cuerpo y proporciona al mismo una fuente de energía. Durante la respiración, el oxígeno (O_2) reacciona con la glucosa ($C_6H_{12}O_6$), y produce dióxido de carbono (CO_2), agua (H_2O) y energía. La ecuación química de la respiración se escribe:

$$C_6H_{12}O_6 + 6O_2$$
$$\downarrow$$
$$6CO_2 + 6H_2O + \text{energía}$$

17. ¿A cuál de éstos se consideraría más probablemente como producto de desecho de la respiración celular?
  (1) glucosa
  (2) oxígeno
  (3) dióxido de carbono
  (4) nitrógeno
  (5) energía

Las *Preguntas 18–19* se basan en los siguientes datos.

Los circuitos eléctricos pueden ser en serie o en paralelo. En los circuitos en serie, la corriente eléctrica sólo puede seguir un trayecto. Una interrupción en cualquier punto de este circuito detiene todo el flujo de corriente.

En los circuitos en paralelo, la corriente eléctrica puede seguir más de un trayecto. Una interrupción en un punto del circuito no impide que la corriente fluya por un segundo (o tercer) trayecto.

CIRCUITO EN SERIE

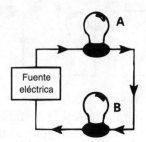

Si la bombilla A se funde, la bombilla B también se apaga.

CIRCUITO EN PARALELO

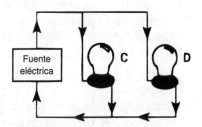

Si la bombilla C se funde, la bombilla D sigue encendida.

18. Cuatro enchufes de pared se colocan en serie con un interruptor de desconexión de emergencia. Si se activa el interruptor de desconexión. ¿qué ocurre con los enchufes de pared?
  (1) Sólo se apaga el enchufe que está más cerca del interruptor.
  (2) Se apagan los cuatro enchufes.
  (3) Los cuatro enchufes permanecen encendidos.
  (4) Se apagan dos de los enchufes, uno a cada lado del interruptor.
  (5) Sólo se apaga el enchufe que está más lejos del interruptor.

19. ¿Qué afirmación es verdadera respecto al circuito que se ilustra abajo?

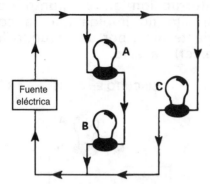

(1) Si se funde la bombilla B, la bombilla A y la bombilla C permanecerán encendidas.

(2) Si se funde la bombilla C, la bombilla A y la bombilla B se apagarán.

(3) Si se funde la bombilla A, la bombilla B se apagará y la bombilla C permanecerá encendida.

(4) Si se funde la bombilla B, la bombilla A y la bombilla C se apagarán.

(5) Si se funde la bombilla A, la bombilla B permanecerá encendida y la bombilla C se apagará.

20. En Estados Unidos se está registrando un aumento en los casos reportados de personas infectadas con el VIH (Virus de Inmunodeficiencia Humana). Es probable que el aumento se deba a todas estas razones *excepto:*

(1) a una mayor atención prestada por los doctores para detectar los síntomas del SIDA.

(2) a un incremento en los esfuerzos por educar a los ciudadanos de EE.UU. acerca de los problemas del SIDA.

(3) a un incremento en la propagación del SIDA.

(4) a un incremento de los exámenes de detección del virus VIH.

(5) a la llegada a Estados Unidos de personas portadoras del virus VIH procedentes de otros países.

21. Dos procesos importantes que realizan las plantas a través de sus hojas son la fotosíntesis y la transpiración. Durante la fotosíntesis, las hojas producen glucosa, una forma de azúcar. Durante la transpiración, las plantas desprenden agua por evaporación de la superficie de las hojas. ¿Cuál es la razón más probable de que las plantas del desierto tengan pocas hojas o ninguna?

(1) aumentar la fotosíntesis

(2) disminuir la fotosíntesis

(3) mantener la fotosíntesis a un nivel constante, noche y día

(4) aumentar la transpiración

(5) disminuir la transpiración

Las *Preguntas 22–23* se basan en la ilustración y el pasaje siguientes.

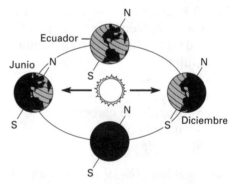

El eje de rotación de la Tierra está inclinado con respecto a la dirección de los rayos del Sol. Esta inclinación permanece constante mientras la Tierra gira alrededor de su eje y alrededor del Sol. La inclinación produce dos importantes efectos en el planeta:

- Es verano en el hemisferio que está inclinado hacia el Sol, mientras que es invierno en el hemisferio que está más alejado del Sol.
- El hemisferio que está inclinado hacia el Sol tiene días más largos y noches más cortas que el hemisferio que está más alejado del Sol.

22. Durante el verano en el hemisferio norte, el Polo Norte experimenta
- **(1)** veinticuatro horas de oscuridad cada día.
- **(2)** veinticuatro horas de luz diurna cada día.
- **(3)** doce horas de luz diurna cada día.
- **(4)** doce horas de oscuridad cada día.
- **(5)** dieciocho horas de luz diurna cada día.

23. ¿Cuál de estas afirmaciones sería verdadera si el eje terrestre no estuviera inclinado?
- **A.** Los días y las noches tendrían la misma duración en cualquier punto de la Tierra.
- **B.** No habría horas de oscuridad en puntos situados a lo largo del ecuador.
- **C.** No habría estaciones en la Tierra.
- **D.** Cada región del planeta tendría la misma fluctuación diaria de temperatura.

- **(1)** A
- **(2)** A y C
- **(3)** A y D
- **(4)** B
- **(5)** B y C

Las *Preguntas 24–25* se basan en la ilustración y el pasaje siguientes.

CEREBRO HUMANO

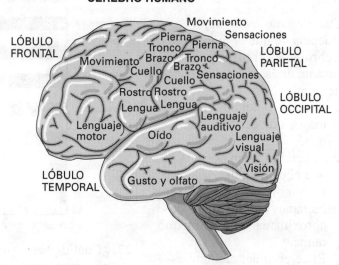

La región de mayor tamaño del cerebro humano es el prosencéfalo. El cerebro consta de dos mitades, o hemisferios, unidos en su centro por medio de un conjunto de fibras nerviosas que se conoce como cuerpo calloso. Cada hemisferio se compone de cuatro partes, o lóbulos, que controlan funciones motoras (movimientos voluntarios) o sensoriales (sensaciones) específicas.

Los científicos saben desde hace mucho tiempo que el hemisferio izquierdo (ilustrado arriba) controla el lado derecho del cuerpo humano y que el hemisferio derecho controla el lado izquierdo. En los últimos años, los científicos también han descubierto que cada hemisferio se especializa en actividades específicas de aprendizaje. Parece que el hemisferio izquierdo está mejor preparado para el lenguaje escrito, las destrezas científicas, las matemáticas y el razonamiento lógico. El hemisferio derecho parece estar más especializado para el arte, la música, la agudeza de ingenio y la imaginación.

24. ¿Qué área del cerebro controla la sensación en el lado izquierdo del rostro de una persona?
(1) el lóbulo occipital derecho
(2) el lóbulo parietal izquierdo
(3) el lóbulo temporal izquierdo
(4) el lóbulo frontal derecho
(5) el lóbulo parietal derecho

25. ¿Cuál de éstas es la mejor evidencia de que el tamaño del cerebro no es el principal causante de las diferencias en inteligencia?
A. El cerebro del adulto es mayor que el cerebro del bebé.
B. El cerebro humano es mayor que el de un gato.
C. El cerebro de todos los seres humanos adultos tiene aproximadamente el mismo tamaño.
D. El cerebro del elefante es mayor que el cerebro humano.
(1) A y B
(2) A y D
(3) B y C
(4) B y D
(5) C y D

26. ¿Cuál de éstas es la mejor evidencia de que la luz se desplaza a mayor velocidad que el sonido?
(1) Los seres humanos tienen distintos órganos sensoriales para la vista y para el oído.
(2) La luz se desplaza por el espacio sideral, pero el sonido no.
(3) La luz atraviesa con facilidad un vidrio grueso, pero el sonido no.
(4) El relámpago se ve antes de que se escuche el trueno.
(5) La frecuencia de la luz visible es mucho mayor que la del sonido.

La *Pregunta 27* se basa en el siguiente gráfico.

PORCENTAJE DE CARBOHIDRATOS EN DETERMINADOS ALIMENTOS

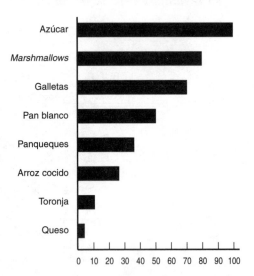

27. ¿Cuál de los siguientes alimentos tiene un contenido de carbohidratos del 50 por ciento o más?
(1) toronja
(2) arroz
(3) *marshmallows*
(4) 1 y 3
(5) 2 y 3

La *Pregunta 28* se basa en el siguiente gráfico.

PRINCIPALES SUSTANCIAS PRESENTES EN AGUA MARINA

(POR PESO)

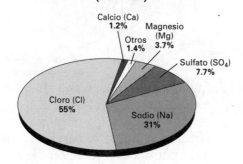

28. Según el gráfico, se puede deducir que la sustancia principal disuelta en el agua de mar es el
    (1) óxido de magnesio (MgO).
    (2) ácido sulfúrico (SO_4H_2).
    (3) cloruro de calcio (Cl_2Ca).
    (4) cloruro de potasio (ClK).
    (5) cloruro de sodio (ClNa).

La *Pregunta 29* se basa en la siguiente ilustración.

BARRA IMANTADA

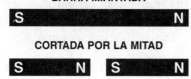

29. Según la ilustración, se puede afirmar que
    (1) la barra imantada tiene más de un polo norte y un polo sur.
    (2) al cortar por la mitad una barra imantada, resultan dos barras imantadas más débiles.
    (3) al cortar por la mitad una barra imantada, resultan dos barras imantadas más cortas.
    (4) al cortar por la mitad una barra imantada, se duplica la fuerza magnética original.

(5) para producir dos barras imantadas, una barra imantada más grande debe cortarse exactamente por la mitad.

La *Pregunta 30* se basa en el siguiente diagrama.

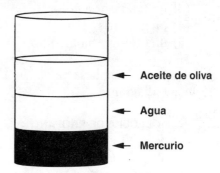

30. En base al diagrama, se puede deducir que la densidad del agua
    A. es menor que la densidad del aceite de oliva.
    B. es menor que la densidad del mercurio.
    C. es mayor que la densidad del hielo.
    D. es mayor que la densidad del aceite de oliva.

    (1) A y B
    (2) B
    (3) B y D
    (4) C y D
    (5) D

La *Pregunta 31* se basa en el siguiente diagrama.

REFRACCIÓN DE LA LUZ BLANCA A TRAVÉS DE UN PRISMA DE VIDRIO

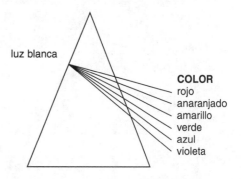

31. ¿Cuál es la mejor evidencia de que la luz del sol es una forma de luz blanca (luz que se percibe blanca pero que en realidad se compone de varios colores)?

(1) un cielo azul y límpido
(2) la luz blanca de la luna
(3) un televisor a color
(4) un arco iris
(5) una fotografía a color

La *Pregunta 32* se basa en el siguiente diagrama.

MOLÉCULA DE PROPANO

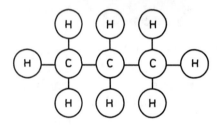

32. El diagrama ilustra la estructura molecular del propano. Cada H representa un átomo de hidrógeno y cada C representa un átomo de carbono. La fórmula de la molécula de propano se escribe:

(1) 3C8H
(2) $3C_8H$
(3) C_3H_8
(4) C_8H_3
(5) C_8H_8

La *Pregunta 33* se basa en el siguiente diagrama.

ARCO REFLEJO SIMPLE

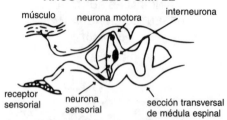

33. En un acto reflejo, como el retirar la mano del fuego, el cerebro no participa inmediatamente. El impulso nervioso que controla esta reacción tiene lugar en un arco reflejo simple, tal como se ilustra en el diagrama. En un arco reflejo simple, la interneurona

(1) inicia el impulso nervioso en el receptor sensorial.
(2) transmite el impulso nervioso a una neurona motora.
(3) transmite el impulso nervioso al cerebro.
(4) transmite el impulso nervioso a la médula espinal.
(5) transmite el impulso nervioso a los músculos, que enseguida reaccionan.

Las respuestas comienzan en la página 487.

PRUEBA POSTERIOR 4: ARTE Y LITERATURA

Instrucciones: La Prueba Posterior de Arte y Literatura consta de 23 preguntas de opción múltiple. Las preguntas se basan en fragmentos de prosa (ficción y no ficción), poesía, teatro, ensayo, discursos y críticas de arte y literatura. Elija la mejor respuesta a cada una de las preguntas que siguen.

Le llevará aproximadamente 33 minutos contestar las preguntas de la prueba. Si, al cabo de los 33 minutos no ha terminado, deténgase y señale hasta dónde ha llegado; luego, termine la prueba y rellene la Tabla de Evaluación para analizar su rendimiento.

PRUEBA POSTERIOR 4: TABLA DE RESPUESTAS DE ARTE Y LITERATURA

1 ① ② ③ ④ ⑤	7 ① ② ③ ④ ⑤	13 ① ② ③ ④ ⑤	19 ① ② ③ ④ ⑤
2 ① ② ③ ④ ⑤	8 ① ② ③ ④ ⑤	14 ① ② ③ ④ ⑤	20 ① ② ③ ④ ⑤
3 ① ② ③ ④ ⑤	9 ① ② ③ ④ ⑤	15 ① ② ③ ④ ⑤	21 ① ② ③ ④ ⑤
4 ① ② ③ ④ ⑤	10 ① ② ③ ④ ⑤	16 ① ② ③ ④ ⑤	22 ① ② ③ ④ ⑤
5 ① ② ③ ④ ⑤	11 ① ② ③ ④ ⑤	17 ① ② ③ ④ ⑤	23 ① ② ③ ④ ⑤
6 ① ② ③ ④ ⑤	12 ① ② ③ ④ ⑤	18 ① ② ③ ④ ⑤	

1. La poetisa Maya Angelou escribió que entre los afroestadounidenses del Sur rural, "La edad se valora más que la riqueza y la piedad religiosa tiene más valor que la belleza". Si se encuestara a los habitantes de la región, ¿cuál de los siguientes individuos, a su parecer, encabezarían la lista de personas más admiradas?
   (1) un actor ganador de un Oscar
   (2) el director de la mayor corporación del país
   (3) un líder religioso local
   (4) la persona más rica del país
   (5) la ganadora de un concurso de belleza del estado

Las *Preguntas 2–5* se basan en el siguiente fragmento extraído de un artículo.

¿TIENE ELLA FUTURO EN EL BÉISBOL?

"Voy a ser la primera mujer que juegue en las grandes ligas". Quien lo dice es mi hija Casey de 10 años.
5 Ella está convencida de que va a ser la futura primera base de los Red Sox: "Si una mujer tiene la misma capacidad atlética que un hombre,
10 ¿por qué no puede jugar en las grandes ligas?" Mucho ha cambiado en los últimos 14 años.

Madre e hija nos sen-
15 tamos en las gradas. Ha habido cientos de escritoras deportivas desde que estoy en Boston. Quisiera poder decir que Casey y yo
20 hablamos de estadísticas de béisbol, pero la verdad es que su padre, un estudioso de la historia de los Red Sox, es quien le ha contagiado su
25 amor por este juego. Aunque sólo tiene 10 años, la niña comprende todos los meca-nismos: ella posee un don especial para analizar a cada
30 uno de los jugadores y evaluar sus capacidades así como el oscurecido destino de su querido equipo de béisbol.

Casey hace comentarios
35 sobre el equipo que tenían los Red Sox en 1993 y tiene una opinión formada acerca del talento de Iván Calderón, Roger Clemens y Frank Viola.
40 Su habitación está repleta de tarjetas de béisbol. Durante las prácticas de bateo de los entrenamientos de primavera, los jóvenes fanáticos, como
45 siempre, tratan de poner las pelotas de béisbol delante de los peloteros, para que se las firmen: "¡Sr. Clemens!" "¡Sr. Calderón!" "Sr. Dawson, por
50 favoooor". Yo me quedo mirando a la muchedumbre de niños: la mitad son niñas. Esto es algo nuevo. En uno de los juegos contra los Minne-
55 sota Twins, noté que el "bat boy" era mujer.

—MARIE BRENNE: "Las chicas del verano", *New York Times,* 5 de abril de 1993. (Fragmento)

2. Casey, la niña de diez años, quiere ser
   (1) escritora deportiva.
   (2) locutora deportiva.
   (3) historiadora de béisbol.
   (4) bateadora.
   (5) primera base.

3. El tema principal del fragmento es
   (1) el creciente número de mujeres que se interesan por los deportes profesionales.
   (2) el de un padre que contagió a su hija su interés por los deportes.
   (3) el de la hija de una escritora deportiva que comparte su amor por los deportes.

(4) la gran asistencia de niñas en los juegos de los Red Sox.

(5) la campaña que están realizando las grandes ligas de béisbol para atraer a las mujeres a la cancha.

4. La finalidad de la última oración es

(1) hacer que el artículo sea más interesante dando detalles específicos.

(2) probar que el equipo no discrimina a las mujeres.

(3) dar un ejemplo de cómo los Red Sox se están preparando para el futuro.

(4) apoyar la idea de que las mujeres están desempeñando un papel más activo en el béisbol de las grandes ligas.

(5) convencer a las niñas a participar en las grandes ligas de béisbol.

5. ¿Cuál de estas afirmaciones habría hecho más probablemente la autora del fragmento?

(1) "Los diamantes de béisbol son los mejores amigos de la mujer".

(2) "Es un mundo de hombres".

(3) "Cuanto más cambian las cosas, tanto más permanecen iguales".

(4) "Todo lo que el hombre puede hacer, la mujer lo puede hacer mejor".

(5) "Las niñas no tienen los mismos intereses que los niños".

Las *Preguntas 6–8* se basan en el siguiente fragmento de un cuerto corto.

¿QUIÉN ESTÁ ESCUCHANDO?

En la sala de estar, el reloj-voz cantaba, ¡Din-din-don, las siete son, qué dormilón, qué dormilón, las
5 siete son! Como si temiera que nadie se levantara de la cama. Era de mañana temprano y la casa estaba desierta; el reloj repetía su
10 incesante cantinela y la lanzaba al vacío. ¡Las siete y diez están por dar, vayan pronto a desayunar, las siete y diez están por dar!

15 En la cocina, el horno-desayuno siseaba con un silbido y expulsaba de sus calientes entrañas ocho trozos de pan perfectamente
20 tostado, ocho huevos y dieciséis lonchas de tocino, dos cafés y dos vasos de leche fría.

"Hoy estamos a 4 de
25 agosto de 2026", dijo una segunda voz proveniente del techo de la cocina, "en la ciudad de Allendale, California"; y repitió la fecha tres
30 veces para que todos la recordaran. "Hoy es el cumpleaños del Sr. Featherstone. Hoy es el aniversario de bodas de Tilita. Hay que
35 pagar el seguro y los recibos del agua, el gas y la luz".

En alguna parte de las paredes, los relés hacían clic, las cintas de memoria se
40 deslizaban bajo células foto-eléctricas.

"¡Las ocho y dos van a ser, a la escuela, al trabajo, a correr, las ocho y dos van a
45 ser!" Pero no se oían portazos ni trajín de zapatos que dejaban su huella en la alfombra. Llovía. La caja del tiempo ubicada en la puerta
50 de entrada cantaba con tranquilidad: "Llueve que te llueve, deja de llover; imper-meable y botas te has de poner. . ." Y el golpear de la
55 lluvia se oía en la casa vacía; y resonaba.

Afuera, el garaje dejaba oír su timbre y abría la puerta para presentar el auto que ya
60 estaba esperando. Tras una larga espera, la puerta volvió a cerrarse.

A las ocho y media, los huevos estaban secos y las
65 tostadas duras como piedra. Una espátula de aluminio los depositó en el fregadero de la cocina, donde un chorro de agua caliente los arrastró
70 hacia abajo, haciendo un remolino por una garganta de metal que los asimiló y envió hacia el mar distante. Los platos sucios se sumergieron
75 en un lavaplatos caliente y volvieron a emerger secos, pulidos y relucientes.

—RAY BRADBURY: *Vendrán lluvias tenues,* 1950. (Fragmento)

6. ¿Cómo están organizados los datos en este pasaje?
   (1) por orden de importancia (de los detalles menos significativos a los más significativos)
   (2) por medio de escenas retrospectivas (sucesos del pasado que alternan con sucesos actuales)
   (3) de lo general a lo específico (exposición general seguida por detalles específicos)
   (4) por orden cronológico (sucesos que se presentan en el orden en que se dieron en la realidad)
   (5) con tema central y ejemplos (idea principal ilustrada con ejemplos específicos)

7. Según la información que presenta el relato, se puede decir que la familia
   (1) disfrutaba haciendo los quehaceres de la casa.
   (2) disfrutaba preparando el desayuno todos juntos.
   (3) opinaba que era importante estar bien organizados.
   (4) prefería que no le dijeran lo que tenía que hacer.
   (5) no tenía trabajo ni dinero.

8. ¿Cuál de estos programas (ficticios) de televisión incluiría más probablemente un episodio basado en el pasaje?
   (1) "Relatos de Ciencia Ficción", que presenta narraciones dramáticas que tratan de la interacción humana con la tecnología del futuro
   (2) "La Casa Modelo", que presenta a posibles compradores de casas equipads con la cantidad mínima de artefactos para el hogar
   (3) "El Mañana es Hoy", que presenta documentales sobre las innovaciones tecnológicas que están inundando al país
   (4) "Escaparate de Comedias", que se especializa en parodias divertidas sobre temas de actualidad
   (5) "Dime Cómo", que presenta nuevos inventos y explica a los niños cómo funcionan y quién los creó

Las *Preguntas 9–11* se basan en el siguiente fragmento extraído de un relato corto.

¿ES ÉL EL PREFERIDO DE LA MADRE?

La vida era extremadamente difícil para los Whipple. Difícil era alimentar tantas bocas hambrientas;

difícil vestir a todos los hijos para que estuvieran bien abrigados durante el, si bien corto, invierno: "Sólo Dios sabe qué sería de nosotros si viviéramos más al norte", decían; difícil era mantenerlos limpios. "Parece que nuestra suerte no va a cambiar nunca", dijo el Sr. Whipple; pero la Sra. Whipple estaba decidida a aceptar lo que fuera y a considerarlo como bueno, sobre todo cuando los vecinos podían escuchar. "No tenemos que dejar nunca que alguien nos oiga quejarnos", decía a su esposo. No podía soportar el que alguien les tuviera lástima. "No, aunque tengamos que vivir en un vagón y recoger algodón por todo el país", decía, "no voy a dar pie a que nadie sienta lástima por nosotros".

La Sra. Whipple quería a su segundo hijo, el enfermo, más de lo que quería a sus otros dos hijos juntos. Ella siempre lo decía; y, cuando hablaba con algunos vecinos, también mencionaba a su marido y a su madre para dar mayor énfasis.

"No es necesario que lo digas a los cuatro vientos", decía el Sr. Whipple; "vas a hacer que la gente piense que no hay nadie más que lo quiera a Él".

"Es algo natural para una madre", le recordaba la Sra. Whipple. "Sabes muy bien que es muy natural que una madre sea así. En cierto modo, la gente no espera mucho de los padres".

Esto no impedía que los vecinos hablaran abiertamente entre ellos. "Si Él se muere, sería por pura misericordia del Señor", decían ellos. "Son los pecados de los padres", concordaban todos. "En algún lugar ha de haber mala sangre y malos actos; de eso pueden estar seguros". Esto lo comentaban a espaldas de los Whipples. Delante de ellos, todos decían, "Él no está tan mal. Puede que se ponga bien. ¡Mira cómo crece!"

La Sra. Whipple detestaba hablar sobre este tema y trataba de no pensar en el asunto; pero, cada vez que alguien ponía un pie en la casa, la persona siempre sacaba a colación el tema y ella tenía que hablar sobre Él primero, antes de poder hablar de cualquier otra cosa. Parecía como que esto la tranquilizaba. "No dejaría que a Él le sucediera nada por nada del mundo; pero parece que no puedo evitar que se haga daño. Él es fuerte y activo y siempre está interesado en todo: era así desde que empezó a andar. A veces me sorprende la capacidad que tiene para hacer cualquier cosa; es muy divertido verlo a Él hacer sus trucos".

—KATHERINE ANNE PORTER: "Él", 1935. (Fragmento)

9. ¿Cuál de las siguientes frases describe mejor a la familia Whipple?
   (1) pobre y luchadora
   (2) aislada y temida
   (3) popular y admirada
   (4) arrogante y presuntuosa
   (5) abierta y honesta

10. ¿Cuál es el temor de la Sra. Whipple?

(1) tener que convertirse en trabajadora agrícola migratoria para ganarse la vida

(2) que los problemas de su segundo hijo sean un castigo de Dios por haber pecado

(3) que su marido y sus hijos piensen que ella no los quiere

(4) que su familia esté enfadada con ella por quejarse demasiado

(5) que los vecinos la menosprecien a ella y a su familia

11. Imagínese que tiene planeado hacer una película en base a ese fragmento. ¿Cuál de los siguientes lugares sería el mejor ambiente para el relato?

(1) un barrio urbano de altos edificios de apartamentos

(2) una exclusiva comunidad vacacional en las montañas

(3) una zona residencial de trabajadores *white-collar* de una gran metrópoli del este del país

(4) un pueblo para jubilados a orillas del mar en la costa oeste del país

(5) un pueblecito del campo en el Sur del país

Las *Preguntas 12–14* se basan en el siguiente poema.

¿DISFRUTARON LOS EX-COMPAÑEROS DE LA REUNIÓN?

25ª reunión de ex-alumnos de la secundaria

Venimos a escuchar el final
de todas las historias
en nuestra antología
de largadas en falso:
5 cómo la chica que parecía

dura como una roca
fue finalmente moldeada;
cómo a los atletas se les
acabaron las carreras;
10 cómo debajo de la piel
nuestros cráneos emergieron
a la superficie
igual que las rocas del lecho
de un río que empieza a
15   secarse.
¡Mira! Todos
hemos llegado a ser
nosotros mismos.

—LINDA PASTAN: 1978

12. Según la voz que narra el poema, los ex-compañeros de secundaria asistieron a la 25ª reunión de ex-alumnos para

(1) ver qué aspecto tenían todos ahora.

(2) enterarse de cómo había cambiado la vida de los demás.

(3) recordar tiempos pasados en la escuela.

(4) homenajear a aquéllos que habían sido las estrellas de la escuela en atletismo.

(5) ver cuánto habían envejecido todos.

13. ¿Qué quiere decir la comparación "debajo de la piel / nuestros cráneos emergieron / a la superficie / igual que las rocas del lecho / de un río que empieza a secarse" (versos 10–14)?

(1) Las características faciales de los ex-compañeros son más marcadas y angulosas al igual que las rocas que se pueden ver en un río.

(2) Las rocas que están debajo de la superficie de un río se hacen visibles cuando el cauce se seca.

(3) De la misma forma en que las rocas se hacen más visibles cuando un río comienza a secarse, los cráneos de los antiguos compañeros se han hecho más prominentes con la edad.

(4) Los estudiantes que antes eran jóvenes son ahora tan viejos y marchitos como un río que se está quedando sin agua.

(5) La forma en que el sol ha secado la piel de los antiguos compañeros es semejante a la manera en que el sol seca las rocas de un río.

14. El lenguaje del poema es más bien

(1) florido y poético.
(2) complejo y oscuro.
(3) formal y erudito.
(4) inusual y original.
(5) sencillo y coloquial.

Las *Preguntas 15–17* se basan en el siguiente fragmento extraído de una obra de teatro.

¿COMPARTEN MADRE E HIJO EL SUEÑO NORTEAMERICANO?

DOLORES: No estaré tranquila hasta que vuelva a mi casa.
JAVIER: [*Cruzando frente a la silla.*] Ay, mamá. . .
5 DOLORES: ¿Pero qué te pasa? El primer cielo que viste fue cielo puertorriqueño. La primera vez que bebiste agua fue agua puertorriqueña. Pero
10 tú no te acuerdas. ¡Eras un bebé! Pero yo sí me acuerdo. Hijo, yo quiero ver a las gallinas cruzar por delante de mi patio todo el año. Quiero
15 oír a todas las personas hablar mi idioma, incluso a los niñitos. El español es tan bello cuando lo hablan los niños. Yo dejé todo lo que era
20 importante para mí cuando salí de Puerto Rico.

JAVIER: ¿Y ésta nunca ha sido tu casa?
DOLORES: Nunca. Este lugar
25 jamás ha sido bueno para ninguno de nosotros.
JAVIER: Ha sido bueno para mí. Creo que aquí podré llegar a ser algiuen. [*Cruza*
30 *hasta donde está Dolores y le toma de la mano.*]
DOLORES: No lo dudo ni por un momento. Pero Ramón no es igual que tú.
35 JAVIER: ¿Es por eso que no puedes aceptar que ésta sea tu casa?
DOLORES: [*Cruza hasta su altar.*] Esta "casa" se llevó a
40 mi niña. . .
JAVIER: Mamá, tienes que aceptar lo que sucedió. Tienes que enterrarla. No puedes culpar a esta casa de. . .
45 DOLORES: ¡Sí puedo!
JAVIER: Podría haber sucedido lo mismo allá. Ella también se habría muerto allá. . .
DOLORES: ¡Ella vivió aquí
50 sólo seis días! ¡Esta casa fría acabó con ella!
JAVIER: Ella nació enfermiza, mamá; le hubiera podido ocurrir cualquier. . .
55 DOLORES: Ella era fuerte. Yo podía sentir lo fuerte que era. Podía sentirlo en sus manos. Podía verlo en su cara rellena y sonrosada. Lo podía oír
60 cuando lloraba. [*Conteniendo las lágrimas.*] Yo cuidaba de ella. Yo la abrigaba. La estrechaba contra mí para protegerla del aire frío de esta
65 casa de la muerte. Seis días estuvo Ramón, tratando de hacer funcionar la calefacción, pero nunca funcionaba. Un día, mientras yo hacía el
70 café, cuando Ramón estaba en el trabajo, ella se murió. Yo. . . me quedé de pie frente a la ventana un día entero,

mirando hacia Puerto Rico. Y,
75 pobre Ramón, casi se vuelve
loco. [*Ella empieza a llorar
amargamente.*]
JAVIER: Mamá, por favor.

—JOSÉ RIVERA: *La casa de Ramón
Iglesia,* 1983. (Fragmento)

15. Según el fragmento, en Dolores
se está librando un conflicto
interno, o una lucha psicológica,
cuyo motivo es
    (1) la actitud negativa que tiene
su hijo hacia la nueva casa.
    (2) la dificultad de hablar
español en una comunidad
de habla inglesa.
    (3) la diferencia entre la vida en
Puerto Rico y la vida en los
Estados Unidos.
    (4) la incapacidad de su marido,
Ramón, para encontrar un
trabajo que tenga futuro.
    (5) el haberse mudado la familia
a una granja avícola en una
comunidad hispana.

16. Lea las acotaciones que corresponden al personaje Javier en
las líneas 3–4 y en las líneas
29–31. Las acciones que realiza
el personaje así como
su conversación con Dolores
revelan que él
    (1) está muy nervioso.
    (2) está a punto de explotar.
    (3) es una persona rígida.
    (4) es un chico tímido.
    (5) es un joven comprensivo.

17. ¿Cómo se siente Javier con
relación a su futuro?
    (1) esperanzado
    (2) preocupado
    (3) deprimido
    (4) disgustado
    (5) confundido

Las *Preguntas 18–20* se basan en el
siguiente fragmento de la crítica de
una obra teatral.

¿DE QUÉ TRATA LA OBRA?

Hace más de cincuenta
años, estalló en Munich una
lucha que, infelizmente, se
podría aplicar a nuestra
5 actualidad: cinco valientes
estudiantes universitarios
publicaron y distribuyeron
por toda Alemania y Austria
unos panfletos anónimos
10 antinazistas titulados "La
Rosa Blanca". Esta campaña
propagandística era un acto
público poco común que
desafiaba al temible Tercer
15 Reich. El 22 de febrero de
1943, los defensores de la
libertad de la Rosa Blanca
fueron arrestados por la
Gestapo y sometidos de
20 inmediato a juicio sumario
por alta traición, sin poder
contar con la defensa de un
jurado, la presencia de la
prensa o la oportunidad de
25 apelación. El castigo era
tristemente previsible.

"La Rosa Blanca", escrita
por Lillian Garrett-Groag,
rinde homenaje a estos
30 jóvenes idealistas y es una
crónica del conflicto moral
que sufre el oficial de
seguridad que tiene que
decidir acerca del destino de
35 estos jóvenes. La obra está
inspirada en parte en la
experiencia vivida por el
padre de la autora, un
austríaco que tuvo que
40 abandonar Viena en 1938
huyendo de la ascensión nazi
al poder.

—LAWRENCE BOMMER: "La Rosa
Blanca es una celebración de los
héroes antinazis", *Chicago
Tribune,* 5 de marzo de 1993.
(Fragmento)

18. Según el fragmento, para escribir "La Rosa Blanca", la autora se inspiró en
(1) su arresto por la Gestapo en la Alemania nazi.
(2) sus experiencias en Munich como periodista durante la Segunda Guerra Mundial.
(3) la experiencia de su padre, que tuvo que huir de los nazis en Viena.
(4) la amistad que tenía con los artistas antinazis en Berlín.
(5) su participación en el juicio contra los defensores de la libertad en Austria.

19. ¿A cuál de los siguientes aconte-cimientos de décadas recientes se parece la situación central de la obra?
(1) La ejecución por parte del gobierno chino de los jóvenes que protestaron en la Plaza Tiananmen pidiendo reformas gubernamentales
(2) La desmembración de la Unión de Repúblicas Socialistas Soviéticas (U.R.S.S.) tras el colapso del gobierno comunista
(3) La misión de las Naciones Unidas de auxilio a Somalia para mantener el orden y distribuir alimentos y medicinas
(4) El conflicto entre habitantes de diferentes grupos étnicos en el antiguo estado comunista de Yugoslavia
(5) El juicio y puesta en libertad en Israel de "Iván el Terrible", obrero jubilado de una fábrica automotriz que fuera acusado de asesinar a prisioneros de un campo de concentración nazi

20. El estilo del crítico de la obra se caracteriza por
(1) el uso de modismos y otras modalidades del lenguaje coloquial.
(2) la ausencia de descripciones y adjetivos vívidos.
(3) su tono amargo y negativo.
(4) el uso de oraciones largas y claras.
(5) la abundancia de juegos de palabras.

Las *Preguntas 21–23* se basan en el siguiente fragmento extraído de la crítica de un libro.

¿DE QUÉ TRATA EL LIBRO *EN MI LUGAR*?

[Charlayne] Hunter-Gault, conocida corresponsal de televisión en la actualidad, fue una de dos estudiantes
5 negros cuyo ingreso en la Universidad de Georgia en 1961—seguido con gran atención por los medios de comunicación nacionales y
10 acompañado de airadas protestas a nivel local—puso término a la segregación racial en esa institución. Sin embargo, en su autobiografía
15 lúcida y circunspecta, se interesa menos por ese triunfo de los derechos civiles que por el hecho de haberse criado dentro de una distin-
20 guida dinastía de predicadores en una comunidad minori-taria que se podría decir autosuficiente.
Los Hunter no eran
25 pobres—el padre era cape-llán del ejército—; y los en-frentamientos desagradables con vecinos blancos o bien le fueron totalmente descono-
30 cidos o se han omitido. El lanzamiento de ladrillos con que se recibió a la autora al

llegar a la universidad se describe sin rencor, de la misma forma que su compromiso con la causa de los derechos civiles se describe sin acaloramiento. El libro nos habla de las escuelas segregadas (equipos deficientes, maestros dedicados), las visitas a los parientes que vivían en el campo y sus mesas espléndidas, los vestidos del baile de graduación, y la temprana afición de la Sra. Hunter-Gault al periodismo a través de las tiras cómicas de Brenda Starr. Gran parte de estos afables recuerdos—entre los que se menciona una clase de economía doméstica en la que la autora aprendió a "hacer salsa blanca"—corren paralelos a la experiencia que tuvo con el mundo blanco. Puede que la implicación de una similitud haya sido precisamente la intención de la Sra. Hunter-Gault. Sólo al final del último capítulo del libro, que transcribe el discurso que pronunció frente a la promoción de egresados de la Universidad de Georgia en 1988, ella habla sin rodeos de la necesidad de "reconocer los principios rectores de la fundamental decencia humana y de vivir conforme a los mismos" en un "mundo expectante y necesitado".

—Crítica de *En mi lugar, The Atlantic,* diciembre de 1992.
(Fragmento)

21. Hunter-Gault describiría su niñez como
(**1**) feliz.
(**2**) violenta.
(**3**) insegura.
(**4**) trágica.
(**5**) solitaria.

22. Gran parte de la crítica se concentra en
(**1**) persuadir a los lectores de que el libro de Hunter-Gault está mal escrito.
(**2**) hacer sugerencias sobre cómo se podría mejorar el libro.
(**3**) señalar y corregir los errores objetivos que presenta el libro.
(**4**) ofrecer una visión general del contenido del libro.
(**5**) proporcionar un resumen de la carrera televisiva de Hunter-Gault.

24. Según la crítica, el libro de Hunter-Gault consiste principalmente en
(**1**) impresiones sobre su infancia y juventud dentro de su familia y su comunidad.
(**2**) una explicación de cómo se desarrolló el movimiento de los derechos civiles en Estados Unidos.
(**3**) recuerdos de actos racistas cometidos por los blancos de su vecindario.
(**4**) una descripción de las profundas diferencias entre negros y blancos según sus vivencias.
(**5**) una descripción de su vida como la primera locutora de televisión afroestadounidense.

Las respuestas comienzan en la página 490.

PRUEBA POSTERIOR 5: MATEMÁTICAS

Instrucciones: La Prueba Posterior de Matemáticas consta de 28 preguntas de opción múltiple y le llevará aproximadamente 45 minutos contestar las preguntas de la prueba. Si, al cabo de los 45 minutos no ha terminado, deténgase y señale hasta dónde ha llegado; luego, termine la prueba y rellene la Tabla de Evaluación para analizar su rendimiento.

En la página 28 encontrará fórmulas útiles para la resolución de algunos de los problemas.

PRUEBA POSTERIOR 5: TABLA DE RESPUESTAS DE MATEMÁTICAS

1 ① ② ③ ④ ⑤	8 ① ② ③ ④ ⑤	15 ① ② ③ ④ ⑤	22 ① ② ③ ④ ⑤
2 ① ② ③ ④ ⑤	9 ① ② ③ ④ ⑤	16 ① ② ③ ④ ⑤	23 ① ② ③ ④ ⑤
3 ① ② ③ ④ ⑤	10 ① ② ③ ④ ⑤	17 ① ② ③ ④ ⑤	24 ① ② ③ ④ ⑤
4 ① ② ③ ④ ⑤	11 ① ② ③ ④ ⑤	18 ① ② ③ ④ ⑤	25 ① ② ③ ④ ⑤
5 ① ② ③ ④ ⑤	12 ① ② ③ ④ ⑤	19 ① ② ③ ④ ⑤	26 ① ② ③ ④ ⑤
6 ① ② ③ ④ ⑤	13 ① ② ③ ④ ⑤	20 ① ② ③ ④ ⑤	27 ① ② ③ ④ ⑤
7 ① ② ③ ④ ⑤	14 ① ② ③ ④ ⑤	21 ① ② ③ ④ ⑤	28 ① ② ③ ④ ⑤

1. Suponiendo que no haya desperdicios, ¿cuántas tablas de $1\frac{1}{2}$ pies de largo se pueden cortar de un tablero de 12 pies de largo?
   (1) 6
   (2) 8
   (3) 9
   (4) 15
   (5) 18

2. Los cuatro miembros de la familia Rodríguez compraron un boleto cada uno para el festival de música. Se vendió un total de 360 boletos. Si se sortean los boletos, ¿cuál es la probabilidad de que gane uno de los miembros de la familia Rodríguez?
   (1) $\frac{1}{200}$
   (2) $\frac{1}{100}$
   (3) $\frac{1}{90}$
   (4) $\frac{1}{36}$
   (5) $\frac{1}{4}$

3. Si $3m + 6 = 30$, ¿cuál es el valor de m?
   (1) 4
   (2) 6
   (3) 8
   (4) 10
   (5) 12

La *Pregunta 4* se basa en los siguientes datos.

Una camisa para hombre vale $30 en un catálogo. A continuación se ofrece una lista con el precio que la misma camisa tiene en varias tiendas.

Clyde's Clothes	$24
Sam's Supply	$32
Florence's Fashion	$33
Dave's Duds	$27
Alma's Apparel	$35

4. ¿En qué tienda se vende la camisa a un precio 10% menor que el precio del catálogo?
   (1) Clyde's Clothes
   (2) Sam's Supply
   (3) Florence's Fashion
   (4) Dave's Duds
   (5) Alma's Apparel

5. ¿Cuál es el valor de $20^2 + 2^3$?
   (1) 46
   (2) 48
   (3) 392
   (4) 408
   (5) 484

6. ¿Cuál es la razón entre el ancho y el alto de la puerta diagramada abajo?

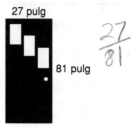

27 pulg

81 pulg

   (1) 2:3
   (2) 1:2
   (3) 1:3
   (4) 2:7
   (5) 1:8

La *Pregunta 7* se basa en el gráfico siguiente, que ilustra la distribución de la población de EE.UU. en las cuatro regiones principales de los Estados Unidos continentales.

DISTRIBUCIÓN DE LA POBLACIÓN DE EE.UU.

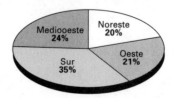

Medioeste 24%
Noreste 20%
Oeste 21%
Sur 35%

7. ¿Qué fracción de la población vive en el Sur?
   (1) $\frac{1}{5}$
   (2) $\frac{1}{4}$
   (3) $\frac{1}{3}$
   (4) $\frac{7}{20}$
   (5) $\frac{13}{20}$

8. Ordene los paquetes que se ilustran abajo de más ligero a más pesado.

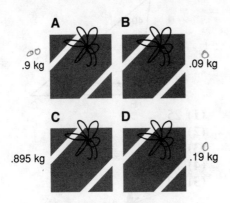

A
.9 kg

B
.09 kg

C
.895 kg

D
.19 kg

(1) A, D, C, B
(2) D, B, C, A
(3) B, D, C, A
(4) A, B, D, C
(5) B, A, C, D

La *Pregunta 9* se basa en la siguiente figura.

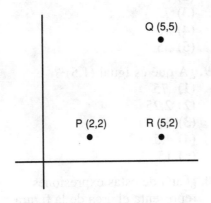

Q (5,5)

P (2,2)   R (5,2)

9. ¿Cuál es la distancia entre P y Q?
(1) 3
(2) $\sqrt{3^2 + 3^2}$
(3) 5
(4) 3^2
(5) 5^2

10. En la figura de abajo se ilustra el plano de una piscina. ¿Cuál de estas medidas se aproxima más en pies al perímetro de la piscina?

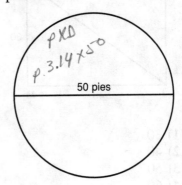

P X D
P. 3.14 x 50

50 pies

(1) 1.57
(2) 15.7
(3) 157
(4) 314
(5) 1963

La *Pregunta 11* se basa en los siguientes datos.

Los Martínez compraron una casa por $80,000 e hicieron un pago inicial de $12,000. Tendrán que pagar $420 al mes de hipoteca y $700 al año en impuestos a la propiedad.

80,000 100%
12,000 x
18%

11. ¿Qué porcentaje del costo total de la casa representa el pago inicial?
(1) 9
(2) 10
(3) 12
(4) 15
(5) 20

12. Un equipo de trabajadores puede ensamblar 15 piezas de máquina en dos horas. ¿Cuántas piezas puede ensamblar en una semana de 40 horas?
(1) 180
(2) 200
(3) 240
(4) 300
(5) 360

13. ¿Cuánto mide la diagonal *JL* del rectángulo de abajo?

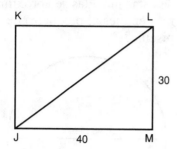

(1) 30
(2) 40
(3) 50
(4) 60
(5) 70

14. ¿Cuál de estas expresiones representa el volumen en pulgadas cúbicas de este paralelepípedo?

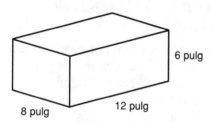

(1) 12 × 8
(2) 12 + 8
(3) 12 × 8 × 6
(4) 2(12 + 8)
(5) 6(8 + 12)

15. Si $12a - 5 = 4a + 11$, entonces $a =$

(1) 2
(2) 3
(3) 5
(4) 8
(5) 12

16. La expresión $3a - 12$ es igual a

(1) $3(a - 4)$
(2) $3(a - 12)$
(3) $12(a - 3)$
(4) $3(4a)$
(5) $3a(12)$

17. Halle la medida en grados del ∠ C del triángulo representado abajo.

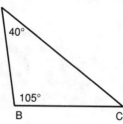

(1) 25
(2) 35
(3) 60
(4) 70
(5) 90

La *Pregunta 18* se basa en la siguiente recta numérica.

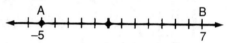

18. ¿Por cuántas unidades están separados los puntos A y B?

(1) 2
(2) 5
(3) 7
(4) 12
(5) 35

19. ¿A qué es igual $(1.5)^2$?

(1) .75
(2) 2.25
(3) 3
(4) 4.5
(5) 15

20. ¿Cuál de estas expresiones representa el área de la figura siguiente?

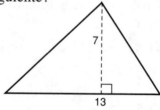

(1) $2 \times 13 \times 7$
(2) 13×7
(3) $2(13) + 2(7)$
(4) $\frac{1}{2}(13 + 7)$
(5) $\frac{1}{2} \times 13 \times 7$

21. Gregorio condujo durante tres horas a una velocidad media de 55 mph y después condujo otras dos horas a 40 mph. ¿Cuál de las expresiones siguientes representa la distancia total recorrida?
(1) 5×45
(2) 5×95
(3) $55 \times 3 + 2$
(4) $55 \times 3 + 40 \times 2$
(5) $\frac{55+40}{5}$

22. En la figura de abajo, $QR = 120$. ¿Cuál es la longitud de PQ?

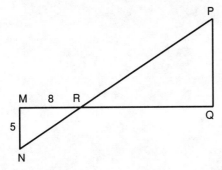

(1) 15
(2) 24
(3) 64
(4) 75
(5) 100

23. Halle la pendiente de la recta que pasa por los dos puntos indicados en el gráfico de abajo.

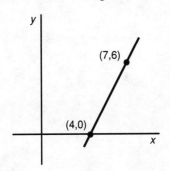

(1) 2
(2) 3
(3) 4
(4) 6
(5) 7

La *Pregunta 24* se basa en el siguiente diagrama.

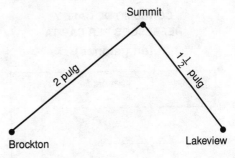

Escala: 1 pulg = 12 mi

24. ¿Cuál es la distancia en millas de Brockton a Lakeview pasando por Summit?
(1) 18
(2) 24
(3) 30
(4) 36
(5) 42

25. Maxine tiene 20 años más que su hija Pilar. Sea y la edad de Maxine. ¿Qué ecuación expresa la suma de las edades de Maxine y de su hija si la suma de ambas es igual a 58?
(1) $y + 20 = 58$
(2) $y - 20 = 58$
(3) $2y - 20 = 58$
(4) $20y = 58$
(5) $\frac{y}{20} = 58$

La *Pregunta 26* se basa en el siguiente gráfico.

CONSUMO DE CAFÉ Y REFRESCOS PER CÁPITA

(en galones)

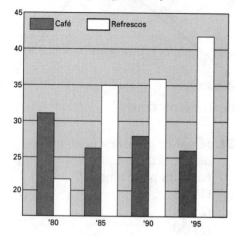

26. ¿En cuántos galones aproximadamente aumentó el consumo anual de refrescos de 1980 a 1995?
(**1**) 5
(**2**) 10
(**3**) 15
(**4**) 20
(**5**) 25

27. En un año reciente, el gobierno de EE.UU. recibió $98,000,000,000 en impuestos a la renta de corporaciones. ¿Cuál de estas expresiones representa ese número en notación científica?
(**1**) 98×10^6
(**2**) 9.8×10^6
(**3**) 9.8×10^8
(**4**) 9.8×10^{10}
(**5**) 9.8×10^{12}

28. Si el pie lineal cuesta $.90, ¿cuál sería el precio de una tabla de 78 pulgadas de largo?
(**1**) $4.95
(**2**) $5.40
(**3**) $5.85
(**4**) $7.02
(**5**) $7.20

Las respuestas comienzan en la página 493.

HOJA DE COMPROBACIÓN DE APTITUD PARA EL GED

Felicitaciones por haber terminado las cinco Pruebas Posteriores, comprobado las respuestas y rellenado las Tablas de Evaluación que se adjuntan al final de cada prueba. Conviene ahora determinar si usted está preparado para el día del examen; por tanto, utilice la tabla y las instrucciones que siguen para analizar su rendimiento.

Con el número de respuestas correctas que ha obtenido podrá estimar lo que se da en llamar su puntuación estándar. Los resultados de todos los que se han examinado para el GED se indican en *puntuación estándar*, razón por la cual es importante comparar su puntuación con la norma.

Prueba	Respuestas correctas	Puntuaciones estándar									Puntuación estándar	Puntuación requerida
		25	30	35	40	45	50	55	60	65		
Expresión Escrita	← Vea la evaluación de la página 431 y luego consulte la *Nota importante* de la página 428 en lo que se refiere a su puntuación final. →											
Estudios Sociales		6	8	10	14	18	22	25	28	29		___ / ___
Ciencias		7	8	10	14	18	22	25	27	29		___ / ___
Arte y Literatura		4	5	8	10	13	16	18	19	20		___ / ___
Matemáticas		6	7	9	12	16	20	22	24	25		___ / ___

Promedio

1. **Escriba en la columna de *Respuestas correctas* el número de respuestas correctas obtenido.** Siga este paso en todas las pruebas excepto en la de Expresión Escrita. (Dado que la evaluación de las composiciones hace más complejo el proceso de puntuación, consulte las páginas 428 y 431 para determinar su aptitud para la Prueba de Expresión Escrita.)

2. **Calcule su puntuación estándar aproximada para cada prueba.** Fíjese en cada fila y busque el número que se aproxime más al número de respuestas correctas que ha obtenido. El número en negrita que encabeza la columna será su **puntuación estándar**.

Por ejemplo, Henry ha contestado correctamente 9 preguntas de la Prueba de Estudios Sociales. El número de la tabla de la fila de Estudios Sociales que más se aproxima a 9 es 10. Fíjese ahora en el número en negrita que encabeza la columna del 10: es 35, la puntuación estándar de Henry en Estudios Sociales. En Ciencias, Henry tiene 19 preguntas bien contestadas. El número de la tabla de la fila de Ciencias que más se aproxima a 19 es 18, el cual también corresponde a una puntuación estándar de 45. Este número será entonces la puntuación estándar de Henry en Ciencias. Como indica este ejemplo, se puede redondear tanto al número superior como al número inferior más cercano, dependiendo de a cuál de éstos se aproxime más.

Acto seguido, estime su puntuación estándar para las Pruebas 2–5.

3. **Compare su puntuación estándar con la puntuación requerida por su estado, provincia o territorio.** Fíjese en la puntuación mínima y en la puntuación mínima media de cada prueba. Para calcular la puntuación requerida del área en que reside, consulte la lista de la página siguiente: escriba la puntuación mínima y la puntuación mínima media de su área en la columna titulada **Puntuación requerida.**

¿Está preparado?

A continuación ofrecemos algunas indicaciones que le aconsejamos seguir para determinar si está preparado o no para examinarse en un área determinada o en todas las áreas del GED.

Si cualquiera de sus puntuaciones estándar es igual o menor que la puntuación mínima de la página 427, se recomienda que haga un repaso general antes de presentarse al Examen del GED. (En la mayoría de los casos, la puntuación mínima es 40.) Si una de sus puntuaciones es inferior a la mínima exigida (número de la izquierda), no podrá aprobar la prueba en cuestión ni obtener la puntuación media que necesita acumular en las cinco pruebas.

En este caso, use las Tablas de Evaluación que se adjuntan a continuación de cada Clave de Respuestas de las Pruebas Posteriores a fin de determinar qué áreas del libro deberá repasar.

Pero si todas sus puntuaciones exceden la mínima de la izquierda y se aproximan más a la segunda (45, en la mayoría de los casos), es probable que ya esté preparado para el Examen del GED. Algunas de sus puntuaciones puede que sean un poco más altas y otras un poco más bajas, debido a que la segunda puntuación de la tabla es un promedio.

No se olvide de considerar su rendimiento en la Prueba Posterior de Expresión Escrita antes de tomar una decisión final.

Recuerde que si se presenta al Examen del GED y no lo aprueba la primera vez, tendrá oportunidad de repasar y volver a hacer el examen en parte o en su totalidad. (Consulte las recomendaciones de la página xvii.)

Puntuaciones mínimas requeridas para la otorgación del Certificado de GED[1]

A continuación se detallan las puntuaciones mínimas exigidas para la expedición del Certificado de GED en los Estados Unidos y sus territorios y en Canadá. Cuando se indican dos números, el **primero** será la **puntuación mínima requerida para cada prueba**, y el segundo la **puntuación mínima media para las cinco pruebas del GED**.

Estados Unidos	Puntuaciones mínimas		Puntuaciones mínimas		Puntuaciones mínimas
Alabama	35 y 45	Kentucky	40 y 45	North Dakota	40 y 45
Alaska	36 Y 45	Louisiana	40 ó 45	Ohio	35 y 45
Arizona	35 Y 45	Maine	35 ó 45	Oklahoma	40 y 45
Arkansas	40 Y 45	Maryland	40 y 45	Oregon	40 y 45
California	40 y 45	Massachusetts	35 y 45	Pennsylvania	35 y 45
Colorado	40 y 45	Michigan	35 y 45	Rhode Island	35 y 45
Connecticut	35 y 45	Minnesota	35 y 45	South Carolina	35 y 45
Delaware	40 y 45	Mississippi	40 ó 45	South Dakota	40 y 45
D.C.	40 y 45	Missouri	40 y 45	Tennessee	35 y 45
Florida	40 y 45	Montana	35 y 45	Texas	40 ó 45
Georgia	35 y 45	Nebraska	40 ó 45	Utah	40 y 45
Hawaii	35 y 45	Nevada	35 y 45	Vermont	35 y 45
Idaho	40 y 45	New Hampshire	35 y 45	Virginia	35 y 45
Illinois	35 y 45	New Jersey	Ver nota 2	Washington	40 y 45
Indiana	35 y 45	New Mexico	40 ó 45	West Virginia	40 y 45
Iowa	35 y 45	New York	40 y 45	Wisconsin	40 y 45
Kansas	35 y 45	North Carolina	35 y 45	Wyoming	35 y 45

Territorios de Estados Unidos	Puntuaciones mínimas	Canadá	Puntuaciones mínimas
American Samoa	45 cada prueba	Alberta	45 cada prueba
Panama Canal Area	40 y 45	British Columbia	45 cada prueba
Guam	35 y 45	Manitoba	45 cada prueba
Kwajalein	35 y 45	New Brunswick	45 cada prueba
Northern Mariana Islands	40 ó 45	Newfoundland	40 y 45
Marshall Islands	40 ó 45	Northwest Territories	45 cada prueba
Micronesia[3]	40 ó 45	Nova Scotia	45 cada prueba
Republic of Palau	40 y 45	Ontario	45 cada prueba
Puerto Rico	35 y 45	Prince Edward Island	45 cada prueba
Virgin Islands	35 y 45	Saskatchewan	45 cada prueba
		Yukon Territory	45 cada prueba

[1] Sistema vigente desde el 1° de enero de 1997. Cada estado o territorio estadounidense así como las provincias canadienses puede que exijan puntuaciones superiores a las indicadas. Por tanto, se recomienda ponerse en contacto con su centro de pruebas a fin de verificar los requisitos de su área.

[2] Las puntuaciones mínimas en New Jersey son 42 para la Prueba 1, 40 para las Pruebas 2 a 4, y 45 para la Prueba 5, con una puntuación total de 225.

[3] Micronesia es un país independiente.

Nota importante

En la Prueba de Expresión Escrita del GED, el examinado recibirá una sola puntuación para las dos partes de la prueba. Esta puntuación compuesta conjuga las puntuaciones de la Parte 1 y la Parte 2 (redacción) de la Prueba de Expresión Escrita en en una proporción determinada por el Servicio de Pruebas del GED. Cada redacción es evaluada por dos lectores de manera holística, es decir, de forma general. Estos lectores califican la redacción en base a una escala que va de 1 (lo mínimo) a 6 (lo máximo). De esta forma, se puede aplicar a la puntuación de la Parte 1 un factor de 2 a 12 puntos. Por lo general, cada punto que se obtiene en la redacción produce una puntuación compuesta que es 2 ó 3 puntos (ó 2% a 4%) más alta.

Por ejemplo, si en la Parte 1 de la Prueba Posterior de Expresión Escrita se ha obtenido una puntuación de 18 y en la Parte 2 (redacción) una puntuación de "2" por dos lectores distintos (igual a 4 puntos), la puntuación compuesta resultante es 41. Sin embargo, si se obtiene la misma puntuación de 18 en la Parte 1 y una puntuación de "4" en la redacción (igual a 8 puntos), la puntuación compuesta resultante será ¡49!

Las pautas que se ofrecen a continuación le ayudarán a determinar a grandes rasgos su grado de aptitud en base a su rendimiento en la Parte 1 de la Prueba Posterior de Expresión Escrita.

0 a 10 ejercicios correctos: Es probable que no esté preparado para la Prueba de Expresión Escrita del GED. En este caso, habría que obtener una puntuación de "6" ó "5" (equivalentes a 12 ó 10 puntos) para alcanzar una puntuación compuesta que le permita aprobar la prueba. Se recomienda un repaso general.

11 a 16 ejercicios correctos: Si es capaz de obtener en la redacción una puntuación de "5" ó "3" (equivalentes a 10 ó 6 puntos), es probable que esté listo para presentarse a la Prueba de Expresión Escrita del GED. Rellene la Tabla de Evaluación de la página 481 y determine las áreas que necesita repasar.

17 a 27 ejercicios correctos: Es probable que esté preparado para la Prueba de Expresión Escrita si es capaz de obtener en la redacción una puntuación de "3" ó "1" (equivalentes a 6 ó 2 puntos). ¡Buena suerte!

CLAVE DE RESPUESTAS PRUEBA PRELIMINAR 1: EXPRESIÓN ESCRITA

Parte 1: Convenciones del español

1. **(2)** El verbo *deber* se escribe con *b*.

2. **(3)** El adjetivo *grande* suele anteceder al nombre al que modifica. En esta posición, se apocopa a *gran*. Las opciones restantes presentan errores de ortografía.

3. **(1)** La mejor opción es, en este caso, la coordinación de las dos oraciones por medio de la conjunción *y*. Los enlaces *o* y *a menos que* desvirtúan el sentido de la oración. La coma no es la puntuación apropiada para finalizar un periodo largo. *Debrá* no es la conjugación correcta de *deber* en futuro imperfecto del indicativo.

4. **(3)** *Lo* es el pronombre adecuado para hacer la concordancia con *extintor*. Según la regla, el pronombre va enclítico al infinitivo.

5. **(5)** El verbo *existir* debe concordar en número con el sujeto. No se debe confundir con *hay*, (*hubo, había*, etc.) que es impersonal y va siempre en singular.

6. **(2)** El párrafo emplea el presente de indicativo en la explicación de su tema; por tanto, el verbo de esta oración deberá utilizar el mismo tiempo verbal. Asimismo, el verbo deberá concordar en número con el sujeto *La mayor parte*, que es singular. Observe que *de los extintores* es un complemento del sujeto.

7. **(5)** Tanto *operación* como *capacitación* se escriben con *c* y con acento pintado en la *o* de la última sílaba.

8. **(1)** *Decisión*, al igual que *comprensión, disensión, colisión* y otros, lleva *s* en la sílaba acentuada.

9. **(1)** Hay una pausa después de *familia*, que indica el final del complemento *Al comprar. . ., al aprender. . ., y al ponerlo. . .* y el inicio de la oración principal *usted estará contribuyendo. . .* Por esta razón se pone una coma.

10. **(1)** Aunque los nombres propios de continentes (por ej.: *Europa*) se escriben con letra inicial mayúscula, los gentilicios derivados de los mismos (por ej.: *europeo, europeas,* etc.) se escriben con minúscula, a menos que encabecen la oración. Es importante notar que en inglés los gentilicios sí llevan mayúscula inicial; razón por la cual se habrá de tener cuidado con estos adjetivos.

11. **(5)** Según la regla, no se escribe *z* sino *c* ante *e* o *i*. Así pues, *veces, hacen* y *ofrecen* se ajustan a la norma. *Asen* es la tercera persona plural del presente de indicativo del verbo *asir,* de significado distinto a *hacer*. No se debe poner coma después de *casa* puesto que la oración subordinada adjetiva que le modifica no es explicativa sino especificativa.

12. **(4)** La opción (4) es la más clara y completa en cuanto al sentido. La versión original presenta un modificador inconexo, ya que la subordinada *Como se sienten. . . como a invitados* se refiere a los

invitados, mientras que la oración principal tiene por sujeto a los anfitriones. Las opciones (1) y (2) omiten parte de la información; y la opción (3) tergiversa el sentido de la oración.

13. (3) La explicación del párrafo se da en presente de indicativo; además, en esta oración se está hablando en general de la gente que se suele alojar en granjas en Wisconsin. En vista de esto, el verbo *hospedar* debería también estar conjugado en presente.

14. (3) La locución adverbial *por su parte* debe ir entre comas.

15. (5) *Viajes* se escribe con *j* y *agencias* se escribe con *g* y *c*. *Disponer + de* quiere decir *contar con*. La expresión *así como* en el sentido de *al igual que* no lleva acento en *como*.

Compruebe sus respuestas de la Prueba Preliminar con la Clave de Respuestas y luego busque en la Tabla de Evaluación que se da abajo el número de los ejercicios que contestó mal y enciérrelo en círculo. De esta manera podrá determinar qué áreas de contenido necesita repasar.

PRUEBA PRELIMINAR 1: TABLA DE EVALUACIÓN DE EXPRESIÓN ESCRITA

Área de contenido	Ejercicio n°
Nombres, Adjetivos, Pronombres	2, 7
Verbos	11
Concordancia	5
Referentes y antecedentes	4
Oraciones simples y compuestas	3, 9
Concordancia de tiempos verbales	6
Modificadores inconexos/traspuestos	12
Paralelismo	13
Uso de mayúsculas	10
Puntuación	14
Ortografía	1, 8
Oraciones que no presentan errores	15

Parte 2: Redacción

De ser posible, pida a un profesor o instructor que evalúe su redacción. Los comentarios que esta persona haga acerca de su composición le servirán para determinar cómo mejorar su modo de escritura.

Pero, si no cuenta con la opción de que alguien lea lo que ha escrito, usted puede intentar evaluar la redacción por su cuenta. Utilice la Guía de Evaluación de Redacción que se ofrece a continuación y conteste las preguntas que se hacen. Si responde *sí* a estas cinco preguntas, es muy probable que su redacción obtenga una puntuación de 4 a 6 en la Parte 2 de la Prueba de Expresión Escrita. Sin embargo, si responde *no* a cualquiera de las preguntas de la Guía de Evaluación, vuelva a leer su composición con detenimiento e identifique sus puntos débiles pensando siempre en una forma de solucionar el problema. Se le recomienda asimismo repasar el Capítulo 4 de la sección de Expresión Escrita.

Guía de Evaluación de Redacción

SÍ   NO

_____ _____ **1.** ¿La redacción contesta la pregunta?

_____ _____ **2.** ¿Está claramente expresado el punto principal de la redacción?

_____ _____ **3.** ¿Presenta cada párrafo información completa, relevante y específica que contribuya a dar apoyo al punto principal?

_____ _____ **4.** ¿Las ideas presentadas están organizadas y estructuradas en oraciones y párrafos coherentes?

_____ _____ **5.** ¿Se ha empleado la lengua con tal efectividad que facilita la lectura y comprensión de la redacción?

CLAVE DE RESPUESTAS PRUEBA PRELIMINAR 2: ESTUDIOS SOCIALES

1. **(3)** Según el principio de la oferta y la demanda, cuando los precios bajan, la demanda sube. Por lo tanto, se habrán de reducir los precios de las computadoras para animar a la gente a que las compre.

2. **(2)** Los actos terroristas reciben siempre gran publicidad. Por esta razón, existe la percepción de que los terroristas se valen de los medios de comunicación para promover su causa.

3. **(2)** La gráfica indica que el promedio de meses de condena cumplidos por delincuentes condenados por jurados es mayor que la condena impuesta por jueces en juicios dictaminados sólo por un juez. En vista de ello, se puede inferir que es más recomendable que los infractores inculpados se declaren culpables y acepten ir a juicio dictaminado por un juez.

4. **(4)** La mayor severidad de las sentencias impuestas por los jurados sugieren que éstos anteponen el bienestar de la comunidad a la clemencia hacia los delincuentes.

5. **(5)** Al igual que la Doctrina Monroe, el Corolario Roosevelt se aplicaba solamente a los países del continente americano. Panamá y Colombia están ubicadas en América Central y América del Sur, respectivamente.

6. **(5)** West Virginia se distinguía de la Virginia oriental en cultura, religión y economía. Conforme a esto, es más lógico concluir que fueran diferencias políticas las causantes de la separación de West Virginia del resto del estado.

7. **(3)** Las opciones (1), (2), (4) y (5) son causas probables de la integración de la mujer al campo laboral. La opción (3) es la explicación menos probable.

8. **(4)** Entre 1970 y 1980, el porcentaje de mujeres casadas empleadas en un trabajo fuera de la casa aumentó en un 15.4 por ciento, pasando del 38.7 al 54.1 por ciento.

9. **(1)** Los rápidos casamientos de los soldados tras su regreso de la guerra constituyen la explicación más probable del aumento de la natalidad. Las opciones (2), (3) y (4) no contribuyeron directamente al "baby boom". La opción (5) no es una explicación plausible.

10. **(1)** Cuando los consumidores gastan más, las empresas aprovechan este aumento del consumo para producir más bienes para vender.

11. **(5)** El programa de la seguridad social sería el más afectado porque a él compete realizar los pagos a los jubilados y los ancianos.

12. **(2)** En el pasaje se menciona que casi la mitad de las exportaciones de Australia van destinadas a Asia. De ahí, se puede decir que unos lazos más estrechos con Asia redundarían en beneficio de la economía del país.

13. **(5)** Tanto Australia como las trece primeras colonias americanas tenían a un monarca británico como jefe de estado. Aunque la reina de Inglaterra no es más que una figura simbólica, el cortar este último lazo con Gran Bretaña se asemejaría más a la decisión de las trece colonias de independizarse que a cualquiera

de las otras opciones, las cuales implican la incorporación de una unidad política a otra.

14. (5) Las regiones del país con el número más alto de habitantes por milla cuadrada están representadas en negro. La parte noreste del país tiene más áreas sombreadas en negro que ninguna otra.

15. (2) La exigencia que hizo Johnson a los estados confederados a que ratificaran una enmienda que abolía la esclavitud no fue una acción a favor del Sur, mientras que todas las demás acciones sí se pueden interpretar como pro-Sur.

Compruebe sus respuestas de la Prueba Preliminar con la Clave de Respuestas y luego busque en la Tabla de Evaluación que se da abajo el número de los ejercicios que contestó mal y enciérrelo en círculo. De esta manera podrá determinar qué destrezas de lectura y qué áreas de contenido necesita repasar. Las destrezas de lectura se abordan en las páginas 33–45; y el número de página correspondiente a las áreas de contenido se cita abajo en la tabla. La capacidad de contestar preguntas que requieren el manejo de las destrezas de lectura y de la información de las áreas de contenido es fundamental para un buen rendimiento en la Prueba de Estudios Sociales del GED. Los números que aparecen en **negrita** son preguntas que se basan en gráficas.

PRUEBA PRELIMINAR 2: TABLA DE EVALUACIÓN DE ESTUDIOS SOCIALES

Destreza de lectura/ Área de contenido	Comprensión	Aplicación	Análisis	Evaluación
Ciencias del Comportamiento (páginas 103–111)		**11**	9	7
Historia de EE.UU. (páginas 112–126)		5	6	15
Ciencias Políticas (páginas 127–138)	3		**2**	**4**
Economía (páginas 139–147)	**8**	10	1	
Geografía (páginas 148–154)	**14**	13		12

CLAVE DE RESPUESTAS
PRUEBA PRELIMINAR 3: CIENCIAS

1. (5) En el pasaje se menciona que los glóbulos blancos combaten las infecciones y que las plaquetas desempeñan un papel importante en la coagulación de la sangre. El combate a las infecciones y la coagulación de la sangre son dos procesos necesarios en la reparación de las heridas.

2. (5) Según el pasaje, la única abertura que tiene la hoja son los estomas. Los estomas son una especie de "boca" por la que respiran las plantas.

3. (5) Correr es la actividad que consume más calorías por hora; de modo que, de entre las actividades que figuran en la lista, correr es la más eficaz para perder peso.

4. (2) Las cargas iguales se repelen; las cargas opuestas se atraen. Los polos norte de los dos imanes son iguales; razón por la cual se repelen.

5. (5) Según el pasaje, las mariposas de color claro fueron devoradas por los pájaros cuando perdieron su capacidad de mimetizarse con el tronco de color claro de los árboles en que vivían cuando éstos empezaron a oscurecerse a causa del hollín.

6. (2) La contaminación industrial de Manchester que oscureció los troncos de los árboles fue causada por los seres humanos.

7. (3) Como la aspirina retarda la coagulación de la sangre, se usa para reducir la posibilidad de derrame cerebral, el cual se produce por obstrucción de las arterias del cerebro debido a un coágulo sanguíneo.

8. (3) El pasaje dice que los primeros períodos geológicos se pueden estudiar con facilidad y precisión.

9. (1) El pasaje compara las formaciones montañosas más antiguas a las más recientes: las montañas bajas son más viejas, mientras que las montañas más altas son más jóvenes.

10. (3) La plata, el cobre, el aluminio y el hierro tienen el coeficiente más alto de conducción de calor; por lo tanto, son los mejores conductores de entre los materiales citados.

11. (4) Todos los demás países listados se encuentran situados en los trópicos ecuatoriales y/o no poseen regiones semiáridas que limitan con desiertos.

12. (2) Las ondas sonoras deben desplazarse a una velocidad constante por el mar para que sea válido el principio en el que se basa el *fathometer* o sondímetro.

13. (1) El pasaje ilustra tanto los efectos beneficiosos como perjudiciales que pueden tener los ácidos orgánicos. El ácido fórmico diluido tiene propiedades germicidas, pero el mismo ácido concentrado es corrosivo y produce quemaduras. El ácido acético es beneficioso porque se usa en la preparación y conserva de alimentos, pero también es dañino porque su olor penetrante puede quemar los orificios nasales.

14. (3) En el pasaje se citan ejemplos de los beneficios de los ácidos orgánicos. Entre éstos se mencionan el ácido fórmico, que se puede usar como germicida, y el ácido acético, que se emplea en la preparación y conserva de alimentos. Ambos ácidos están aquí usados en forma diluida.

15. (1) La persona de tipo sanguíneo O puede donar sangre a personas de cualquier tipo sanguíneo, razón por la cual se le llama donante universal.

Compruebe sus respuestas de la Prueba Preliminar con la Clave de Respuestas y luego busque en la Tabla de Evaluación que se da abajo el número de los ejercicios que contestó mal y enciérrelo en círculo. De esta manera podrá determinar qué destrezas de lectura y qué áreas de contenido necesita repasar. Las destrezas de lectura se abordan en las páginas 33–45; y el número de página correspondiente a las áreas de contenido se cita abajo en la tabla adjunta. La capacidad de contestar preguntas que requieren el manejo de las destrezas de lectura y de la información de las áreas de contenido es fundamental para un buen rendimiento en la Prueba de Ciencias del GED. Los números que aparecen en **negrita** son preguntas que se basan en gráficas.

PRUEBA PRELIMINAR 3:
TABLA DE EVALUACIÓN DE CIENCIAS

Destreza de lectura/ Área de contenido	Comprensión	Aplicación	Análisis	Evaluación
Biología (páginas 157–172)	1	5, 6	**15**	**3**
Ciencias de la Tierra (páginas 173–190)	8	9	11	
Química (páginas 191–204)	13	2	7	14
Física (páginas 205–218)	**10**	**4**		12

CLAVE DE RESPUESTAS PRUEBA PRELIMINAR 4: ARTE Y LITERATURA

1. (2) La palabra *Rey* connota alabanza. El pasaje nos habla de los comienzos de la carrera de Presley y evidencia la admiración del autor hacia el cantante.

2. (5) Aunque el esfuerzo y la dedicación son fundamentales, estar en el lugar preciso en el momento preciso también contribuye al éxito. El hecho de que Presley se mudara a Memphis y de que le oyera el presidente de una compañía discográfica fueron circunstancias que contribuyeron de manera crucial a que saltara a la fama.

3. (4) Abraham Lincoln, que había nacido en una cabaña de madera y llegó a ser presidente, es la única figura de origen humilde de las opciones citadas. Todos los demás personajes citados han nacido en el seno de familias adineradas.

4. (4) Según el fragmento, el personaje "no había tenido ni el espíritu ni la energía ni la presencia de ánimo para haberlas hecho con más tiempo o con más dedicación"; es decir que no le importaba mucho lo que iba a regalar.

5. (3) El extracto se basa casi enteramente en los pensamientos íntimos del personaje. No se utiliza ninguno de los otros métodos citados.

6. (3) El título y la referencia que se hace de los demás personajes implican que Tom, un hombre ya fallecido, es el narrador que relata la historia en primera persona.

7. (4) El poema está escrito en verso libre; es decir, carece de rima y de una pauta rítmica regular.

8. (4) Las frases de Higgins: "siempre que dejo que una mujer haga amistad conmigo" y "siempre que yo me hago amigo de una mujer" nos indican que éste ha tenido experiencias previas.

9. (3) La referencia a las direcciones diferentes implica que las parejas suelen acordar seguir una dirección que no es del agrado de ninguno de los dos.

10. (1) La primera oración asevera que los hispanos constituyen el "grupo minoritario de más rápido crecimiento en EE.UU."

11. (5) En el pasaje, Sánchez se queja de que, por ser norteamericano de origen cubano, sólo le ofrecían papeles estereotipados. Luego explica que su madre le sugirió que se cambiara de nombre. La implicación era que su nombre hispano estaba impidiendo que le ofrecieran una variedad más amplia de papeles que interpretar.

12. (2) Sánchez dice: "No puedo expresar lo frustrante que era ir a las audiciones sabiendo que iba a ser considerado para representar cuatro posibles papeles: el de traficante de drogas, el de miembro de una pandilla, el de amante o el de joven que se ha criado en la calle pero que tiene un corazón de oro". Es muy probable que Sánchez desee tener la oportunidad de actuar en una comedia shakespeariana para salir del encasillamiento causado por esos papeles estereotipados.

Compruebe sus respuestas de la Prueba Preliminar con la Clave de Respuestas y luego busque en la Tabla de Evaluación que se da abajo el número de los ejercicios que contestó mal y enciérrelo en círculo. De esta manera podrá determinar qué destrezas de lectura y qué áreas de contenido necesita repasar. Las destrezas de lectura se abordan en las páginas 33–45; y el número de página correspondiente a las áreas de contenido se cita abajo en la tabla. La capacidad de contestar preguntas que requieren el manejo de las destrezas de lectura y de la información de las áreas de contenido es absolutamente esencial para un buen rendimiento en la Prueba de Arte y Literatura del GED.

PRUEBA PRELIMINAR 4: TABLA DE EVALUACIÓN DE ARTE Y LITERATURA

Destreza de lectura/ Área de contenido	Comprensión	Aplicación	Análisis
La narrativa de ficción (páginas 221–233)	4		5
La poesía (páginas 234–246)	6		7
El teatro (páginas 247–256)	8		9
Literatura de no ficción (páginas 257–268)	2	3	1
Comentarios (páginas 268–273)	10	12	11

CLAVE DE RESPUESTAS PRUEBA PRELIMINAR 5: MATEMÁTICAS

1. 590

$$\begin{array}{r} 590 \\ 9\overline{)5310} \\ -45 \\ \hline 81 \\ 81 \\ \hline 00 \end{array}$$

2. .95

$$\begin{array}{r} .95 \\ .4.\overline{)3.80} \\ 36 \\ \hline 20 \\ 20 \\ \hline 0 \end{array}$$

3. $53

Primero, halle el total de los cheques:
$16.75 × 4 = $67
Después halle la diferencia:
$120 − $67 = $53

4. $\frac{1}{2}$

$$\begin{array}{r} 1\frac{1}{4} = \frac{5}{4} \\ -\frac{3}{4} \quad \frac{3}{4} \\ \hline \frac{2}{4} = \frac{1}{2} \end{array}$$

5. $2\frac{1}{10}$

$4\frac{1}{5} × \frac{1}{2}$
$\frac{21}{5} × \frac{1}{2} = \frac{21}{10} = 2\frac{1}{10}$

6. $3 millones

De 1995 a 1999:
$\frac{904,400}{323,000} = $ las ventas casi se triplicaron
De 1999 a 2003:
904,400 × 3 = 2,713, 200 ó 3,000,000 (redondeado al millón más cercano)

7. 416 millas

$\frac{312 \text{ millas}}{6 \text{ horas}} = \frac{x}{8 \text{ horas}}$
$= \frac{312×8}{6} = 416$

8. $252

$\frac{x}{$350} = \frac{72}{100}$
$= \frac{$350×72}{100} = \frac{$2,200}{100} = 252
ó:
350 × .72 = 252

9. 13 pies

$a^2 = b^2 + c^2$
$a^2 = 12^2 + 5^2$
$a^2 = 144 + 25$
$a^2 = 169$
$a = \sqrt{169} = 13$

10. $367.50

Halle las horas trabajadas incluyendo sobretiempo:
40 horas normales; 3 horas de sobretiempo
Halle la paga total de Nick:
40 × $8.40 = $336.00
+ 3 × $12.60 = $37.00
$373.80

11. (2) (3.14)(6)

La fórmula de la circunferencia es $C = \pi d$; d = doble del radio
ó: 2 • 3 = 6
$C = \pi d$
$C = (3.14) (6)$

12. $2.73 × 10^5$

13. 218 millones de galones

Aumento mínimo:
85 millones − 80 millones = 5 millones
Aumento máximo:
790 − 567 = 223 millones
Halle la diferencia:
223 − 5 = 218 millones

14. 78.5 yd²

$A = \pi r^2$
$A = \pi 15^2$
$A = 3.14 • 225$
$A = 706.5 \text{ pies}^2$
$A = 706.5 \text{ pies} ÷ 9 = 78.5 \text{ yd}^2$

15. 102° $180° - 78° = 102°$

16. 105° El ángulo que está arriba de la estación es de 75°, el mismo ángulo que está arriba de Main Street. Para hallar su suplemento: $180° - 75° = 105°$

17. $x = 70$
$$14 = \tfrac{x}{5}$$
$$14 \cdot 5 = x$$
$$70 = x$$

18. $x = 4$
$$4x - 9 = 7$$
$$4x = 7 + 9$$
$$4x = 16$$
$$x = \tfrac{16}{4} = 4$$

19. $x = 7$
$$3(x - 2) - 3 = x + 5$$
$$3x - 6 - 3 = x + 5$$
$$3x - 9 = x + 5$$
$$3x - x - 9 + 9 = x - x + 5 + 9$$
$$2x = 14$$
$$x = 7$$

20. –5 $-4 + (-3) - (-2)$
$$-4 - 3 + 2$$
$$-7 + 2 = -5$$

21. 13 $5y - 3x^2$
$$5(5) - 3(-2)^2$$
$$25 - 3(4)$$
$$25 - 12 = 13$$

22. 3 *quarters*, 4 *dimes*, 7 *nickels*

Sea x = *quarters*
$x + 1$ = *dimes*
$x + 1 + 3$ = *nickels*
$$x + x + 1 + x + 1 + 3 = 14$$
$$3x + 5 = 14$$
$$3x = 14 - 5$$
$$3x = 9$$
$$x = \tfrac{9}{3} = 3$$
$x = 3$ *quarters*
$x + 1 = 4$ *dimes*
$x + 4 = 7$ *nickels*

23. 30° $\angle C = 180° - 110° = 70°$
$$\angle B = 180° - 100° = 80°$$
$$\angle A = 180° - (80° + 70°)$$
$$= 30°$$

24. pesa más
$$\frac{1 \text{ kg.}}{2.2 \text{ lb}} = \frac{3 \text{ kg}}{x \text{ lb}}$$
$$= \frac{3 \times 2.2}{1} = 6.6 \text{ lb}$$

Por lo tanto, el paquete de 3 kg pesa más que el paquete de 6 lb.

25. $16\tfrac{1}{2}$ pies
$$\frac{3}{4} = \frac{x}{22}$$
$$= \frac{22 \times 3}{4} = \frac{66}{4} = 16\tfrac{1}{2}$$

26. $2\sqrt{5d} = \sqrt{\left(x_2 + x_1\right)^2 + \left(y_2 + y_1\right)^2}$
$$= \sqrt{(5 - 1)^2 + (4 - 2)^2}$$
$$= \sqrt{4^2 + 2^2}$$
$$= \sqrt{16 + 4}$$
$$= \sqrt{20} = \sqrt{4 \cdot 5} = 2\sqrt{5}$$

27. $\tfrac{1}{2}$ $\frac{y2 - y1}{x2 - x1}$
$$\frac{4 - 2}{5 - 1} = \frac{2}{4} = \frac{1}{2}$$

28. 70°
Primero, halle el $\angle c$:
El ángulo c mide 55°, ya que tanto el lado ab como el lado bc mide 6 pulgadas.
Después, halle $\angle b$:
$$180° - 2(55°) =$$
$$180° - 110° = 70°$$

29. $\tfrac{1}{13}$ $\frac{4 \text{ ases}}{52 \text{ cartas}} = \frac{1}{13}$

30. 139 $\sqrt{25} + (4 \times 3)^2 - (5 \times 2)$
$$5 + 122 - 10$$
$$5 + 144 - 10 = 149 - 10$$
$$= 139$$

Compruebe sus respuestas de la Prueba Preliminar con la Clave de Respuestas y luego busque en la Tabla de Evaluación que se da abajo el número de los ejercicios que contestó mal y enciérrelo en círculo. De esta manera podrá determinar qué áreas de contenido necesita repasar. El número de página correspondiente a las áreas de contenido se cita abajo en la tabla. Los números que aparecen en **negrita** son preguntas que se basan en gráficas.

PRUEBA PRELIMINAR 5:
TABLA DE EVALUACIÓN DE MATEMÁTICAS

Área de contenido	Ejercicio n°	Páginas a repasar
Números enteros y decimales	1, 2, 3	277–286
Fracciones	4, 5	287–300
Razón y proporción	**6**, 7	301–304
Porcentajes	8	305–311
Medidas	**10**, 24	312–322
Gráficos, estadística y probabilidad	**13**, 29	323–330
Numeración	12, 30	331–336
Geometría	**9**, 11, **14**, **15**, **16**, **23**, **25**, **28**	337–349
Álgebra	17, 18, 19, 20, 21, 22, **26**, **27**	350–374

CLAVE DE RESPUESTAS
PRUEBA 1: EXPRESIÓN ESCRITA

CAPÍTULO 1: USO BÁSICO DEL ESPAÑOL

Ejercicio 1: Número de los nombres
página 52

1. países (4)
2. hogares (4)
3. negocios (1)
4. aleaciones (4)
5. carros (1)
6. bidés (2)
7. trenes (4)
8. vidas (1)
9. mujeres (4)
10. papás (3)

Ejercicio 2: Género de los nombres
página 52

1. congresista (A)
2. acción (F)
3. crin (F)
4. caparazón (M)
5. cutis (M)
6. tez (F)
7. espesor (M)
8. acidez (F)
9. álbum (M)
10. élite (F)
11. joven (A)
12. carácter (M)
13. crisis (F)
14. emblema (M)
15. oxímoron (M)

Ejercicio 3: Tiempos simples
página 54

Verbo	Indicador Temporal
1. hablaré	mañana
2. ve	hoy
3. plantó	año pasado
4. salía	ayer
5. puedes, podrás	(contexto)
6. estés	(contexto)
7. fuera	(contexto)

Ejercicio 4: Tiempos compuestos
página 55

1. ha asistido (*pretérito perfecto de indicativo*)
2. había trabajado (*pretérito pluscuam-perfecto de indicativo*)
3. había enviado (*pretérito pluscuamperfecto de indicativo*)
4. habría llamado (*potencial compuesto*)
   o
   hubiera/-ese llamado (*pretérito pluscuamperfecto de subjuntivo*)
5. haya hecho (*pretérito perfecto de subjuntivo*)
   o
   hubiera/-ese hecho (*pretérito pluscuamperfecto de subjuntivo*)

Ejercicio 5: Imperativo
página 56

1. salgan, salid
2. ayuda
3. haz
4. sé
5. inmiscuyas

Ejercicio 6: Verbos irregulares
página 57

1. quepo
2. satisfizo
3. oigo
4. haya
5. Estése

Ejercicio 7: Uso de los tiempos verbales
página 57

1. (3) Se recomienda el indicativo en este caso.
2. (2) La concordancia exige el singular.
3. (4) El contexto exige el presente.
4. (5) Es más apropiado el pretérito imperfecto en la condición.

Ejercicio 8: Concordancia
página 59

1. **asistió** — El sujeto es *grupo* (singular).
2. **va, van** — Se pueden usar indistintamente.
3. **nuevos** — La concordancia exige el masculino plural.
4. **coreaba** — *Multitud* es nombre colectivo singular.
   venían — Aunque *gente* es colectivo, en este caso está usado en plural.
5. **están sentados** — El verbo y el adjetivo conciertan en masculino plural.
6. **estaba** — *Todo* resume la serie de elementos anterior y es singular.

Ejercicio 9: Adjetivos
página 60

1. su
2. tus, sus
3. este, esa
4. estas, esas
5. nuestra

Ejercicio 10: Pronombres personales
página 61

1. **Repítamelo** — *Le* es siempre objeto indirecto.
2. **se me** — *Me se* es incorrecto.
3. **Le dirás** — Si se pospone el pronombre, debe ir enclítico.
4. **Vayámonos** — Se elide la *s* ante *nos*.
5. **Digámosle** — No se elide la *s* ante *le*.

Ejercicio 11: Pronombres demostrativos y posesivos
página 62

1. **la tuya** — *Piscina* es femenino singular.
2. **aquél** — *Aquel* es adjetivo y no pronombre.
3. **eso** — El pronombre neutro no lleva acento pintado.
4. **al mío** — *Al mío* reemplaza a *a mi sistema.*
5. **Aquello** — El pronombre neutro no lleva acento pintado.

Ejercicio 12: Pronombres relativos e interrogativos
página 62

1. **Quién, quién** — El primer *quién* está usado en una pregunta directa; el segundo es parte de una pregunta indirecta.
2. **Qué, que** — El primer pronombre es interrogativo; el segundo es relativo y está determinado por *lo.*
3. **cuál** — El pronombre es interrogativo y encabeza una pregunta indirecta.
4. **cuyo** — *Cuyo* es relativo y su antecedente es *el abogado.*
5. **que, cual** — Ambos pronombres son relativos.

Ejercicio 13: El pronombre y su referente
página 63

Pronombre	Referente
1. los que	Aquellos hermanos
2. te	tú
3. míos	yo
4. conmigo	yo
5. me	yo
6. les	Aquellos hermanos

Ejercicio 14: Ambigüedad del referente
página 64

1. **(4)** Con las opciones (1) y (5) no se sabe si Federico es el hermano de Jorge o de Natalia y Adriana. Las opciones (2) y (3) desvirtúan el sentido de la oración.

2. **(5)** La opción (1) es ambigua: no se sabe si el coche es de Jorge o de Federico o de Natalia y Adriana o del padre de estos tres hermanos. Las opciones (2) y (4) especifican que el dueño del coche es varón, pero todavía no se puede determinar de quién. La opción (3) es agramatical.

CAPÍTULO 2: ESTRUCTURA DE LA ORACIÓN

Ejercicio 1: Corrección de frases incompletas
página 65

Se ofrece abajo una nueva versión del párrafo que no necesariamente habrá de coincidir con la suya. Las modificaciones aparecen en **negrita**.

En su discurso inaugural de 1960, el presidente John F. Kennedy dijo: "No pregunten lo que puede hacer su país por ustedes; pregunten lo que ustedes pueden hacer por su país". Esta filosofía redundó en gran beneficio de los ciudadanos de **EE.UU. y también** de los países en vías de desarrollo. **Tenemos, por ejemplo, el caso del Cuerpo de Paz, programa** que envió a **estos países** voluntarios especializados en distintas **áreas, como** construcción, agricultura, ganadería, salubridad y otros. Los voluntarios del Cuerpo de Paz se dedicaron a transmitir a los ciudadanos de dichos países sus conocimientos. Su fin **era** mejorar **el nivel de vida de estas**

poblaciones así como mejorar las relaciones entre Estados Unidos **y las naciones en vías de desarrollo.**

Ejercicio 2: Oraciones coordinadas
página 66

1. Vamos a dar una fiesta el viernes **y** esperamos que puedan venir.
2. No estudió para su examen, **pero** lo aprobó. (*o:* **sin embargo, no obstante, mas**)
3. Diseñemos la nueva estructura **e** iniciemos el proyecto.
4. Ya llueva, ya nieve, José es siempre puntual; **pero** yo no. (*o:* **mas, sin embargo**)
5. No quiere trabajar **ni** tampoco quiere estudiar. (*o:* **y, pero**)

Ejercicio 3: Introducción a las oraciones subordinadas
Parte A
página 68

Los ejemplos que siguen presentan posibles combinaciones de oraciones. Las conjunciones subordinantes así como la puntuación adecuada a cada caso se indican en negrita. Recuerde que hay oraciones que admiten más de una conjunción.

1. **A pesar de que** le tenía mucho miedo al agua, se inscribió a la clase de natación. (*o:* **Aunque**)
2. No voy a ir a la reunión de ex-alumnos **porque** mis mejores amigos no van a estar. (*o:* **pues, puesto que, ya que,** etc.)
3. Cecilia se quedó con su madre **hasta que** volvió la enfermera.

Parte B
página 68

1. **Como** llegamos tarde a la iglesia, nos perdimos la ceremonia de la boda. (*o:* **debido a que, dado que,** etc.)
2. Rosa se enojó con la niñera; **así que** dijo que no la volvería a contratar.
3. **Cuando** llegamos al estacionamiento, observamos que la tienda estaba cerrada.

Ejercicio 4: Práctica de oraciones subordinadas
páginas 68–69

1. (b) porque
2. (a) desde que

3. (b) para que
4. (c) por lo tanto
5. (c) a pesar de que
6. (a) en caso de que
7. (b) luego que
8. (b) Así pues
9. (a) Aunque
10. (c) Después que

Ejercicio 5: Puntuación de las oraciones compuestas
página 69

Los ejemplos que se ofrecen abajo ilustran modos posibles de puntuar la oración. Recuerde que, aunque su puntuación difiera de ésta, no necesariamente habrá de ser incorrecta.

1. La miró por largo rato, trató de llamar su atención, se le acercó; pero ella no le hizo caso.
2. Por más que me lo pidas, no podré hacerlo.
3. Fue a su casa; pero, cuando trató de abrir la puerta, no pudo.
4. No logró obtener la puntuación necesaria; por lo tanto, no podrá apobar el curso.
5. Si consigue lo que se propone, podrá mejorar su vida.

Ejercicio 6: Errores frecuentes de puntuación
página 70

Los ejemplos que se dan a continuación presentan posibles modos de puntuar la oración. Tenga presente que el español es bastante flexible en lo que a puntuación se refiere; no obstante, existen reglas básicas que se habrán de observar.

1. Vine, vi, vencí.
2. La llamé a su casa, **pero** me dijeron que ya se había ido. **Volví** entonces a la oficina.
3. (*no es necesario hacer correcciones*)

Ejercicio 7: Práctica de construcción de oraciones
página 71

Posible respuesta con modificaciones indicadas en negrita:

(1) Un grupo de sicólogos ha realizado una investigación acerca del orden de nacimiento de los **hijos. Las** conclusiones obtenidas sugieren que el orden en que nace el niño relativo a sus hermanos influye en el

desarrollo de **su** personalidad **e** inteligencia. (2) Una de **las teorías de este grupo de investigadores** postula que el primogénito recibe más atención de los padres que sus **hermanos; razón** por la cual los primogénitos tienden a ser más intelectuales. (3) El **segundogénito, así como los que lo siguen,** se ven obligados a compartir a sus padres con el primerizo **y** adaptan su comportamiento al de los hermanos mayores.

Ejercicio 8: Otras expresiones de enlace
página 71

1. **(a)** La oración expresa una relación causa-efecto. *Sin embargo* indica un contraste; *de pronto* indica una situación repentina, inesperada.
2. **(b)** El que la comida sea sabrosa, no la hace necesariamente económica; así que *en consecuencia* estaría fuera de lugar. Tampoco se puede emplear *por ejemplo,* puesto que no se ilustra ningún concepto en la oración.
3. **(a)** Aunque *sin embargo* expresa una contraposición, no expresa una condición. No aprobar un curso no es consecuencia plausible de haber estudiado con más ahínco.

Ejercicio 9: Práctica de oraciones compuestas
página 72

Los ejemplos que se dan a continuación presentan posibles modos de combinar y puntuar las oraciones. Recuerde que, aunque las conjunciones y puntuación que haya usado difieran de éstas, no necesariamente habrán de ser incorrectas.

1. La vendedora era muy cortés; **así que** escuchó pacientemente todas mis quejas. (*o:* **por lo que, y**)
2. Mis amigos me aconsejan, **pero** no siempre les escucho. (*o:* **aunque, mas, sin embargo,** etc.)
3. Puedo llevarte al trabajo por la mañana **o,** si prefieres, puedes ir en el subterráneo. (*o:* **o bien, pero**)

Ejercicio 10: Construcción y uso
páginas 72–73

1. **(4)** *Sin embargo* indica que lo que sigue se contrapone a lo dicho.

2. **(1)** no es necesario hacer correcciones
3. **(4)** La segunda parte de la oración presenta información adicional sin contraponerse a lo dicho en la primera parte. *Además* sería una opción válida si no estuviera mal escrita la palabra.
4. **(2)** Es necesario poner una coma para separar la condición de la oración principal.
5. **(1)** no es necesario hacer correcciones

Ejercicio 11: Concordancia de los tiempos verbales
página 73

1. **fuese** — Es incorrecto el empleo del potencial en la condición.
2. **hubieses** — ídem
3. **acudieras** — *Aunque* presenta una hipótesis y requiere el uso del subjuntivo.
4. **hubo** — El pretérito anterior precede a la acción de la oración principal.

Ejercicio 12: Modificadores inconexos y traspuestos
página 74

Posibles respuestas:

1. <u>Clavado en la pared</u>, Ricardo vió el letrero de "No fumar".
   Nueva versión: Ricardo vio el letrero de "No fumar" clavado en la pared.
2. <u>Estando en la ducha</u>, sonó el teléfono.
   Nueva versión: El teléfono sonó cuando estaba en la ducha.
3. <u>De viaje por Colorado</u>, mi equipaje se perdió en el tren.
   Nueva versión: Mi equipaje se perdió en el tren, cuando estaba de viaje por Colorado.
4. El perro estaba debajo de la mesa <u>pidiendo comida a todos los comensales</u>.

Ejercicio 13: Paralelismo
páginas 74–75

1. **(b)** La serie exige que sus elementos sean nombres.
2. **(a)** La serie exige que sus elementos sean infinitivos.
3. **(b)** ídem

Ejercicio 14: Construcción y uso
páginas 75–76

1. **(3)** El complemento *de cinco y seis años* debe colocarse junto a *niños,* vocablo al que modifica.

2. **(4)** Este tipo de estructura pasiva es innecesario, puesto que el equivalente activo es más claro y conciso.

3. **(4)** A fin de guardar el paralelismo, es preferible que los tres elementos de la serie sean adjetivos: *interesantes, motivadoras* y *no desalentadoras.*

4. **(5)** Las opciones (1), (2) y (3) fragmentan la idea de la oración. La opción (4) es incorrecta puesto que *vistos* sólo puede desempeñar papel de adjetivo y no de participio pasado.

CAPÍTULO 3: ORTOGRAFÍA Y PUNTUACIÓN

Ejercicio 1: Reglas sobre el uso de las mayúsculas
página 78

Los cambios se indican en negrita.

1. El alcalde de **Chestertown** solicitó la asistencia del **Gobernador Kelly.**

2. Nos reuniremos con el **senador** el **miércoles,** 9 de **agosto,** en el Lincoln Center de **Memphis.**

3. Siga en dirección **norte** hasta la avenida **Baker,** luego doble a la izquierda en el Kennedy Expressway.

4. El río **Ohio** es muy bonito.

Ejercicio 2: El uso de la coma
página 79

Querida mamá:

Como me queda poco **dinero,** no podré ir a casa en las vacaciones de primavera. Por lo **tanto,** me quedaré aquí en Des Moines estudiando. Debo confesar **que,** aunque no malgasté el **dinero,** tampoco ahorré lo suficiente para el boleto de avión. Así **pues,** espero que lo entiendas. Por **último,** quería pedirte que llamaras a Daniel y Estela y les dijeras que no voy.

Un abrazo, *Delia*

Ejercicio 3: Repaso de puntuación
página 80

1. Para quitar la pintura, **necesitarás:** un galón de aguarrás, trapos, pincel y máscara protectora.

2. Elisa no ha devuelto el vestido a la **tienda** porque ha perdido el recibo.

3. Aunque me acueste **tarde,** siempre me despierto a la misma hora.

4. En esta caja están los platos **blancos;** en la otra, los platos azules.

5. Jimena **contestó:** "Cumpliré con mi promesa".

CAPÍTULO 4: CÓMO PREPARARSE PARA LA PRUEBA DE COMPOSICIÓN

Ejercicio 1: Precalentamiento
página 82

Habrá variación en las respuestas; sin embargo, cuando escriba, cerciórese de verificar la gramática y construcción de las frases, el uso de las mismas, el léxico empleado, la puntuación y ortografía así como la claridad, efectividad y concisión de sus ideas.

Ejercicio 2: Tema, público y propósito
página 82

1. *tipo de escrito:* nota de justificación
2. *tema:* necesidad de un niño de ausentarse de clase
3. *propósito:* solicitar permiso para que Erik pueda faltar a clase el viernes próximo
4. *público:* un profesor

Ejercicios 3–9
páginas 84–89

Habrá variación en las respuestas; sin embargo, asegúrese de haber seguido las instrucciones que se dan en el manual.

Ejercicio 10: Causa y efecto
página 89

Los seis *efectos* del divorcio de los Wilson son:

1. La casa de la familia se pondrá a la venta.

2. Se habrá de llegar a un acuerdo con respecto a la propiedad familiar.

3. Es probable que la Sra. Wilson busque un trabajo a tiempo completo.

4. El Sr. Wilson se ha mudado a un apartamento.

5. La Sra. Wilson y los niños se han ido a vivir con la hermana de ésta.

6. La vida de los Wilson ha cambiado radicalmente.

Ejercicios 11–14
páginas 90–96

Habrá variación en las respuestas.

CLAVE DE RESPUESTAS
PRUEBA 2: ESTUDIOS SOCIALES

CAPÍTULO 1: CIENCIAS DEL COMPORTAMIENTO

Ejercicio 1: Antropología física y cultural
página 104
Aplicación

1. **F** Los huesos fósiles constituyen un aspecto físico de los seres humanos.
2. **C** Los jeroglíficos (tipo de escritura) representan un aspecto cultural del ser humano.
3. **C** Los hábitos alimentarios son un aspecto cultural.

Ejercicio 2: Grupo primario y secundario
página 106
Aplicación

1. **S** La clase de matemáticas es un grupo secundario porque la interacción es breve y general.
2. **P** La familia es el más primario de todos los grupos.
3. **S** Aunque se conozca a todos los habitantes del pueblo, no es posible entablar una relación estrecha y personal con cada uno de ellos.

Ejercicio 3: Familia nuclear y extendida
páginas 106–107
Aplicación

1. **E** El hecho de que haya tres generaciones que cohabitan en el hogar indica que padres, hijos y abuelos viven bajo un mismo techo, lo cual corresponde a una familia extendida.
2. **N** Cuando en el hogar conviven dos generaciones —los padres y los hijos—, tenemos el caso de una familia nuclear.
3. **E** Según el pasaje, en la familia extendida cohabitan en el hogar otros parientes, además de los padres y los hijos.

Ejercicio 4: Estratificación social
página 107
Aplicación

1. **CL** El sistema de clases fomenta la autosuperación y la realización personal.
2. **CA** El sistema de castas es estricto y rígido.
3. **CL** El sistema de clases ofrece la posibilidad de optar por distintas profesiones u oficios.

Ejercicio 5: Tipos de aprendizaje
páginas 108–109
Aplicación

1. **(1)** La niña aprende a responder (dejar de llorar) a un estímulo (la luz), al asociar el estímulo a una recompensa (el que la tomen en brazos y la conforten).
2. **(4)** El niño sigue un proceso de razonamiento lógico y adapta la información para distinguir entre el pájaro y el avión.

Ejercicio 6: Mecanismos de defensa
página 111
Aplicación

1. **(4)** El zorro se inventa una excusa (las uvas estaban amargas de todas formas) cuando no logra alcanzarlas. Éste es un ejemplo de racionalización.
2. **(3)** Miguel dirige su enojo hacia su perro en lugar de dirigirlo hacia la verdadera causa: el hecho de que su equipo perdiera el juego. Este mecanismo de defensa es de desplazamiento.

CAPÍTULO 2: HISTORIA DE EE.UU.

Ejercicio 1: Una nueva nación
página 113
Análisis

1. (c) 2. (a) 3. (b)

Ejercicio 2: Los comienzos del gobierno americano
página 114
Comprensión

1. V 2. V 3. F

Ejercicio 3: Disputas, concesiones y acuerdos
páginas 114–115
Análisis

1. (2) Al contar a cada esclavo como sólo tres quintos de persona, se favorecía a los estados del Norte; porque, de esta manera, se limitaba el número de escaños que tenía el Sur en la Cámara de Representantes.

Aplicación

2. (1) Según el pasaje, los anti-federalistas temían un control autoritario por parte de un gobierno central. Asimismo, los conservadores de los dos partidos actuales dan primacía a la soberanía de los estados sobre la soberanía federal.

Ejercicio 4: La Guerra de 1812
página 116
Comprensión

(4) Según el pasaje, los acontecimientos que contribuyeron al sentir nacionalista de Estados Unidos después de la Guerra de 1812 fueron la expansión hacia el oeste (Destino Manifiesto) y la creciente necesidad de manufacturar los productos dentro del país en razón del bloqueo naval británico.

Ejercicio 5: Una nación dividida
páginas 117–118
Aplicación

1. (3) La soberanía popular permitía que la gente aprobara o desaprobara las decisiones legislativas; por lo tanto, de entre las opciones propuestas, la soberanía popular es la que más se asemeja al referéndum.

Evaluación

2. (5) Al dictaminar la Corte Suprema que Dred Scott podía ser devuelto a su amo, validaba así la práctica vigente de tratar a los esclavos como objetos de propiedad.

Ejercicio 6: El voto sobre la secesión
página 118
Comprensión

1. (b) Virginia se dividió en dos por el tema de la secesión; y la parte occidental (que ahora se conoce como West Virginia) permaneció leal a la Unión.

2. (c) Texas se separó de la Unión a pesar de que sólo la parte oriental del estado había votado a favor de esta decisión.

3. (a) Como "estado fronterizo", Kentucky permaneció en la Unión a pesar de ser un estado esclavista.

Ejercicio 7: Desarrollo de grandes empresas
página 119
Aplicación

Las opciones 2 y 3 se refieren a actividades económicas donde no interviene el gobierno. La opción 1 se refiere a una medida tomada por un organismo del gobierno, por la que se exige a una empresa que proceda de una manera determinada.

Ejercicio 8: Estados Unidos se urbaniza
página 120
Comprensión

1. (a) en la década de 1920
   (b) 70 millones

Evaluación

2. (5) En 1930, la barra correspondiente a la población rural de EE.UU. indica unos 52 millones de habitantes; y la barra de la población urbana, unos 68 millones de habitantes. Sumando ambas cifras, vemos que la población total (rural y urbana) de la época era de unos 120 millones, que es aproximadamente un medio de la población actual de 248 millones de habitantes.

Ejercicio 9: Estados Unidos se convierte en potencia mundial
páginas 121–122
Análisis

1. (3) Las Islas Filipinas fueron cedidas a Estados Unidos en virtud del tratado que puso fin a la Guerra Hispano-Estadounidense; por lo tanto, el establecimiento por parte de EE.UU. de bases militares en las islas es el resultado de una política expansionista estadounidense de control sobre otras áreas.

2. (4) La explicación más probable de la postura aislacionista que mantuvo Estados Unidos desde el final de la Guerra Civil hasta el desencadenamiento de la Guerra Hispano-Estadounidense es que el país estaba más preocupado en recuperarse y reconstruir el Sur una vez finalizada la contienda civil.

Ejercicio 10: La Primera Guerra Mundial
página 122
Comprensión

(1) Aliados
(2) el Tratado de Versalles
(3) la Liga de Naciones
(4) aislacionismo

Ejercicio 11: El *New Deal*
página 122
Aplicación

1. (a)   2. (c)   3. (b)

Ejercicio 12: La Segunda Guerra Mundial
página 124
Comprensión

1. V   2. V   3. F

Ejercicio 13: Las décadas recientes
página 126

1. (d)   2. (f)   3. (a)   4. (c)   5. (e)
6. (b)

CAPÍTULO 3: CIENCIAS POLÍTICAS

Ejercicio 1: Métodos para obtener el poder
página 128
Aplicación

1. (4) El derrocamiento de la monarquía francesa y su reemplazo con una forma republicana de gobierno es un ejemplo de revolución.

2. (3) Hitler llegó al poder en Checoslovaquia gracias a una conquista militar.

Ejercicio 2: Representación legislativa
páginas 129–130
Aplicación

1. (3) Como Alaska tiene la menor población de entre los estados representados, tendrá por lo tanto el menor número de representantes en la Cámara.

Análisis

2. (5) Dado que el número de representantes delegados por cada estado se basa en su población, se puede deducir que New Jersey, a pesar de su reducido tamaño, es un estado urbano, industrializado y densamente poblado. La densidad de población es característica de los estados urbanos e industrializados.

Ejercicio 3: El poder legislativo
página 130
Aplicación

1. E La facultad de imponer sanciones económicas no está contemplada en la Constitución; por lo tanto, se aplica la cláusula elástica.

2. C La facultad de aprobar leyes impositivas está contemplada en la Constitución.

3. C La facultad de presentar proyectos de ley está contemplada en la Constitución.

Ejercicio 4: El poder ejecutivo
página 131
Aplicación

1. (5) En el pasaje se expresa que los presidentes de tipo "fuerte" hacen con frecuencia uso de su poder de veto y tratan de imponerse al poder legislativo. Las acciones de Andrew Jackson se ajustan a esta descripción.

Análisis

2. (5) El Vicepresidente desempeña un gran número de funciones dentro del poder ejecutivo. Por lo tanto, si el presidente y el vicepresidente pertenecieran a distintos

partidos políticos, esta situación podría obstaculizar la eficacia y la capacidad de gobernar del presidente.

Ejercicio 5: El poder judicial
página 132
Comprensión
(4) La autoridad de decidir la constitucionalidad o inconstitucionalidad de una ley (que compete a la Corte Suprema) recibe el nombre de revisión judicial.

Ejercicio 6: Derechos estatales versus derechos individuales
páginas 132–133
Aplicación
1. (No)
2. **I** Al prohibir que los estados pudieran declarar la ilegalidad del aborto en ciertos casos, la Corte Suprema defendió los derechos individuales de las personas.
3. **I** Al dictaminar que un acusado debe ser informado de sus derechos, la Corte Suprema defendió los derechos de los individuos.

Ejercicio 7: La promulgación de una ley
página 133
Evaluación
(2) La opción (2) se ve respaldada por la parte del cuadro que indica que todo proyecto de ley se debe presentar a un comité de conferencia para la realización de concesiones y acuerdos. El cuadro no indica que el proyecto de ley se pueda presentar directamente al presidente. Las maniobras dilatorias son un medio aceptable para retrasar la votación de un proyecto de ley. Los proyectos de ley presentados por *cualquiera* de las cámaras pueden recibir enmiendas tal como se observa en la ilustración. El cuadro muestra que los proyectos de ley se pueden convertir en leyes sin contar con la firma del presidente si son aprobados por dos tercios de las dos cámaras.

Ejercicio 8: Sistema de control y equilibrio de poderes
página 134
Comprensión
1. (a) ejecutivo   (b) judicial
2. (a) legislativo   (b) ejecutivo
3. (a) judicial   (b) legislativo

Ejercicio 9: Facultades del gobierno estatal
página 135
Aplicación
1. A   2. F   3. E

Ejercicio 10: El espectro político
página 136
Aplicación
1. (2) Dado que la cita apoya una mejora social (mejora de programas bilingües) a través de la acción gubernamental, se puede decir que la afirmación refleja una ideología liberal.
2. (4) Dado que la cita está a favor del mantenimiento del orden social existente, se puede clasificar esta afirmación como conservadora.
3. (1) Dado que la cita se inclina a cambios rápidos y fundamentales en las leyes, se puede decir que evidencia una ideología radical.

Ejercicio 11: Los partidos políticos
página 137
Aplicación
1. **R** Los republicanos son, por lo general, partidarios de una mayor autoridad estatal y local.
2. **D** Los demócratas apoyan generalmente los objetivos de los sindicatos.
3. **D** Los demócratas abogan por el gasto público en favor de los desfavorecidos y de las minorías.

Ejercicio 12: La elección del presidente
página 138
Comprensión
1. (c)   2. (a)   3. (b)

Ejercicio 13: El proceso electoral
página 138
Evaluación
(2) Dado que la finalidad de las primarias cerradas es dar a los miembros de un partido la oportunidad de expresar sus preferencias por el candidato que se ha de postular a la elección general, se puede colegir que los votantes tienen que declarar su afiliación partidaria; de no ser así, las elecciones primarias no tendrían razón de ser.

CAPÍTULO 4: ECONOMÍA
Ejercicio 1: Factores de producción
página 140
Aplicación
1. **C** Las herramientas del fontanero son equipo que se utiliza para proveer un servicio.
2. **N** Los diamantes son materia prima que se encuentra en la naturaleza.
3. **T** Los agricultores que plantan las cosechas realizan un trabajo.

Ejercicio 2: Los sistemas económicos y los gobiernos
página 141
Comprensión
1. (1) La cita alude a una política de no interferencia gubernamental, característica del sistema capitalista.
2. (4) Como el capitalismo y el comunismo ocupan los extremos del continuo, se puede deducir que son opuestos.

Ejercicio 3: Oferta, demanda y equilibrio
página 143
Comprensión
1. (4) El punto donde se intersectan las líneas corresponde aproximadamente a 250 dólares.
Análisis
2. (3) A medida que baja el precio, aumenta la demanda.

Ejercicio 4: El dinero y la política monetaria
página 146
Comprensión
1. V
2. V

3. **F** La *tasa de redescuento* es la tasa de interés que carga la Reserva Federal a los bancos que toman dinero prestado; la *tasa preferencial,* no mencionada en el pasaje, es la tasa que cargan los bancos a sus mejores clientes.

Ejercicio 5: Política monetaria y fiscal
página 147
Comprensión
1. **disminuir; bajar:** Ambas medidas ponen una mayor cantidad de dinero a disposición de los consumidores.
2. **disminuir; elevando; aumentando:** La inflación es un incremento en la cantidad de dinero circulante. Para reducir la inflación, la Reserva Federal reduce la cantidad de dinero en circulación aumentando la tasa de redescuento. Esto hace que sea más costoso para los bancos pedir dinero prestado a la Reserva Federal. Al aumentar el coeficiente de reserva, la Reserva Federal reduce la cantidad de dinero que pueden dar en préstamo los bancos.

CAPÍTULO 5: GEOGRAFÍA
Ejercicio 1: Medir distancias
página 149
Comprensión
1. 900 millas
2. 1,050 millas

Ejercicio 2: Husos horarios
página 151
Aplicación
1. (2) La ciudad de Los Ángeles está situada en el huso horario del Pacífico, lo cual significa que está tres horas más atrasada que el huso horario del Este, que corresponde a Philadelphia.
Análisis
2. (5) El noroeste de Indiana se encuentra económicamente unido al área metropolitana de Chicago; por lo tanto, por razones económicas, se lo sitúa dentro del huso horario del Centro.

Ejercicio 3: Topografía de EE.UU. página 152

Análisis

1. (3) Denver (conocida como la "Ciudad a una milla de altura") está ubicada en las altiplanicies del borde oriental de las Montañas Rocosas. Ninguna de las demás ciudades citadas se encuentra cerca de regiones montañosas.

2. (3) New Orleans es la única ciudad representada que está por debajo del nivel del mar; y sufre inundaciones debido a su proximidad al Río Mississippi. Las Vegas está ubicada en un desierto; Phoenix está ubicada en una región seca del país. Ni New York ni Atlanta están por debajo del nivel del mar.

Ejercicio 4: El subcontinente indio página 153

Comprensión

1. (4) El Everest, cuya cima alcanza una altitud de 29,028 pies por encima del nivel del mar, no sólo es el punto más alto de la cordillera del Himalaya sino que es también la montaña más alta del mundo.

2. (5) Un vistazo al mapa del subcontinente indio muestra que la parte más extensa del terreno se encuentra entre el nivel del mar y los 1,000 pies de altitud. En la leyenda, el blanco indica este nivel de elevación.

CLAVE DE RESPUESTAS
PRUEBA 3: CIENCIAS

CAPÍTULO 1: BIOLOGÍA

Ejercicio 1: Estructura de la célula
página 158
Comprensión
  1. (c)   2. (a)   3. (b)   4. (d)

Ejercicio 2: Las células
página 159
Comprensión
  1. (4) Las opciones (1), (2), (3) y (5), a pesar de afirmaciones verdaderas, no expresan la idea principal. Los datos del pasaje dan apoyo a la idea central de que la célula es una estructura altamente organizada y compleja.

Análisis
  2. (5) Los cloroplastos desempeñan un papel fundamental en el proceso de elaboración de alimentos en las plantas. En vista de que la célula animal carece de cloroplastos, se puede deducir que los animales deben obtener su alimento de fuentes externas.

Aplicación
  3. (5) El orgánulo presente en las plantas pero no en los animales que produce la energía necesaria para la realización de la actividad celular es el cloroplasto.

Ejercicio 3: Las células y el transporte activo
página 160
Comprensión
  1. alta; baja
  2. baja; alta

Ejercicio 4: Difusión y ósmosis
página 160
Análisis
  1. (3) Según el pasaje, la difusión es el movimiento de moléculas desde un área de *alta* concentración a un área de *baja* concentración. Este proceso permite una distribución uniforme de sustancias por todas las células del cuerpo.
  2. (5) Mediante el proceso de ósmosis, el agua se desplaza de una concentración más *baja* a otra más *alta*. Como la solución salina del plasma sanguíneo está más concentrada, la célula perderá agua. Al perder agua, se encogerá.

Ejercicio 5: Mitosis
página 162
Comprensión
  1. (a)   2. (b)   3. (d)   4. (c)

Ejercicio 6: Meiosis
página 163
Comprensión
4, 1, 3, 2

Ejercicio 7: División celular
página 163
Comprensión
  1. (3) Debido al intercambio y recombinación del material cromosómico, el método de reproducción que posibilita una mayor variedad en la descendencia es la reproducción sexual.

Análisis
  2. (3) Como las células cancerosas se extienden por el organismo invadiendo las células sanas, se puede inferir que las células cancerosas se dividen de forma menos predecible que las células normales.

Ejercicio 8: Genética y herencia
páginas 164–165
Comprensión
  1. (4) En el diagrama se puede observar que sólo un hijo de cuatro no presenta el gen dominante de ojos verdes o el gen dominante de ojos marrones. Éste es el único hijo que va a tener ojos azules; por lo tanto, existe la probabilidad de que el 25 por ciento de los hijos tengan ojos azules.

Análisis
  2. (3) El padre es el portador del cromosoma "Y", que determina el sexo de un niño.

Ejercicio 9: El ciclo del nitrógeno
página 166
Análisis

1. **(1)** El único caso que muestra una relación mutuamente beneficiosa entre dos organismos distintos es el de las bacterias que sólo habitan en el estómago de los ungulados y les ayudan en el proceso de digestión.

Aplicación

2. **(4)** La soja es una legumbre que desempeña un papel preponderante en el proceso de fijación del nitrógeno. La rotación de los cultivos con una plantación de soja aumenta la posibilidad de reponer el nitrógeno del suelo.

Ejercicio 10: La fotosíntesis
páginas 166–167
Análisis

1. **(5)** Las plantas que carecen de clorofila deben valerse de un proceso distinto al de la fotosíntesis para obtener la energía que necesitan. Uno de dichos procesos es el parasitismo, en virtud del cual un organismo se alimenta de otro.

2. **(1)** El pigmento verde indica la presencia de clorofila. Las secciones de la hoja del coleus que eran originalmente verdes contenían almidón, el cual se produce por medio de la fotosíntesis. El almidón, a su vez, se vuelve marrón cuando se le aplica yodo.

Ejercicio 11: La respiración celular
páginas 167–168
Análisis

1. **(1)** Las moléculas de glucosa tienen que estar presentes para que se pueda llevar a cabo la respiración celular. Como las moléculas de glucosa son el producto final de la fotosíntesis en las plantas, se puede inferir que la fotosíntesis debe preceder a la respiración celular.

Aplicación

2. **(4)** Cuanto más activa es la persona, más energía gasta y más dióxido de carbono exhala. Los atletas son más activos que el común de la gente; por tanto tendrán ritmos de respiración celular más elevados.

Evaluación

3. **(4)** El ritmo de respiración celular se ve afectado por el estado de reposo o de actividad física en que se encuentre la persona. Las opciones (3), (4) y (5) incluyen ambos criterios; sin embargo, la opción (4) prueba un número mayor de estudiantes, obteniéndose así unos datos más fiables.

Ejercicio 12: Clasificación de los organismos
páginas 169–170
Aplicación

1. **(1)** El estreptococo es un organismo unicelular de la familia de las bacterias y pertenece al reino de los moneras.

2. **(3)** El moho carece de clorofila y obtiene su alimento de otro organismo. Pertenece al reino de los hongos.

Ejercicio 13: La evolución y la selección natural
páginas 170–171
Aplicación

1. **(3)** Según el pasaje, ciertas formas de vida sufrieron adaptaciones para poder afrontar las exigencias del medio ambiente. El hecho de que el ornitorrinco se encuentre solamente en Australia respalda la hipótesis de que este animal se desarrolló independientemente en un medio ambiente cerrado durante la etapa inicial de la evolución de los mamíferos.

Análisis

2. **(1)** La opción (1) es la mejor respuesta porque las opciones (3), (4) y (5) no son verdaderas. La opción (2) tampoco es válida porque las formas más altas de vida animal son mamíferos placentarios.

Evaluación

3. (4) De las opciones citadas, la foca es el único mamífero cuyo cuerpo está también adaptado para la vida acuática: medio ambiente atípico de los mamíferos.

Ejercicio 14: La ecología y los ecosistemas
página 172
Aplicación

1. pastos
2. ganado vacuno y ciervos
3. puma

Análisis

4. La erradicación d**el puma** provocó un aumento en la población de animales que se alimentan de pasto, como **el ciervo** y **el ganado vacuno,** lo cual condujo a la **denudación** de la tierra y posteriormente a su **erosión** debido a copiosas lluvias.

CAPÍTULO 2: CIENCIAS DE LA TIERRA

Ejercicio 1: Estrellas y galaxias
página 174
Comprensión

3, 4, 1, 2

Ejercicio 2: El sistema solar
página 175
Aplicación

(4) Según el cuento de "Ricitos de Oro (*Goldilocks* en inglés) y los Tres Osos", Ricitos de Oro probó un tazón de avena que estaba demasiado frío, otro que estaba demasiado caliente y un tercero que tenía la temperatura justa. Esto se corresponde con el hecho de que Marte sea demasiado frío, Venus demasiado caliente y la Tierra que tiene la temperatura adecuada para sustentar la vida.

Ejercicio 3: Los planetas
página 176
Comprensión

1. la Tierra; Marte
2. Mercurio
3. Venus

Ejercicio 4: La tectónica de placas
página 178
Comprensión

(5) En el pasaje, los terremotos, volcanes y montañas, así como la teoría de la deriva continental, se explican gracias a la teoría de la tectónica de placas.

Ejercicio 5: Los terremotos
página 178
Evaluación

(3) Según el mapa, es probable que la costa oeste sea víctima de la mayor parte de los daños producidos por terremotos moderados y de alta intensidad. La evidencia del mapa contradice las opciones (1), (2) y (4). La opción (5) no es un dato sino una opinión.

Ejercicio 6: Deriva continental
páginas 178–179
Análisis

(3) Esta opción refleja una comprensión del concepto de deriva continental. La opción (1) es falsa y la opción (2) ofrece una explicación insatisfactoria.

Ejercicio 7: Medición del tiempo geológico
página 180
Comprensión

1. (5) De acuerdo con el texto, las rocas sedimentarias están depositadas cerca de la superficie y las rocas metamórficas están justo debajo de las rocas ígneas.

Análisis

2. (5) Es probable que las rocas de trilobites sean más antiguas que las de los corales porque, cuanto mayor es la profundidad a la que se encuentra un fósil, más antiguo tiende a ser éste.

Ejercicio 8: Minerales y rocas
página 181
Análisis

1. (3) El potasio, que constituye un 1.85 por ciento de la corteza terrestre, es el único elemento que ocupa un espacio tres veces mayor que el silicio.

2. (5) La capacidad que tiene el oxígeno de combinarse con la mayor parte de los elementos de la Tierra es la razón por la que constituye una parte tan grande de la corteza terrestre. Las opciones (1), (2) y (3) no son verdaderas. La opción (4) no guarda relación con el tema de la composición de la corteza terrestre.

Ejercicio 9: Una Tierra cambiante
página 182
Aplicación

(5) La opción (5) es el procedimiento utilizado por la gran mayoría de los agricultores para aumentar la probabilidad de una buena cosecha, y no tiene nada que ver con la prevención de la erosión.

Ejercicio 10: Cambios en el nivel del mar
página 183
Comprensión

(5) Según la gráfica, hace unos 18,000 años el nivel del mar se encontraba a casi 400 pies por debajo del nivel del mar actual.

Ejercicio 11: El origen de los mares
página 184
Comprensión

1. (4) A un 0.001 por ciento, el vapor de agua presente en la atmósfera es la fuente que produce la menor cantidad de agua en la Tierra.

Análisis

2. (4) Según el texto, muchos científicos creen que los mares se formaron al liberarse el agua contenida en el interior de la Tierra.

Ejercicio 12: Las mareas
páginas 184–186
Análisis

1. (5) Según la ilustración, la Luna está alineada con el Sol y recibe la fuerza de atracción solar más intensa. Este fenómeno se da en luna llena y en luna nueva.

Aplicación

2. (2) La condición opuesta a la sicigia produce mareas inusualmente bajas, porque la fuerza gravitacional de la Luna y el Sol ejercida sobre la Tierra se encuentra en su punto de intensidad más bajo.

Ejercicio 13: Capas de la atmósfera terrestre
páginas 186–187
Comprensión

1. (4) La ionosfera se extiende a una altitud de 30 a 300 millas de la atmósfera de la Tierra. Las nubes noctilucas se encuentran a alturas superiores a las 40 millas.

2. (3) Las ondas de radio de la capa "D" se hallan al mismo nivel que las nubes noctilucas, es decir, en la parte inferior de la ionosfera.

3. (5) Las nubes (situadas en la troposfera) aparecen en el diagrama al mismo nivel que el Monte Everest, por lo que es factible que las nubes oculten la cumbre de esta montaña.

Ejercicio 14: El ozono en la atmósfera
páginas 187–188
Análisis

(2) El smog es visible y, por consiguiente, permanece en la troposfera, la capa atmosférica más próxima a la superficie terrestre.

Ejercicio 15: El ciclo del agua
página 189
Comprensión

5, 3, 1, 4, 2

Ejercicio 16: Humedad
página 189
Análisis

1. (4) Según el pasaje, el aire cálido es capaz de contener una mayor cantidad de humedad que el aire frío; por lo tanto, cuando la temperatura baja, el aire ya enfriado no puede contener la cantidad de humedad que contenía cuando estaba caliente. De esta manera, el aire alcanza su punto de saturación y elimina el exceso de humedad. A 45 grados, es muy probable que la precipitación se produzca en forma de lluvia.

2. (3) En un momento dado, la cantidad de vapor de agua presente en el aire es constante. Sabemos que el aire frío contiene menos humedad que el aire cálido y que, cuando el aire se calienta, tiene la capacidad de contener más agua. Si no se agrega humedad al aire, el nivel de humedad baja.

Ejercicio 17: Masas de aire, frentes y tiempo atmosférico
página 190
Comprensión

1. (2) Según el pasaje, los frentes cálidos producen nubes bajas, vientos constantes y lloviznas.

Evaluación

2. (5) El pasaje trata sobre todas las propiedades que afectan a los frentes, excepto la dirección en que se mueve la masa de aire.

CAPÍTULO 3: QUÍMICA

Ejercicio 1: Estructura atómica
página 192
Comprensión de ideas

**1. (d)   2. (e)   3. (f)   4. (b)   5. (c)
6. (a)**

Ejercicio 2: Energía nuclear
página 193
Aplicación

1. (4) Según el pasaje, la fusión consiste en la unión de dos núcleos de un elemento químico a alta temperatura y presión para formar un nuevo elemento. El hidrógeno, el elemento más ligero, es el único de la lista cuyo núcleo, durante la fusión, puede formar el segundo elemento más ligero: el helio.

2. (1) De acuerdo con el pasaje, la fisión implica la división del núcleo de un elemento pesado. El plutonio no es un gas y, por lo tanto, es el único elemento pesado de las opciones citadas.

Ejercicio 3: Elementos isotópicos
páginas 193–194
Aplicación

1. (3) Según el cuadro, el número másico del litio es 6.94. De todos los elementos mencionados, es el que tiene más probabilidades de tener un isótopo de 6. Si se fusionaran dos isótopos de litio, la masa atómica del nuevo elemento sería 12: número másico del carbono 12.

2. (1) Según el pasaje, los isótopos son formas distintas de un mismo elemento determinadas por el número de neutrones presentes en el núcleo. El único elemento representado capaz de duplicar o triplicar su masa hasta adquirir una masa final de 2 ó 3 sería el hidrógeno, que tiene un número másico de 1.01.

Ejercicio 4: Los elementos y la periodicidad
página 196
Aplicación

1. (4) En el pasaje se menciona que, a medida que aumenta el número atómico de los elementos de una columna, las propiedades químicas similares ocurren con mayor regularidad y en mayor grado. La única propiedad *física* que tendría el oro en un grado mayor sería la maleabilidad, ya que es un metal blando y dúctil. Las opciones (1), (2) y (5) no son propiedades físicas. La opción (3) no es válida para el oro ni los demás metales.

Evaluación

2. (4) El hecho de que el radón se encuentre en el suelo, opción (1), sugiere que es más denso y pesa más que los demás. Asimismo, el hecho de que tenga un número atómico más alto, opción (2), indica que sus propiedades (peso y densidad inclusive) son mayores que las de los demás elementos de su familia.

Ejercicio 5: Ecuaciones equilibradas
página 197
Comprensión

1. E Tanto al inicio como al final de la reacción tenemos dos átomos de nitrógeno (N) y dos átomos de oxígeno (O).

2. D La reacción se inicia con un átomo de hierro (Fe), un átomo de hidrógeno (H) y un átomo de cloro (Cl). Sin embargo, termina con un átomo de hierro, dos átomos de hidrógeno y tres átomos de cloro. Por lo tanto, no está equilibrada.

3. E La reacción comienza y termina con dos átomos de hidrógeno (H) y un átomo de oxígeno (O).

Ejercicio 6: Reacciones químicas
páginas 197–198
Análisis

1. (2) Las opciones (1), (3) y (5) no se inician con una molécula de dióxido de carbono (CO_2) y una molécula de agua (H_2O). La opción (4) sí comienza con dióxido de carbono y agua pero no está equilibrada la ecuación.

Comprensión

2. (2) Según el pasaje, una ecuación química está equilibrada cuando cumple con la ley de la conservación de la materia, que establece que la materia no se crea ni se destruye.

Evaluación

3. (4) La formación de una capa de cobre en el aluminio es la única evidencia citada que puede probar que se ha producido un cambio químico.

Ejercicio 7: Tipos de sustancias
página 199
Aplicación

1. (1) La sal es un compuesto formado por los elementos sodio y cloro que tiene propiedades distintas a las de sus componentes.

2. (2) El aire es una mezcla compuesta por cuatro gases por lo menos. Cada gas retiene sus propiedades particulares.

Ejercicio 8: Compuestos y enlaces químicos
página 200
Comprensión

1. (2) De acuerdo con el pasaje, el enlace iónico se logra mediante la transferencia de electrones.

2. (1) Según el pasaje, un enlace es covalente cuando los átomos forman moléculas compartiendo electrones.

Ejercicio 9: Ácidos, bases y sales
páginas 201–202
Análisis

1. (4) El ácido acético, un ácido suave presente en el vinagre, se encontraría en la parte ácida de la escala de pH cerca del punto de neutralidad: entre los valores 4 y 5. Las opciones (1) y (5) representan grados de alcalinidad, no de acidez; y las opciones (2) y (3) indican un alto grado de acidez.

2. (3) El agua no es ácida ni alcalina; por lo tanto, se ubicaría en el punto neutro de la escala de pH.

Evaluación

3. (5) Una sustancia es ácida si tiene un sabor amargo, opción (2), o si neutraliza a una base, opción (3). Los ácidos tienen un pH inferior a 7; así que la opción (1) queda eliminada.

Ejercicio 10: La batería de automóvil
páginas 202–203
Aplicación

1. (2) En el ejemplo, el ácido sulfúrico, que es conductor de la electricidad, está disuelto en agua.

2. (1) Según el pasaje, el plomo pierde dos electrones cuando reacciona con el ácido sulfúrico; por lo tanto, se puede decir que el plomo se oxida.

3. (2) El ácido sulfúrico es el agente oxidante porque hace que el plomo de la batería pierda electrones. El dióxido de plomo es el agente reductor porque hace que el ácido sulfúrico gane electrones.

Análisis

4. (4) La batería se descarga totalmente cuando el ácido sulfúrico ya no es capaz de oxidar el plomo y el dióxido de plomo ya no es capaz de reducir el ácido sulfúrico; razón por la cual no puede ya llevarse a cabo el proceso de oxidación-reducción que es lo que genera el flujo de corriente eléctrica.

Ejercicio 11: Velocidad de reacción, catalizadores y equilibrio
página 204
Análisis

1. (3) Los catalizadores son agentes que aceleran la velocidad de las reacciones químicas sin sufrir ellos ninguna alteración química. La lipasa acelera la velocidad con que las grasas se convierten en ácidos grasos. Como la lipasa se encuentra en el cuerpo, puede describirse como un catalizador biológico. Los catalizadores negativos (2) inhiben, es decir, retardan la velocidad de las reacciones químicas.

Aplicación

2. (5) Según el pasaje, el equilibrio químico se produce cuando la velocidad de reacción inicial se equilibra con la velocidad de reacción inversa. En la fotosíntesis (2), las plantas asimilan agua y dióxido de carbono del aire para producir almidón con la ayuda de la luz solar. El oxígeno derivado se libera. El caso inverso de este proceso es la respiración (3), o sea, la captación del oxígeno por los animales y la combinación del oxígeno con el almidón para formar dióxido de carbono y agua, que las plantas utilizan en la fotosíntesis. Por lo tanto, la reacción inicial, dada por la fotosíntesis, se equilibra por la reacción inversa, dada por la respiración, resultando así en un equilibrio químico.

CAPÍTULO 4: FÍSICA

Ejercicio 1: Las leyes de la fuerza y el movimiento
página 206
Aplicación

1. FA   2. AR   3. G   4. I

Ejercicio 2: La fuerza gravitacional
página 206
Comprensión

(1) El peso es una función de la fuerza de atracción de un objeto sobre otro. Según el pasaje, la intensidad de la fuerza depende de la masa de los objetos. Como Júpiter es mayor que la Tierra, la fuerza de atracción de aquél es mayor, lo que produce un incremento en el peso del astronauta relativo a su peso en la Tierra.

Ejercicio 3: Formas de energía
página 207
Aplicación

1. C   2. P

Ejercicio 4: Tipos de energía
página 208
Aplicación

1. (1) La energía nuclear es el resultado de la división de un átomo de un elemento químico pesado como el U-235.

2. (2) El gas y el aire son mezclas. Cuando se inflaman, se produce combustión, la cual es un proceso químico.

Ejercicio 5: Máquinas simples
página 209
Análisis

(3) Según el pasaje, cuanto mayor sea la distancia entre el punto de apoyo y la fuerza aplicada, menor será la fuerza requerida para realizar el trabajo. Si la distancia se incrementa a 20 pies, el esfuerzo se reduciría a la mitad.

$100 \div 2 = 50$ libras de fuerza aplicada

Ejercicio 6: Teoría cinética de la materia
página 210
Comprensión

1. V   2. F   3. V

Ejercicio 7: Calor y temperatura
páginas 210–211
Análisis

(4) El hormigón armado (o concreto reforzado) no podría mantener su durabilidad si los dos materiales, concreto y acero, se expandieran y contrayeran a distintas temperaturas; de modo que (1) es una opción correcta. Además, como el hormigón armado no se pandea (encorva) como el asfalto, se puede deducir que el hormigón se debe expandir a una temperatura más alta que el asfalto; de modo que la respuesta (2) también es correcta. La opción (3) no es verdadera puesto que es sabido que el hormigón armado se expande y contrae.

Ejercicio 8: Tipos de ondas
página 212
Aplicación

1. T   2. L   3. T

Ejercicio 9: Propiedades de las ondas
páginas 212–213
Comprensión

(3) El pasaje expresa que la longitud de onda es la distancia entre dos crestas de onda sucesivas o dos senos de onda sucesivos. Los puntos Z e Y son dos crestas de onda sucesivas.

Ejercicio 10: El principio fotoeléctrico
página 214
Evaluación

(5) Según el pasaje, una sustancia activa emite electrones cuando la luz incide sobre la misma. La intensidad de la luz determina la fuerza de la corriente generada por la emisión de los electrones. Esto sugiere que la energía luminosa se transmite en paquetes y manojos y refuta la creencia de que la luz existe solamente en forma de onda continua.

Ejercicio 11: Propiedades de las ondas lumínicas
página 215
Aplicación

1. (2) La refracción es el cambio de dirección de las ondas lumínicas al pasar de un medio a otro; en este caso, del agua al aire.

2. (1) La reflexión es el retorno de una onda lumínica cuando incide sobre una superficie brillosa.

Ejercicio 12: Electricidad y magnetismo
página 217
Análisis

1. (1) Según la información del texto, la fuerte atracción magnética proveniente del núcleo de la Tierra tiende a alinear la aguja de la brújula en la dirección de norte-sur.

Comprensión

2. (4) Un objeto magnetizado puede atraer a cualquiera de los polos de un objeto sin magnetizar que esté hecho de hierro, acero, níquel o cobalto; pero sólo atraerá al polo opuesto de otro objeto magnetizado. No se puede atraer al aluminio, al latón o al estaño.

Ejercicio 13: Conductores y aislantes
página 218
Aplicación

1. A   2. C   3. A   4. C   5. A

Ejercicio 14: Electroimanes
página 218
Análisis

(3) De la lista, la única razón plausible para no colocar el radio cerca de los instrumentos de navegación es que el electroimán del radio ejercería una fuerza de atracción sobre la brújula del barco o del avión, haciendo que salgan de su curso. Las opciones (1) y (2) no tienen nada que ver con los instrumentos de navegación. Las opciones (4) y (5) no son plausibles ni verdaderas.

CLAVE DE RESPUESTAS
PRUEBA 4: ARTE Y LITERATURA

CAPÍTULO 1: LA NARRATIVA DE FICCIÓN

Ejercicio 1: La atmósfera como parte del ambiente
página 223
Deducción

Algunas de las frases que contribuyen a crear una atmósfera de miedo son: *Tengo que esconderme, Su pecho palpitaba, esperaba agazapado, esquina oscura, Me están buscando por todas partes, Se acercó sigilosamente, Se quedó agarrotado, Apretó los dientes.*

Pero son sobre todo las imágenes las que crean ese ambiente: la imagen del hombre buscado que huye; la oscuridad de una noche lluviosa; el silbido de la sirena del coche-patrulla; el temor y ansiedad del personaje; y otros.

Ejercicio 2: Identificar al narrador
páginas 226–227
Aplicación

Los nombres y pronombres que debió haber subrayado aparecen en *cursiva* y los que debió encerrar en círculo aparecen en **negrita.**

Macomber salió por la curvada abertura lateral del asiento delantero y puso los pies en el suelo. El **león** estaba todavía allí mirando majestuosa y fríamente hacia el objeto del que sólo veía la silueta, y cuyo volumen era como el de un enorme rinoceronte. El viento no llevaba hasta **sus** fosas nasales el olor de *hombre* y tenía los ojos fijos en aquella forma [el jeep], moviendo un poco **su** enorme cabeza de un lado a otro.

Luego, mientras miraba hacia aquel objeto, sin temor alguno, pero dudando antes de decidir**se** a bajar a beber a la ribera con una cosa semejante frente a **él,** vio destacar**se** del conjunto la *figura* de un *hombre*, y dando vuelta rápidamente, corrió a acoger**se** al abrigo de los árboles. En aquel momento, oyó un estampido seco y sintió el golpe de una sólida bala 30–36 de 150 gramos, que **le** mordía el flanco y la ardiente y repugnante brecha abierta en **su** estómago. Trotó, sintiendo las patas pesadas, y con **su** enorme panza herida, corrió por entre los árboles a buscar refugio en las altas hierbas. Nuevamente, el estampido volvió a alcanzar**lo** y pasó a **su** lado desgarrando el aire. Luego estalló una vez más y entonces sintió el golpe en **sus** costillas inferiores y la boca se **le** llenó de pronto de sangre caliente y espumosa. Galopó hacia los altos pastos donde podría ocultar**se** aplastado contra el suelo y lograr que esa cosa se acercara para saltarle encima y cazar al *hombre* que la llevaba.

Ejercicio 3: Deducir el tema
páginas 227–228
Deducción

1. (5) El fragmento expone la lucha de la Srta. Strangeworth contra el mal que "estaba acechando muy cerca".

2. (3) Por más que la Srta. Strangeworth creyese que estaba siendo bien intencionada, sus actos perjudicaban a personas inocentes.

Ejercicio 4: Tono y personajes
página 229
Análisis

1. (4) Las dos últimas oraciones indican un tono de voz sarcástico y divertido.

2. (3) Parece que el autor piensa que las personas como la madre de Julian necesitan más tolerancia y simpatía.

Ejercicio 5: Identificar el estilo del autor
página 230
Análisis

Las descripciones y las imágenes que evocan los sentidos aparecen en *cursiva.*

El chirrido de ruedas de carreta que lanzó la soprano castigó mis oídos. El sol que se filtraba por las persianas llenó la habitación de una sulfurosa luz. No sabía por cuánto tiempo había dormido, pero *sentí un leve temblor de agotamiento.*

La cama gemela que había junto a la mía estaba vacía y sin hacer.

A las siete *había oído cómo mi madre se levantaba, se ponía rápidamente la ropa y salía en puntillas de la habitación.* Luego *pude oír el zumbido del exprimidor de naranjas* que venía de la planta baja, y *sentir el olor a café y tocino que se colaba por debajo de la puerta.* Luego, *el agua del fregadero salió del grifo y los platos tintinearon* cuando mi madre los secó y los puso en el armario.

Luego, *la puerta principal se abrió y se cerró.* Luego *se abrió y se cerró la puerta del garaje; el motor del auto hizo brum-brum* y, avanzando con un *crujir de grava, se perdió en la distancia.*

Ejercicio 6: Comentarios sobre ficción
páginas 232–233
Literal
1. (2) La crítica expresa que "uno preferiría seguir la vida de Putus como mujer joven en lugar de volver a ella unas décadas después. . . "

Deducción
2. (1) La última oración de la crítica deja en claro que el crítico admira la habilidad narrativa de la escritora.

Aplicación
3. (4) Según la crítica, se puede clasificar el libro en la categoría de drama de la vida real.

CAPÍTULO 2: LA POESÍA

Ejercicio 1: Interpretar dos poemas
páginas 234–235
1. (4) Este poema trata de los efectos del amor en el enamorado.
2. (3) El soneto presenta una rima consonante o perfecta.

Ejercicio 2: La forma de la poesía
páginas 236–237
Literal
1. Hay tres oraciones. (Hay un punto al final de cada oración.)

Deducción
2. Al final de la segunda estrofa, la abuela sonríe. *Sonrió* nos da la clave del estado de ánimo de la abuela.
3. El narrador es el nieto de una trabajadora agrícola migrante de origen hispano.

Ejercicio 3: La musicalidad en la poesía
página 238
Análisis
1. (1) *Coco, cacao / cacho, cachaza*
   (2) *diga despierto / lo que le pasa*
2. Las palabras que riman son: *cachaza, abrasa, pasa, casa.* Estas palabras tienen en común el sonido final -*asa* (o -*aza*, que en el español de América no se distingue).

Deducción
3. En el poema riman los versos pares solamente.

Ejercicio 4: Vocablos que imitan sonidos
página 239
Análisis
1. aliteración: (a) *999 calorías. / Azulea y ríe su gran cachaza*
   (b) *Remeda al cuco. Rooooooooeeeeis. . . tierno autocarril, móvil de sed, que corre hasta la playa.*

   repetición: *Quién como los hielos. Pero no. Quién como lo que va ni más ni menos. Quién como el justo medio.*

2. onomatopeya

Ejercicio 5: Inferir el sentido
páginas 240–241
Deducción
1. Inferencia: El hombre es el padre.
   Versos 2–3
   Palabras clave: *nuestros niños*
2. Inferencia: El hombre era una persona muy atlética.
   Verso 6
   Palabras clave: *una vez lanzó juegos de béisbol perfectos*
3. Inferencia: El hombre es ahora un anciano.
   Versos 11–12
   Palabras clave: *ahora se arquea crudamente para agarrar una caña de bambú.*
   Verso 14
   Palabras clave: *inclinas con reverencia tu cuerpo para rezar*

Ejercicio 6: Lenguaje poético
página 243
Análisis

Verso 1: imaginería

Verso 2: personificación

Verso 3: personificación

Ejercicio 7: Más práctica de intepretación de poemas
páginas 244–245
Literal

1. 1 (b)   2 (c)   3 (a)   4 (e)   5 (d)

Análisis

2. (3) La Muerte y la Inmortalidad son personajes que acompañan a la narradora en el carruaje.

Deducción

3. (5) Según la última estrofa podemos deducir que la poetisa cree que, aunque la narradora ya no se encuentra en este mundo, sigue, sin embargo, viviendo.

Ejercicio 8: Crítica de un poema
página 246
Deducción

1. (2) El crítico (citando a Hamlet de Shakespeare) afirma que "las hondas y las flechas de la mala fortuna" suelen ser dones que nos fortalecen.

2. (1) Esta opción es una versión más sencilla del clisé.

CAPÍTULO 3: EL TEATRO

Ejercicio 1: Diálogo y puntuación
página 248
Literal

1. **Edward y Victoria:** Los corchetes indican que Catherine interrumpe la conversación de Edward.

2. **Edward:** Edward se siente molesto por la interrupción de Catherine.

3. **Edward:** El tono y las respuestas de Victoria a Edward indican que ella está disgustada con él.

Ejercicio 2: Deducir el clima de un diálogo
página 249
Análisis

(1) La rudeza de Edward para con Catherine, las contestaciones de Victoria a Edward y la salida abrupta de Catherine indican que el clima de la escena es de tensión.

Ejercicio 3: Comprender el personaje
páginas 251–252
Deducción

1. (3) En esta escena, Mama hace a Jessie una serie de preguntas; entre ellas, dónde había puesto Jessie sus lentes. Lo que dice la madre al principio ("me gustaría saber por qué") y la contestación de Jessie ("Tú no tienes la menor idea de lo que yo siento.") nos dan a entender que existe una falta de comunicación entre madre e hija. Ninguna de las demás opciones encuentra apoyo en el diálogo de la escena.

2. (4) En varias partes del diálogo, la madre critica a Jessie tildándola de desagradecida y distante. Asimismo, la madre culpa a la hija de que Cecil la haya dejado.

Análisis

3. (4) El tono acusatorio y el disgusto de la madre al igual que las respuestas de Jessie indican un clima de tensión.

Ejercicio 4: Apoyar datos e inferencias
página 252
Deducción

1. Se puede inferir que Jessie está separada de Cecil en base a las siguientes frases: "¿Por qué te dejó Cecil?"; "Cecil me dejó porque me hizo escoger entre él y el cigarrillo" y "Cecil se fue prácticamente por la misma razón".

2. Podemos decir que Jessie no sabe muy bien lo que su madre quiere saber en base a las siguientes frases: "¿Tan alejada de la realidad?" y "¿Qué dices?"

3. Se puede afirmar que la madre de Jessie no cree la versión de los hechos que la hija había dado del accidente si consideramos la siguiente oración: "¿Cómo te caíste del caballo, de verdad?"

Ejercicio 5: Interpretar una escena de una obra
páginas 253–254

1. **(3)** La segunda frase de Alice, en la que ésta sugiere que se busque un hogar para su padre (igual que su marido Sidney había hecho con sus padres) y la conversación acerca de un poder notarial nos da a entender que ella y Gene son hermanos. Otra indicación dada acerca de la relación que existe entre éstos se ofrece más adelante en la escena: "Por muchos años, le destrozó el corazón a nuestra madre con esto".

Aplicación

2. **(5)** La primera frase de Alice, en la que dice "Yo hago mucho por mis hijos pero no espero que algún día me lo retribuyan" sugiere que, a su parecer, los padres no deben esperar que los hijos se hagan cargo de ellos en la ancianidad.

Deducción

3. **(2)** Según lo que dice Gene, él no se siente aliviado, sino avergonzado por no poder ofrecerle a su padre que viva con él.

Literal

4. **(4)** La frase de Gene que dice "No puedo decirte lo avergonzado que me siento. . . de no poder decir con los brazos abiertos, 'Papá, vente a vivir conmigo. . . te quiero, papá, y quiero cuidar de ti'" demuestra que Gene se siente culpable por no poder querer a su padre.

Ejercicio 6: Leer la crítica de una película
páginas 254–256
Análisis

1. **(2)** El hecho de que la novela *El último de los magnates* estuviera inconclusa y de que, no obstante, Pinter y Kazan fueran capaces de plasmar el libro en una "película fascinante y mesurada" connota admiración.

Literal

2. **(1)** El pasaje afirma que "Stahr es un ser humano imperfecto".

Deducción

3. **(5)** Como los "defensores de la máquina hollywoodiana" tienden siempre de apoyar el sistema en vigor en Hollywood y suelen ser a menudo productores de películas, se puede inferir que la película ofenderá a los productores de cine de Hollywood.

CAPÍTULO 4: LITERATURA DE NO FICCIÓN
Ejercicio 1: Biografía
páginas 257–259
Análisis

1. **(5)** La importancia del traslado de Thoreau a la laguna Walden radica en el hecho de que se realizara un 4 de julio, aniversario de la independencia de la nación. En esa fecha, Thoreau declaró su propia independencia.

Aplicación

2. **(4)** Recluido en el bosque, Thoreau pudo reflexionar acerca del sentido y la belleza de la vida. Las otras opciones no guardan relación con la búsqueda del significado de la vida.

Literal

3. **(1)** El pasaje indica que el ensayo "Sobre el deber de la desobediencia civil" influyó en las obras de Gandhi y Martin Luther King, Jr.

Deducción

4. **(2)** El pasaje indica que Thoreau fue encarcelado por no pagar un impuesto de capitación para financiar la guerra contra México. La acción de Thoreau es un ejemplo de resistencia no violenta a una ley injusta.

Ejercicio 2: Historia oral
páginas 259–260
Literal

1. F El pasaje es agridulce y nos habla al mismo tiempo de tristeza y de esperanza. La manera de afrontar la situación en ese entonces era, según Chávez, "no [dejar] que que eso te [influyera] negativamente".

2. V De acuerdo con la opinión de Chávez, los niños no cuestionan la situación y siguen yendo por inercia.

3. V Según el pasaje: " 'Siguiendo las cosechas', perdimos muchos días de clase".

4. F El pasaje es en su totalidad una descripción de los efectos que produjo la Depresión en la familia de Chávez.

Ejercicio 3: Autobiografía
páginas 261–262
Deducción

1. (5) El pasaje nos da a entender que la maestra, al parecer, desconocía la situación del niño (el autor) y mostraba desinterés e indiferencia hacia él. El autor no la pinta como docente sensible y comprensiva.

Análisis

2. (4) La única semejanza entre la niñez de Chávez y la de Gregory es que ambos salieron adelante en la vida a pesar de la pobreza sufrida. Las opciones (1), (2), (3) y (5) no son válidas en lo que se refiere a la niñez de estos dos hombres.

3. (5) El título nos da a entender que la opinión que tiene cada uno de sí no es necesariamente la misma que tiene un tercero. Las opciones restantes no encuentran apoyo en el pasaje.

Ejercicio 4: Anotaciones de un diario
página 262
Deducción

1. (5) La cita nos dice que la vida es un constante experimentar y que los experimentos como tales conllevan un riesgo. La cita no presenta argumentos que respalden a las demás opciones.

Aplicación

2. (3) La ocupación de astronauta es la que presenta el mayor grado de riesgo físico de entre las opciones citadas.

Ejercicio 5: Ensayo de tipo formalista
páginas 263–264
Deducción

1. (4) La palabra *deber* connota obligación; por lo tanto, el título da a entender que la persona está obligada a desobedecer una ley que sea injusta.

2. (3) El gobierno representa a los habitantes de un país y es el instrumento a través del cual éstos llevan a cabo su voluntad. Las otras opciones no aciertan en la definición.

3. (1) Según el ensayo, "El gobierno. . . es sólo la modalidad que ha escogido la gente para ejecutar su voluntad".

Ejercicio 6: Comparación y contraste de estilos
páginas 264–266
Análisis

1. (3) Todas las opciones presentan rasgos característicos del texto, excepto la opción que se refiere a largos párrafos explicativos.

Deducción

2. (4) La aseveración y la fuerza del pasaje ponen en evidencia la dependencia total del agente por la computadora.

Análisis

3. (4) El pasaje 2 carece del humor del pasaje 1.

Deducción

4. (3) A lo largo del fragmento, la autora habla de los problemas sicológicos causados por las oficinas electrónicas, entre ellos "un aumento pronunciado de soledad y desconexión".

Aplicación

5. (4) Los Pasajes 1 y 2 mencionan nuestra dependencia y confianza en las computadoras. Los autores de estos pasajes opinan que el ser humano debe retener el control sobre las computadoras.

Ejercicio 7: Práctica de lectura de discursos
páginas 267–268
Análisis

1. (4) Dado que es su discurso inaugural, Kennedy desea impresionar a los oyentes e inducirlos a que obren de una manera determinada.

2. (3) El penúltimo párrafo exhorta de manera poderosa y efectiva a los habitantes a servir a su patria: "no pregunten lo que puede hacer su país por ustedes; pregunten lo que ustedes pueden hacer por su país".

3. (1) El discurso carece de rima o ritmo.

Ejercicio 8: Leer la crítica de un libro
páginas 268–269
Análisis

1. + 2. – 3. F

Ejercicio 9: Leer la crítica de una novela
páginas 269–270
Análisis

1. (5) Ésta es la única opción que refleja la habilidad de la autora en caracterizar a sus personajes.

Aplicación

2. (2) Las afirmaciones "El almuerzo con un productor en Sardi es absurdo" y "el estereotipadamente descrito mundo del espectáculo de New York o Hollywood" reflejan la opinión del crítico de que las escenas de New York no han sido bien logradas.

Ejercicio 10: Leer una crítica de música
páginas 270–271
Deducción

1. (2) El crítico describe a Marsalis como perteneciente a una élite, es decir, a un grupo selecto. Esta afirmación expresa admiración por el músico.

Aplicación

2. (2) *Fomentar* quiere decir "promover el desarrollo de una persona o una cosa". Esto nos da a entender que el crítico apoya los cambios bien logrados que hace Marsalis en la tradición musical.

Ejercicio 11: Leer una crítica de arte
páginas 271–272
Literal

1. (5) El único tema que no aborda la crítica es el costo de las pinturas de Wyeth.

Deducción

2. (3) El pasaje alude en dos ocasiones al estilo llano y simple de Wyeth: " 'La sencillez' es característica de Wyeth" y "La sencillez de la obra de Wyeth se opone a la complejidad de pensamiento".

Ejercicio 12: Leer una crítica de televisión
páginas 272–273
Deducción

1. (5) El crítico dice del clásico M*A*S*H que "nos hizo reír hasta que llorábamos".

Aplicación

2. (2) El crítico dice que, "Al igual que las otras grandes comedias, [M*A*S*H] tuvo éxito principalmente explorando, de hecho celebrando, las relaciones entre los personajes".

Análisis

3. (1) El crítico pone de manifiesto su admiración de las comedias tratadas.

CLAVE DE RESPUESTAS
PRUEBA 5: MATEMÁTICAS

CAPÍTULO 1: DECIMALES

Ejercicio 1: Lectura de decimales
página 278

1. .05
2. 100.002
3. (a) .7   (c) 305.056
   (b) 2000.08   (d) .0065

Ejercicio 2: Comparación de decimales
página 279

1. (a) .05   (c) .7
   (b) 4.10   (d) .51
   (e) 1.033
2. 4.67; 4.067; 4.0067

Ejercicio 3: Redondeo de decimales
página 280

1. .375 se redondea a **.38**
2. 8.275 se redondea a **8.3**
3. 101.68 se redondea a **102**

Ejercicio 4: Suma y resta de decimales
página 281

1. **17.91**
$$\begin{array}{r} 5.9 \\ 2.46 \\ 6 \\ 3.07 \\ +\ .48 \\ \hline 17.91 \end{array}$$

2. **37.8**
$$\begin{array}{r} 43.0 \\ -\ 5.2 \\ \hline 37.8 \end{array}$$

3. **968.749 metros**
$$\begin{array}{r} 237.42 \\ 150.045 \\ 186.21 \\ 298.674 \\ +\ 96.4 \\ \hline 968.749 \text{ metros} \end{array}$$

4. **$357.56**

PASO 1
$$\begin{array}{r} \$42.87 \\ 5.93 \\ 10.00 \\ 17.48 \\ +\ 38.40 \\ \hline \$114.68 \end{array}$$

PASO 2
$$\begin{array}{r} \$472.24 \\ -\ 114.68 \\ \hline \$357.56 \end{array}$$

5. **$265.27**

PASO 1
Sumar las piezas:
$$\begin{array}{r} \$17.50 \\ 4.95 \\ 6.00 \\ 13.44 \\ +\ 60.75 \\ \hline \$102.64 \end{array}$$

PASO 2
Sumar:
Piezas	$102.64
Mano de obra	160.00
Impuestos	+ 2.63
	$265.27

Ejercicio 5: Multiplicación y división de decimales
página 284

1. **.513**
$$\begin{array}{r} .342 \\ \times\ 1.5 \\ \hline 1710 \\ 342 \\ \hline .5130 = .513 \end{array}$$

2. **$22.75**
$$\begin{array}{r} \$6.50 \\ \times\ 3.5 \\ \hline 3\,250 \\ 19\,50 \\ \hline \$22.750 = \$22.75 \end{array}$$

3. **120.1**

$$120.1$$
$$.05\overline{)6.005}$$
$$\begin{array}{r} 5 \\ \hline 1\ 0 \\ 1\ 0 \\ \hline 0 \\ 0 \\ \hline 05 \\ 5 \\ \hline 0 \end{array}$$

4. **.004**

$$.004$$
$$3\overline{)\,.012}$$
$$\begin{array}{r} 0 \\ \hline 01 \\ 0 \\ \hline 12 \\ 12 \\ \hline 0 \end{array}$$

5. $472 \times 10,000 = $ **4,720,000**
6. $456.12 \div 100 = $ **4.5612**
7. **(3)** $(3.5 \times 1.19) + (2 \times 2.30)$

Ejercicio 6: Estimación
página 285

1. *estimado:* $9 \times 10 = $ **$90**
2. *estimado:* $36 \div 2 = $ **18**

Ejercicio 7: Problemas de enunciado verbal con decimales
páginas 285–286

1. **(2) 3**

$$3.75$$
$$3.2\overline{)12.0\,00}$$
$$\begin{array}{r} 9\ 6 \\ \hline 2\ 4\ 0 \\ 2\ 2\ 4 \\ \hline 1\ 6\ 0 \\ 1\ 6\ 0 \\ \hline 0 \end{array}$$

Se pueden cortar 3.75 estantes, pero sólo se pueden cortar 3 estantes *completos.*

2. (3) 8.6408

$$\begin{array}{r} 3.086 \\ \times\ \ 2.8 \\ \hline 2\ 4\ 688 \\ 6\ 1\ 72\ \ \\ \hline 8.6\ 408 \end{array}$$

3. (2) \$320.54

Ganancia bruta:	Total de deducciones:	Paga neta:
\$265.72	\$27.03	\$434.47
+ 168.75	+ 86.93	− 113.93
\$434.47	\$113.93	\$320.54

4. (2) 16.1

Millas recorridas:	Millas por galón:

$$\begin{array}{r} 8747.6 \\ -\ 7353.2 \\ \hline 1394.4 \end{array}$$

16.13 se redondea a 16.1

$$86.4\overline{)1394.4\ 00}$$
$$\begin{array}{r} 864\ \ \ \ \ \ \\ \hline 530\ 4\ \ \ \ \\ 518\ 4\ \ \ \ \\ \hline 12\ 0\ 0\ \ \\ 8\ 6\ 4\ \ \\ \hline 3\ 3\ 60 \\ 2\ 5\ 92 \\ \hline 7\ 68 \end{array}$$

CAPÍTULO 2: FRACCIONES

Ejercicio 1: Tipos de fracciones
página 287

1. fracciones semejantes y fracciones impropias
2. números mixtos
3. fracciones propias y fracciones desemejantes

Ejercicio 2: Ampliación y reducción de fracciones
páginas 288–289

1. (a) $\frac{9}{24}$

   (b) $\frac{6}{7} \frac{(\times 4)}{(\times 4)} = \frac{24}{28}$

2. (a) $\frac{3}{4}$

   (b) $\frac{30}{42} \frac{(\div 6)}{(\div 6)} = \frac{5}{7}$

3. (a) $\frac{6}{8} \frac{(\div 2)}{(\div 2)} = \frac{3}{4}$

   (b) $\frac{25}{30} \frac{(\div 5)}{(\div 5)} = \frac{5}{6}$

Ejercicio 3: Conversión de fracción a decimal
página 290

1. (a) $\frac{7}{100}$

   (b) $.32 = \frac{32}{100} \frac{(\div 4)}{(\div 4)} = \frac{8}{25}$

   (c) $3.1 = 3\frac{1}{10}$

2. (a)
$$.37 = .37\tfrac{4}{8} = .37\tfrac{1}{2}$$
$$8\overline{)3.00}$$
$$\begin{array}{r} 2\ 4 \\ \hline 60 \\ 56 \\ \hline 4 \end{array}$$

(b)
$$1.33 = \mathbf{1.33\tfrac{1}{3}}$$
$$3\overline{)4.00}$$
$$\begin{array}{r} 3\ \ \\ \hline 1\ 0 \\ 9 \\ \hline 10 \\ 9 \\ \hline 1 \end{array}$$

(c)
$$.83 = .83\tfrac{2}{6} = \mathbf{.83\tfrac{1}{3}}$$
$$6\overline{)5.00}$$
$$\begin{array}{r} 4\ 8 \\ \hline 20 \\ 18 \\ \hline 2 \end{array}$$

Ejercicio 4: Conversión de fracción impropia a número mixto y viceversa
página 291

1. (a) $12\tfrac{1}{4} = \frac{(12\times 4)+1}{4} = \frac{48+1}{4} = \frac{49}{4}$

   (b) $6\tfrac{2}{3} = \frac{(6\times 3)+2}{3} = \frac{18+2}{3} = \frac{20}{3}$

2. (a)
$$\frac{9}{9} = 9\overline{)9}\ \ \begin{array}{l} 1 = 1 \\ \underline{9} \\ 0 \end{array}$$

   (b)
$$\frac{17}{5} = 5\overline{)17}\ \ \begin{array}{l} 3 = 3\tfrac{2}{5} \\ \underline{15} \\ 2 \end{array}$$

Ejercicio 5: Comparación de números
página 294

1. (a) $\frac{7}{8} > \frac{3}{5}$ $\frac{7}{8} \frac{(\times 5)}{(\times 5)} = \frac{35}{40}$
   $\frac{3}{5} \frac{(\times 8)}{(\times 8)} = \frac{24}{40}$

   (b) $\frac{2}{3} > \frac{4}{9}$ $\frac{2}{3} \frac{(\times 3)}{(\times 3)} = \frac{6}{9}$
   $\frac{4}{9} = \frac{4}{9}$

2. (a) $3 < 8$

   (b) $\frac{3}{4} = \frac{9}{12}$
   $\frac{2}{3} = \frac{8}{12}$
   $\frac{3}{4} > \frac{2}{3}$

(c) $2\frac{3}{8} = \frac{19}{8}$

$\frac{5}{2} = \frac{20}{8}$

$2\frac{3}{8} < \frac{5}{2}$

(d) $\frac{9}{9} = 1$

$\frac{2}{2} = 1$

$\frac{9}{9} = \frac{2}{2}$

(e) $.07 = .0700$

$.0873 = .0873$

$.07 > .0873$

Ejercicio 6: Suma y resta de fracciones
página 296

1. $\frac{11}{12}$ $\quad \frac{2}{3} = \frac{8}{12}$

$+ \frac{1}{4} = \frac{3}{12}$

$\overline{\phantom{+\frac{1}{4}} \frac{11}{12}}$

2. $10\frac{1}{24}$ $\quad 3\frac{7}{8} = 3\frac{21}{24}$

$2\frac{5}{6} = 2\frac{20}{24}$

$+ 3\frac{1}{3} = 3\frac{8}{24}$

$\overline{\phantom{+3\frac{1}{3}=} 8\frac{49}{24} = 8 + 2\frac{1}{24} = 10\frac{1}{24}}$

3. $\frac{3}{5}$ $\quad \frac{9}{10}$

$- \frac{3}{10}$

$\overline{ \frac{6}{10} = \frac{3}{5}}$

4. $\frac{3}{10}$ $\quad \frac{4}{5} = \frac{8}{10}$

$- \frac{1}{2} = \frac{5}{10}$

$\overline{\phantom{-\frac{1}{2}=} \frac{3}{10}}$

5. $13\frac{2}{3}$ $\quad 25\frac{1}{6} = 25\frac{1}{6} = 24\frac{7}{6}$

$- 11\frac{1}{2} = 11\frac{3}{6} = 11\frac{3}{6}$

$\overline{\phantom{-11\frac{1}{2}=11=} 13\frac{4}{6} = 13\frac{2}{3}}$

6. $6\frac{15}{17}$ $\quad 10 = 9\frac{17}{17}$

$- 3\frac{2}{17} = 3\frac{2}{17}$

$\overline{\phantom{-3\frac{2}{17}=} 6\frac{15}{17}}$

Ejercicio 7: Multiplicación de fracciones
página 298

1. $\frac{3}{8} \times \frac{2}{15} \times \frac{6}{7} = \frac{6}{140} = \frac{3}{70}$

2. $8\frac{1}{6} \times 4 = \frac{49}{6} \times \frac{4}{1} = \frac{98}{3} = \mathbf{32\frac{2}{3}}$

3. $2\frac{1}{2} \times 2\frac{1}{3} = \frac{5}{2} \times \frac{7}{3} = \frac{35}{6} = \mathbf{5\frac{5}{6}}$

4. $2\frac{3}{4} \times \frac{6}{7} = \frac{11}{4} \times \frac{6}{7} = \frac{33}{14} = \mathbf{2\frac{5}{14}}$

Ejercicio 8: División de fracciones
página 298

1. $\frac{2}{5} \div 4 = \frac{2}{5} \times \frac{1}{4} = \frac{1}{10}$

2. $\frac{3}{7} \div \frac{6}{35} = \frac{3}{7} \times \frac{35}{6} = \frac{5}{2} = \mathbf{2\frac{1}{2}}$

3. $9 \div 2\frac{1}{2} = \frac{9}{1} \times \frac{2}{5} = \frac{18}{5} = \mathbf{3\frac{3}{5}}$

Ejercicio 9: Grupos de información
página 300

1. (3) $\frac{19}{40}$ **de milla**

Información: $\frac{7}{8}$ de milla; $\frac{2}{5}$ de milla (según diagrama)

Longitud de Pine Way:

$\frac{7}{8} - \frac{2}{5} = \frac{35}{40} - \frac{16}{40} = \frac{19}{40}$ de milla

2. (4) $1\frac{1}{8}$ **millas**

Información: $\frac{19}{20}$ y $\frac{3}{10}$ para Birch Trail (según diagrama); $\frac{19}{40}$ para Pine Way (según resultado de la *Pregunta 1*)

Longitud de Birch Trail:

$\frac{19}{20} - \frac{3}{10} = \frac{19}{20} - \frac{6}{20} = \frac{13}{20}$

Total de ambas calles: $\frac{13}{20} + \frac{19}{40} = \frac{26}{40} + \frac{19}{40} = \frac{45}{40} = 1\frac{5}{40} = 1\frac{1}{8}$ millas.

3. (5) no se da suficiente información
Es necesario conocer el ancho de la Zona de acampado A, pero el dato no está dado.

CAPÍTULO 3: RAZÓN Y PROPORCIÓN

Ejercicio 1: Razón
página 301

1. Primero, convierta 1 hora a 60 minutos para que las unidades a comparar sean semejantes.

$\frac{30 \text{ minutos}}{1 \text{ hora}} = \frac{30 \text{ minutos}}{60 \text{ minutos}} = \frac{1}{2}$

2. $\frac{3 \text{ libras}}{4 \text{ personas}} = \frac{3}{4}$

3. $\frac{88 \text{ pies}}{8 \text{ segundos}} = \frac{11}{1}$

4. $\frac{\$80}{12 \text{ tablas}} = \frac{20}{3}$

Ejercicio 2: Aplicación de razones
página 302

1. $\frac{\text{costo de materiales}}{\text{total de gastos}} = \frac{\$120}{\$200} \div \frac{40}{40} = \frac{3}{5}$

2. $\frac{\text{total}}{\text{transporte}} = \frac{\$200}{\$40} \div \frac{40}{40} = \frac{5}{1}$

3. $\frac{\text{dividendo}}{\text{acciones}} = \frac{\$729}{300} = \mathbf{\$2.43 \text{ por acción}}$

Ejercicio 3: Regla de tres
página 303

1. $m = 4$ $\quad \frac{2}{5} = \frac{m}{10}$

$\frac{2 \times 10}{5} = 4$

2. $x = 1$ $\quad \frac{x}{7} = \frac{3}{21}$

$\frac{7 \times 3}{21} = \frac{21}{21} = 1$

3. $y = 6\frac{2}{3}$ $\quad \frac{5}{y} = \frac{15}{20}$

$\frac{20 \times 5}{15} = \frac{100}{15} = 6\frac{2}{3}$

Ejercicio 4: Aplicación de proporciones
página 304

1. **$11\frac{1}{5}$ pulgadas de alto**

$$\frac{5 \text{ pulgadas de ancho}}{7 \text{ pulgadas de largo}} = \frac{8 \text{ pulgadas de ancho}}{p \text{ (pulgadas de largo)}}$$

$$\frac{7 \times 8}{5} = \frac{56}{5} = 11\frac{1}{5} \text{ pulgadas de alto}$$

2. **40 gerentes**

$$\frac{2 \text{ gerentes}}{9 \text{ vendedores}} = \frac{g \text{ (gerentes)}}{180 \text{ vendedores}}$$

$$\frac{180 \times 2}{9} = \frac{360}{9} = 40 \text{ gerentes}$$

3. **420 calorías**

$$\frac{2 \text{ panqueques}}{120 \text{ calorías}} = \frac{7 \text{ panqueques}}{c \text{ (calorías)}}$$

$$\frac{120 \times 7}{2} = \frac{840}{2} = 420 \text{ calorías}$$

CAPÍTULO 4: PORCENTAJES

Ejercicio 1: Conversión de fracción a decimal
página 306

1. $\frac{87}{100}$ $87 \times \frac{1}{100} = \frac{87}{1} \times \frac{1}{100} = \frac{87}{100}$
   .87 $87 \times .01 = .87$

2. $\frac{2}{3}$ $66\frac{2}{3} \times \frac{1}{100} = \frac{200}{3} \times \frac{1}{100} = \frac{2}{3}$
   .66$\frac{2}{3}$ $66\frac{2}{3} \times .01 = .66\frac{2}{3}$

3. $\frac{1}{8}$ $12.5 \times \frac{1}{100} = 12\frac{1}{2} \times \frac{1}{100} =$
   $\frac{25}{2} \times \frac{1}{100} = \frac{1}{8}$

4. $\frac{9}{50}$ $18 \times \frac{1}{100} = \frac{18}{1} \times \frac{1}{100} = \frac{9}{50}$
   .18 $18 \times .01 = .18$

5. $\frac{1}{200}$ $\frac{1}{2} \times \frac{1}{100} = \frac{1}{200}$
   .005 $\frac{1}{2} \times .01 = .5 \times .01 = .005$

Ejercicio 2: Conversión a porcentaje
página 307

1. $\frac{3}{8} \times \frac{100}{1} = \frac{300}{8} = \mathbf{37\frac{1}{2}\%}$

2. $4.5 \times 100 = \mathbf{450\%}$

3. $.625 \times 100 = \mathbf{62.5\%}$

4. $2\frac{1}{4} \times 100 = \frac{9}{4} \times \frac{100}{1} = \frac{900}{4} = \mathbf{225\%}$

Ejercicio 3: Problemas sobre porcentajes
página 308

1. **1.2**   Se pide la parte:
   $\frac{n}{30} = \frac{4}{100}$
   Multiplique en diagonal:
   $30 \times 4 = 120$
   Divida: $120 \div 100 = 1.2$

2. **400**   Se pide el total:
   $\frac{10}{n} = \frac{2.5}{100}$
   Multiplique en diagonal:
   $10 \times 100 = 1000$
   Divida: $1000 \div 2.5 = 400$

3. **9%**   Se pide el porcentaje:
   $\frac{30.60}{340} = \frac{n}{100}$
   Multiplique en diagonal:
   $30.60 \times 100 = 3060$
   Divida: $3060 \div 340 = 9$

4. **.31**   Se pide la parte:
   $\frac{n}{62} = \frac{\frac{1}{2}}{100}$
   Multiplique en diagonal:
   $62 \times \frac{1}{2} = 31$
   Divida: $31 \div 100 = .31$

Ejercicio 4: Problemas sobre porcentajes
página 309

1. **$252**   Estamos buscando la parte que ahorra Jesse cada mes.
   $\frac{n}{2100} = \frac{12}{100}$
   Multiplique en diagonal:
   $2100 \times 12 = 25,200$
   Divida: $25,200 \div 100 = \$252$

2. **$12,000**   Estamos buscando el costo total del carro.
   $\frac{1800}{n} = \frac{15}{100}$
   Multiplique en diagonal:
   $1800 \times 100 = 180,000$
   Divida: $180,000 \div 15 = \$12,000$

3. **36% de indecisos**   Primero, halle el número total de votantes:
   $200 + 120 + 180 = 500$
   Después, halle el porcentaje de indecisos:
   $\frac{180}{500} = \frac{n}{100}$
   Multiplique en diagonal:
   $180 \times 100 = 18,000$
   Divida: $18,000 \div 500 = 36\%$ de indecisos

4. **$17.98**   Primero, halle el costo total de los casetes:
   $\$7.49 \times 3 = \$22.47$
   Después, halle el descuento de Hosea:
   $\frac{n}{22.47} = \frac{20}{100}$
   Multiplique en diagonal:
   $22.47 \times 20 = 449.40$
   Divida: $449.40 \div 100 = \$4.49$
   Halle el costo final de Hosea:
   $\$22.47 \div \$4.49 = \$17.98$

Ejercicio 5: Problemas de interés
página 311

1. (3) $31,968.75 Primero, halle el interés del préstamo durante 1 año:
$$\frac{n}{31,000} = \frac{12.5}{100}$$
Multiplique en diagonal:
$31,000 \times 12.5 = 387,500$
Divida:
$387,500 \div 100 = \$3875$ por 1 año
Después, halle el interés en 90 días:
$\frac{90}{360} = \frac{1}{4}$ de año
$\$3875 \times \frac{1}{4} = \$968.75$ en 90 días
Finalmente, halle la cantidad total que debe pagarse:
$\$31,000 + 968.75 = \$31,968.75$

2. (1) $\dfrac{1500 \times 8\frac{1}{2}}{100}$

Esta expresión representa cómo resolver la proporción:
$$\frac{n}{1500} = \frac{8\frac{1}{2}}{100}$$
Multiplique en diagonal: $1500 \times 8\frac{1}{2}$
Divida: $(1500 \times 8\frac{1}{2}) \div 100$ ó
$$\frac{1500 \times 8\frac{1}{2}}{100}$$

3. (4) $4,500 Halle el total para calcular cuánto tomó prestado:
$$\frac{360}{n} = \frac{8}{100}$$
Multiplique en diagonal:
$360 \times 100 = 36,000$
Divida: $36,000 \div 8 = \$4500$

CAPÍTULO 5: MEDIDAS

Ejercicio 1: Conversiones
página 313

1. Convierta una unidad menor (horas) a una mayor (días). Divida 96 por el número de horas que tiene el día
(24 hr = 1 día): $96 \div 4 = $ **4 días**

2. Convierta una unidad menor (cuartos) a una mayor (galones). Divida 20 por el número de cuartos que hay en un galón
(4 qt = 1 gal): $20 \div 4 = $ **5 galones**

3. Convierta una unidad mayor (días) a una menor (minutos). Primero, calcule el número de minutos que tiene el día
(1 día = 24 hr y 1 hr = 60 min):
$24 \times 60 = $ **1440**
Después, multiplique el total por 2 para calcular 2 días:
$1440 \times 2 = $ **2880 minutos**

4. Convierta una unidad menor (pies) a una mayor (millas). Divida 14,110 por el número de pies que hay en una milla
(5280 pies = 1 milla):
$14,110 \div 5280 = 2.67 = $ **2.7 millas**
(redondeada al décimo más cercano)

Ejercicio 2: Operaciones básicas con medidas
páginas 314–315

1. 7 pies 6 pulg

```
        7 pies   6 pulg
    3)22 pies   6 pulg
      21 pies
         1 =   +12 pulg
               18 pulg
               18 pulg
                    0
```

2. 40 min

```
       0 hr      40 min
    8)5 hr       20 min
      0
      5 hr =   +300 min
               320
               320
                 0
```

3. 7 oz
```
    1 lb   4 oz        20 oz
  -      13 oz    =  - 13 oz
                        7 oz
```

4. (4) 19($415)
1 lb 3 oz = 16 oz + 3 oz = 19 oz

5. (5) $107.50 Primero, halle el número total de horas:
```
    2 hr 30 min
    3 hr
    4 hr 45 min
    7 hr 15 min
  + 4 hr
   20 hr 90 min = 21 hr 30 min = 21½ hr
```
Después, halle la paga total:
$21\frac{1}{2}$ hr $\times \$5 = \frac{43}{2} \times \frac{5}{1} = \$107.50$

Ejercicio 3: Medidas métricas
página 317

Esta tabla le ayudará a seguir las soluciones dadas a continuación:

kilo	hecto	deca	unidad	deci	centi	mili

1. Primero, sume:
400 cm + 15 cm + 1285 cm + 15 cm
= 1715 cm

Segundo, convierta 1715 centímetros a metros:
Corra el punto decimal 2 lugares a la izquierda.
1715 cm = **17.15 m**

2. Primero, una semana = 7 días
857 mg × 7 = 5999 mg
Segundo, convierta 5999 miligramos a gramos:
Corra el punto decimal 3 lugares a la izquierda.
5999 mg = 5.999 g

3. $\frac{1\,km}{.621\,mi} = \frac{80\,km}{n}$
$\frac{.621 \times 80}{1}$ = 49.68 mph en Canadá.
En EE.UU. la máxima es 55 mph y en Canadá 49.68 mph.
En EE.UU. se permite conducir a mayor velocidad.

4. 1000 metros a kilómetros: Corra el punto decimal 3 lugares a la izquierda.
1000 m = 1.000 km = 1 km

5. **(2)** .75 x $6.40

Ejercicio 4: Problemas con dinero página 318

1. **(3) $200** Primero, halle el número de libras que hay en dos toneladas:
$\frac{1\,T}{2000\,lb} = \frac{2\,T}{n\,lb}$
$\frac{2000 \times 2}{1}$ = 4000 lb
Después, halle el número total de bolsas:
4000 lb ÷ 50 = 80 bolsas
Después, calcule los beneficios:
$5.95 × 80 = $476 de ingresos
2 × $138 = $276 de gastos
$476 − $276 = $200 de beneficios

2. **(2) $15.68** Primero, halle el número de yardas que hay en 48 pies:
$\frac{1\,yd}{3\,pies} = \frac{n\,yd}{48\,pies}$
$\frac{1 \times 48}{3} = \frac{48}{3}$ = 16 yd
Después, calcule el costo total:
16 × $.98 = $15.68

3. **(2) 12¢**
$\frac{\$6.48}{36}$ = $.18 por cápsula
$.18 × 2 = $.36 por dosis
$\frac{\$4.32}{36}$ = $.12 por cápsula
$.12 × 2 = $.24 por dosis
$.36 − $.24 = $.12

Ejercicio 5: Problemas sobre tiempo páginas 319–320

1. **(3) $4\frac{1}{2} \times 8 \times 5 \times 4$**
Primero:
10 A.M. a mediodía =   2 hr
mediodía a 2:30 P.M. = $+ 2\frac{1}{2}$ hr
                    $4\frac{1}{2}$ hr por día
Segundo:
Multiplique $4\frac{1}{2}$ horas por día por $8 por hora por 5 días a la semana por 4 semanas.

2. **(5) $4\frac{3}{4}$**
5 / 20   8   hr
5 / 21 $9\frac{1}{2}$ hr
5 / 22 $10\frac{3}{4}$ hr
5 / 23   8   hr
5 / 24 $+ 8\frac{1}{2}$ hr
Total $44\frac{3}{4}$ hr
$44\frac{3}{4} - 40 = 4\frac{3}{4}$ hr de sobretiempo

3. **(4) $371**
40 × $7.85 = $314
$4\frac{3}{4}$ × $12   = + 57
Total $371

4. **(4) $248.57**
1% + 25% + 7% = 33%
33% × $371 = $122.43 de deducciones
$371 − $122.43 = $248.57 de paga neta

5. **(2) $960 \times \frac{1}{3}$**
            $d = vt$
(20 min = $\frac{1}{3}$ hr)
        = $960(\frac{1}{3})$ ó $960 \times \frac{1}{3}$

Ejercicio 6: Escalas y medidores página 322

1. **(3) 1 pulg = 200 mi**
$\frac{2000\,mi}{10\,pulg} = \frac{n\,mi}{1\,pulg}$
$\frac{2000 \times 1}{10}$ = 200 millas

2. **(1) $113.63**
Nueva lectura   4752 kwh
Lectura anterior   −3843 kwh
diferencia   909 kwh
$\frac{\$.125}{1\,kwh} = \frac{n\,dólares}{909\,kwh}$
$\frac{\$.125 \times 909}{1}$ = $113.625 ó $113.63

CAPÍTULO 6: GRÁFICOS, ESTADÍSTICA Y PROBABILIDAD

Ejercicio 1: Media y mediana
página 324

1. **44 puntos**
   37 + 63 + 42 + 24 + 44 + 51= 261
   261 ÷ 6 = 43.5 = 44 puntos

2. **61 puntos**
   Halle los números del medio:
   45   48 $\boxed{53 \quad 68}$ 72   74
   Halle el promedio: 53 + 68 = 121
   121 ÷ 2 = 60.5 ó 61 puntos

3. **$44.80**
   Ordene de menor a mayor y halle el número del medio:
   $39.95 $42.88 $\boxed{\$44.80}$ $48.95 $52.25

Ejercicio 2: Gráficos circulares
página 325

1. **$666.67**
   Primero, calcule los gastos anuales de alquiler:
   $\frac{n}{32,000} \times \frac{25}{100} = \frac{32,000 \times 25}{100} = \$8000$
   Después, calcule los gastos mensuales de alquiler:
   $8000 ÷ 12 = $666.67

2. **(5)   no se da suficiente información**
   El gráfico no hace mención alguna sobre la ropa.

3. **(1)   1 a 10**
   $\frac{ahorros}{total} = \frac{10\%}{100\%} = \frac{10}{100} = \frac{1}{10}$

Ejercicio 3: Gráficos de barras
página 325

1. **$19,750**
   Primero, halle el total:
   13,000 + 20,000 + 21,000 + 25,000 = $79,000
   Después, halle el promedio:
   $79,000 ÷ 4 = $19,750

2. **(2) $2,000**
   $23,000 – $21,000 = $2,000

Ejercicio 4: Gráficos lineales
páginas 326–327

1. ventas; 1992; 1995
2. decenas de millares de dólares
3. $60,000
4. más altas

Ejercicio 5: Práctica mixta de gráficos
páginas 327–328

1. **$1,750**
   $\frac{n}{25,000} = \frac{7}{100}$ $\frac{25,000 \times 7}{100} = \$1750$

2. **$33,333.33**
   $\frac{20,000}{n} = \frac{37}{100}$ $\frac{20,000 \times 100}{60} = \$33,333.33$

3. **$15,120**
   Primero, halle las deducciones totales:
   27% + 7% + 3% = 37%
   $\frac{n}{24,000} = \frac{37}{100}$ $\frac{24,000 \times 37}{100} = \$8880$
   Ahora, reste para calcular el salario neto de Mike:
   $24,000 – 8880 = $15,120

4. **200 pies**   1450 – 1250 = 200 pies

5. **2.45 veces más alto**
   $\frac{\text{World Trade Center}}{\text{Monumento a Washington}} = \frac{1350}{550} = 2.45$

6. **1125 pies**
   1000 + 1250 = 2250
   2250 ÷ 2 =1125 pies

7. **Abril y julio**

8. **$69,750**
   Jóvenes: 4000 a $5.75 = $23,000
   Adultos: 5500 a $8.50 = $46,750
   $\overline{}$
   $69,750

Ejercicio 6: Probabilidad
páginas 329–330

1. $\frac{1}{52}$ $\frac{\text{1 as de espadas}}{\text{52 cartas}} = \frac{1}{52}$

2. **25%** $\frac{\text{13 corazones}}{\text{52 cartas}} = \frac{1}{4} = 25\%$

3. **(1)** $\frac{1}{6}$ $\frac{\text{1 posibilidad}}{\text{6 ases}} = \frac{1}{6}$

4. **(5)   50%** $\frac{\text{3 posibilidades}}{\text{6 caras}} = \frac{3}{6} = 50\%$

5. **(1)   0**   Esto no es posible.

6. **(3)** $\frac{1}{2}$ $\frac{\text{1 cara}}{\text{2 posibilidades}} = \frac{1}{2}$

Ejercicio 7: Probabilidad dependiente
página 330

1. $\frac{1}{17}$ $\frac{\text{3 ases}}{\text{51 cartas}} = \frac{1}{17}$

2. $\frac{4}{51}$ $\frac{\text{4 ases}}{\text{51 cartas}} = \frac{4}{51}$

3. $\frac{2}{9}$ $\frac{\text{2 quarters}}{\text{9 monedas}} = \frac{2}{9}$

4. $\frac{1}{4}$ $\frac{\text{2 quarters}}{\text{8 monedas}} = \frac{1}{4}$

CAPÍTULO 7: NUMERACIÓN

Ejercicio 1: Potenciación
página 331

1. **25**   5 × 5 = 25
2. **729**   9 × 9 x 9 = 729
3. $\frac{27}{64}$ $\frac{3}{4} \times \frac{3}{4} \times \frac{3}{4} = \frac{27}{64}$
4. **1**   1 elevado a cualquier potencia es siempre 1.

5. 1 Cualquier número elevado a la potencia 0 es 1.

6. .008 $(.2)(.2)(.2) = .008$

7. 0 $0 \times 0 = 0$

Ejercicio 2: Simplificación de raíces cuadradas
página 332

1. $4\sqrt{3}$ $\quad \sqrt{48} = \sqrt{16 \cdot 3} = 4\sqrt{3}$

2. $2\sqrt{2}$ $\quad \sqrt{8} = \sqrt{4 \cdot 2} = 2\sqrt{2}$

3. $3\sqrt{3}$ $\quad \sqrt{27} = \sqrt{9 \cdot 3} = 3\sqrt{3}$

Ejercicio 3: Raíces cuadradas
página 332

1. 9

2. 1

3. 5.3 (aprox.); $\quad \sqrt{4 \cdot 7} = 2\sqrt{7}$ (simplificada)

4. 7.2 (aprox.); $\quad \sqrt{4 \cdot 13} = 2\sqrt{13}$ (simplificada)

5. 3.2 (aprox.)

6. 4

7. 15

Ejercicio 4: Orden de operaciones
página 333

1. 0 $\quad 7 - 5 + 3 - 5$
$\qquad 2 + 3 - 5 = 0$

2. 23 $\quad 8 + 3 \times 5$
$\qquad 8 + \quad 15 = 23$

3. 8 $\quad 6 + 21 \div 3 - 5$
$\qquad 6 + \quad 7 - 5 = 8$

4. 33 $\quad 4 + 3^3 + 3 \times 2 - 2^2$
$\qquad 4 + 27 + 3 \times 2 - 4$
$\qquad 4 + 27 + \quad 6 - 4 = 33$

Ejercicio 5: Evaluación de fórmulas
página 335

1. 125 pulg^3 $\quad V = l^3$
$\qquad V = 5^3 = 125$

2. \$288 $\quad i = c\%t$
$\qquad i = (800)(.12)(3) = \$288$

3. 28.26 pulg^2 $\quad A = \pi r^2$
$\qquad A = (3.14)(3^2)$
$\qquad A = (3.14)(9) = 28.26$

4. 40 pies $\quad P = 2l + 2a$
Convierta 2 yardas a 6 pies:
$\qquad P = 2(14) + 2(6)$
$\qquad P = 28 + 12 = 40$

Ejercicio 6: Notación científica
página 336

1. 8.2×10^{-3}

2. 3.82×10^4

3. $1.624 \times 1000 = \mathbf{1624}$

4. $3.12 \times .10 = \mathbf{.312}$

CAPÍTULO 8: GEOMETRÍA

Ejercicio 1: Pares de ángulos
página 339

1. 38° porque $\angle DBC$ y $\angle ABD$ son ángulos suplementarios.
$180° - 142° = 38°$

2. 38° porque $\angle ABE$ y $\angle DBC$ son ángulos opuestos por el vértice.

3. 142° porque $\angle EBC$ y $\angle ABD$ son ángulos opuestos por el vértice.

4. 38° $\quad 90° - 52° = 38°$

Ejercicio 2: Ángulos de triángulos
página 340

1. $\angle B = 70$
Sume los dos ángulos conocidos:
$70° + 40° = 110°$
Reste el total de 180°:
$180° - 110° = 70°$

2. $\angle Q = 125°$
Sume los dos ángulos conocidos:
$30° + 25° = 55°$
Reste el total de 180°:
$180° - 55° = 125°$

3. $\angle X = 90°$
Sume los dos ángulos conocidos:
$30° + 60° = 90°$
Reste el total de 180°:
$180° - 90° = 90°$

4. $\angle E = 60°$
Sume los dos ángulos conocidos:
$60° + 60° = 120°$
Reste el total de 180°:
$180° - 120° = 60°$

Ejercicio 3: Tipos de triángulos
páginas 340–341

1. (a) Triángulo escaleno: porque sus tres lados tienen longitudes distintas

(b) Triángulo isósceles: porque tiene iguales dos lados y dos ángulos

(c) Triángulo equilátero: porque tiene los tres lados iguales

(d) Triángulo rectángulo: porque $\angle C$ es un ángulo recto

2. **76°** Halle el total de los ángulos de la base:

$52° \times 2 = 104°$

Reste del total de grados que hay en un triángulo:

$180° - 104° = 76°$

3. **30°** Halle el total de los ángulos conocidos. Como datos tenemos que el triángulo es rectángulo (tiene un ángulo de 90°) y que otro ángulo mide 60°.

$90° + 60° = 150°$

Reste del total de grados que hay en un triángulo:

$180° - 150° = 30°$

Ejercicio 4: Triángulos semejantes
página 342

1. **9 pulg**

$\frac{DF}{AC} = \frac{DE}{AB}$

$\frac{DF}{15} = \frac{6}{10}$

$\frac{15 \times 6}{10} = \frac{90}{10} = 9$ pulg

2. **12 pies**

$\frac{t}{8} = \frac{18}{12}$

$t = \frac{18 \times 8}{12} = \frac{144}{12} = 12$ pies

3. (a) Primero identifique dos triángulos semejantes y trácelos. Establezca una proporción: $\frac{d}{b} = \frac{c}{a}$

(b) **150 pies** $\frac{d}{6} = \frac{50}{2}$

$d = \frac{50 \times 6}{2} = \frac{300}{2} = 150$ pies

Ejercicio 5: El teorema de Pitágoras
páginas 343–344

1. $a = 15$

$a^2 = b^2 + c^2$
$a^2 = 9^2 + 12^2$
$a^2 = 81 + 144$
$a^2 = 225$
$a = \sqrt{225} = 15$

2. $c = 25$ pulg

$a^2 = b^2 + c^2$
$a^2 = 225 + 400 = 625$
$a = \sqrt{625} = 25$

3. (3) **100**

$a^2 = b^2 + c^2$
$a^2 = 60^2 + 80^2$
$a^2 = 3600 + 6400 = 10,000$
$a = \sqrt{10,000} = 100$

4. (2) **12** Primero, trace un diagrama con los datos del problema

$a^2 = b^2 + c^2$
$13^2 = 5^2 + c^2$
$169 = 25 + c^2$
$169 - 25 = c^2$
$144 = c^2$
$\sqrt{144} = c$
$12 = c$

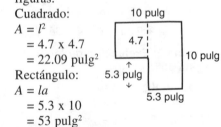

Ejercicio 6: Perímetro
páginas 346–347

1. **360 pies** $P = 4l$

$P = 4 \times 90 = 360$ pies

2. **49.9 pulg** $P = a + b + c$

$P = 16.5 + 12.4 + 21$
$= 49.9$

3. **$2961** Primero, calcule el perímetro total:

$P = 2l + 2a$
$= 2(400) + 2(224)$
$= 800 + 448 = 1248$ yd

Después, convierta a pies:

$1248 \times 3 = 3744$ pies

Después, halle el número de secciones de 8 pies:

$3744 \div 8 = 468$ secciones

Finalmente, calcule el costo total:

$468 \times 5\frac{3}{4} = \frac{468}{1} \times \frac{23}{4} = 117 \times 23 = \$2691$

4. **70 m** Primero, calcule las longitudes de los lados no marcados:

$20 - 15.3 = 4.7$
$10.8 + 4.2 = 15.0$

Después, sume todos los lados:

$20 + 4.2 + 4.7 + 10.8 + 15.3 + 15$
$= 70$m

5. **194 pies** Halle el perímetro:

$P = 2l + 2a$
$= 2(7) + 2(48) = 236$

Reste la longitud de la casa:

$236 - 42 = 194$ pies

Ejercicio 7: Área
página 348

1. **75.09 pulg2**

Esta figura se compone de dos figuras.

Cuadrado:

$A = l^2$
$= 4.7 \times 4.7$
$= 22.09$ pulg^2

Rectángulo:

$A = la$
$= 5.3 \times 10$
$= 53$ pulg^2

Sume para hallar el área total:

$53 + 22.09 = 75.09$ pulg^2

2. **$2.\frac{11}{14}$ pulg^2** $A = \pi r^2$

$= \frac{22}{7} \times (\frac{1}{2})^2$
$= \frac{22}{7} \times \frac{1}{4}$
$= \frac{11}{7} \times \frac{1}{2} = \frac{11}{14}$ pulg^2

3. 50 yd²   Primero, halle el área del cuarto:

$$30 \times 15 = 450 \text{ pies}^2$$

Después divida por 9 yardas para obtener el número de yardas cuadradas:

$$450 \div 9 = 50 \text{ yd}^2$$

4. 78.5 pies²

El mayor diámetro posible para esta alfombra es de 10 pies; por lo que el radio es de 5 pies.

El área es: $A = \pi r^2$

$$= 3.14\,(5^2)$$
$$= 78.5 \text{ pies}^2$$

Ejercicio 8: Volumen
página 349

1. 45 galones

Halle el volumen del acuario:

$V = (18)(12)(48)$
$\quad = 10{,}368 \text{ pulg}^3$

Halle la capacidad del tanque en galones:

$$10{,}368 \div 231 = 44.9 = 45 \text{ galones}$$

2. 500 pies³

Convierta 6 pulgadas a $\frac{1}{2}$ pie:

$V = (25)(40)(\frac{1}{2})$
$\quad = 500 \text{ pies3}$

3. 25,872 pies³

$V = \pi r2h$

$\quad = \frac{22}{7}(14^2)(42)$
$\quad 22(196)(6) = 25{,}872 \text{ pies}^3$

CAPÍTULO 9: ÁLGEBRA
Ejercicio 1: Términos
página 351

1. $8x; +7y; -5$

2. $2x^2; -\frac{3}{x}$

3. $8ab; +12$

Ejercicio 2: Ecuaciones
página 352

1. 5 más 7 veces un número (y) es igual a 19.

2. Un número (a) menos 5 es igual a 23.

3. 10 dividido por un número (y) menos 5 es igual a 0.

Ejercicio 3: Ecuaciones de un paso
página 353

1. $x = 4$ $3 + x = 7$

$$3 - 3 + \underbrace{x = 7}_{0} - 3$$

2. $x = 36$ $\frac{x}{3} = 12$

$$\frac{3}{1} \cdot \frac{x}{3} = 12 \cdot 3$$
$$x = 36$$

3. $x = 8$ $x - 8 = 0$

$$x - \underbrace{8 + 8}_{0} = 0 + 8$$
$$x = 8$$

4. $x = 15$ $5x = 75$

$$\frac{5x}{5} = \frac{75}{5}$$
$$x = 15$$

Ejercicio 4: Traducción de español a álgebra
página 355

1. $\frac{x-y}{3}$

2. $x^2 + y^2$

3. $4(x + 10)$

4. $2x - 7$

5. $\frac{x^3}{4}$

6. $\frac{5x}{2x}$

Ejercicio 5: Traducción de frases a ecuaciones
páginas 356–357

1. $\frac{1}{4}x = 18$ ó $\frac{x}{4} = 18$

2. $9 + \frac{1}{2}x = 13$ ó $9 + \frac{x}{2} = 13$

3. $x - y = 8$

4. $2x - 3 = 5x + 9$

5. (1) $x - 5 = 19$

6. (4) $\frac{x}{7} = 5$

7. (1) $x + 6 = \frac{7}{6}x$

Ejercicio 6: Resolución de problemas de un paso
página 357

1. $x = \$20$ $\frac{1}{8}x = 2.50$

$$\frac{8}{1} \cdot \frac{1}{8}x = 2.50 \cdot 8$$
$$x = \$20$$

2. $x = \$192$ $72 = x - 120$

$$72 + 120 = x - \underbrace{120 + 120}_{0}$$
$$\$192 = x$$

3. $x = 12$ pies $x - 5\frac{1}{2} = 6\frac{1}{2}$

$$x - \underbrace{5\frac{1}{2} + 5\frac{1}{2}}_{0} = 6\frac{1}{2} + 5\frac{1}{2}$$
$$x = 12$$

4. $x = \$5973.75$ $\qquad$ $927 = .16x$

$$\frac{927}{.16} = \frac{.16x}{.16}$$

$$927 \div .16 = x$$

$$\$5793.75 = x$$

Ejercicio 7: Combinación de términos semejantes
página 358

1. $9x + 9y$

2. $7x^2 + 5x$

3. $x + y$

4. $12a^2 + 5a$

5. $9xy + 6x - 3y$

Ejercicio 8: Eliminación de los signos de agrupación
página 359

1. $5(3x + 2) = \mathbf{15x + 10}$

2. $6x + 2(12x - 7) = 6x + 24x - 14$
$\qquad\qquad\qquad\quad = \mathbf{30x - 14}$

3. $3(2x = 4 - 3y) = \mathbf{6x + 12 - 9y}$

4. $-6(5x - 12) = \mathbf{-30 + 72}$

5. $2(x - y) = \mathbf{2x - 2x}$

Ejercicio 9: Resolución de ecuaciones de pasos múltiples
página 360

1. $x = 14$ $\qquad$ $2x - 26 = 2$
$\qquad\qquad$ $2x - 26 + 26 = 2 + 26$
$\qquad\qquad\qquad\quad 2x = 28$
$\qquad\qquad\qquad\quad\; x = 14$

2. $x = 15$ $\qquad$ $\frac{x}{3} + 4 = 9$
$\qquad\qquad$ $\frac{x}{3} + 4 - 4 = 9 - 4$
$\qquad\qquad\qquad\quad \frac{x}{3} = 5$
$\qquad\qquad\qquad\quad x = 15$

3. $x = 21$ $\qquad$ $\frac{4x}{3} - 14 = 14$
$\qquad\qquad$ $\frac{4x}{3} - 14 + 14 = 14 + 14$
$\qquad\qquad\qquad\quad \frac{4x}{3} = 28$
$\qquad\qquad\qquad\quad 4x = 84$
$\qquad\qquad\qquad\quad\; x = 21$

4. $x = 1$ $\qquad$ $2(5x - 11) + 12x = 0$
$\qquad\qquad$ $10x - 22 + 12x = 0$
$\qquad\qquad$ $22x - 22 + 22 = 0 + 22$
$\qquad\qquad\qquad\qquad 22x = 22$
$\qquad\qquad\qquad\qquad\;\; x = 1$

Ejercicio 10: Planteo y resolución de ecuaciones de pasos múltiples
páginas 360–361

1. **(4)** $\;3(x + 32) = 123$

2. **(4)** $\;2x + 24 = 56$

3. **(4)** $\;(2x - 6) + x = 42$

4. **(5)** $\;4800 + 36x = 10,200$

5. **(5) no se da suficiente información**
No se sabe cuántos boletos gratis se dieron.

Ejercicio 11: Recta numérica
página 362

1. $1\frac{1}{2} > -1$ $\qquad$ **2.** $-4 < -2\frac{1}{2}$

Ejercicio 12: Números con signo
página 362

1. -3 yd

2. $+4\frac{1}{2}$ pt

3. $-9 < -4$

4. $-3 < 1$

5. $-\frac{1}{4} > -\frac{1}{2}$

6. $2\frac{1}{3}$

7. 3

Ejercicio 13: Combinación de números con signo
página 363

1. -17 $\qquad$ **3.** -33 $\qquad$ **5.** -19

2. -2 $\qquad$ **4.** -3 $\qquad$ **6.** -7.7

Ejercicio 14: Eliminación de signos dobles
página 364

1. **1** $\;-6 + (-2) - (-9) = -6 - 2 + 9 = \mathbf{1}$

2. ganancia total de 22 yardas
$\quad +23 \quad -4$
$\quad\; +8 \quad -6$
$\quad \underline{+3} \quad \underline{-2}$
$\quad\;\; 34 \quad -12$
$\quad +34 - 12 = +22$

3. **19°** $\;12 - (-7) = 12 + 7 = 19$

4. **$158**
$\quad +140 \qquad -14$
$\quad\; +56 \qquad -32$
$\quad\; +26 \qquad -18$
$\quad +222 \qquad -64$
$\quad +222 + (-64) = +158$

Ejercicio 15: Multiplicación y división de números con signo
página 365

1. 40

2. -144

3. -84

4. -5

5. 3

6. −4

7. − **$22,284**   (−$2476)(9) = −$22,284

Ejercicio 16: Inecuaciones de un paso
página 366

1. $x > -2$ $x - 3 > -5$
$$x - 3 + 3 > -5 + 3$$
$$x < -2$$

2. $x < -7$ $-3 + x < -10$
$$-3 + 3 + x < -10 + 3$$
$$x < -7$$

3. $x < -36$ $\frac{x}{-3} < 12$
$$-3 \cdot \frac{x}{-3} > 12 \cdot (-3)$$
$$x > -36$$
Observe el cambio de sentido.

4. $x \le 4$ $x - 5 \le -1$
$$x - 5 + 5 \le -1 + 5$$
$$x \le 4$$

5. $x < 4$ $-4x > -16$
$$\frac{-4x}{-4} < \frac{-16}{-4}$$
$$x < 4$$
Observe el cambio de sentido.

Ejercicio 17: Multiplicación de expresiones algebraicas
página 368

1. $24x^3$ $8x \cdot 3x2 =$
$$8 \cdot 3 \cdot x \cdot x2 = 24x^3$$

2. $-28x^2y$ $7xy(-4x) =$
$$7 \cdot (-4) \cdot x \cdot x \cdot y = -28x^2y$$

3. $-18a^3b^2$ $(-6ab^2)(3a^2) =$
$$-6 \setminus 3 \setminus a \setminus a^2 \setminus b^2 =$$
$$-18a^3b^2$$

4. $6y^3 - 12y^2 - 21y$
$$3y(2y^2 - 4y - 7) =$$
$$3y(2y^2 + 3y(-4y) + 3y(-7) =$$
$$6y^3 - 12y^2 - 21y$$

Ejercicio 18: Máximo común factor
página 368

1. $7x^2(3x - 2)$
$$21x^3 - 14x^2 =$$
$$7x^2(3x) + 7x^2(-2) =$$
$$7x^2(3x - 2)$$

2. $11p^4(11p - 3)$
$$121p^5 - 33p^4 =$$
$$11p^4(11p) + 11p^4(-3) =$$
$$11p^4(11p - 3)$$

3. $9x^2y^2(x + 4y)$
$$9x^3y^2 + 36x^2y^3 =$$
$$9x^2y^2(x) + 9x^2y^2(4y) =$$
$$9x^2y^2(x + 4y)$$

4. $5x^2(x^2 + 5x - 4)$
$$5x^4 + 25x^3 - 20x^2 =$$
$$5x^2(x^2) + 5x^2(5x) + 5x^2(-4) =$$
$$5x^2(x^2 + 5x - 4)$$

Ejercicio 19: Factorización por agrupación
página 369

1. $(x + 4)(x + 3)$
$$x^2 + 4x + 3x + 12$$
$$x(x + 4) + 3(x + 4)$$
$$(x + 4)(x + 3)$$

2. $(4y + 3z)(2y + 3z)$
$$8y^2 + 6yz + 12yz + 9z^2$$
$$2y(4y + 3z) + 3z(4y + 3z)$$
$$(4y + 3z)(2y + 3z)$$

Ejercicio 20: Pares ordenados
página 371

1. $A (2, 2)$ **4.** $G (0, -2)$
2. $C (-3, 1)$ **5.** $H (1, -1)$
3. $F (-1, -4)$

Ejercicio 21: Distancia por conteo
página 372

1. 9   **2.** 9   **3.** 6

Ejercicio 22: Distancia entre dos puntos
página 372

1. **5** $(x_1, y_1) = (0, -2)$
$$(x_2, y_2) = (4, -5)$$
$$d = \sqrt{(4 - 0)^2 + (-5 - (-2))^2}$$
$$d = \sqrt{4^2 + (-3)^2}$$
$$d = \sqrt{16 + 9}$$
$$d = \sqrt{25} = 5$$

2. **6** E y F están en la misma línea vertical. Cuente las unidades de $(1, 4)$ a $(1, -2)$; $d = 6$

3. **5√2** $(x_1, y_1) = (-2, 3)$
$$(x_2, y_2) = (-1, -4)$$
$$d = \sqrt{(-1 - (-2))^2 + (-4 - 3)^2}$$
$$d = \sqrt{(-1 + 2)^2 + (-7)^2}$$
$$d = \sqrt{1^2 + (-7)^2}$$
$$d = \sqrt{1 + 49}$$
$$d = \sqrt{50} = \sqrt{25 \cdot 2} = 5\sqrt{2}$$

Ejercicio 23: Pendiente de una recta página 374

1. $\frac{4}{3}$ $\frac{4-0}{3-0} = \frac{4}{3}$

2. $\frac{1}{11}$ $\frac{0-(-1)}{6-(-5)} = \frac{1}{6+5} = \frac{1}{11}$

3. 1 $\frac{2-3}{-1-0} = \frac{-1}{-1} = 1$

4. 0 La recta es paralela al eje x; la pendiente es 0.

CLAVE DE RESPUESTAS PRUEBA POSTERIOR 1: EXPRESIÓN ESCRITA

Parte 1: Convenciones del español

1. (1) La versión original es la más adecuada. *Uno* debe concordar en género con *métodos* y no con *meditación. Meditación* se escribe con *c* y con acento pintado en la *o* de la última sílaba.

2. (5) La opción (5) enlaza de manera acertada las dos oraciones por medio de la conjunción coordinada *y.* En las opciones (1) y (3), el enlace desvirtúa el sentido de la oración. Las opciones (2) y (4) son ambiguas en cuanto al referente de la oración encabezada por gerundio.

3. (4) El uso de la forma reflexiva *apóyese* es incorrecto. *Apoye* en este caso es verbo transitivo con complemento directo *los pies.*

4. (2) *Cómo* es pronombre relativo interrogativo y lleva acento pintado. Equivale a *de qué manera.*

5. (5) El pronombre debe concordar en género y número con su antecedente; en este caso: *las preocupaciones. Las* es la forma más apropiada del pronombre por ser femenina plural.

6. (2) Tanto *haya avanzado* como *haya podido* están regidos por *Una vez.* El segundo verbo debe, por tanto, ir en subjuntivo para guardar el paralelismo.

7. (1) El sujeto de la oración es *promedio,* en razón de lo cual el verbo *desechar* debe concertar con éste en número. *Desechó* es singular y es por ello la forma adecuada del verbo.

8. (3) La puntuación más apropiada en este caso son los dos puntos porque preceden a la oración que sirve de comprobación a lo establecido en la anterior. (Obsérvese que no es necesario encabezar la oración que sigue con mayúscula.) La coma no es adecuada para separar dos oraciones tan extensas. La raya es típica del inglés, pero no aplicable en este ejemplo en español.

9. (3) El verbo *acostumbraba* debe concordar en número con su sujeto *mayoría.*

10. (4) *Por* es la preposición correcta que acompaña a *optar.*

11. (2) La relación que existe entre las dos oraciones es de causa-efecto. La primera oración expresa el efecto, la segunda la causa. La conjunción causal *porque* es el enlace apropiado.

12. (1) A fin de guardar el paralelismo en la estructura de la oración, es preferible el uso del infinitivo en lugar del gerundio. Tanto *eliminar* como *preparar* son los núcleos del predicado nominal de la oración.

13. (2) En este caso de sujeto compuesto, los tres elementos del mismo deben presentar la misma construcción: *pastas* y *arroz* son nombres, por lo que convendría fueran seguidos de otro nombre y no de una frase de infinitivo: *comer otros granos y cereales.* Al eliminar el infinitivo, se subsana el problema y la construcción se ajusta a una estructura paralela.

14. (5) El uso del pretérito imperfecto de subjuntivo es incorrecto. Es más adecuado a la oración el presente de subjuntivo *vaya.*

15. (3) El sujeto de esta oración coordinada es *gente,* que es un nombre colectivo singular. En consecuencia, el verbo deberá también concertar en singular.

16. (5) *Resfríos* es palabra llana terminada en vocal seguida de *s;* sin embargo, lleva acento en la *i* para romper el diptongo. *Exponerse* se escribe con *x,* como *experimentar* o *exportar.* No hay que confundir la escritura de estas palabras con la ortografía de vocablos como *esponja* o *espirar.*

17. (3) El párrafo realiza la explicación de su tema en presente de indicativo. La concordancia de los tiempos verbales en este discurso expositivo exige el uso del presente. Por esta razón, el verbo *acabar* debe estar conjugado en presente. La opción (4) con construcción en gerundio no es gramatical. La opción (5) tergiversa el sentido de la oración.

18. (4) La conjunción *aunque* es el enlace más adecuado en esta oración. *Por lo tanto* expresa una consecuencia y *ya que, dado que* y *como* indican una causa; no obstante, la oración no expresa ni causa ni consecuencia.

19. (5) A fin de mantener una coherencia en la estructura de la oración, es recomendable sustituir el nombre *la buena alimentación* por la frase de infinitivo *alimentarse bien.* Así pues, se conserva una estructura paralela.

20. (3) Esta oración coordinada posee dos verbos en imperativo. El primer verbo *seguir* está conjugado en la segunda persona del singular (*tú*) y no concuerda con el segundo verbo de la oración y los demás verbos en imperativo del resto del párrafo, los cuales están conjugados en tercera persona (*usted*).

21. (4) *Ay* es una interjección, mientras que *hay* es la forma impersonal de *haber.*

22. (4) El sujeto de la oración principal es *mayor parte;* por lo que el verbo *descomponerse* debe concertar con el mismo en singular.

23. (1) *Han encontrado* no es la forma correcta del impersonal ni de la pasiva refleja.

24. (3) La expresión comparativa es *mismo. . . que.*

25. (5) *También* es adverbio de modo que significa *asimismo* o *además. Se ha descubierto* es una pasiva refleja singular cuyo sujeto es la subordinada sustantiva de la oración. *Tanto* es invariable en este caso y pertenece a la expresión *tanto. . . como.*

26. (3) Es necesario poner una coma para separar la subordinada *siempre que se encuentran. . . salvado* de la oración principal.

27. (2) *Contenido* es un nombre singular, por lo que el verbo *variar* debe concordar con el sujeto en singular.

Compruebe sus respuestas de la Prueba Posterior con la Clave de Respuestas y luego busque en la Tabla de Evaluación que se da abajo el número de los ejercicios que contestó mal y enciérrelo en círculo. De esta manera podrá determinar qué áreas de contenido necesita repasar. El número de página correspondiente a las áreas de contenido se cita abajo en la tabla.

PRUEBA POSTERIOR 1: TABLA DE EVALUACIÓN DE EXPRESIÓN ESCRITA

Área de contenido	Ejercicio nº	Páginas a repasar
Nombres, Adjetivos, Pronombres	19	51–52, 59–62
Verbos	3, 10, 20	52–57
Concordancia	7, 15, 27	58–59
Referentes y antecedentes	1, 5, 9, 22	63–64
Oraciones simples y compuestas	2, 11, 18, 24	65–69
Concordancia de tiempos verbales	14, 17	73
Modificadores inconexos/traspuestos	23	73–74
Paralelismo	6, 12, 13	74–76
Uso de mayúsculas	8	77–78
Puntuación	26	69–71, 78–80
Ortografía	4, 21	80
Oraciones que no presentan errores	16, 25	

Parte 2: Redacción

De ser posible, pida a un profesor o instructor que evalúe su redacción. Los comentarios que esta persona haga acerca de su composición le servirán para determinar cómo mejorar su modo de escritura.

Pero si no cuenta con la opción de que alguien lea lo que ha escrito, usted puede intentar evaluar la redacción por su cuenta. Utilice la Guía de Evaluación de Redacción que se ofrece a continuación y conteste las preguntas que se hacen. Si responde *sí* a estas cinco preguntas, es muy probable que su redacción obtenga una puntuación de 4 a 6 en la Parte 2 de la Prueba de Expresión Escrita. Sin embargo, si responde *no* a cualquiera de las preguntas de la Guía de Evaluación, vuelva a leer su composición con detenimiento e identifique sus puntos débiles pensando siempre en una forma de solucionar el problema. Se le recomienda asimismo repasar el Capítulo 4 de la sección de Expresión Escrita.

Guía de Evaluación de Redacción

SÍ   NO

_____ _____ **1.** ¿La redacción contesta la pregunta?

_____ _____ **2.** ¿Está claramente expresado el punto principal de la redacción?

_____ _____ **3.** ¿Presenta cada párrafo información completa, relevante y específica que contribuya a dar apoyo al punto principal?

_____ _____ **4.** ¿Las ideas presentadas están organizadas y estructuradas en oraciones y párrafos coherentes?

_____ _____ **5.** ¿Se ha empleado la lengua con tal efectividad que facilita la lectura y comprensión de la redacción?

CLAVE DE RESPUESTAS PRUEBA POSTERIOR 2: ESTUDIOS SOCIALES

1. **(1)** El diagrama de ingresos muestra que el 30 por ciento proviene de la Seguridad Social y otros impuestos personales, el 35 por ciento viene del impuesto a la renta y el 7 por ciento de otros impuestos gravados a los individuos.

2. **(2)** Lo recaudado en Seguridad Social, Medicare, desempleo y otros, ascendió al 30 por ciento; sin embargo, el monto expendido fue de un 32 por ciento. Ninguna de las opciones restantes encuentran apoyo en las cifras de los gráficos.

3. **(1)** La opción (2) es una definición de aprendizaje cultural. Las opciones (3) y (4) son ejemplos de aprendizaje cultural en los seres humanos. La opción (5) es un hecho observable en otros animales. Todas estas afirmaciones respaldan la conclusión de que sólo los seres humanos se valen del aprendizaje cultural.

4. **(2)** Los Federalistas se basaban en el supuesto de que el gobierno federal no tenía autoridad sobre lo decidido por los estados. La opción (1) se refiere a la posición de los anti-federalistas.

5. **(3)** Los fundadores de la nación se dividieron en dos grupos respecto al tema de la declaración de derechos. Esta división estaba arraigada en las ideas que tenían éstos acerca de los derechos y poderes del gobierno central.

6. **(4)** Reponer árboles y arbustos cuyas raíces retengan el suelo sería una solución práctica. Las ovejas (1) serían incluso más destructivas que el ganado vacuno. El proceso natural (2), el regado intenso (3) o la incrementación de la tala de bosques (5) daría como resultado una mayor erosión del suelo.

7. **(4)** El grupo descrito se inició con características de multitud expresiva, puesto que sus miembros estaban compartiendo una experiencia de diversión. Pero el desborde de emociones hizo que se descontrolara la muchedumbre y se convirtiera así en multitud activa.

8. **(1)** Según el pasaje, las adivinanzas, que son una forma de juego verbal, además de divertir sanamente al niño, estimulan el desarrollo de sus capacidades lingüísticas y lógicas; de modo que la opción (5) es errónea. Los psicólogos tienen razón en dar tanta importancia a los juegos sociales; así que la opción (4) es también incorrecta. No hay evidencia que respalde las afirmaciones de las opciones (2) y (3).

9. **(1)** Sería el Departamento de Comercio y, en consecuencia, su secretario, el encargado de fomentar el desarrollo de nuevas empresas.

10. **(3)** Como los parques nacionales son terreno público, este organismo dependería del secretario del interior.

11. **(3)** Si hay más casas en el mercado, los vendedores se darían cuenta de que los compradores tienen más opciones para elegir y es probable que acepten una oferta más baja. Las opciones (1) y (2) se aplican a situaciones en las que el número de compradores excede al de vendedores: si hay

muchas casas en el mercado, los propietarios no tendrían mucho incentivo en poner sus casas a la venta. La opción (5) alude a un comprador que no conoce bien el mercado inmobiliario.

12. (5) La comida china es muy popular, como lo demuestra el número de restaurantes chinos que existe. Las opciones (1) y (2) no son ejemplos de aculturación. Las linternas chinas se usan esporádicamente y no suponen una adaptación cultural. Las bicicletas no constituyen un medio de transporte exclusivamente chino.

13. (1) El punto más alto en el nivel de población de los países tanto desarrollados como en vías de desarrollo se ha dado en 1990 o antes. Después de ese período, se proyecta una disminución en el nivel poblacional de ambas regiones.

14. (3) El gráfico muestra que la población de las naciones en vías de desarrollo aumentó abruptamente entre 1950 y 1990. La mejora en la nutrición y en las condiciones de salubridad e higiene se tradujo en una mayor natalidad y una menor mortandad en la población infantil. Como consecuencia de esto, la población adulta capaz de procrear aumentó, lo cual acarreó un crecimiento marcado en la población. La opción (1) no es muy plausible, ya que es más probable que una mejora en el control de la natalidad conlleve una disminución de la población, y no un aumento. Lo mismo se diría de la opción (2), que se refiere a la emigración desde las regiones en vías de desarrollo a las regiones desarrolladas. La opción (4) tampoco es válida, debido a que la caída en la tasa de embarazos en las regiones desarrolladas no pudo afectar a las regiones en vías de desarrollo.

15. (2) Toda mejora en los envíos de correo se traduciría en mejoras en las comunicaciones. Las demás opciones no son razones valederas para desear una mejora de los envíos postales.

16. (5) El cable transatlántico unió dos lugares distantes gracias a una tecnología más avanzada. Ninguno de los demás cambios produjo un mejoramiento de las comunicaciones ni supuso un avance tecnológico importante.

17. (2) Al forzar la retirada del proyecto de ley, los republicanos pusieron en evidencia su desaprobación respecto al proyecto de ley, que es justamente lo opuesto de la opción (3). La opción (1) puede ser verdadera, pero no hay ningún dato acerca del tiempo que emplearían hablando los demócratas si quisieran hacerlo. No hay evidencia que respalde las opciones (4) ó (5).

18. (1) El artista compara la cartografía con el arte de la guerra. El caricaturista asemeja el salón de actualización de mapas de una compañía de cartografía a la sala de operaciones de un centro de mando en que se planean las estrategias de guerra.

19. (4) La protección del medio ambiente es un tema de interés público.

20. (5) Este grupo centra su interés en una sola ley.

21. (1) En la preparación de la sopa de verduras entra una gran variedad de ingredientes que retienen sus propias características y que ni se mezclan tan íntimamente como para producir una consistencia única, opción (2), ni están tan desligados como para estar en constante rivalidad entre ellos, opción (3).

22. **(4)** La curva que indica el control de los costos de salud pública reducirá el déficit a 0 hacia el año 2003. Las otras curvas muestran un déficit federal persistente.

23. **(1)** El pasaje afirma que la lluvia ácida se puede extender a muchas millas de su punto de origen, de modo que no es un problema local. El ser humano no puede controlar el ciclo natural del agua; así que es difícil contener la lluvia ácida en áreas específicas.

24. **(2)** Los propietarios de restaurantes están restringidos por el número de licencias que hay disponibles. Hasta que no obtengan la licencia correspondiente, no podrán competir con otros negocios que sirvan bebidas alcohólicas.

25. **(4)** Las otras dos tiendas de video ya están atendiendo a las necesidades del mercado y, por tanto, limitarán el número de clientes que pueda tener la pareja.

26. **(2)** Baird había infringido la ley. Como candidata a la posición jurídica más alta del país, sería un mal ejemplo para el pueblo estadounidense. Se nombró entonces a otra mujer; de modo que la opción (1) es incorrecta. Las demás opciones no encuentran apoyo en ningún dato del párrafo.

27. **(2)** El accidente de tráfico es el único suceso aterrador *sufrido* por la persona. En los demás casos, la persona ha sido testigo o se ha enterado o ha sido informada de un suceso.

28. **(4)** Según el pasaje, las relaciones encabezan la lista de causantes de felicidad. La fe ocupa el tercer lugar. Las demás opciones no se citan como causas de la felicidad.

29. **(3)** El primer párrafo ofrece varias definiciones de felicidad, pero termina diciendo que, en lo que respecta a la misma, "todo depende". La información presentada no respalda las demás conclusiones.

30. **(3)** Los emigrantes que cruzaron el océano para llegar a América venían en busca de mejores trabajos y de una vida mejor para sus familias, es decir, con los mismos objetivos con que ahora vienen los inmigrantes mexicanos. Colón cruzó el océano por razones económicas. Los esclavos africanos vinieron a América en contra de su voluntad. Las otras dos opciones se refieren a sucesos militares.

31. **(2)** Según la clave, el símbolo que aparece en el mapa especifica los blancos de ataques aéreos.

32. **(5)** Al concentrarse en la destrucción de los centros militares, los Aliados planeaban debilitar las defensas de Irak, hasta el punto en que se viera obligado a rendirse.

Compruebe sus respuestas de la Prueba Posterior con la Clave de Respuestas y luego busque en la Tabla de Evaluación que se da abajo el número de los ejercicios que contestó mal y enciérrelo en círculo. De esta manera podrá determinar qué destrezas de lectura y qué áreas de contenido necesita repasar. Las destrezas de lectura se abordan en las páginas 33–45; y el número de página correspondiente a las áreas de contenido se cita abajo en la tabla. La capacidad de contestar preguntas que requieren el manejo de las destrezas de lectura y de la información de las áreas de contenido es fundamental para un buen rendimiento en la Prueba de Estudios Sociales del GED. Los números que aparecen en **negrita** son preguntas que se basan en gráficas.

PRUEBA POSTERIOR 2: TABLA DE EVALUACIÓN DE ESTUDIOS SOCIALES

Destreza de lectura/ Área de contenido	Comprensión	Aplicación	Análisis	Evaluación
Ciencias del Comportimiento (páginas 103–111)	3	7, 12	27, 28	8, 29
Historia de EE.UU. (páginas 112–126)	**30**	16, 21	4, **31**	5, 15
Ciencias Políticas (páginas 127–138)	17	9, 10	19, 20	26
Economía (páginas 139–147)	**2**	24, 25	11, **22**	**1**
Geografía (páginas 148–154)	**13**	6, 32	**14**, **18**	23

CLAVE DE RESPUESTAS
PRUEBA POSTERIOR 3: CIENCIAS

1. **(4)** Aunque las cinco opciones presentan datos, sólo la opción (4), que afirma que los globos cargados de helio se elevan en el aire, expresa una relación entre el peso relativo del helio y el aire.

2. **(2)** Las bases neutralizan a los ácidos. La opción (1) aumenta la acidez. La opción (3) es incorrecta porque una sustancia neutra como el agua no tendría ningún efecto. Las opciones (4) y (5) no se pueden colegir de las medidas tomadas por los científicos.

3. **(4)** Además de la luz solar, tanto el dióxido de carbono (anhídrido carbónico) como el agua tienen que estar presentes para que se pueda realizar la fotosíntesis. En este caso, sólo se menciona el agua como una de las opciones. La glucosa, opción (1), es un producto de la fotosíntesis; el oxígeno, opción (2), es un derivado del proceso; el nitrógeno, opción (3), casi no existe en estado libre.

4. **(3)** El polvo no es un tipo de precipitación del agua.

5. **(3)** La epidermis es un tejido, ya que es una capa de células organizadas que se asocian para desempeñar una misma función.

6. **(4)** El páncreas es un órgano, puesto que es una unidad estructural integrada por varios tipos de tejidos.

7. **(4)** Las opciones A y D son hechos observables, pero ninguno de ellos presenta evidencia de que la luz solar se pueda convertir en energía calorífica.

8. **(3)** Esta afirmación es una hipótesis porque ofrece una explicación razonable, aunque no probada, de por qué el apio contribuye a la reducción de la presión arterial.

9. **(2)** Cualquier descubrimiento o producto que resulta de un experimento se clasifica como hallazgo.

10. **(3)** Un auto con las ventanillas cerradas es prácticamente idéntico a un invernadero. El vidrio deja pasar la energía luminosa pero impide que se escape la energía calorífica.

11. **(5)** A medida que aumente la temperatura de la Tierra, es probable que se deshielen los casquetes polares. El agua resultante del derretimiento del hielo ocasionaría un aumento en el nivel del mar.

12. **(1)** Al reducir nuestra dependencia de todos los tipos de combustibles fósiles, se reduciría la cantidad de gases de invernadero que se emiten a la atmósfera.

13. **(3)** La opción A es incorrecta porque no se detalla el porcentaje de helio presente en la muestra de aire seco puro. La opción D tampoco es correcta porque la tabla se basa en una muestra de aire seco, no húmedo.

14. **(3)** La cantidad de dióxido de carbono disminuye a medida que aumenta la temperatura de la bebida. La bebida gaseosa perdería entonces el gas.

15. **(5)** El peso del agua desplazada por cualquier objeto que flota en ella es igual al peso total del objeto, sin importar que sólo una parte del objeto esté sumergida.

16. **(3)** Como se puede observar en la ilustración, la corriente de convección es el movimiento de aire causado por diferencias en la temperatura. En el mar se producen las corrientes acuáticas de convección.

17. (3) La energía y el agua que se producen en el proceso de respiración celular son utilizadas por el cuerpo. El CO_2 (dióxido de carbono) es expulsado por los pulmones como producto de desecho.

18. (2) Como el interruptor y los enchufes están ordenados en serie, al apagarse uno, se apagan todos. Cuando se activa el interruptor, se interrumpe el circuito y todos los enchufes se apagan.

19. (3) Sólo la opción (3) es verdadera. Las bombillas A y B son parte del mismo circuito en serie; y, si se apaga una, también se apaga la otra. La bombilla C, no obstante, permanecerá encendida sin importar lo que ocurra con las bombillas A y B.

20. (2) El aumento de los programas de concientización y educación de la población acerca del SIDA no contribuye al crecimiento del número de casos reportados de esta enfermedad.

21. (5) El cacto y otras plantas del desierto sólo pueden sobrevivir en el desierto si conservan el agua de forma efectiva. A raíz de esto, las plantas del desierto han evolucionado poco y sus hojas carecen de superficie que posibilite la transpiración.

22. (2) Durante los meses de verano, el Polo Norte está inclinado hacia el Sol y recibe luz solar veinticuatro horas al día.

23. (2) Según el pasaje, la inclinación del eje terrestre es responsable de las diferencias en la duración del día y la noche, así como de las diferencias de estación.

24. (5) El lado izquierdo del rostro está controlado por el lado derecho del cerebro. El lóbulo parietal es el que controla las sensaciones faciales.

25. (5) Las opciones A y B insinúan que a mayor cerebro, mayor inteligencia. Las opciones C y D sugieren que el tamaño del cerebro no determina necesariamente el grado de inteligencia.

26. (4) Cuando se produce una descarga eléctrica en una nube, se origina tanto el trueno como el relámpago. El relámpago se ve antes de que se oiga el trueno, porque la luz se desplaza con mayor rapidez que el sonido.

27. (3) Los *marshmallows* contienen alrededor de un 80 por ciento de carbohidratos; las demás opciones contienen menos de un 50 por ciento de carbohidratos.

28. (5) Las dos sustancias más importantes presentes en el agua del mar son el cloro (Cl) y el sodio (Na), es decir, los dos elementos que forman el cloruro de sodio (ClNa), conocido como sal común.

29. (3) Sólo se puede deducir que del corte resultan dos imanes más cortos. En base al dibujo solamente, no se puede determinar la potencia de estos imanes.

30. (3) Cuando los líquidos no se mezclan uniformemente, el de mayor densidad va al fondo, mientras que el de menor densidad asciende a la superficie.

31. (4) El arco iris se forma porque las gotas de lluvia en suspensión actúan como prismas diminutos y hacen que la luz solar (luz blanca natural) se descomponga en los colores que la integran.

32. (3) La forma correcta de representar una molécula de tres átomos de carbono y ocho átomos de hidrógeno es mediante la fórmula C_3H_8.

33. (2) Como se aprecia en el dibujo, la interneurona recibe el impulso nervioso de la neurona sensorial y lo transmite a la neurona motora.

Compruebe sus respuestas de la Prueba Posterior con la Clave de Respuestas y luego busque en la Tabla de Evaluación que se da abajo el número de los ejercicios que contestó mal y enciérrelo en círculo. De esta manera podrá determinar qué destrezas de lectura y qué áreas de contenido necesita repasar. Las destrezas de lectura se abordan en las páginas 33–45; y el número de página correspondiente a las áreas de contenido se cita abajo en la tabla. La capacidad de contestar preguntas que requieren el manejo de las destrezas de lectura y de la información de las áreas de contenido es fundamental para un buen rendimiento en la Prueba de Ciencias del GED. Los números que aparecen en **negrita** son preguntas que se basan en gráficas.

PRUEBA POSTERIOR 3: TABLA DE EVALUACIÓN DE CIENCIAS

Destreza de lectura/ Área de contenido	Comprensión	Aplicación	Análisis	Evaluación
Biología (páginas 157–172)	**24**, 27	5, 6, 8, 9	21, **33**	20, **25**
Ciencias de la Tierra (páginas 173–190)	**16, 22**	4, 10	11, **23**	12
Química (páginas 191–204)	**13, 32**	2, 14	3, 17, **28**	1
Física (páginas 205–218)	**29, 30**	15, **18**	7, **19**	26, **31**

CLAVE DE RESPUESTAS PRUEBA POSTERIOR 4: ARTE Y LITERATURA

1. **(3)** De acuerdo con la cita, ni a la riqueza (4) ni a la belleza (5) se tiene en tanta estima como a la piedad religiosa. Según lo afirmado, se puede decir que a estos habitantes sureños no les impresiona ni la fama (1) ni el poder (2).

2. **(5)** Las líneas 5–7 expresan que Casey anhela convertirse en primera base de los Red Sox.

3. **(1)** A lo largo del fragmento, la autora da ejemplos de la participación de las mujeres y las niñas en el béisbol. Ella menciona a escritoras deportivas, a aficionadas del deporte y a una bateadora.

4. **(4)** En las líneas 41–53, la autora escribe: "Durante las prácticas de bateo de los entrenamientos de primavera. . . me quedo mirando a la muchedumbre de niños: la mitad son niñas. Esto es algo nuevo." La oración final ofrece un ejemplo específico de otro suceso novedoso dentro del béisbol: el papel tradicionalmente masculino de "bat boy" está siendo ahora desempeñado por una niña.

5. **(1)** A lo largo del fragmento, la autora apoya el interés que tiene su hija, así como otras mujeres, por el béisbol.

6. **(4)** Los datos están organizados por orden cronológico. Al inicio del extracto son las 7:00 de la mañana. Las acciones relevantes subsiguientes tienen lugar a las 7:09, 8:01 y 8:30.

7. **(3)** Dado el número de mensajes electrónicos hablados que recuerdan a la familia las fechas importantes (un cumpleaños, un aniversario, los pagos que hay que hacer), se puede deducir que la familia opinaba que era importante estar bien organizados.

8. **(1)** El fragmento trata principalmente de la interacción humana con la tecnología del futuro y, más en particular, de lo absurda que es una tecnología divorciada de la humanidad.

9. **(1)** De acuerdo con las dos primeras oraciones del fragmento: "La vida era extremadamente difícil para los Whipple. Difícil era alimentar tantas bocas hambrientas; difícil vestir a todos los hijos para que estuvieran bien abrigados durante el, si bien corto, invierno. . ."

10. **(5)** En la mitad del primer párrafo la autora escribe que ". . . la Sra. Whipple estaba decidida a aceptar lo que fuera y a considerarlo como bueno, sobre todo cuando los vecinos podían escuchar. . . No podía soportar el que alguien les tuviera lástima. . ."

11. **(5)** Según los datos que se ofrecen en el primer párrafo, la historia se desarrolla en un lugar donde los inviernos son cortos y es posible ganarse la vida recogiendo algodón. Los detalles apuntan hacia un pueblito del campo en el sur del país.

12. **(2)** En los dos primeros versos del poema, el narrador dice: "Venimos a escuchar el final / de todas las historias".

13. **(3)** Esta comparación tan compleja se apoya en dos analogías. Por un lado, la autora asemeja un río que se está secando a una persona que está envejeciendo y cuya vida se está "secando". Por otro lado, se comparan las

rocas que sobresalen en un río que se está secando a la prominencia cada vez más evidente de las facciones de una persona que está envejeciendo. Observe que todas las comparaciones del poema desarrollan la idea de personas que están cambiando y que "llegan a ser ellos mismos" con el transcurso del tiempo.

14. (5) Típico del lenguaje del poema es el vocabulario de los tres últimos versos: "¡Mira! Todos / hemos llegado a ser / nosotros mismos". Observe que el lenguaje de estos versos es llano, informal y conversacional.

15. (3) El conflicto interno de Dolores se expresa en la primera línea del fragmento: "No estaré tranquila hasta que vuelva a mi casa".

16. (5) La forma en que Javier se dirige a su madre así como sus acciones revelan que el joven se interesa por los sentimientos de ella. Por ejemplo, cuando su madre se pone a llorar, Javier trata de calmarla: "Mamá, por favor".

17. (1) Javier tiene esperanzas en el futuro cuando dice: "Creo que aquí podré llegar a ser alguien".

18. (3) La última oración dice que la autora se inspiró en la vida de su padre, quien se vio obligado a salir de Viena para escapar de los nazis que habían ascendido al poder.

19. (1) Tanto en el incidente de la Rosa Blanca como en el de la Plaza Tiananmen fueron ejecutados estudiantes universitarios por protestar contra un gobierno que ellos consideraban inmoral.

20. (4) La estructura de la oración de la crítica tiende a ser bien elaborada. La mayoría de las oraciones son complejas y hasta las oraciones más simples contienen una gran cantidad de complementos.

21. (1) Las anécdotas que Hunter-Gault decidió incluir en su relato—recuerdos de cenas en las granjas de los parientes, la compra del vestido para el baile de graduación de la escuela y la lectura de las tiras cómicas de los periódicos—ilustran una niñez feliz y normal. Observe que el crítico califica los recuerdos de Hunter-Gault como "afables".

22. (4) El fragmento es principalmente informativo, centrándose en el contenido del libro en lugar de en la crítica del mismo. Observe que el crítico no menciona nunca la calidad de la escritura ni los puntos fuertes o débiles del texto.

23. (1) La segunda oración del fragmento dice: "Sin embargo, en su autobiografía lúcida y circunspecta, se interesa menos por ese triunfo de los derechos civiles [*la desegregación de la Universidad de Georgia*] que por el hecho de haberse criado dentro de una distinguida dinastía de predicadores en una comunidad minoritaria que se podría decir autosuficiente".

Compruebe sus respuestas de la Prueba Posterior con la Clave de Respuestas y luego busque en la Tabla de Evaluación que se da abajo el número de los ejercicios que contestó mal y enciérrelo en círculo. De esta manera podrá determinar qué destrezas de lectura y qué áreas de contenido necesita repasar. Las destrezas de lectura se abordan en las páginas 33–45; y el número de página correspondiente a las áreas de contenido se cita abajo en la tabla. La capacidad de contestar preguntas que requieren el manejo de las destrezas de lectura y de la información de las áreas de contenido es fundamental para un buen rendimiento en la Prueba de Arte y Literatura del GED.

PRUEBA POSTERIOR 4: TABLA DE EVALUACIÓN DE ARTE Y LITERATURA

Destreza de lectura/ Área de contenido	Comprensión	Aplicación	Análisis
La narrativa de ficción (páginas 221–233)	7, 9, 10	8, 11	6
La poesía (páginas 234–246)	12		13, 14
El teatro (páginas 247–256)	15, 17		16
Literatura de no ficción (páginas 257–268)	2, 3	1, 5	4
Comentarios (páginas 268–273)	18, 21, 22, 23	19	20

CLAVE DE RESPUESTAS PRUEBA POSTERIOR 5: MATEMÁTICAS

1. (2) 8

$12 \div 1\frac{1}{2} =$

$\frac{12}{1} \div \frac{3}{2}$

$\frac{12}{1} \times \frac{2}{3} = \frac{24}{3} = 8$

2. (3) $\frac{1}{90}$

$\frac{\text{miembros de la familia}}{\text{total de boletos}} \quad \frac{4}{360} = \frac{1}{90}$

3. (3) 8

$3m + 6 = 30$

$ - 6 - 6$

$\frac{3m}{3} = \frac{24}{3}$

$m = 8$

4. (4) Dave's Duds

$\frac{x}{\$30} = \frac{10}{100}$

$100x = \$300$

$x = \$3 \qquad \qquad \$30$

$ \underline{-\$3}$

$ \$27$

5. (4) 408

$20^2 + 2^3 =$

$20 \times 20 + 2 \times 2 \times 2 =$

$400 + 8 = 408$

6. (3) 1:3

ancho:alto $= 27:81 = 1:3$

7. (4) $\frac{7}{20}$

$35\% = \frac{35}{100} = \frac{7}{20}$

8. (3) B, D, C, A

$A = 0.9 = 0.900$

$B = 0.09 = 0.090$

$C = 0.895$

$D = 0.19 = 0.190$

9. (2) $\sqrt{3^2 + 3^2}$

$d = \sqrt{(x_2 - x_1)^2 + (y_2 - y_1)^2}$

$d = \sqrt{(5-2)^2 + (5-2)^2}$

$d = \sqrt{3^2 + 3^2}$

10. (3) 157

$C = \pi d$

$C = 3.14 \times 50$

$C = 157$

11. (4) 15

$\frac{\$12{,}000}{\$80{,}000} = \frac{3}{20}$

$\frac{3}{20} = \frac{x}{100}$

$20x = 300$

$x = 15\%$

12. (4) 300

$\frac{\text{piezas}}{\text{horas}} \quad \frac{15}{2} = \frac{x}{40}$

$2x = 600$

$x = 300$

13. (3) 50

$a^2 = b^2 + c^2$

$a^2 = 40^2 + 30^2$

$a^2 = 1600 + 900$

$a = \sqrt{2500}$

$a = 50$

14. (3) $12 \times 8 \times 6$

$V = lah$

$V = 12 \times 8 \times 6$

15. (1) 2

$12a - 5 = 4a + 11$

$\underline{-4a -4a}$

$8a - 5 = 11$

$ + 5 + 5$

$\frac{8a}{8} = \frac{16}{8}$

$a = 2$

16. (1) $3(a - 4)$

Divida cada término entre 3:

$3a - 12 = 3(a - 4)$

17. (2) 35

$105° \qquad \qquad 180°$

$\underline{+ 40°} \qquad \qquad \underline{- 145°}$

$145° \qquad \qquad 35°$

18. (4) 12

El punto A está 5 unidades a la izquierda de 0.
El punto B está 7 unidades a la derecha de 0.
Los puntos distan 5 + 7 = 12 unidades uno del otro.

19. (2) 2.25

$(1.5)^2 = 1.5 = 2.25$

20. (5) $\frac{1}{2} \times 13 \times 7$

$A = \frac{1}{2}bh$
$A = \frac{1}{2} \times 13 \times 7$

21. (4) $55 \times 3 + 40 \times 2$

22. (4) 75

$$\frac{MR}{MN} = \frac{QR}{PQ}$$
$\frac{8}{5} = \frac{120}{x}$
$8x = 600$
$x = 75$

23. (1) 2

$\frac{\text{variación en } y}{\text{variación en } x} \quad \frac{6}{3}$

24. (5) 42

$2 + 1\frac{1}{2} = 3\frac{1}{2}$
$3\frac{1}{2} \times 12 =$
$\frac{7}{2} \times \frac{12}{1} =$
$\frac{84}{2} = 42$

25. (3) 2y – 20 = 58

Maxine = y
Pilar = $y - 20$
suma = $y + y - 20 = 58$
$2y - 0 = 58$

26. (4) 20

1990	42 gal
1975	– 22
	20 gal

27. (4) 9.8×10^{10}

28. (3) $5.85

78 pulg = $6\frac{1}{2}$ pies
$6\frac{1}{2} \times \$.90 =$
$\frac{13}{2} \times \$\frac{.90}{1} = \$5.85$

Compruebe sus respuestas de la Prueba Posterior con la Clave de Respuestas y luego busque en la Tabla de Evaluación que se da abajo el número de los ejercicios que contestó mal y enciérrelo en círculo. De esta manera podrá determinar qué áreas de contenido necesita repasar. El número de página correspondiente a las áreas de contenido se cita abajo en la tabla. Los números que aparecen en **negrita** son preguntas que se basan en gráficas.

PRUEBA POSTERIOR 5:
TABLA DE EVALUACIÓN DE MATEMÁTICAS

Área de contenido	Ejercicio n°	Páginas a repasar
Números enteros y decimales	19, 28	277–286
Fracciones	1, **7**	287–300
Razón y proporción	**6**	301–304
Porcentajes	4, 11	305–311
Medidas	**18**, 21, 24	312–322
Gráficos, estadística y probabilidad	2, **26**	323–330
Numeración	**8**	331–336
Geometría	5, **10**, **13**, 14, **17**, **20**, 22	337–349
Álgebra	3, 9, 12, 15, 16, 23, 25, 27	350–374

ÍNDICE

Cultural,
  antropólogo ~, 103
  relatividad ~, 105
  universal ~, 104
Cúmulo (*meteorología*),
  190
Curvas de nivel, 152

D
Dalton, John, 191
Darwin, Charles, 170
Decimal,
  cero en número ~, 278
  número ~, 277
  punto ~, 277
Decimales,
  ~ mixtos, 278
  comparación de ~,
    278–279, 292
  división de ~, 282–284
  empleo de los ~,
    277–278
  fracciones ~, 277
  fracciones y ~, 294
  multiplicación y
    división de ~,
    281–282
  orden de los ~, 278
  porcentajes y ~, 306
  posiciones (*lugares*) ~,
    277
  redondeo de ~, 279–280
  suma y resta de ~,
    280–281
Decisión Dred Scott, 116
Declaración de
    Independencia, 113
Deductivo, razonamiento,
    37
  (*Véase también* Razo-
    namiento crítico.)
Defensa,
  mecanismos de ~, 111
Déficit presupuestario, 146
Deflación, 144
Del origen de las especies
    (Charles Darwin),
    170
Deltas, 182
Demanda, 141
  (*Véase* Oferta y
    Demanda.)

Democracia, 127
  ~ pura, 127
  ~ representativa, 127
Demostrativo,
  adjetivo ~, 59
  pronombre ~, 61–62
Depresión
  (*Véase* Recesión;
    Colapso de la bolsa
    de valores.)
Derecho divino, 128
Derechos civiles,
  movimiento de los ~,
    124
Deriva continental,
  teoría de la ~, 176
Descriptiva,
  escritura ~, 88–89
Desegregación, 123
  (*Véase también*
    Movimiento de los
    derechos civiles.)
Desenlace
  ~ en narrativa, 225
  ~ en teatro, 250
Desigualdades, 365
Desplazamiento
  (*psicología*), 110
  (*Véase* Mecanismos de
    defensa.)
Destino Manifiesto, 115
Destrezas de lectura, 33
  (*Véase* Razonamiento
    crítico.)
Détente, 124
Diálogo,
  ~ en narrativa de
    ficción, 223
  ~ en teatro, 248–249,
    251
Diámetro, 345
Diarios, 262
Dictadura, 127
Difracción, 214
Difusión, 159
Dígitos, 277
Dinero,
  problemas matemáticos
    con ~, 308–311
Diploide,
  célula ~, 163
Discriminación racial, 124

Discurso,
  ~ directo, 223–224
  ~ indirecto, 224
Distensión
  (*Véase Détente.*)
División
  ~ de decimal entre
    decimal, 283–284
  ~ de decimales, 282–286
  ~ de fracciones, 298
  ~ de número entero
    entre decimal, 283
  ~ de números con
    signo, 364–365
Doctrina Monroe, 115
Dólares
  ~ constantes, 145
  ~ corrientes, 145
  (*Véase también* Política
    fiscal.)
Dominios magnéticos, 216
Dorsal oceánica, 182
Dred Scott,
  decisión ~, 116

E
Ecología, 171–172
Economía, 139–147
  ~ mixta, 141
  ~ y gobierno, 140
Económico,
  indicador ~, 145
  sistemas ~, 140–141
Ecosistema, 171–172
Ecuaciones
  ~ algebraicas, 351
  ~ químicas, 196
  ~ químicas
    equilibradas, 197
  resolución de ~ de
    pasos múltiples, 359
  resolución de ~ de un
    paso, 357
  traducción de ~,
    354–356
Ecuador,
  línea del ~, 149
Ego, 109
Eisenhower, Dwight, 123
Eje,
  ~ *x,* 369
  ~ *y,* 369

NOTAS